Y0-CCG-140

NORTH ATLANTIC BIOTA

AND THEIR HISTORY

NORTH ATLANTIC BIOTA
AND THEIR HISTORY

A Symposium

held at the University of Iceland, Reykjavík

July 1962

under the auspices of the University of Iceland

and the Museum of Natural History

EDITORS

ÁSKELL LÖVE and DORIS LÖVE

SPONSORED BY THE

NATO ADVANCED STUDY INSTITUTES PROGRAM

A Pergamon Press Book

THE MACMILLAN COMPANY

NEW YORK

1963

THE MACMILLAN COMPANY
60 Fifth Avenue,
New York 11, N.Y.

This book is distributed by
THE MACMILLAN COMPANY · NEW YORK
pursuant to a special arrangement with
PERGAMON PRESS LIMITED
Oxford, England

Library of Congress Card No. 62-22038

Printed in Great Britain by Page Bros. (Norwich) Ltd.

To the bicentennial anniversary of

SVEINN PÅLSSON
25 April 1762 to 23 April 1840

the distinguished Icelandic naturalist
and
pioneer glaciologist

CONTENTS

FOREWORD

þat er ok mannsins náttúra at forvitna ok sjá þá hluti, er hánum eru sagðir, ok vita, hvárt svá er sem hánum er sagt eða eigi.

Konungsskuggsjá

It is in man's nature to wish to see and experience the things that he has heard about and thus learn whether the facts are as told or not.

King's Mirror

(Transl. by L. M. Larson: *Scandinavian Monographs*, vol. III, New York, 1917.

These lines from the *King's Mirror*, the important Old Norse book which contains, among other things, valuable information on geography and natural history, express better than we can say what has been in our minds when we were editing this book. It is intended not only as a presentation of the current status of our knowledge on the distribution and history of plants and animals in the North Atlantic area, but also as a review of current trends in biogeographical and geological investigations concerning these problems. The papers included were delivered at a symposium held at the University of Iceland, Reykjavík, 12–25 July 1962. During the meeting 29 lectures were given, followed by discussion periods, and one long and several smaller excursions were made to parts of Iceland of interest in this connection.

Although the subject matter of the symposium, North Atlantic biota and their history, has been much discussed for almost a century, this is the first attempt to present in one volume a reasonably many-sided evaluation of the problems involved. It is evident that although many specialists from different branches of the life and earth sciences are represented in this book, the number of contributors had to be limited and, thus, also the points of view. There is, however, reason to believe that this compilation will be of value to those students who specialize in similar problems, and that it will help forward their research. Since the situation of Iceland and its unique Tertiary and Pleistocene deposits seem to make this country ideal for such studies, it was selected as the meeting-place for the symposium in the hope that this would advise the scientific world about the importance of much increased scientific studies of this and other North Atlantic "stepping stones".

The symposium was organized by a small committee consisting of Áskell Löve, president; Ármann Snævarr and Sigurdur Thorarinsson, vice-presidents and representing, respectively, the University of Iceland and the Museum of Natural History in Reykjavík; Eythor Einarsson from the Museum of Natural History, secretary and organizer of the excursions; and Sigurdur J. Briem, representing the Icelandic Ministry of Education.

The committee acknowledges gratefully the encouragement and financial support received from the NATO Advanced Study Institutes Programme, which made possible both this symposium and the publication of this book. It is also indebted to the University of Iceland and the Museum of Natural History, under whose auspices the symposium was organized. Its gratitude is also extended to the Pergamon Press for valuable assistance in editing the papers, and to Miss Virginia Weadock, who had the task of correcting the language of the foreign manuscripts. Last but not least all the contributors are to be thanked for having given of their time and experience to make this venture possible.

Montreal, August 1962

ÁSKELL LÖVE
DORIS LÖVE

INTRODUCTION

ÁSKELL LÖVE

Institut Botanique de l'Université de Montréal, Montréal, Canada

THE dispersal of plants and animals is one of the great problems in the field of evolution. It is also one of the most fascinating questions of the biological sciences, since it is concerned not only with understanding a distant past but also with knowledge of present conditions. In addition, it is not a problem to be solved by the biologist alone; his conclusions must be confirmed by aid of palynology telling us about biological and climatical changes in the recent past, and by aid of historical geology regarding the more distant past. The history and evolution of all living beings is closely related to their distribution, which in turn is intimately associated with the geological history of continents and oceans.

It has long been known that a considerable number of species of plants and animals belonging to seemingly identical species inhabit both sides of the Atlantic Ocean. Already Humboldt has raised the interesting question whether any of these species are originally common to both continents or whether those species, externally so similar as to be known by the same name, are in fact identical to each other.

The analogy of the animal kingdom seems to favor the negative of this question, since no quadruped or terrestrial bird, and even no reptile and not even an insect is said to be naturally common to the equinoctial regions of the Old and New Worlds. The same may be true also for higher plants in these regions. But as we go farther north and approach higher latitudes, the probability of finding animals and plants of identical species on both sides of the Ocean becomes increasingly greater. In northern Europe there are rare plants, not related to any others on that continent, but of identically the same species as are widespread in North America; similarly, there are plants in eastern North America, whose closest or even identical relatives all occur in Europe. The same is also the case for some lower animals which are unable to fly or swim across the Ocean and are as confined to a terrestrial habitat as ever any plants.

The observation that identical animals and plants occur on both sides of the North Atlantic led, late in the last century, to the launching of a theory of so-called Pleistocene survival. However, this theory did not solve any questions, it only moved the problem farther back in time. The outstanding unsolved problem in historical biogeography in the North Atlantic still is, whether certain flora and fauna elements on both sides of the Ocean reached their present areas by dispersal over the existing lands of the continents and subsequently became extinct in interior parts of these lands where they do not appear today, as maintained by some biogeographers, or, whether these continents in a not too remote past were in direct contact with each other; furthermore, in case such a contact existed, whether they might have been united by land-bridges that have later mysteriously disappeared or by a continuity that has been subsequently broken by some kind of a displacement?

In recent years so many new facts have been brought into light regarding the old problem of the history of the North Atlantic biota that a fresh attack on their problems seems almost overdue. It also seems as if we were nearing the stage when the geological information permits us to construct a somewhat better timetable for possible dispersal periods. Even the biological facts and methods concerning studies of the evolution of the biota themselves have increased and improved so that we now are able to evaluate their true relationships better and attack many of the problems experimentally.

Since the problems of the history of the North Atlantic biota cannot easily be understood by studying the continental conditions alone, it seemed advisible to search for a concrete foundation of the discussion and to restrict this broad subject in space and time. This is one of the reasons that we held this first symposium in Iceland, since this automatically concentrates the discussions to studies of the present conditions in light of our knowledge of the Pleistocene and the Tertiary. Not only is this island a "stepping stone" between the continents, but it may in itself harbor such data that are the key to the solution of many of the problems to be considered.

This symposium was organized to clarify what are the facts, or to permit the presentation of available evidence on certain phases of an important scientific problem. It is meant as an opportunity to state in one issue what has been gathered and to gain new insights and outlooks from different fields of science. It is, however, not meant to prove a certain theory or to disprove another. A scientist's aim in a discussion with his colleagues is not to persuade but to clarify. It is the hope of the organizers and sponsor of this meeting that we will leave it better informed than we came, ready to reconstruct and construct anew on the foundations laid down here.

SOME CHAPTERS OF THE TERTIARY HISTORY OF ICELAND

TRAUSTI EINARSSON

University of Iceland, Reykjavík, Iceland

THE oldest rocks in Iceland are Tertiary plateau basalts. These basalts, which form the western, northern, and eastern parts of the country, are remnants of a 5–7 km thick pile or plateau of lava flows. The plateau must originally have had a much greater extension than the present island, as is evidenced by the truncation of the plateau at the coasts. The lowest accessible parts are of Early Tertiary, probably Eocene or possibly Uppermost Cretaceous age, while the highest parts are of Upper, possibly Uppermost Tertiary age. The lavas were formed entirely on land. Their base is unknown.

The Icelandic basalts are usually grouped with similar rocks in northwestern Britain, the Faeroe Islands, Greenland, Spitsbergen, and Franz Josef's Land under such names as the North Atlantic, Brito-Arctic, or Thulean plateau basalts. The lowest parts of the Icelandic plateau and the basalts in Britain, the Faeroe Islands, and Greenland seem to be of a similar age, whereas the basalts of Spitsbergen are somewhat older. In Iceland no marine fossils, nor fossil land fauna, are associated with the main part of the plateau and the age is based on lignites which are found at a number of horizons. This means that the age determinations are considerably uncertain.

The assumption was made long ago that the plateau lavas were formed on an extensive land mass occupying the area of the present North Atlantic or at least large parts of it, and successive foundering of much of the land has been postulated. The question is naturally important in the present context and we shall therefore consider some aspects of it, although it must be said at the outset that we can say very little with any certainty.

Postulation of a large-scale foundering of a continental area cannot be made without consideration of the isostatic equilibrium. This leads to speculation about processes in deep-crustal or sub-crustal regions. Foundering could have taken place if a relatively light deep layer grew thinner by spreading or if such a layer became denser by crystallization. Thus, foundering is not definitely excluded, but by postulating it we introduce inevitably deep- or subcrustal processes of a wholly hypothetical character.

Paleontologically, there is no strong evidence that Iceland was connected with Europe or America in the Lower Tertiary. On the contrary, the flora suggests lack of such a land connection.

There is, in my opinion, one main evidence which suggests rather great Tertiary changes in the North Atlantic area. I am referring to the sea-bottom topography. This looks relatively fresh and is suggestive of considerable tectonic changes which might have taken place in the Upper Tertiary. There is one important tectonic event of which we know: the uplift of Iceland, Greenland, Scandinavia, and Britain from low lands to the present mountainous countries took place in the Upper Tertiary. At the same time it is possible that the ocean floor changed considerably.

The geophysicists are today inquiring into the origin and history of ocean basins by way of seismic studies and through the examination of bottom sediments. It is advisable to await more such investigations in the North Atlantic and Arctic area before drawing further conclusions regarding the geographic development in this area in the Tertiary. But palynological studies also seem quite promising.

As matters stand today, we must face the possibility that the North Atlantic Ocean existed in the Lowest Tertiary and that the various remnants of plateau basalts indicate as many separate and distinct volcanic regions. To see, for instance, how Iceland might have originated in a deep ocean, the following hypothesis may be considered (cf. Einarsson, 1960):

Submarine volcanism produced a pile of relatively light pyroclastic material, and in spite of corresponding isostatic sinking of the base of the pile, a large island would eventually be formed. Assuming at the beginning a 3 km deep ocean, then a 6.2 km thick pile of density 2.2 would reach the surface of the sea. Adding a 6 km thick pile or plateau of subaerial basalts of mean density of 2.7 would, in equilibrium, give a land surface at 1100 m above sea level, if there was no compaction of the underlying pile.

I shall now consider the Icelandic rocks more specifically. Intercalated between the lava banks are very often thin seams of terrestrial sediments. They consist mostly of windblown sand or dust, whereas conglomerates are very rare, except in the higher parts. The sediments of the lower parts hence suggest in the first place a dry lava desert, but in a few cases one also finds indications of the existence of rivers. The clearest case, I think, is the well-known locality Brjánslaekur. As shown in Fig. 1 we find evidence that three times a lava filled up the river bed until at last more intense volcanic production so completely altered the drainage that sedimentation at this place came to an end.

In the Skardsströnd area we have sediments with a total thickness of about 50 m. A few lavas flowed during the period of sedimentation and one of these is seen to have flowed over soft mud. The lignite seams found in this area are very variable from place to place. There is a seam of 80–90 cm thickness at one place (Tindar), whereas at another place (Nípur) there is a succession of many 5–10 cm seams separated by sandstone. I think that these sediments have been formed by a sluggish river in a wide flat depression. As long as there was only an occasional lava flow at extended intervals the course of the river changed little. But in the end more intensive volcanism set

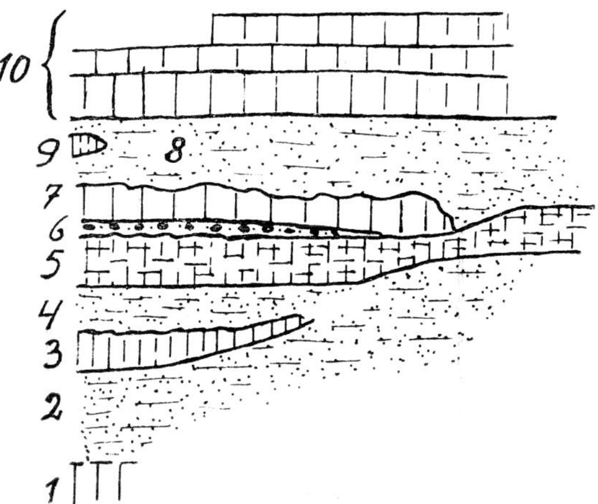

FIG. 1. Section through the western part of the Brjánslaekur sediments (looking S.–SW.). On top of a lava (1) of normal magnetization, there is a mainly barren lower part (2) of sediments: dark, brown, and yellow clay. A new, normally magnetized, lava (3) filled a groove (water course) which had been eroded into the lower sediments. This lava was previously considered a sill, but distinct magnetization of the clay at the lower contact, and absence of any magnetization at the upper contact as well as the difference of the under- and overlying sediments tend to confirm the present interpretation. The main fossiliferous sediments (4) follow. The lignite forms many thin layers, which are embedded in clay and consist to a considerable part of wood chips and numerous leaves, apparently carried by a sluggish river and buried in its muddy bottom. A new lava (5), of normal magnetization, again filled the water course and covered its surroundings. The lava has a blocky (kubbaberg) structure and is partly a typical "palagonite" breccia as might be found in the much younger "Móberg" formation. The river dug a new shallow bed at the same place as before and deposited a new layer (6) of coarser, fluviatile material. Again a lava (7), of reverse magnetization, filled the bed, but a clear trace of this is now lost in the section. A coarser sediment, (8), mainly non-fossiliferous, was deposited before a new and more intense volcanic period, represented by basalt lavas (10) put an end to sedimentation in this locality. At (9) is an intrusive basalt of reverse magnetization.

in, there came a rapid succession of lava floods, with the result that sedimentation came to an end here, i.e. the river was diverted to another area or perhaps it disappeared completely into the porous group of young lavas, the water flowing as ground water and not as a river.

When speaking of a lava desert, I have in mind conditions somewhat similar to those of the present Ódádahraun lava field. All the precipitation is lost into the porous lavas and flows as ground water on a deeper impervious floor until it emerges as large springs in the outskirts of the lava field. Within the dry lava field the lavas weather into sand or dust that is moved by the wind and settles in the depressions. Vegetation is naturally very sparse here, and fossilization would be most unlikely. Only around the springs at the rim of the lava field does the vegetation thrive and here it could be fossilized.

The picture of the Lower Tertiary landscape which I have in mind is that of a very extensive flat lava desert. It is mostly dry and without vegetation, only in occasional depressions is there sufficient moisture to sustain an oasis. Rivers are formed during long periods of relative volcanic quiescence and deposit sand and mud in their lower parts. But when a new intensification of volcanism sets in these rivers may disappear. Thus the vegetation is subject to often repeated changes in the water supply. While an oasis or a river bank is destroyed by a lava flow in one place, a wet depression is formed far away at the front of a new lava flow. The species we would find here after a short time possibly give no true picture of the climate or the vegetation of the country as a whole but may rather reflect which species migrate most rapidly into a new, isolated, wet place.

Practically every place, where we can study a thick section of the plateau basalts, we find that alternating with sections where a thin sediment separates every two lava banks, there are one or more such parts of the section, containing 10–20 lavas, with no sediments at all. These lava successions seem to represent great intensification of the volcanic activity and it seems most likely that during such periods vegetation must have been largely destroyed over an extensive area.

How large such an area may have been we cannot easily answer at present, because the individual lava groups have not been traced in sufficient detail and over sufficiently large areas.

In the lower parts of the plateau, traces of frost action are unknown, but in the topmost plateau group such signs are common. In addition there occur moraine-like conglomerates, and sometimes distinct moraines, resting on a striated floor. The conglomerates probably are mainly of fluvial nature, but they often seem to have been reworked by frost. In some cases they also show clear signs of erosion by sandstorms, among them the so-called "dreikanters". Thus, in this topmost group we have clear signs of a severe climate.

The age of this group is a very important question, but one not yet fully settled. It may be of Upper Pliocene age, and this is suggested by some approaches to the problem. On the other hand this plateau group is older than a complete peneplanation of the country, a differential uplift, a modelling of the landscape at a base level some 300 m above the present one, and finally a general uplift of 300 m in two or more steps, and a grading of the landscape to the lower base levels. One of the later episodes in this story was the formation of a strandflat at a sea level some 100 m above the present one, and after this strandflat had been formed there flowed lavas that have reverse magnetic polarity which indicates Lower Pleistocene age.

If we were free to base our estimate of age on this tectonic and erosional history, it seems most likely that a Lower Pliocene or even Miocene age should be assumed for the topmost plateau group. But the relations to the Upper Pliocene sediments in Tjörnes, although not at all very clear, seem to indicate a Late Pliocene age for the plateau group. This would demand on the

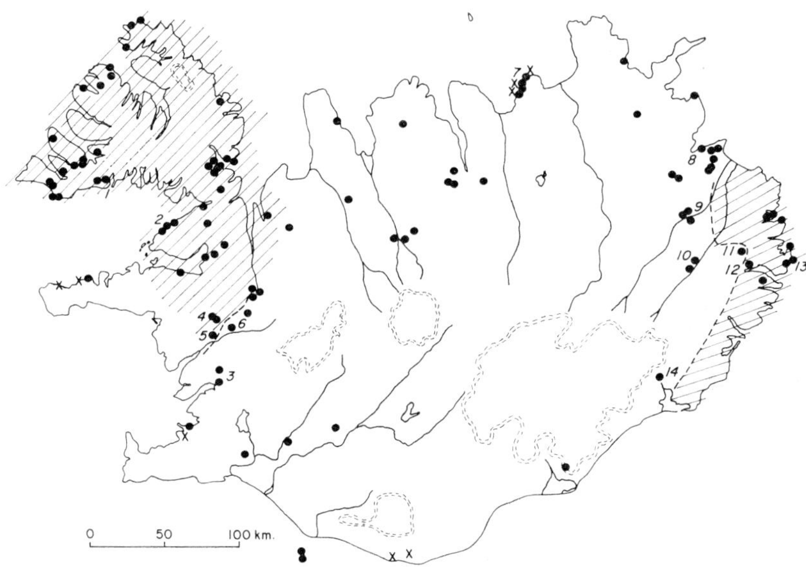

FIG. 2. Localities for fossil plants (dots) and marine fauna (crosses) in Iceland from earlier than Late and Post-glacial times. A few uncertain localities of surtarbrandur on Snaefellsnes and the Northwest Peninsula have been ignored. Hatching indicates the areas in which Pflug's "first type" of Icelandic flora occurs (cf. the text, p. 5). 1, Brjánslaekur; 2, Skardsströnd; 3, Litlisandur; 4, Hredavatn; 5, Stafholt; 6, Sleggjulaekur; 7, Tjörnes; 8, Vopnafjördur; 9, Jökuldalur; 10, Bessastadaá and Hengifoss; 11, Tungufell; 12, Hólmatindur; 13, Gerpir; 14 Hoffell.

other hand that peneplanation and valley erosion in Iceland had been extremely rapid, and this is not at all easy to comprehend. Absolute dating of the topmost plateau group is very much to be desired.

A fossil flora is found at a number of horizons in the plateau (Fig. 2). In the lowest ones, a temperate or warm-temperate climate is indicated. But with increasing height the flora takes on a cooler character. Pflug (1959) has divided the flora into several types:

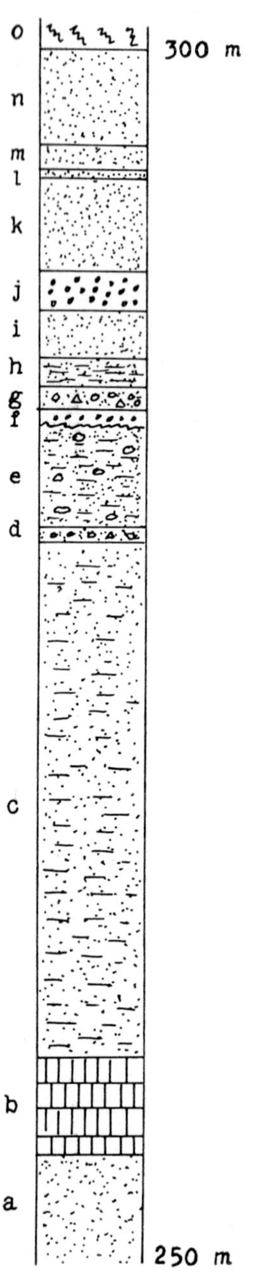

FIG. 3. The Litlisandur Glacial Horizon, 250–300 m above sea level. (a) Brown sandstone; (b) some lavas with strong reverse magnetization, basis of the regional magnetic group R_3; (c) light and dark brown clay and fine sandstone, 20 m thick, the surface of which is distinctly glacially striated (direction N. 50° W.); (d) grey-brown conglomerate with striated basalt cobbles (moraine), ½ m thick; (e) a 5 m thick layer of reddish-grey clay with scattered striated basalt stones (moraine), the reddish color of which was acquired probably before the deposition of (f). The surface of (e) is broken up (frost action), and debris from (e) is incorporated in (f); (f) conglomerate containing scattered basalt blocks, larger than are found in (e); (g) a 1 m thick, brown conglomerate with glacially striated basalt blocks (moraine); (h) a 1 m thick varve-clay with grey and reddish layers; (i) brown sandstone, 2 m thick; (j) 1–2 m of fine basalt gravel with numerous rhyolite pebbles; (k) a 4 m thick brown sandstone layer; (l) a thin layer, 10–20 cm thick, of greenish-grey clay, possibly mud from the bottom of a lake; (m) 1 m light brown loess with plant remains (leaves), suggesting willows, birch and alder; pollen has not been found; (n) 4 m of brown sandstone; (o) a very thick layer of primary volcanic "palagonite" breccia of reverse magnetization.

(1) A Deep-Lower Tertiary flora of warm character.
(2) A mixed flora with warm and cool elements.
(3) A Tertiary flora of Hoffell and Tjörnes type, ranging perhaps from Upper Miocene to Upper Pliocene.
(4) An Upper Tertiary and Pleistocene type flora.
(5) A Pleistocene type flora.

This scheme represents in a very broad sense a chronological order. But it has been revealed that rather early there were considerable fluctuations between "warm" and "cool" floras, whether or not this is a reflection of climatic alternations or of the repeated and rapid changes in the other external conditions which I have mentioned earlier.

In western Iceland the localities of Skardströnd and the Northwestern Peninsula belong to Pflug's first type. Hredavatn and Stafholt in Borgarfjördur still belong to this group, but Sleggjulaekur, a little higher than Hredavatn, pertains to the second type. In the topmost plateau group we then have the horizon of Litlisandur (Hvalfjördur) with a leaf bed in loess above varve-clay and a moraine on a clearly glacier-striated floor (Fig. 3). This is the lowest known glacial horizon in western Iceland. Above it are certainly three reverse magnetic periods and three normal ones, and more probably the total number of magnetic periods above this horizon is closer to 10. Pollen has not been found in this horizon nor have the leaves been analyzed by experts. They seem to belong to willows, birch, and alder.

FIG. 4. Drawing of the impression of a plant on the lower face of a basalt lava. The plant stem is about 25 cm long, and the width of it and the branches is 3–5 mm From Grafardalur near Hvalfjördur. The lower surface of the lava must have consolidated before the plant was burned.

In eastern Iceland the lowest plant horizon is that of Gerpir. It is considered as Lowest Tertiary or even Uppermost Cretaceous by Pflug (1959).

On top of this we have a 4500 m thick pile of lavas that have been mapped by Walker (1959). Near the top of the pile, in which Walker did not find any unconformity, are the lignite seams of Hólmatindur and Tungufell. The former seems to belong to the Lower Tertiary on palynological grounds (Schwarzbach, private communication) and this is in keeping with the lack of an unconformity between it and Gerpir. But a widely divergent view has been expressed concerning Tungufell to which I shall return soon.

Farther inland we have still higher members of the plateau basalts. These form a thick group that contains lignites of a much cooler character than that of Gerpir; they belong to Pflug's third or fourth types. Rather high up in this group the locality Bessastadaá has a flora comparable to that of the warmest zone of the Pliocene Tjörnes sediments (Pflug, 1959). In the close neighborhood, and almost certainly below Bessastadaá, the locality Hengifoss shows a flora of a much cooler character. Pflug interprets it as a cold period at the beginning of or at the end of a glacial time.

A number of localities at Jökuldalur and Vopnafjördur, which belong to this group of basalts, have a flora comparable to that of Bessastadaá, but it has also been found that the flora is horizontally quite variable (Jux, 1960). Pflug and Jux place this flora into the Upper Tertiary, or even the Upper Pliocene.

Let us now return to Tungufell. According to the mapping by Walker, this locality should be close to the Hólmatindur lignite and we must put this far below the above-mentioned Upper Tertiary inland basalts. However, Meyer and Pirrit (1957) give an Upper Pliocene or Lower Pleistocene age for Tungufell on a palynological basis. Also Jux (1960) concludes that the Tungufell flora shows a striking similarity to the flora of the inland basalts, which he is inclined to put into the Upper Pliocene. The conditions are thus quite perplexing. A possible solution of the difficulties is the assumption that the warm flora of the Lowest Tertiary in Iceland was very soon replaced by a much cooler flora that, with little variation, persisted throughout all the rest of the Tertiary.

In the Icelandic lignites Pflug has found some 50 pollen species, including nearly 20 new ones, i.e. not previously found elsewhere. He points out that whereas European and North American pollen types of this time are considered nearly identical, the Icelandic types show marked differences. They present closer affinity with the Paleocene of Spitsbergen and with the Lower Tertiary of Japan. Macroscopic remains have also rendered about 50 species if we include the old determination made by Heer (1868).

The results of Pflug's work suggest that in the Lower Tertiary, and perhaps still later, Iceland was not connected with lands in the east or west but instead there were rather connections with more northerly lands.

Finally, it may be recalled that, on the basis of the Eocene flora, Chaney (1940) concluded that the poles and the continents in the Arctic to Sub-Arctic areas were practically at their present relative position. The same data would seem, among others, to indicate that the influence of the Atlantic waters was felt in Spitsbergen as it is today. Provisional results of paleomagnetism in Iceland (Th. Sigurgeirsson, private communication) give for the Lower Tertiary pole a position of about 75°N., 70°W. (Smith Sound) which would imply a latitude of 70° for Iceland, instead of the present 65°. On the other hand, the paleomagnetically located pole for the Upper Tertiary in Iceland (Sigurgeirsson, 1957) shows no sure difference from the present geographic pole.

REFERENCES

ÁSKELSSON, J. (1954). Some Tertiary plants from Iceland. *Náttúrufr.* **24**, 92–96.

CHANEY, R. W. (1940). Tertiary forests and continental history. *Bull. Geol. Soc. Amer.* **51**, 469–486.

EINARSSON, Tr. (1957). Der Paläomagnetismus der isländischen Basaltes und seine stratigraphische Bedeutung. *Neues Jahrb. Geol. Paläontlog.* Mh. 159–175.

EINARSSON, Tr. (1960). The plateau basalt in Iceland. Int. Geol. Congr. XXI. Guide to excursion No. A2 (Iceland): 5–20.

HEER, O. (1868). *Flora fossilis Arctica I.* Zürich.

JUX, U. (1960). Zur Geologie des Vopnafjord-Gebietes in Nordost-Island. *Geologie* **9**, Bh. 28, 1–57.

MEYER, B. L. and PIRRIT, J. (1957). On the pollen and diatom flora contained in the surtarbrandur of East Iceland. *Proc. Roy. Soc. Edinb.* **61**, 262–275.

PFLUG, H. D. (1959). Sporenbilder aus Island und ihre stratigraphische Deutung. *Neues Jahrb. Geol. Paläontolog.* Abh. 107, 141–172.

SCHWARZBACH, M. (1955). Allgemeiner Überblick der Klimageschichte Islands. *Neues Jahrb. Geol Paläontolog* Mh. 97–130.

SCHWARZBACH, M. (1959). Die Beziehungen zwischen Europa und Amerika als geologisches Problem. Kölner Universitätsreden, No. 23: 1-39.

SCHWARZBACH, M. and PFLUG, H. D. (1957). Das Klima des jüngeren Tertiärs in Island. *Neues Jahrb. Geol. Paläontolog.* Abh. 104: 279–296.

SIGURGEIRSSON, Th. (1957). Direction of magnetization in Icelandic basalts. *Phil. Mag.* Suppl. 6 (22), 240–246.

WALKER, G. P. L. (1959). Geology of the Reydarfjördur Area, Eastern Iceland. *Quart, J. Geol.* **114**, 367-393.

THE GEOLOGICAL KNOWLEDGE OF THE NORTH ATLANTIC CLIMATES OF THE PAST

MARTIN SCHWARZBACH

Geologisches Institut, Universität Köln, Cologne, Germany

THE climatic history of the northern Atlantic is of great importance for the understanding of the history of the biota in this region. But we can reconstruct it only in fragments. This is caused partly by the fact the the sea-covered areas of the Earth give only few outcrops and insights to the geologist; the islands are an exception, but there are not many in the northern Atlantic. It is true that the situation has improved since it is now technically possible to bring up cores from the ocean floor. Thus we can gain at least some additional facts about the Quaternary and in part the Tertiary too, and this is, of course, the time which is especially interesting for us. But as concerns the Pre-Tertiary period, we can rely only on the adjacent continental areas, i.e. Europe and North America, and on Greenland and some other islands.

Here we have to wholly disregard Iceland, at least at first, for there are no known sediments older than Tertiary. The oldest rocks of the island are basalts. It is not impossible that this volcanism began in the Upper Cretaceous as it is supposed to have done in Greenland, but that is without special importance for the climatic history, and only the plant-bearing Tertiary beds of Iceland reveal something about it.

We can distinguish 4 or 5 great divisions in this climatic history. Their time-span varies greatly, and they are known to be very different in kind. In part they differ considerably as regards climate. Their respective boundaries are arbitrary, partly conditioned by the state of the investigation. These divisions are:

1. Pre-Cambrian.
2. Eocambrian.
3. Paleo- and Mesozoic.
4. Tertiary.
5. Quaternary.

1. PRE-CAMBRIAN

The Pre-Cambrian, i.e. the period which is older than 600 million years, can be treated in a few sentences because we know nearly nothing of it. Neither the large Pre-Cambrian areas of Scandinavia nor those of Canada or

Greenland with their generally highly metamorphic rocks give us sufficient paleoclimatic information. Moreover, we do not know the paleographic situation in the North Atlantic region at that time. It is true that the Lewisian gneisses of the Scottish Hebrides are regarded as equivalents of the Canadian–Greenlandian shield. Hans Stille (1958), for instance, draws an eastern projection of this shield which comprises the northern Atlantic including Iceland; he called it "Laurentia Minor" (in analogy to the projection of Asia Minor). But that is an hypothetical, though possible, idea.

It is, therefore, impossible to say how far the North Atlantic region was temporarily influenced by a glacial climate like the one presumed for Canada in Huronian time—perhaps 1 billion years B.P.—taking the cobalt tillites into consideration.

2. EOCAMBRIAN

The first important fix-point at the turn of the Pre-Cambrian to Cambrian is in the so-called Eocambrian. This period is short, extending approximately some 100,000 or, at most, some million years; it has an age of perhaps 600 million years. But in many places it is characterized very well by moraine-like sediments, the so-called "tillites". There is no doubt that many of these are not true morainal deposits but pseudo-tillites. The stratigraphical position is also uncertain in many cases, but there remains a lot of localities where we must suppose glacial activities, especially in regions surrounding the North Atlantic. Investigation of those phenomena started first in the Norwegian mountains. Now we do also know such deposits from Sweden, Spitsbergen, eastern and northern Greenland, and farther—but more doubtfully—from the British Isles, Normandy, and eastern Bohemia. At typical localities we find polished and striated boulders, striated pavement, and superposition of fossiliferous Cambrian. Not so clear are the occurrences in North America. But the above-mentioned tillites found between Greenland and Sweden make it nearly certain that there was an Arctic climate with big glaciers or inland ice in the North Atlantic area during the Eocambrian.

It is remarkable that nearly all these tillites are situated in regions with a recent or Pleistocene glaciation. Therefore they should actually present no more problems than the Quaternary Ice Ages do. However, there are also occurrences in other continents, and these make the Eocambrian Ice Age a puzzle.

3. PALEO- AND MESOZOIC

The following division of the Paleo- and Mesozoic comprises *ca.* 500 million years—a very long period. But it is possible to treat it collectively for it presents rather uniform climatic features. There is much climatic information available in Europe and North America, Greenland, and Spitsbergen.

Not only floras and faunas, but also sediments give valuable information, especially the rather thick limestones and the evaporites.

If we consider only Greenland and the other Arctic islands in this connection, we must mention the limestones of the Cambrian and Ordovician, the Old Red beds in east Greenland, the coals of the Upper Devonian and Lower Carboniferous on Bear Island and Spitsbergen, gypsum beds in the Upper Carboniferous of Spitsbergen and Greenland, reefs in the Rhaeto-Liassic of Jameson Land, in the Cretaceous of Kome, Atane, and Patoot in western Greenland, Spitsbergen, and King Charles Land.

All these occurrences prove the same thing: that for a very long time there was a climate completely different from today. There was no Arctic; not just a moderate, but a warm or very warm climate existed. In another connection I have explained comprehensively that the North Atlantic belonged to the tropical reef-belt during the Paleozoic; Franz Lotze (1957) has shown that also the Paleozoic belt of the northern evaporite zone, i.e. the hot desert belt of the Earth, was situated there. In the Mesozoic, the temperatures were already somewhat lower, e.g. in Greenland, and the northern boundary of the reef corals shifted farther to the south. But the Mesozoic floras prove that very favorable climatic conditions were still present.

The Rhaeto-Liassic floras of Jameson Land alone have revealed some 200 different species. I mention further the famous leaves and fruit of the bread-fruit tree, *Artocarpus*, described in 1890 by Nathorst from the Cretaceous of Greenland.

I would like to add that the modern direct measurements of temperature with the aid of O^{18}/O^{16} isotopes fit in rather well with the geologically determined climate. Belemnites from the Scottish Jurassic gave sea temperatures of 17–23°C, from Alaska of 17°. That is somewhat more than 10° higher than today.

It is not yet possible to say if there were large climatic fluctuations in the Paleo- and Mesozoic of the northern Atlantic. Their existence seems possible, especially at the turn of the Carboniferous-Permian with the big inland glaciations of the Southern Hemisphere. But the influence of the Gondwana Ice Ages must not have been large, in analogy with the small influence which the Quaternary glaciations did show in the tropics.

In any case, we do not find positive indications for cool temperatures in the northern Atlantic and its surroundings. There are almost no tillites of Paleo- or Mesozoic age. What has been described as such is very uncertain, taking for instance the much-mentioned Squantum tillite near Boston; its glacial origin is as doubtful as its stratigraphic position.

This is not the right occasion to discuss the cause of the warm climate in the North Atlantic region during Paleo- and Mesozoic time. But it must be emphasized that another position of the pole and the equator would be a very good explanation, at least in the Paleozoic. This fits in very well with modern paleomagnetic results as well as with paleoclimatic reconstructions in other continents. The climatic map of Devonian time which I published some time ago may illustrate this problem (see also Fig. 1).

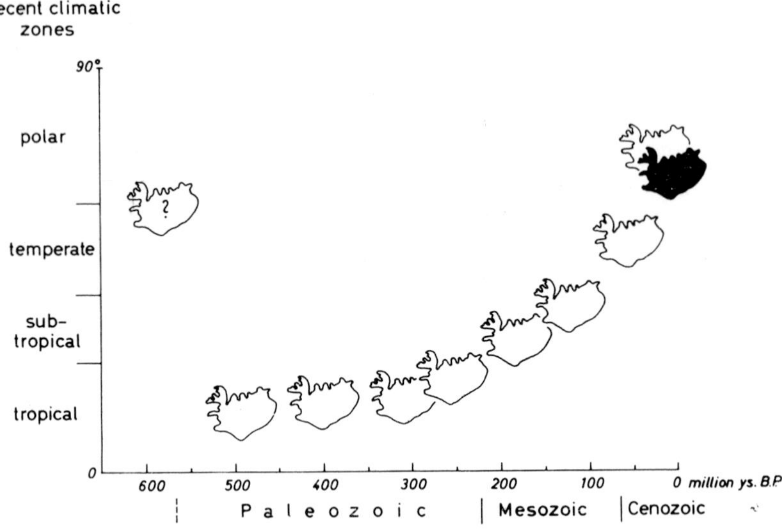

FIG. 1. The climatic position of Iceland, according to geological results, during the last 600 million years. Only the recent position (shown in black) is definite, all others are more or less hypothetical, and more so the farther back we go into the past. Paleomagnetic data were not used in the construction of the figure. The shifting position may be due (especially in the Paleozoic time) in part to continental drift. Design by Dr. L. Ahorner.

4. TERTIARY

There is no sharp boundary between the Mesozoic and the Tertiary, a period which lasted from *ca.* 70 to 1 million years B.P. At least in the Lower Tertiary we find climatic conditions similar to those in the Cretaceous and the temperatures of high latitudes were much higher than today. There existed no polar ice caps, but instead rich tree vegetation even on the islands nearest the pole.

Nevertheless we will consider the Tertiary separately; first, because the climate changed decisively in the younger Tertiary; second, because we now have much more and better climatic indicators, also from Iceland, as I mentioned earlier.

The Tertiary tree floras of Iceland were the very first to be known, for as early as in 1772 (190 years ago), Eggert Ólafsson from Iceland carefully described the plant impressions of Brjánslaekur in northwestern Iceland. Afterwards many other polar floras were discovered. "Polar flora" means all

Arctic floras, especially of the Tertiary, but partly also of Pre-Tertiary age, which contrast so impressively with the poorer recent vegetation. The pioneer paleo-botanist of the polar floras was the Swiss Oswald Heer who published his famous *Flora fossilis arctica* in 1868 and later.

We must mention here especially the following places where Tertiary Arctic floras have been found: Iceland, Greenland, Spitsbergen, King Charles Land and Grinnell Land.

The southernmost occurrences are those in Iceland. Heer (1868) cited 41 plant species from here; he and other authors mention *Pinus*, *Picea*, *Abies*, *Tsuga*, *Sequoia*, *Cryptomeria*, *Liriodendron*, *Laurus*, *Sassafras*, *Platanus*, *Planera*, *Dombeyopsis*, *Acer*, *Rhus*, *Rhamnus*, *Vitis*, *Alnus*, *Betula*, *Corylus*, *Fagus*, *Quercus*, *Juglans*, *Salix*, *Ulmus*, *Vaccinium*, *Viburnum*. However, the determinations are based on leaf impressions and therefore they are in part very uncertain. Berry (1930), who revised critically all polar floras in 1930, let pass as plants that might justly be considered of a cool temperate climate only the following: *Platanus*, *Liriodendron*, *Acer*, *Juglans*, *Gingko*, *Fraxinus*, and *Hicoria*. Heer (*loc. cit.*) inferred a climate with an annual average temperature of at least 9°C. That may be rather true.

Later on, Áskelsson (1946) has described also some pollen, and at my suggestion Pflug (1956, 1959) studied in more detail the pollen floras of Iceland, especially from the lignites (Icelandic: surtarbrandur). Also Meyer and Pirrit (1957) and Jux (1960) made pollen-analytical investigations here. But the pollen has more importance as regards stratigraphy and not so much concerning paleoclimatology.

Finally, E. Schönfeld (1956) studied fossil Icelandic woods. He found among others, *Ilex* and supposed that the Icelandic *Ilex* and also *Picea* had their nearest relations in North American species.

In Greenland the leaves of willow, poplar, birch, and hazel dominate according to the revisions of Berry (1930). But there also are represented *Liquidambar*, *Ulmus*, *Platanus*, *Sassafras*, *Fraxinus*, *Cornus*, *Liriodendron*, *Acer*, and *Vitis*.

In a rather new paper Schloemer-Jaeger (1958) cites from Spitsbergen above all *Sequoia langsdorfic*, *Metasequoia occidentalis*, and *Cercidiphyllum arcticum*. The average January temperature must have been higher than 0°C. There are also pollen-analytical studies by Manum (1954).

Grinnell Land is the locality nearest to the Pole, 82° N. Lat. According to Berry (1930) its Tertiary flora consists of *Equisetum*, *Taxodium*, *Pinus*, *Abies*, *Populus*, *Betula*, and *Corylus*.

This last locality, especially, shows that the Tertiary polar floras have nothing to do with tropical or even only subtropical vegetation; they are ordinary floras of moderate climate. They fit in with the picture of the Tertiary climatic belts of the whole Earth, and these belts were generally shifted polewards (cf. Chaney, 1940; Schwarzbach, 1946).

With higher temperatures in the polar region there is, of course, no change in the unusual distribution of day and night so characteristic for high latitudes; that means we have the additional problem of the polar night, of short- and long-day plants. But, considering the successful cultivation of hundreds of plants by Icelandic greenhouse gardeners, among them many plants from subtropical regions, we must admit that this problem cannot be a difficult one.

There exists the real difficulty that we do not know the exact age of the Tertiary polar floras. In part they seem to be of older Tertiary age. Pollen-analysis also points in that direction. But we can only express conjectures as long as we have no reference to securely dated beds of mammals or marine faunas or have no absolute age determinations.

We must suppose—as everywhere on the Earth—that the younger Tertiary was cooler than the older, and that there was a gradual transition to the Quaternary Ice Age. The Pliocene marine beds of Tjörnes in northern Iceland—the only Pre-Quaternary marine sediments of the island—indeed show such faunas. The faunas of the lower parts of the Tjörnes beds required higher temperatures than the recent sea. (I have supposed a difference of 5°C according to the faunal list of Bárdarson, 1925.) But the temperatures of the youngest Pliocene can have been only slightly higher than now.

Of special interest in this connection are the studies by Jón Jónsson (1954) in the region of Hornafjördur, southeastern Iceland. He found tillites there, overlain by lignites. The pollen-analytic investigations by Pflug (1956) in the Geological Institute of Cologne showed that the lignites may be from younger Tertiary, meaning that moraine-depositing glaciers already existed before this time (i.e. also in Early Tertiary time). We do not need to imagine a large Vatnajökull at this time, but at least we must take into account small Tertiary glaciers. The general gradual climatic deterioration of the Tertiary in Iceland led temporarily and locally to glacial climatic conditions. We know nothing—at least not directly—of the other North Atlantic regions in this respect, but we can suppose similar conditions in Greenland and Spitsbergen; all the more so because Early Tertiary glaciers already existed in Alaska, according to studies by Miller (1953).

For the problem of the development of biota in the North Atlantic it is of great interest to know a little not only about the Tertiary climate but also about paleogeographic conditions on the whole. Generally we can say that the climatic picture allows no room for continental drift, at least not on a big scale. That is in agreement with paleo-magnetic results. We must suppose that the cause of the warm Tertiary climate in Europe was partly a powerful Gulf Stream which could flow unchecked far to the east and northeast. Therefore, paleoclimatologists have no reason to construct a land-bridge between Europe and North America; on the contrary, the evidence speaks more *against* an emerged Faeroes–Iceland ridge. I mention, by the way, that the distribution of Tertiary mammal faunas in Europe–Asia–North America do not require such a land-bridge.

It is to be hoped that the study of deep-sea cores will give more certain answers to these questions.

5. QUATERNARY

The Quaternary Ice Age which began *ca.* 1 million years ago is of greatest importance for the recent flora and fauna of the North Atlantic regions. Nevertheless, we can treat it relatively briefly. One fact stands without doubt: that these areas were covered more or less completely by ice during Glacial times; looking out of the windows of the University of Reykjavík, we see ice-polished rocks all around us.

But there remain some questions of special interest:

1. What was the detailed course of the Ice Age, i.e. the succession of Glacials and Interglacials?
2. Where were the ice-free refugia?
3. What about Quaternary land-bridges?

The *first* question concerning the stratigraphy of the Quaternary Ice Age can be answered only on a large scale. Generally ice-bordered and temporarily ice-covered areas are much less fit for a detailed stratigraphic division than more distant regions. This is due to the fact that ice-erosion often removes older deposits completely. But still it is certain also that in the polar regions Glacial periods alternated with Interglacials in which climate, and vegetation, were about the same as today or even a little more favorable. There are several known Interglacials in Iceland, for instance from Snaefellsnes and from the neighborhood of Reykjavík, and Thórarinsson will tell us something about new finds in southern Iceland. Likewise, it seems to be certain that these Interglacial floras and faunas belong to several, i.e. temporally different, Interglacial periods.

There are also Interglacials in Greenland, from where Bryan (1954) described an occurrence of *Picea mariana*, and also in Alaska and Arctic Canada (Terasmae *et al.*; cf. Craig and Fyles, 1961).

Until now it has been completely impossible to equate all these Interglacials with the standard divisions of Europe or North America.

But the studies of deep-sea sediments will perhaps help us to get better results. The cores from the floor of the oceans prove a repeated alternation of warm and cool periods, confirmed by foraminiferal faunas or directly isotopic temperatures. The core no. 280, for instance—from the northern Atlantic at 35° N. Lat.—shows according to Emiliani (1958) a change between temperatures of 11° and 18°C. The 11° record corresponds to a Glacial, the 18° to an Interglacial time, with perhaps an age of 90,000 years. But most age calculations are very uncertain, especially for the periods beyond C^{14} determinations, i.e. older than 50,000 years. Therefore we will get valuable new results for Quaternary stratigraphy and chronology only with better age determinations and a more sure correlation with continental events.

The *second* question concerns the ice-free refugia during Glacial times. They can originate where precipitation is too low to produce glaciers, though temperatures may be sufficiently low; for example, the recent Peary Land in north Greenland. Ice-free refugia can also occur where steep mountain ranges prevent snow accumulation. All regions with pronounced relief, for instance Iceland, had such places. Thórarinsson (1937) has given a map which indicates the rather large areas without inland ice or at best local glaciation. We can suppose that the glacial climate at these places was about the same as it is near the border of recent inland ice areas.

Finally, the *third* question: Quaternary land-bridges have been demanded as an explanation in certain Ice Age hypotheses or to explain the peculiarities of the recent or Interglacial flora and fauna, especially in Iceland. But the geologist must be skeptical of such suppositions, for he cannot find any indications that at any time in the Quaternary parts of the Wyville-Thompson ridge emerged from the sea. Of course, this ridge was about 100 m shallower during Glacial time because of eustatic fluctuations. But for zoo- or phyto-paleography not the Glacials but, on the contrary, the Interglacials are important—and there we must expect even higher sea levels than today!

Properly that paleoclimatologist now ought to treat the Post-glacial time accordingly, for this period has especially close relations to the recent distribution of flora and fauna. But there will be special papers regarding this problem in this symposium, and I can forego speaking on this last chapter of climatic history.

REFERENCES

Áskelsson, J. (1949). Er hin smásaeja flóra surtarbrandslaganna vaenleg til könnunar? *Sk rsla Menntaskólans í Reykjavík* **1945–46**, 1–9.

Áskelsson, J. (1956). Myndir úr jardfraedi Íslands IV. Fáeinar plöntur úr surtarbrandslögunum. *Náttúrufr.* **26**, 44–48.

Áskelsson, J. (1960). Pliocene and Pleistocene fossiliferous deposits. Int. Geol. Congr. XXI. Guide to excursion No. A2 (Iceland): 28–32.

Bárdarson, G. G. (1925). A stratigraphical survey of the Pliocene deposits at Tjörnes in northern Iceland. *Kgl. Danske Vidensk. Selsk. Biol. Medd.* **55** (5), 1–118.

Berry, E. W. (1930). The past climate of the north polar region. *Smithsonian Inst. Misc. Coll.* **82** (6), 1–29.

Bryan, M. S. (1954). Interglacial pollen spectra from Greenland. *Danmarks Geol. Unders. II. Raekke*, No. 80. 65–72.

Chaney, R. W. (1940). Tertiary forests and continental history. *Geol. Soc. Amer. Bull.* **51**, 486–486.

Craig, B. C. and Fyles, J. G. (1961). Pleistocene geology of Arctic Canada. In G. O. Raasch (ed.). *Geology of the Arctic*, Toronto, 403–420.

Emiliani, C. (1958). Paleotemperature analysis of core 280 and Pleistocene correlations. *J. Geol.* **66,** 264–275.

Heer, O. (1868). *Flora fossilis arctica.* I. Island. Zürich.

Jónsson, J. (1954). Outline of the geology of the Hornafjördur region. *Geogr. Ann.* **36**, 146–161.

JUX, U. (1960). Zur Geologie des Vopnafjord-Gebietes in Nordost-Island. *Geologie* **9**, Bh. 28, 1–57.

LOTZE, F. (1957). *Steinsalz und Kalisalze. I.* 2nd ed. Berlin.

MANUM, S. (1954). Pollen og sporer i tertiaere kull fra Vestspitsbergen. *Norsk Polarinstitutt Skr.* **79**, 1–10.

MEYER, B. L. and PIRRIT, J. (1957). On the pollen and diatom flora contained in the surtarbrandur of East Iceland. *Proc. Roy. Soc. Edinb.* **B61**, 262–275.

MILLER, D. J. (1953). Late Cenozoic marine glacial sediments and marine terraces of Middleton Island, Alaska. *J. Geol.* **61**, 17–40.

NATHORST, A. G. (1890). Über die Reste eines Brotfruchtbaums, *Artocarpus Dicksoni* n.sp., aus cenomanen Kreideablagerungen Grönlands. *Sv. Vet. Akad. Handl.* N.F. **27** (1), 1–10.

PFLUG, H. D. (1956). Sporen und Pollen von Tröllatunga (Island) und ihre Stellung zu den pollenstratigraphischen Bildern Mitteleuropas. *Neues Jahrb. Geol. Paläontolog.* Abh. 102, 409–430.

PFLUG, H. D. (1959). Sporenbilder aus Island und ihre stratigraphische Bedeutung. *Neues Jahrb. Geol. Paläontolog.* Abh. 107, 141–172.

SCHLOEMER-JAEGER, A. (1958). Alttertiäre Pflanzen aus Flözen der Brögger-Halbinsel Spitzbergens. *Palaeontogr.* **B 104**, 39–103.

SCHÖNFELD, E. (1956). Fossile Hölzer von Island. *Neues Jahrb. Geol. Paläontolog.* Abh. 104, 191–225.

SCHWARZBACH, M. (1946). Klima und Klimagürtel im Alttertiär. *Naturwiss.* **33**, 355–361.

SCHWARZBACH, M. (1949). Fossile Korallenriffe und Wegeners Drifthypothese. *Naturwiss.* **36**, 229–233.

SCHWARZBACH, M. (1955). Allgemeiner Überblick der Klimageschichte Islands. *Neues Jahrb. Geol. Paläontolog.* Mh. 97–130.

SCHWARZBACH, M. (1961). *Das Klima der Vorzeit.* 2 ed. Stuttgart.

SCHWARZBACH, M. and PFLUG, H. D. (1956). Das Klima des jüngeren Tertiärs in Island. *Neues Jahrb. Geol. Paläontolog.* Abh. 104, 279–298.

STILLE, H. (1958). Die assyntische Tektonik im geologischen Erdbild. *Beih. Geol. Jahrb.* **22**, 1–255.

TERASMAE, J. (1960). Contributions to Canadian palynology. No. 2. *Geol. Survey Canada, Bull.* **56**, 1–41.

THÓRARINSSON, S. (1937). The main geological and topographical features of Iceland. *Geogr. Ann.* **19**, 161–175.

THE ATLANTIC FLOOR*

Bruce C. Heezen and Marie Tharp

Columbia University, Department of Geology and Lamont Geological Observatory, Palisades, New York

Former continental connections across present seas have been frequently proposed by botanists, zoologists and paleontologists striving to understand the affinities and routes of dispersal of land biota. Land connections across present epicontinental seas have clearly occurred during the Pleistocene due to eustatic fluctuations of sea level. More difficult is the question of earlier connections across the deep seas (Heezen *et al.*, 1959).

FORMER LAND CONNECTIONS ACROSS THE DEEP SEA

Geophysicists and oceanographers have long been skeptical of sunken ancient continents or sinuous isthmian links across the deep sea (Bucher, 1952; Ewing, 1952). The structure of the ocean floor in depths greater than 4000 m is fundamentally different from that beneath the continents. The Mohorovicic discontinuity, the boundary between the crust and mantle, lies at some 30 to 40 km below the continents. However, below the ocean's surface the Mohorovicic discontinuity lies at a depth of only 10 to 12 km. The rocks lying immediately above the Mohorovicic discontinuity are known entirely on the basis of their seismic-wave velocities. In a typical deep-sea crustal section $\frac{1}{2}$ to 1 km of sediment lies above a thin 1 to 2 km layer in which the seismic-wave velocity is between 4 and 5 km/sec (Hill, 1957). This second layer is sometimes ascribed to altered basalt and sometimes to lithified sediments, although it seems more likely that the material is igneous rather than sedimentary. Beneath this lies a layer 3 to 5 km thick which has a velocity of about 6.5 km/sec. The mantle below the Mohorovicic discontinuity has a velocity of about 8.2 km/sec. Hundreds of measurements beneath the deep-sea floors have revealed this column to be essentially universal. However, in the central part of the Mid-Oceanic Ridge, in the Norwegian Sea, in the northern North Atlantic and in other areas (primarily where the depth is less than 4000 m), the crustal structure is quite different, the seismic velocity of the deepest observed layer ranging between 6.8 and 7.5 km/sec. Recent seismological studies in Iceland have led Tryggvason (1962) to conclude that the 7.4 km/sec layer reaches to tens of kilometers depths below Iceland, an emerged portion

* Lamont Geological Observatory Contribution No. 577.

of the Mid-Oceanic Ridge. The same velocity material has been found beneath the crest of the Mid-Atlantic Ridge and over much of the floor of the Norwegian Sea and the Labrador Sea (Ewing and Ewing, 1959).

If a continent subsided to oceanic depths (greater than 4000 m), one would expect the crustal structure to be markedly different in the area formerly occupied by the continent. In addition, in order to maintain isostatic balance, a yet unknown process, whereby a thick section of continental-type crustal rocks is transformed into thin section oceanic crustal rocks, is required. Thus, in view of these difficulties, it seems necessary to limit any consideration of land connections across the deep sea to "island stepping stones" and to continental displacements.

Flat-topped seamounts of the central Pacific were islands in the Cretaceous (Hamilton, 1956). Thus numerous "stepping stones" did exist across many parts of the Pacific in the Cretaceous. These flat-topped seamounts (guyots) are less plentiful in the Atlantic. Botanists in particular have serious reservations about a "stepping stone" type of land bridge, for they maintain that small islands would not develop continental-type vegetation and therefore would not act as a bridge.

The continental displacement hypothesis, once rejected for lack of a mechanism, has received new support in the last decade from the results of the studies of paleomagnetism. The gradual opening of the Atlantic by 2000 miles in the Mesozoic and Early Tertiary is supported by a consistent discrepancy between paleomagnetic measurements made in North America and Europe (Runcorn, 1959). The fact that no sediments older than Cretaceous have been found on the Atlantic deep-sea floor is not in opposition to this view, although it might be argued that the few hundred outcrops of Tertiary and Cretaceous sediment constitute too small a sample upon which to base such an important generalization (Ericson *et al.*, 1961). Recently, detailed studies of the thickness of the sedimentary layer which lies above the oceanic crust have been made by the seismic-reflection technique (Ewing, 1961). In general it is found that there is an exceptionally homogeneous 1–2 km layer which overlies a layer of similar thickness which in turn rests on an intensely irregular sub-bottom topography. The material lying beneath the second sedimentary layer is presumably one which refraction measurements have indicated to have a crustal velocity of 4.5 to 5.5 km/sec. Both sedimentary layers thicken markedly upon approaching the continents, apparently in response to greater rates of sedimentation.

When approaching the Mid-Oceanic Ridge, the thickness of sediment thins markedly. On the flanks of the Mid-Atlantic Ridge the irregular deeper layer apparently reaches the surface in many areas, sediment being restricted to the bottoms of occasional intermontane basins. Near the crest of the Mid-Oceanic Ridge sediment is virtually absent. The absence of sediment from the crest of the Mid-Oceanic Ridge has been taken as evidence of the recent origin of this topography (Heezen, 1960). The continental displacements which may have created the Atlantic in the Mesozoic and Tertiary may be the result of a process which continually added material along the crest of the Mid-Oceanic Ridge. The mechanism of this continual addition of new crust has been variously ascribed to mantle convection currents which rise beneath the ridge, diverge and carry the oceanic crust toward the continents (Dietz, 1961). The sinking of these currents below the continents may, in turn, cause compression and uplift in the continents. However, others prefer to explain the displacement of continents through an overall expansion of the interior of the earth (Heezen, 1960; Wilson, 1960). Needless to say, for students of the Atlantic it makes little difference which of the two hypotheses is favored, for in regard to the Atlantic the effects of either mechanism would be identical.

It might occur to some that the absence of sediments from the crest of the Mid-Atlantic Ridge could be explained in terms of a recent emergence. It might be argued that the sediments were eroded from the Mid-Atlantic Ridge by subaerial erosion and that the ridge has only recently been submerged beneath the ocean. However, if this were true one would expect to find exceptionally thick deposits of sediment on the margins of the Mid-Oceanic Ridge near the former shorelines. The recent data indicate that the entire width of the Mid-Atlantic Ridge from deep basin on one side to deep basin on the other is nearly devoid of sediment. This would require that the entire Mid-Atlantic Ridge some 1200 miles wide be raised 3 or 4 km above the adjacent basins in order to affect denudation and that the products of denudation lie in the basins. However, the pattern of distribution of sediment thickness in the basins does not support this view, for there is a gradual increase in thickness toward the continents and no evidence of thickening along the margins of the Mid-Oceanic Ridge. The discovery of a few freshwater diatoms in a core from the crest of the equatorial Mid-Oceanic Ridge at one time led certain investigators to propose an emergence of a short duration (Kolbe, 1957). However, it need only be mentioned that, (1) the layer of freshwater diatoms is approximately a millimeter thick interbedded with typical deep-sea sediments, and (2) the winds blowing off Africa often carry such large quantities of diatom tests as to lay down layers of appreciable thickness on the decks of ships.

We may conclude that land connections across the deep basins of the Atlantic have not existed in the form of sunken continents, isthmian links, or closely-spaced insular "stepping stones". But it is now probable that a displacement of Europe and North America has occurred and that at some time in the Paleozoic or Early Mesozoic parts of Europe and America lay adjacent to one another without an intervening ocean. It seems unlikely that once the two continents were displaced from one another that any land connections existed where there is now deep sea.

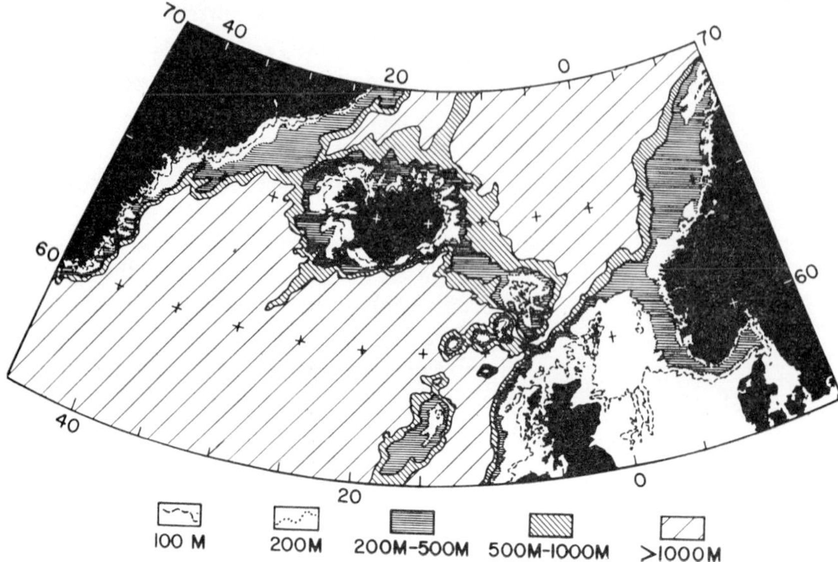

FIG. 1. Bathymetric chart of the Faeroe–Iceland–Greenland Ridge.

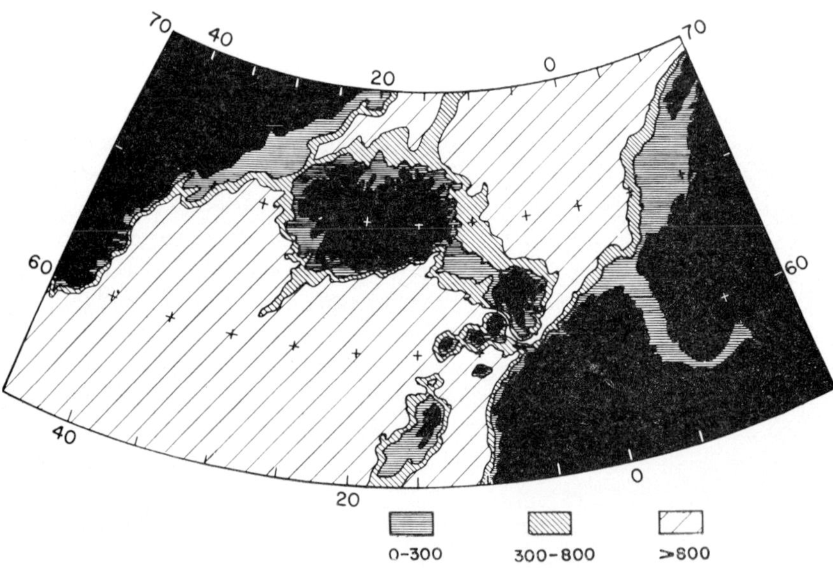

FIG. 2. Hypothetical bathymetric chart of the Faeroe–Iceland–Greenland Ridge if sea level were lowered 200 m. Current estimates of the maximum Pleistocene lowering of sea level do not exceed 160 m; thus, even if the maximum lowering of sea level during penultimate glaciation were 40 m greater than current estimates, the Faeroe–Iceland–Greenland Ridge would not provide a continuous land bridge from Europe to Iceland and Greenland. If such a connection is required by studies of the geology of the ridge or of the biota of the area, a substantial subsidence of this ridge must be assumed to have occurred in the Late Pleistocene.

FORMER LAND CONNECTIONS ACROSS SHALLOW SEAS

As shallow seas we will consider those areas considerably less than 4000 m in depth. For the Atlantic this actually consists of one connection across the Faeroe–Iceland–Greenland–Canada Ridge. Although it may well be that a connection existed between Spitzbergen and Greenland,* if a connection did exist across the Nansen Straits its disruption was probably due to the opposed continental displacements of Europe and North America.

At the present time, the 500 m contour connects almost completely across the Faeroe–Iceland–Greenland Ridge from Europe to Greenland (Fig. 1). In two small gaps, one near the Faeroes and another in Denmark Strait, depths are slightly greater. Little can be said concerning the geological history and origin of this ridge for at present no cores nor dredge hauls of ancient rock have been reported from anywhere along the ridge. Since the top of this ridge lies close to sea level, minor vertical movements of the Earth's crust could either cause an emerged land link or a submerged sill. At the present time it would seem that the Tertiary history of a possible land bridge across the Faeroe–Iceland–Greenland Ridge could be best estimated from data obtained from the fossil and contemporary biota (Löve and Löve, 1956).

On the other hand, we can perhaps be somewhat more definite about possible land connections in the Middle and Late Pleistocene. Due to the relatively short interval of time involved we can perhaps exclude really large tectonic changes in the absolute elevation of the ridge and restrict ourselves to considerations of the effects of glacial eustatic changes of sea level. In recent years studies of eustatic changes in sea level have been made in widely separated parts of the world (Fairbridge, 1961). A prominent submerged shoreline found in depths of 160 m off of North America, South America and Africa is generally ascribed to the sea level associated with the penultimate glaciation. Studies of the probable ice volume based on the distribution of ice and studies of its probable thickness based on Post-glacial rebound of the land have allowed the calculation of the probable volume of water tied up in the glaciers of the penultimate glaciation (Donn *et al.*, 1962). This volume as given by Donn, Farrand and Ewing is approximately 85–100 $\times$ 10^6 km^2. This would account for lowering of sea level of approximately 140–160 m. Their estimates for the two ultimate glaciations are 70–84 and 75–88, with resulting sea level lowerings of 105–123 m and 114–134 m (Table 1). It is generally considered that the earlier glaciations were less extensive, that the maximum lowering of sea level should have occurred during the penultimate glaciation (Farrand, 1962). If the Iceland–Greenland Ridge has neither been elevated nor depressed nor seriously eroded during the past 200,000 years, then no land bridge could have existed across the Faeroe–Iceland–Greenland

* Depths in this area exceed 3000 m, recent Soviet expeditions having disproved the existence of the so-called Nansen Sill (Hope, 1959).

TABLE 1*

	Ultimate (Wisconsin)		Penultimate (Illinoian)
	Late	Early	(Maximum)
	Ice	Volumes	10^6km^2
Total glacier ice	71–84	74–88	84–99
Volume of modern glaciers†	28–35	28–35	28–35
Volume of ancient glaciers minus modern volume	43–49	46–53	56–64
Water equivalent (ice density 0.9)	38–45	41–48	50–58
	Sea-level lowering (meters)		
(Surface area of world oceans 361 × 10^6km^2)	105–123	114–134	137–159

* After Donn, W. L., Farrand, W. R. and Ewing, M. (1962).

† Minimum volume after Crary (1960), maximum after Novikov (1960), estimates of Antarctic ice.

Ridge (Fig. 2). Gaps of over 200 miles must have existed between Faeroes and Iceland and between Iceland and Greenland with prevailing depths of 100 or 200 m. Thus, if a nearly continuous land bridge between Europe and Iceland is required, it must be assumed that the Iceland–Faeroe Ridge has subsided slightly more than 200 m in the last 200,000 years since eustatic lowering alone is insufficient to account for the emergence of a land bridge during the penultimate glaciation. Such a subsidence cannot be considered geologically unreasonable, but the ultimate proof will lie in geological exploration of the ridge and in the results of the study of North Atlantic biota.

REFERENCES

BUCHER, W. H. (1952). Continental drift versus land bridges. In E. MAYR (ed.): The problem of land connections across the South Atlantic, with special references to the Mesozoic. *Bull. Amer. Mus. Nat. Hist.* **99**, 93–103.

CRARY, A. P. (1960). Status of United States scientific programs in the Antarctic. I.G.Y. Bull. 39, *Amer. Geophys. Union Trans.* **41**, 521–532.

DIETZ, R. S. (1961). Continent and ocean-basin evolution by spreading of the sea floor. *Nature* **190**, 854–857.

DONN, W. L., FARRAND, W. R., and EWING, M. (1962). Pleistocene ice volumes and sea-level lowering. *J. Geol.* **70**, 206–214.

ERICSON, D. B., EWING, M., WOLLIN, G. and HEEZEN, B. C. (1961). Atlantic deep-sea sediment cores. *Geol. Soc. Amer. Bull.* **72**, 193–286.

EWING, J. I. and EWING, W. M. (1959). Seismic refraction measurements on the Atlantic Ocean basins, Mediterranean Sea, on the Mid-Atlantic Ridge and in the Norwegian Sea. *Geol. Soc. Amer. Bull.* **70**, 291–318.

EWING, M. (1952). The Atlantic Ocean Basin. In E. MAYR (ed.): The problem of land connections across the South Atlantic, with special references to the Mesozoic. *Bull. Amer. Mus. Nat. Hist.* **99**, 87–91.

EWING, M. (1961). Address to American Geographical Society, November 1961.

FAIRBRIDGE. R. W. (1961). Eustatic changes in sea level. In L. H. AHRENS and others (ed.): *Physics and Chemistry of the Earth.* Vol. IV, 99–185. Pergamon Press, London.

FARRAND, W. (1962). Post-glacial uplift in North America. *Amer. J. Sci.* **260**, 181–199.

HAMILTON, E. L. (1956). Sunken islands of the Mid-Pacific mountains. *Geol. Soc. Amer. Memoir* **64**, 1–97.

HEEZEN, B. C. (1960). The rift in the ocean floor. *Scientific American* **203**, 98–110.

HEEZEN, B. C., THARP, M. and EWING, M. (1959). The floors of the oceans. I. The North Atlantic. *Geol. Amer. Spec. Paper* 65, 1–122.

HILL, M. N. (1957). Recent geophysical exploration of the ocean floor. In L. H. AHRENS and others (ed.): *Physics and Chemistry of the Earth*, 129–163. Pergamon Press, London.

HOPE, E. R. (1959). Geotectonics of the Arctic Ocean and the Great Arctic Magnetic Anomaly. *J. Geophys. Research* **64**, 407–427.

KOLBE, R. W. (1957). Fresh-water diatoms from Atlantic deep-sea sediments. *Science* **126**, 1053–1056.

LÖVE, A. and LÖVE, D. (1956). Cytotaxonomical conspectus of the Icelandic flora. *Acta Horti Gotoburg.* **20**, 69–291.

NOVIKOV, V. (1960). The study of the Antarctic is continuing. *Priroda* **8**, 43–52 (in Russian).

RUNCORN, S. K. (1959). Rock magnetism, *Science* **129**, 1002–1012.

TRYGGVASON, E. (1962). Crustal structure of the Iceland region from dispersion of surface waves. *Seismo, Soc. Amer. Bull.* **52** (2), 359–388.

WILSON, J. T. (1960). Some consequences of expansion of the earth. *Nature* **185**, 880–882.

RECENT STUDIES ON THE GEOLOGY OF THE FAEROES

JÓANNES RASMUSSEN

Museum of Natural History, Tórshavn, Faeroes

APART from papers written during the seventeenth and eighteenth centuries on Faeroese minerals and coal measures, the geology of the Faeroe Islands is not mentioned in the literature until about 1800.

Without going into tiring, historical details, I shall very briefly list the most important works on the geology of the Faeroes in the nineteenth century, namely the papers by Sir George Mackenzie and Th. Allan in 1814, by J. G. Forchhammer and W. C. Trevelyan in 1823–24, and by A. Helland and J. Geikie in 1880.

Sir George Mackenzie, together with Thomas Allan, paid a visit to the Faeroe Islands in 1812. The purpose of their journey was to ascertain whether special geological features observed in Iceland, where Sir George Mackenzie had visited in 1810, were to be found also in the Faeroes. In his work, Mackenzie describes some geological observations and concludes that the islands are of submarine volcanic origin. Allan shares Mackenzie's view of the volcanic origin, but does not agree with his opinion regarding the submarine eruptions. Allan's observations of striae and his words concerning them are of interest: "The rock appears to have been worn down by the friction of heavy bodies."

Eleven years later, in 1821, Forchhammer visited the Faeroe Islands together with Trevelyan, the British mineralogist and botanist. In Forchhammer's paper (1824) we find the first complete account of the geology of the Faeroe Islands. Forchhammer divides the rocks into 4 groups: (1) Trap without glassy feldspar, (2) Coal measures, (3) Porphyritic rocks, and (4) Irregular trap (dykes and sills). He shows the regional extension of these rock types on an accompanying small map.

During the next 58 years we find only a few fragmentary works on the geology of the Faeroe Islands, but in 1879 Helland and Geikie visited the Faeroe Islands. The particular purpose of the journey was to examine the glacial geology of the islands, which hitherto was as good as unknown. Basing their statements on the radiating direction of the striae and the total absence of foreign rocks, Helland (1880) and Geikie (1880) concluded that the Faeroes have had a glaciation of their own. In Helland's as well as in

Geikie's works we find, besides the glacial geology, a comprehensive account of the general geology of the Faeroes. Helland retains Forchhammer's classification of the rocks, but he uses other terms, e.g. "Anamesite" instead of "Trap without glassy feldspar", and "Dolerite" instead of "Porphyritic rocks".

While the papers by Mackenzie (1814) and Allan (1814) cannot be considered of essential importance to later geological works, this is, however, not the case with the publications by Forchhammer (1824), Helland (1880), and Geikie (1880). They have laid the basis for later studies even though points of view have changed a great deal, especially thanks to work by Peacock (1928), Walker and Davidson (1936) and subsequent investigators.

The present short account of investigations on the geology of the Faeroes in more recent years, is chiefly based on results obtained during the systematical geological mapping of the Faeroes under the auspices of the Geological Survey of Denmark.

This project was begun in 1939, but was suspended during the war. In the beginning it was conducted by Professor Arne Noe-Nygaard, and later (from 1951) it was carried on by this author at a permanent station in the Faeroes, and is now about to be concluded by both of us.

It must be emphasized that the geological mapping of the Faeroes has not been concerned solely with rock types, but also with geological development, or rather, with development of the plateau basalt volcanism. Thus, the series delimited by the mapping represent stages in volcanic development.

Attempts were made to make the map on the basis of different types of basalt, but in our experience, many difficulties arose and this system in several cases proved quite impractical. Among the problems encountered, the following may be mentioned: (1) the characteristic tapering out and overlapping of strata in the plateau basalts; (2) the very thin lava flows of varying types in certain series occurring in a large number; (3) the horizontal changes in the same lava flows, consequential to the sinking of heavier minerals.

The Faeroes belong geologically to the large Brito-Arctic, North Atlantic, or Thulean igneous region and appear as a geographically bounded link between the Scoto-Irish region and Iceland.

The geological structure of the Faeroes is very simple: a regular alternation of lava beds with pyroclastic materials, and very subordinate intra-basaltic sediments. The whole series, having a total thickness of about 3000 m, is traversed by intrusive bodies. No eruptive rocks are known from the Faeroes—neither effusive nor intrusive—of a composition other than basalt, and the substratum of these basalts is completely unknown.

As far as the age of the Faeroes is concerned, it is difficult to determine, even roughly. Only two definable species of plant fossils have been found (*Sequoia langsdorfii* and *Taxodium distichum*). However, compared with conditions in the Scoto-Irish region and in Iceland, it is reasonable to estimate the age as Eocene–Oligocene.

In the following, I shall try to give a brief account of the geological development of the Faeroes, based upon a purely schematic cut through the whole sequence of rock layers and on surface map sections of some significant localities.

THE LOWER BASALT SEQUENCE

In all probability the volcanic activity started with large fissure eruptions, and this phase is represented by a basalt series nearly 1000 m thick and petrographically very uniform, referred to below as the Lower Basalt sequence.

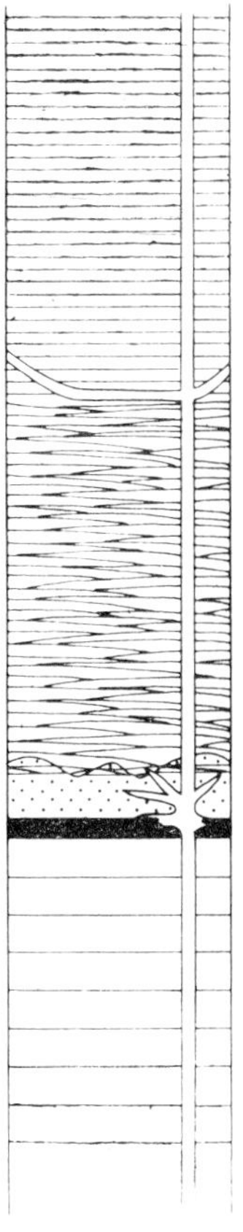

FIG. 1. Schematic cut through the Faeroean sequence: Lower Basalt sequence, Upper Basalt sequence (lower zone), and Upper Basalt sequence (upper zone). Black: Coal-bearing series; dotted: Tuff–Agglomerate zone; white: intrusions.

The Lower Basalt sequence, the oldest stratum, is exposed on Suduroy, Mykines, and Vágar beneath the Coal-bearing series (Figs. 1 and 2). As the dip on Suduroy is 3°–6° NNE., NE., and ENE., on Mykines 8°–13° ESE. and

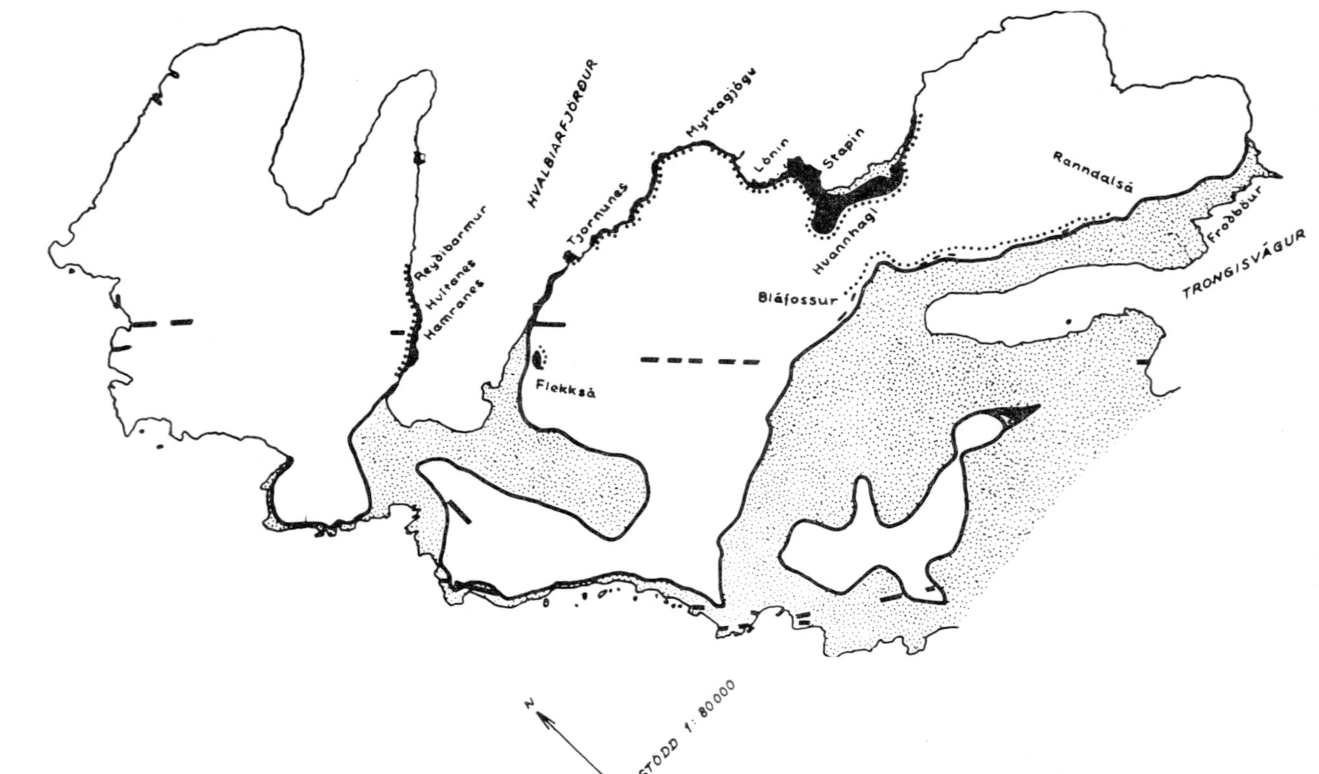

FIG. 2. Section of northern Suduroy. Fine-dotted: Lower Basalt sequence; black line: Coal-bearing series; black- and large-dotted: Tuff–Agglomerateand intrusion zone; white: Upper Basalt sequence; double line: dykes.

SE. and on Vágar 3° ESE., this sequence goes below sea level in the northern part of Suduroy, and in the western part of Vágar. An excellent view of this sequence is to be had in the naked, steep, sometimes quite vertical, rocky wall to the west. The thickness of the individual basalt beds generally ranges from 10 to 30 m, although thinner beds do occur; the greatest measured thickness of a basalt bed in this sequence is about 70 m. Petrographically the flows are very uniform. They consist of homogeneous, hard, dark, fine grained, only exceptionally porphyritic basalts often with a well-developed columnar structure. The surface of the individual flows is slaggy, porous, red, due to either the oxidation or to the heating effect of the overlying flow.

Intrabasaltic sediments are of rather subordinate significance. Besides the prevailing tuff layers, 1 to 4 m in thickness, intrabasaltic, fluvial, conglomerates and shales of almost the same thickness as the tuff layers occur, sometimes containing sporadic coal in very thin layers or lenses.

All the known part of the Lower Basalt sequence (about a 1000 m thick) is of subaerial, volcanic origin. However, since its substratum and consequently the absolute thickness of the whole sequence is unknown, as mentioned above, nothing can be stated regarding a possible earlier submarine volcanic phase.

THE COAL-BEARING SERIES

Subsequent to the formation of the Lower Basalt sequence there occurred a quiet period in the volcanic activity, an interval of a rather long duration, represented by a Coal-bearing series (Fig. 1). This rests immediately on the surface of the Lower Basalt sequence and occurs thus in the northern part of Suduroy and in the westernmost part of Vágar. On Suduroy (Fig. 2) the Coal-bearing series has its highest position in the southwest at about 425 m, and on Vágar in the northwest at about 250 m above sea level. The surface of the Lower Basalt sequence has undergone a rather high degree of subaerial weathering, and the Coal-bearing series, therefore, rests on a strongly undulating surface. The coals in the Coal-bearing series are the only ones in the Faeroes of any economical interest. They are allochtonous, deposited in a basin or a lake, and cover an area of about 23 km². In Fig. 3 is drawn a characteristic profile section through the Coal-bearing series, the thickness of which usually reaches 10–15 m. The sequence is as follows:

1. Light grayish-yellow or gray bottom clay (Faeroic: Banki).
2. Lower coal band (Faeroic: Stabbi).
3. Dark shale (Faeroic: Rann). Some coals often occur in this shale, especially in the southern area.
4. Upper coal band (Faeroic: Kolband).
5. Roof clay (Faeroic: Tak).

The roof clay is of rather variable nature, and sometimes fluvial conglomerates entirely of basaltic origin occur. They occur mainly towards the outer boundary of the coal area. The clays are all fire-resistant and without plasticity. The thickness of the individual coal bands in the profile section varies some-

FIG. 3. Profile through the Coal-bearing series.

what from place to place. In the northern area the lower coal band is thicker than the upper one, whereas the contrary is the case in the southern area.

At the transition between the two areas several coal bands often occur. The total thickness of the two coal bands ranges generally from 50 to 150 cm with an average thickness of $\frac{3}{4}$ m for the western part of the area. Towards the east and north the coals taper out.

The coals must be classified somewhere between lignite and bituminous, and appear as two types: glossy (Vitrite) and dull (Durite). The glossy coals are lustrous, hard, with conchoidal fracture and very pure. Their caloric value lies between 6000 and 6300 kcal; the ash content being below 5 per cent. The dull coals are streaky, brittle, crumble easily, and are less pure. Their caloric value lies generally between 5000 and 5500 kcal and the ash content is often close to 20 per cent, sometimes even higher.

Leaf fossils are very scarcely represented, possibly because the coals are allochtonous. As mentioned above, only two definable species have been found: *Sequoia langsdorfii* and *Taxodium distichum*.

THE TUFF–AGGLOMERATE ZONE

After the long rest period renewed volcanism set in, and the eruptive activity in the intial stage was highly explosive with a production of predominantly pyroclastic material. The deposits of pyroclastics overlying the Coal-bearing series and underlying the Upper Basalt sequence have been described as the Tuff–Agglomerate zone (Fig. 1).

The Tuff–Agglomerate zone occurs on the east side of Suduroy, on Tindhólmur, and on the west side of Vágar. On Suduroy (Fig. 2) it appears as an elongated belt, 2 to 3 km in width and about 10 km long, from the north side of Trongisvágur. It can be studied in ravines and in coastal cross-sections, where it is evident that it overlies the Coal-bearing series and is overlain, sometimes with interbeddings, by the Upper Basalt sequence. Since the deposit almost entirely consists of pyroclastic materials such as ash, lapilli, and volcanic bombs, the thickness varies considerably from place to place. Generally it is 20 to 30 m. However, thinner as well as much thicker layers occur.

It is likely that the Tuff–Agglomerate zone on Suduroy and on Vágar, where the conditions are quite analogous, covers the eruption fissures which have been feeding the Lower Basalt sequence, as well as their closest surroundings. Furthermore, since they appear along and follow the direction of the Suduroyarfjördur and the Mykines fjördur, it is tempting to suppose—as will be discussed later on—that the orientation of the inter-island straits is determined by the longitudinal bearing of these eruption fissures.

THE UPPER BASALT SEQUENCE

The explosive eruption activity was succeeded immediately by a volcanism which resulted in the formation of the Upper Basalt sequence (cf. Fig. 1). This is most likely what happened, since the Tuff–Agglomerate zone, at the boundary of the Upper Basalt sequence, alternates with thin beds belonging to this sequence. Likewise, it must be assumed that during the following stage, the volcanism was more localized along the old fissures, respresented by the numerous necks which are visible in cross- as well as longitudinal sections in coastal profiles along the straits running NW.–SE. between the northern islands.

The basalts in the Upper Basalt sequence display far greater variation from bed to bed than do those of the Lower Basalt sequence. The following main types occur: (1) dense, dark basalts without phenocrysts; (2) plagioclase-porphyritic, grayish basalts with characteristic subtypes; (3) olivine basalts, varying from ordinary olivine basalts to oceanities. All transitions between these main types occur.

While the thickness of the Lower Basalt sequence is about 1000 m, the Upper sequence is considered to be about 2000 m, so that the whole Faeroic sequence will be about 3000 m. However, in the geologic mapping work it has proved justified and adquate to divide the Upper Basalt sequence into a Lower and an Upper zone. In the *Lower zone*, comprising a little more than two-thirds of the sequence, the individual lava flows are generally of slight thickness, often 1 to 2 m or less; however, beds of somewhat greater thickness occur. The very thin lava flows, about 20 to 30 cm thick, appear frequently in large numbers and may be explained as having run out through breaks in thicker lava layers. Tuff layers are very uncommon in this zone, and the individual flows are usually separated by porous inter-zones and distinct ropy-lava surfaces. Therefore, it must be assumed that the whole zone was formed by a steady, continuous volcanic activity. In the *Upper zone*, comprising barely one-third of the Upper Basalt sequence, the individual flows are usually about 10 m thick, and tuff layers are common between the individual beds.

The boundary between the two zones is usually distinct in the field and clearly expressed in the topography. The Lower zone is exposed on the northern part of Suduroy, on Vágar and on the northern part of Streymoy, whereas it is partly covered by the Upper zone on the southern part of Streymoy, Eysturoy, and the northern islands, except Fugloy and Svínoy where only the Upper zone prevails.

After the basalt plateau was completed, unequal withdrawal of the substratum resulted in readjustment movements which led to the formation of fracture lines (master joints). Further readjustment movements along the same lines of fractures results in "lamellae zones" which traversed the whole sequence. Subsequently we have basaltic intrusions in these "lamellae zones" and in other zones of weakness in the plateau.

INTRUSIVES

Intrusive formations occur as (1) irregular intrusive formations; (2) sills; and (3) dykes.

The dykes are intruded in the above "lamellae zones" and traverse the entire plateau. The two other intrusion forms, irregular intrusive formations and sills, occur, as indicated by Fig. 1, in two different intrusion levels: a lower one, where the Coal-bearing series and the Tuff–Agglomerate zone have acted as a zone of weakness; and an upper one, where the boundary between the lower and the upper zones in the Upper Basalt sequence apparently acted as a zone of weakness.

Since the dykes have been observed as irregular intrusive formations as well as sills, we must assume that all the above forms of intrusions belong roughly to the same phase of eruption.

Irregular intrusive formations. The irregular intrusive formations are intruded in the Coal-bearing series and especially in the overlying Tuff–Agglomerate zone. Since the latter is often strongly porous and not very resistant to magma pressures in different directions, these intrusions will have quite an irregular shape. Such irregular intrusive formations appear in the north-easterly part of Suduroy, on Tindhólmur, and in the western most part of Vágar.

On Suduroy they are present at the coast on the northern side of Hvalbiarfjördur and along the eastern coast of Suduroy to Hvannhagi, as shown by Fig. 2. On the northern side of Trongisvágur they can be studied in ravines in the vegetation-covered terrain. They are also visible on the south side of the fjord at the easterly boundary of the Coal-bearing series. In the north the intrusive formations reach a height of up to 35 m above sea level, and in the south they attain thicknesses of about 100 m at some places. By the intrusion the easterly coal-area has been strongly dislocated and destroyed with regard to coal mining. Occasionally long apophyses are visible in the Upper Basalt sequence.

On Tindhólmur and on the westernmost part of Vágar the irregular intrusive formations—like on Suduroy—are intruded in the Coal-bearing series and in the overlying Tuff–Agglomerate zone.

Sills. Sills occur on Streymoy, Eysturoy, Svínoy, and Fugloy (Figs. 4–6).

The large *Streymore* sill (Fig. 4) extends in an almost true NW.–SE. direction. It is about 9 km long and varies in width from 1 to 2 km in the north and from 2 to 3 km in the south. At one place the erosion has been so deep that the sill has been divided into a northerly and a southerly part. The lowest position of the sill is along its central part in the west, about 300 m above sea level, where it more or less follows the regular basalt bedding. To the north, south and east it is strongly transgressive. The thickness is greatest towards the west, up to about 60 m, whereas it is strongly decreasing towards the east, down to 10 m, in some parts even to 5 m.

The Eysturoy sill (Fig. 5) extends about 6 km in a NW.–SE. direction and ranges in width between 2 and 3.5 km. It is most conspicuous towards the west where it forms prominent columnar structures. Like the Streymoy sill, the lower sill boundary on the west side has a smooth, winding course, whereas in the north, south, and east it is strongly transgressive. Again, like the Streymoy sill, the Eysturoy one has its lowest position and greatest thickness—up to

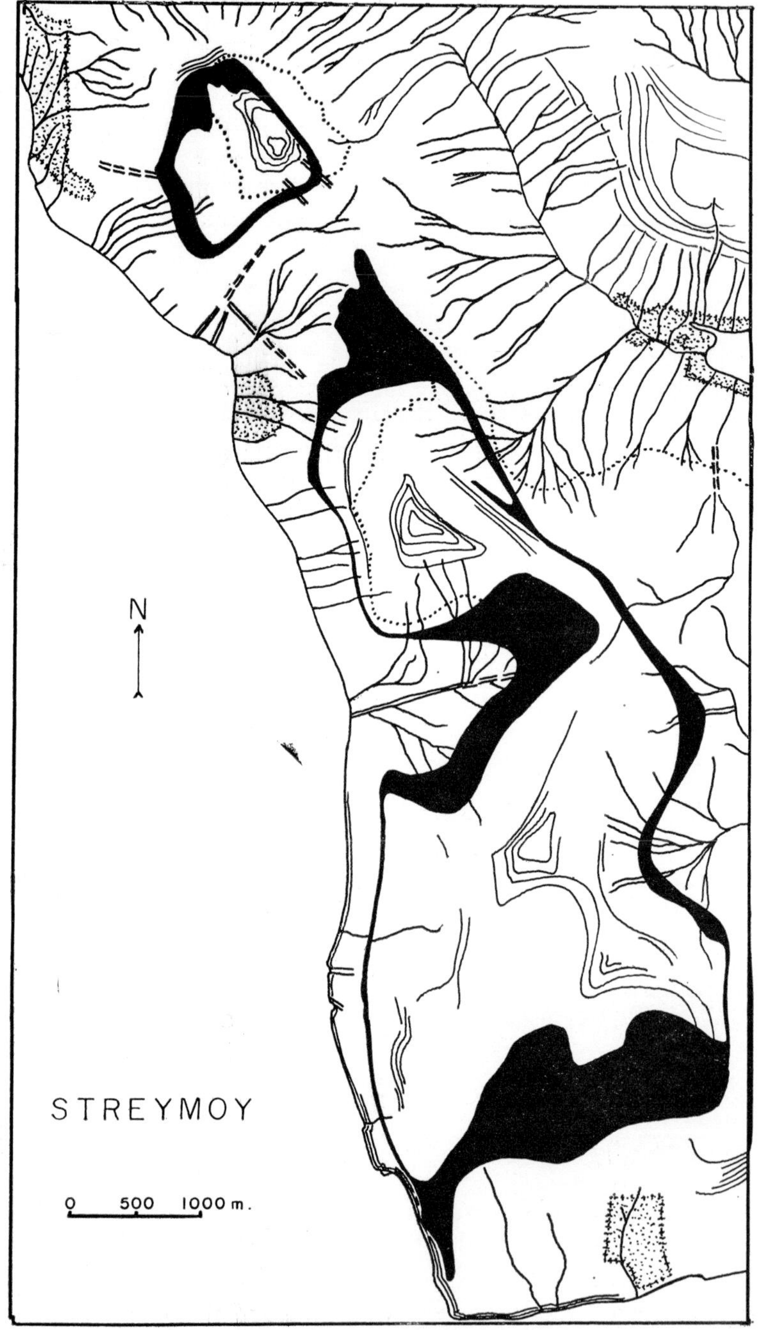

FIG. 4. The Streymoy sill. Black: Sills. Double line: Dykes. Dotted line: Border between lower and upper part of Upper Basalt Sequence. Stippled areas: Settlements.

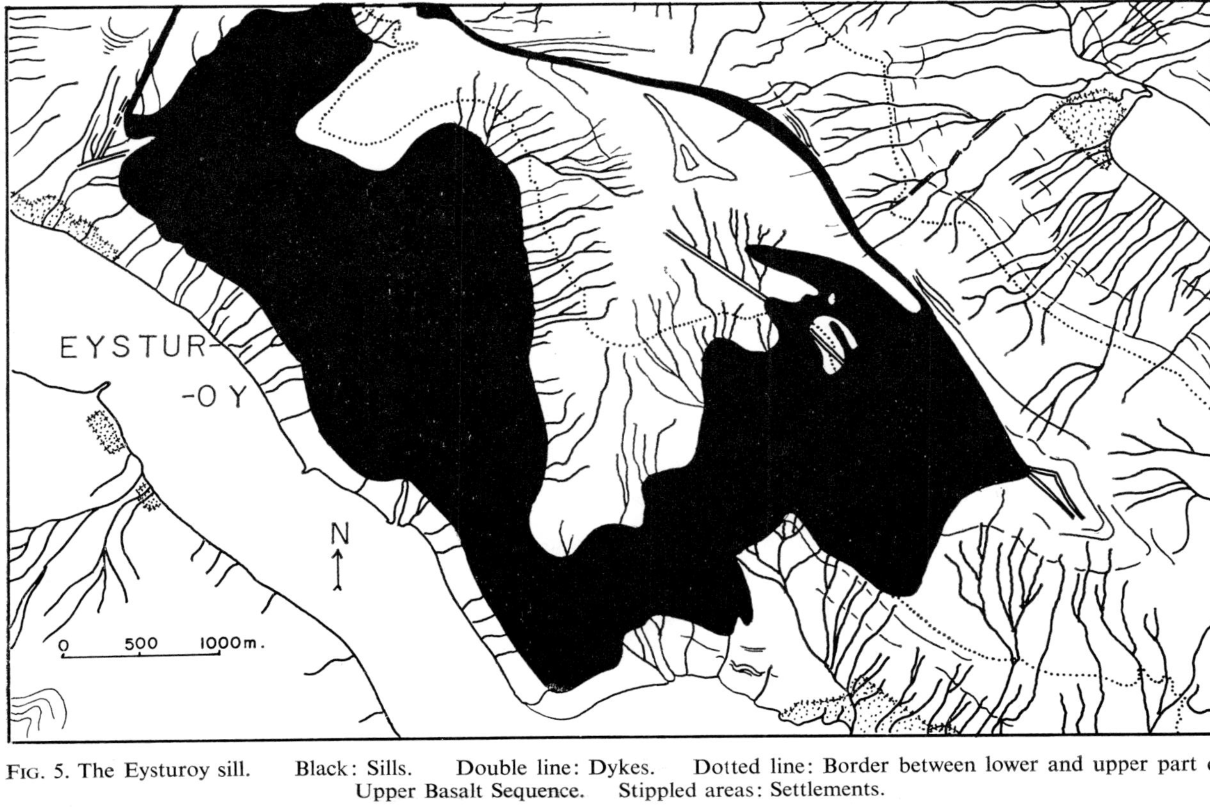

FIG. 5. The Eysturoy sill. Black: Sills. Double line: Dykes. Dotted line: Border between lower and upper part of Upper Basalt Sequence. Stippled areas: Settlements.

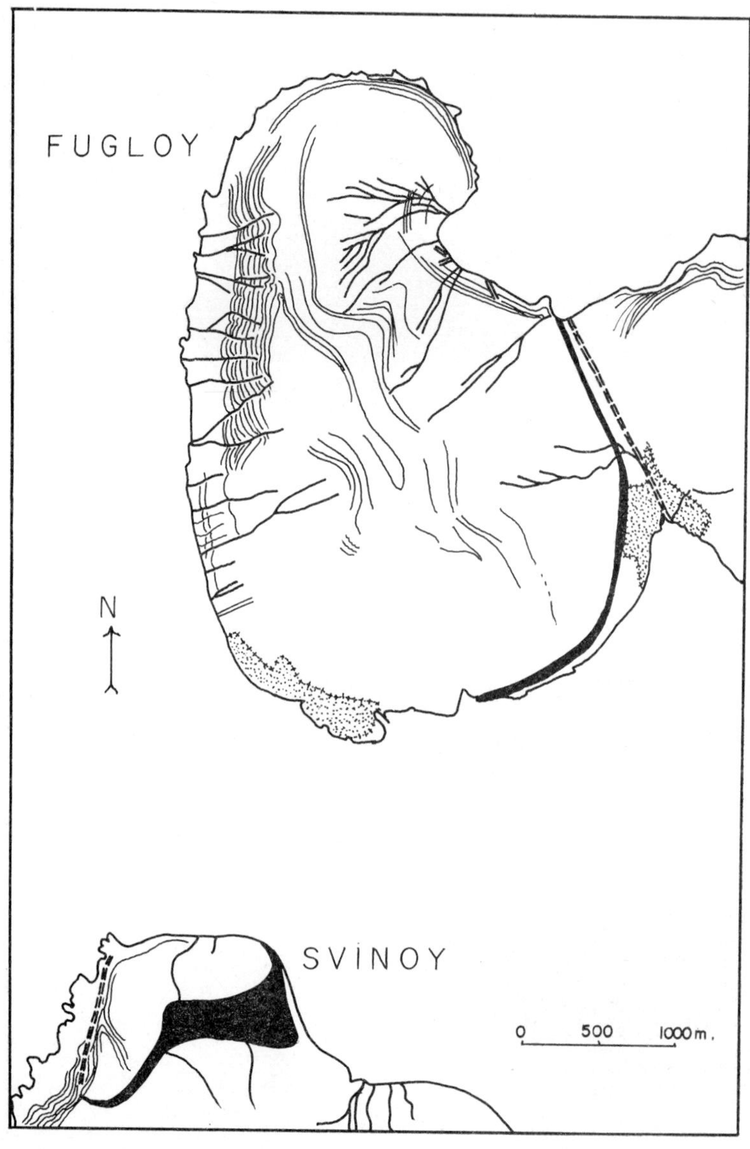

FIG. 6. The Fugloy and Svínoy sill. Black: Sills. Double line: Dykes. Stippled areas: Settlements.

100 m—in the central area in the west. It decreases in thickness with increasing transgressivity in the east, where the peripheral part of the sill is locally almost perpendicular. It is most likely that the *Fugloy* sill and the *Svínoy* sill (Fig. 6) belong to the same intrusive formation, later on divided by the Fugloyarfjördur. The thickness of these sills is only 15 to 30 m.

As is evident from what is said above we find a morphologically common feature in these sills, a characteristic semi-saucer-shaped form. The sills run rather concordantly in the central area, where they reach their greatest thickness, while in the peripheral area they become strongly transgressive, at the same time decreasing considerably in thickness.

Dykes. Dykes occur everywhere, but are most abundant along a belt running NE.–SW. across the northern group of islands. They represent roughly the same main types as are found in the plateau basalt. The course of the dykes is usually a straight lined, but sometimes rather winding. It looks as if the feldspar dykes have a more winding course than the dense, dark basalt dykes. General thickness is 2 to 4 m; the greatest thickness observed is 20 m. Geikie (1880) gives the main direction as NNE.–SSW. and ENE.–WSW. Noe-Nygaard (1940) proves that the dominating direction of 76 dykes on Kallsoy and Kunoy is NNE.–ENE. to SSW.–WSW. On Suduroy the main orientation is approximately NW.–SE.

After the intrusion of irregular intrusive formations, sills, and dykes, there occurred again a tectonic period.

If we draw a line from Mykines to Fugloy, it will hit the deepest points in the straits and the greatest heights in the valleys running in the direction of the straits. North of this line the dip is roughly towards the ENE., and south of this line it is approximately ESE. The line thus forms the present main water-shed of the islands.

On western Mykines the dip is 13°, on eastern Mykines 8°, on western Vágar 3°, on Streymoy and Eysturoy 2°–3°, and on the northern islands the dip is even smaller. This indicates a movement along the line with upheaval of the land to the west. By this movement fracture lines and "lamellae zones" have arisen in the plateau—running NE.–ENE. north of the line and SE.–ESE. south of the line—and where they cross dykes, horizontal dislocation of the dykes are visible in the direction of the "lamellae zones". Thus the movement, which has resulted in the above-mentioned water-shed in the plateau, is younger than the dyke intrusion and consequently is Late Tertiary.

While the Tertiary geology of the Faeroes in recent years has been the object of a systematical geological mapping, the Quaternary geology has only been dealt with fragmentarily.

As already shown by Helland (1880) and Geikie (1880) the Faeroes had a glaciation of their own. The aforementioned hinge-line (the water-shed of the

Late Tertiary and the present), during the widest extension of the Pleistocene ice, formed an "ice-shed" for one ice flow running northwards and another southwards. However, at more advanced stages the ice direction was decided by the local topographic forms.

Moraine deposits occur everywhere in the lowlands, but the cover is rather thin, only exceptionally reaching 4 to 5 m in thickness. Terminal moraines have not been observed, and the poor moraine cover can be explained, on the whole, by the fact that the greater part of the material was carried out to sea by the ice. As shown by previous investigators, no boulders of foreign origin occur in the Faeroic moraines.

The problem of the thickness of the ice has frequently been touched upon in previous literature, and it has generally been assumed that the ice did not reach above 500 m since striae have not been observed above that height. Otherwise, however, observation of striae is difficult at that height on account of the extensive weathering, and locally the very dense, resistant rocks (as, for example, the sills) are distinctly glaciated up to far greater heights.

As to the extension of the ice, naturally, nothing can be suggested, but remnants of cirques and valley slopes, particularly on the west and north coasts, show that the ice has extended a good deal farther than the present coast line, and that the postglacial coast erosion on the west and on the north is considerable.

A glance at the map of the Faeroes shows an obvious NW.–SE. running dominance of the fjord direction. The same orientation prevails in the traversing valleys (e.g. Millum Fjarda, Sandsdalur).

The origin of the fjord system, including the traversing valleys, has been discussed frequently. Mackenzie (1814) suggested that they resulted from removal by erosion of great dykes. Geikie (1880) showed that the ice followed the Pre-Glacial topography and explained the fjord system as a consequence of river action assisted by Glacial erosion. Grossman and Lomas (1895) proposed that the ice did little more than modify pre-existing valleys. Gregory (1913) assumed that the fjord system was preglacial in age, and that its formation thus could not be due to glacial erosion. Peacock (1928) suggested that the fjord system was derived from an earlier goe-system, and that it therefore had its ultimate origin in a system of master joints related to an episode of crustal movement which took place after the volcanic period but before the Ice Age.

When mentioning the Tuff–Agglomerate zone it was pointed out that the agglomerates most likely covered the eruption fissures which were feeding the Lower Basalt sequence, and that those occur along the fjords following them. In the same manner the numerous vents, which probably were supplying the Lower Basalt zone in the Upper Basalt sequence, occur along the fjords. No vents have been observed outside the fjord system although the opportunities for observation are excellent. It might therefore be tempting to assume that the volcanic activity was localized throughout along the old fissures and that the ultimate origin of the fjord system was determined by these fissures.

Lakes are numerous in the bottom of the traversing valleys as well as in the cirques. Most of them occupy true rock basins excavated under varying conditions. Formerly they were, no doubt, much more abundant, as many of them are now being silted up and replaced by alluvium.

Alluvial deposits are rather insignificant in the Faeroes. Marine alluvium is quite lacking and freshwater alluvial layers show far less variety and far less thickness than elsewhere.

Peat occurs everywhere in the lowlands along the slopes of the valleys as well as on their bottoms. The thickness of the peat is generally 1 or 1.5 m, rarely up to 3 m. The greatest thickness of biogene freshwater alluvium has been measured to 5.5 m.

Our knowledge of the Faeroic bogs is limited to a joint study by Jessen and Rasmussen (1922) on a section of a bog in the Faeroes, and to work by Jessen (1923) alone on the stratigraphy of Faeroic bogs.

The most important alluvial freshwater layers according to Jessen (1923) are: mud, rarely in thick layers; *Equisetum*-peat, not common in thick layers; and low-bog peat, which appears in two forms, *Sphagnum*-peat and *Eriophorum angustifolium*-peat. The latter constitutes the bulk of the peat in the Faeroes. The most important fossils in the Faeroic low-bog peat are *Eriophorum angustifolium*, *Carex stellulata*, and *Ranunculus flammula*. Moreover, there is a *Calluna*-peat with twigs and roots of *Calluna vulgaris* and *Juniperus communis*. Pure *Sphagnum*-peat is very rare. Clay, sands, and gravel often form a considerable part of the bog sections.

The *Calluna*-peat, according to Jessen and Rasmussen (1922), occurs as a horizon dividing the Faeroic bogs, and the authors are of the opinion that it is contemporaneous with Upper Forrestian and the Sub-Boreal period.

Submarine bogs occur frequently along the eastern shores of the Faeroe Islands, indicating that a depression has taken place in Post-Glacial time According to Jessen and Rasmussen (1922), the land has been submerged at least 3.5 m after the formation of these bogs.

Therefore, since distinctive features of a Post-Glacial upheaval of the land are visible along the western coasts (Mykines, Vágar, Hestoy) and recent movements can be indicated in the "lamellae zones", it is tempting to conclude that the Late Tertiary movement is still active along the Mykines–Fugloy axis with an upheaval to the west and a submergence to the east.

REFERENCES

ALLAN, Th. (1814). An account of the mineralogy of the Faroe Islands. *Trans. Roy. Soc. Edinb.* **7**, 229–67.

FORCHHAMMER, J. G. (1824). Om Faeröernes geognostiske Beskaffenhed. *Kgl. Danske Vidensk. Selsk. Skr.* **2**, 159–206.

GEIKIE, J. (1880). On the geology of the Faeroe Islands. *Trans. Roy. Soc. Edinb.* **30**, 217–69.

GREGORY, J. W. (1813). *The Nature and Origin of Fiords.* London.

GROSSMAN, K. and LOMAS, J. (1895). On the glaciation of the Faeroe Islands. *The Glaciol. Magazine*, 1895, 1–15.

HELLAND, AMUND (1880). Om Faeröernes geologi. *Geogr. Tidsskr.* **4**, 149–79.

JESSEN, K. and RASMUSSEN, R. (1922). Et Profil gennem en Törvemose paa Faeröerne. *Danm. Geol. Undersög.* **4** (1), 1–13.

JESSEN, K. (1925). De faeröske Mosers Stratigrafi. Det 17. Skand. Naturforskarmötet i Göteborg 1923, 185–190.

MACKENZIE, SIR GEORGE (1814). An account of some geological facts observed in the Faeroe Islands. *Trans. Roy. Soc. Edinb.* **7**, 213–27.

NOE-NYGAARD, A. (1940). Om Gjógv-Systemernes Alder paa Faeröerne. *Medd. Dansk Geol. Foren.* **9**, 542–7

NOE-NYGAARD, A. (1946). Some petrogenetic aspects of the Northern basalt Plateau. *Medd. Dansk Geol. Foren* **11**, 55–65.

NOE-NYGAARD, A. (1951). Den geologiske Kortlaegning af Faeröerne 1938–50. *Medd. Dansk Geol. Foren.* **12**, 163.

NOE-NYGAARD, A. and RASMUSSEN, J. (1957). The making of the basalt plateau of the Faeroes. *Congreso Geol. Intern. Mexico 1956*, 299–407.

PEACOCK, M. A. (1928). Recent lines of fracture in the Faeroes, in relation to the theories of fiord formation in the northern basalt plateau. *Trans. Geol. Soc. Glasgow* **18**, 1–26.

RASMUSSEN, J. (1951a). Nyere synspunkter vedrörende de faeröske kullags stratigrafi. *Medd. Dansk Geol. Foren.* **12**, 164.

RASMUSSEN, J. (1951b). Transgressive sillintrusioner i Faeröplateauet. *Medd. Dansk Geol. Foren.* **12**, 164.

RASMUSSEN, J. (1952). Bidrag til forstaaelse af den faeröske lagseries opbygning. *Medd. Dansk Geol. Foren.* **12**, 275–83.

RASMUSSEN, J. (1955). Nøkur ord um gjáir í Føroyum—uppruna teirra og aldur (Notes on origin and age of goes). *Fróðskaparrit* (*Ann. Soc. Sci. Faeroensis*), **4**, 108–24.

RASMUSSEN, J. (1957a). Yvirlit yvir innskotin grótsløg í Føroyum (General view of intrusive rocks of the Faeroe Islands). *Fróðskaparrit* (*Ann. Soc. Sci. Faeroensis*), **6**, 61–96.

RASMUSSEN, J. (1957b). Iles Faeröe. *Lexique stratigraphique international.* Paris, **1**, 13–17.

TREVELYAN, W. C. (1823). On the mineralogy of the Faeroe Islands. *Trans. Roy. Soc. Edinb.* **9**, 461–4.

WALKER, F. and DAVIDSON, C. F. (1936). A contribution to the geology of the Faeroes. *Trans. Roy. Soc. Edinb.* **58**, 869–97.

PHYTOGEOGRAPHICAL CONNECTIONS OF THE NORTH ATLANTIC

ERIC HULTÉN

Department of Botany, State Museum of Natural History, Stockholm 50, Sweden

THE present study is based on distributional maps of all plants known to occur in Iceland, Greenland, Spitsbergen, Jan Mayen, Bear Island, and the Faeroe Islands. The maps have been divided into 23 groups according to their general geographical area: Circumpolar, European, American, Amphi-Atlantic, and so on.

The number of species belonging to each group and found in certain localities distributed all over the map of the northern Atlantic have been counted, and places with the same number of species in each category have been united with lines. In this way an idea has been gained as to how many species of each group occur at different places. We find, for instance, how many Circumpolar plants occur on Iceland or on Spitsbergen, and how many species with their main area in continental Europe exist on these islands. The maps should give a good idea of the relationship of the floras of the above-mentioned Atlantic islands to each other as well as to adjacent continental Europe and America.

To each map has been added a sketch of the world range of all species belonging to the group in question. As these ranges are very variable in different species, these sketches can only give a general idea of their distribution. However, the sketches will help make the conditions understandable.

Of fundamental importance for the phytogeography of the North Atlantic is the question as to whether the species are native or introduced. Communication between Iceland, Europe, Greenland, and America has been intense and has been going on for several centuries. Very many weeds, or plants otherwise not native, have been added to the natural floras. It is desirable to exclude them from this discussion as they do not concern the older history of the flora. About 210 such species, recognized by most botanists as not belonging to the native flora, occur within the area; most of them are of European origin, and only about ten are American.

In Iceland, Greenland, and Newfoundland, however, there are European species considered native by botanists dealing with the respective floras, but whose character suggests that they possibly have been originally introduced. They occur in the natural vegetation, but this is hardly a reliable indication that they belong to the native flora. If, for instance, a European species is introduced to Newfoundland and the climate there is suitable, it might well be able to compete with the native vegetation and become a member of the natural plant societies after some centuries. Personally, I believe that not a few of the European plants in Iceland, Greenland, and Newfoundland fit into this category, as for instance, some of the species occurring around Reykjavík only.

As plants occurring in central Europe must have a different history from those not reaching south of Scandinavia, they have here been referred to other groups. The Circumpolar plants lacking in Greenland, for instance, have been divided into two sets, those occurring in central Europe (Fig. 1), and those not reaching that far south (Fig. 2).

A review of the groups represented by the maps follows.

In Fig. 1 are shown the ranges of those Circumpolar, or nearly Circumpolar, plants which do not occur in Greenland, nor in central Europe: 27 species. Only one of them, *Ranunculus pallasii*, exists in Spitsbergen but not in Iceland.

Figure 2 includes Circumpolar plants not occurring in Greenland, but found in central Europe: 64 species. They are of a more southern affinity but 16 of them have reached Iceland.

Figures 3, 4, and 5 correspond to Figs. 1 and 2, but include species occurring also in Greenland. Figure 3, comprising those species not occurring in central Europe, has an Arctic or Arctic-montane character. Species found also in central Europe have been divided into two groups, namely one with an Arctic-montane character (Fig. 4) and another with a more boreal character (Fig. 5). No sharp line of demarcation can be drawn between Figs. 4 and 5, but as their areas are quite different it is impractical to include them in the same map.

These three groups (Figs. 3, 4, 5) comprise altogether 197 species, all of a more or less Circumpolar character and all found in Greenland or on the Atlantic islands. They form the main element of the Atlantic flora. It should be noted that all of them have northern ranges around the Pole with 131 of them occurring on Iceland, 98 on Spitsbergen, 22 on Bear Island, 24 on Jan Mayen, and 58 on the Faeroe Islands.

Figures 6 and 7 consist of nearly Circumpolar plants which show the same behavior in the Atlantic sector as the other Circumpolar plants but have a peculiar gap in their total range in northern Asia, as for instance, *Silene acaulis*, *Loiseleuria procumbens*, and *Rhododendron lapponicum*. Here they are treated separately only because it can be suspected that they have a different history from those with more or less continuous distribution all around the Pole. The total area of some of them approaches that of the Amphi-Atlantic plants. As seen from the maps illustrating their total ranges, they are Arctic-montane species, but sometimes with very split-up areas. They seem to have had an earlier continuous connection also in northern Asia, but at a later stage have lost part of their area owing to changes in the climate. From an

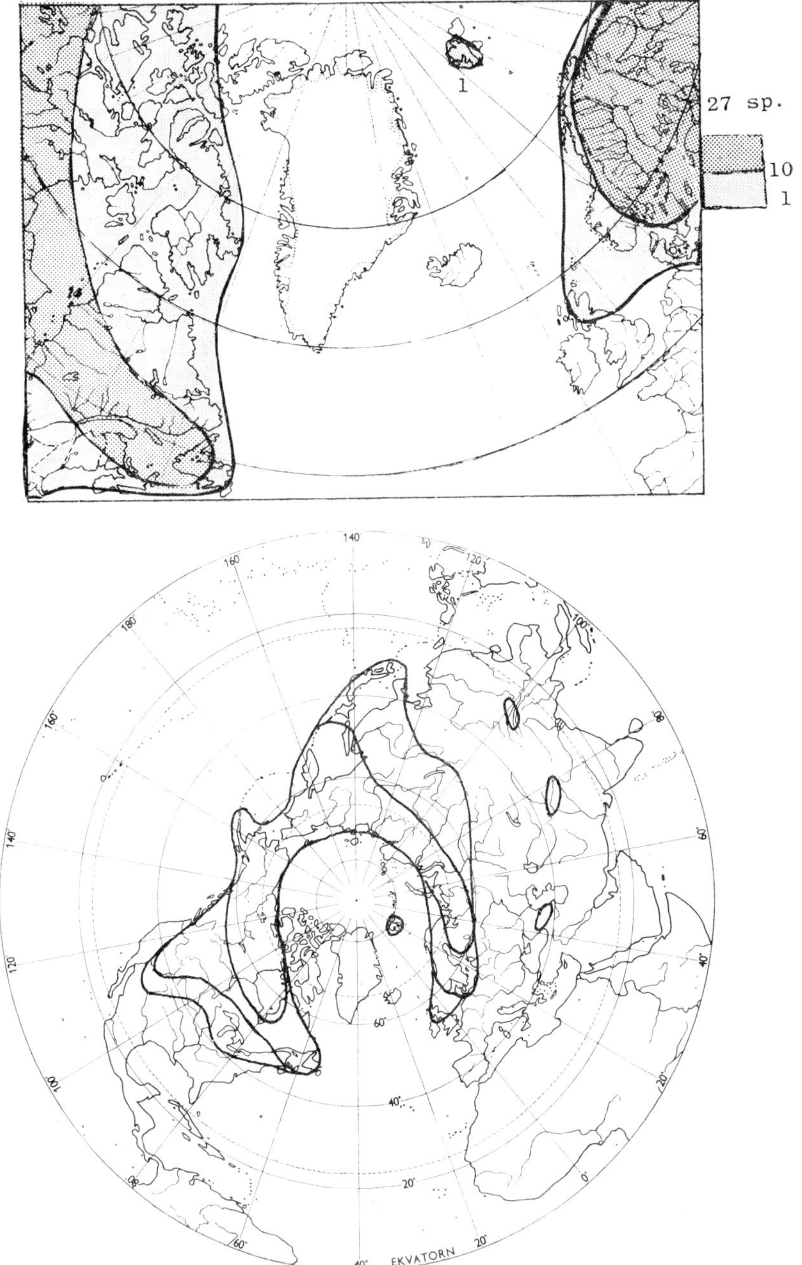

FIG. 1. Circumpolar plants lacking in Greenland and central Europe.

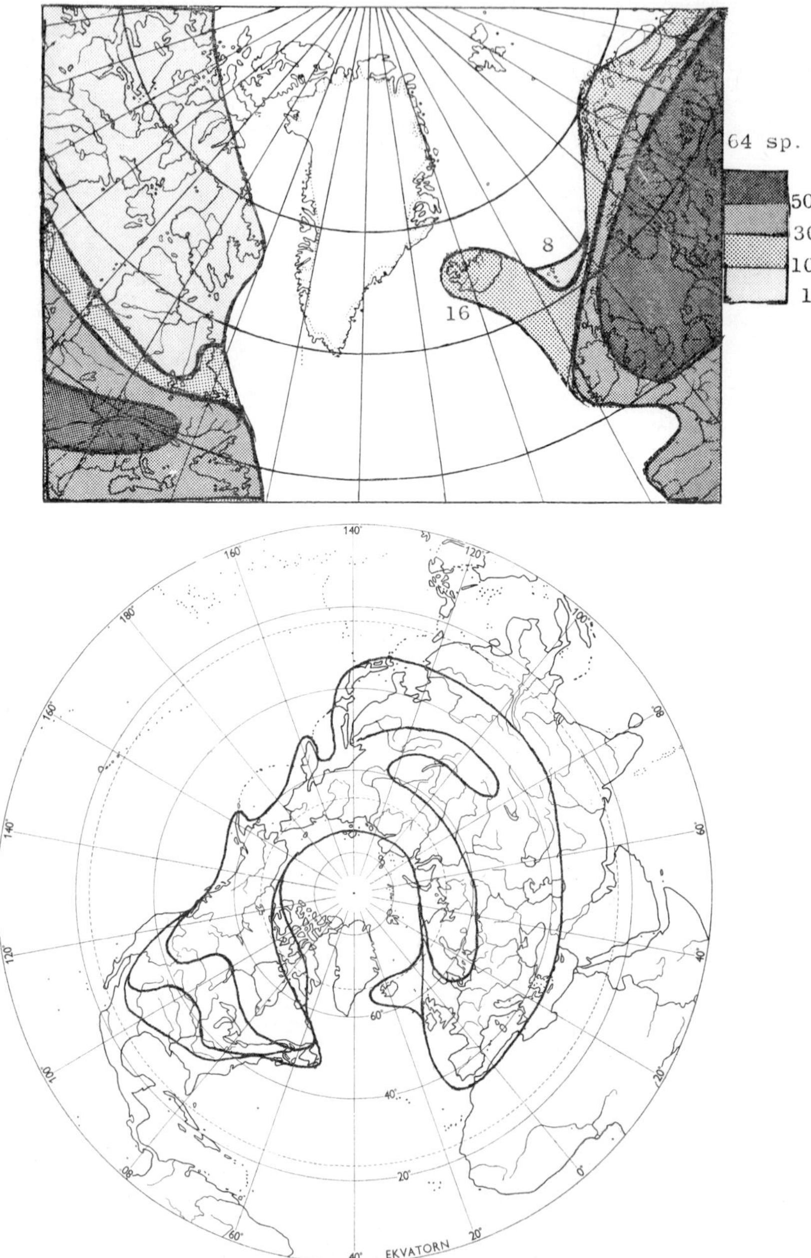

FIG. 2. Circumpolar plants lacking in Greenland but occurring in central Europe.

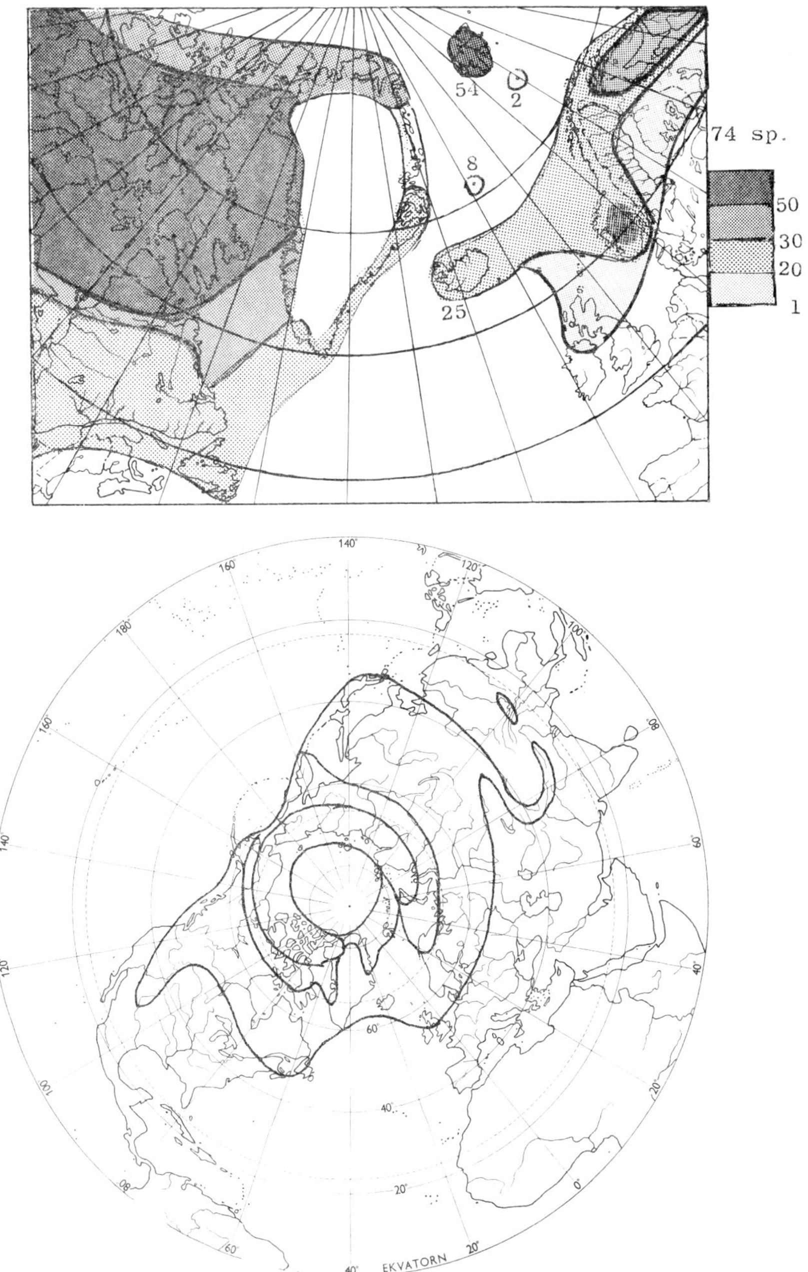

FIG. 3. Circumpolar plants occurring in Greenland but lacking in central Europe.

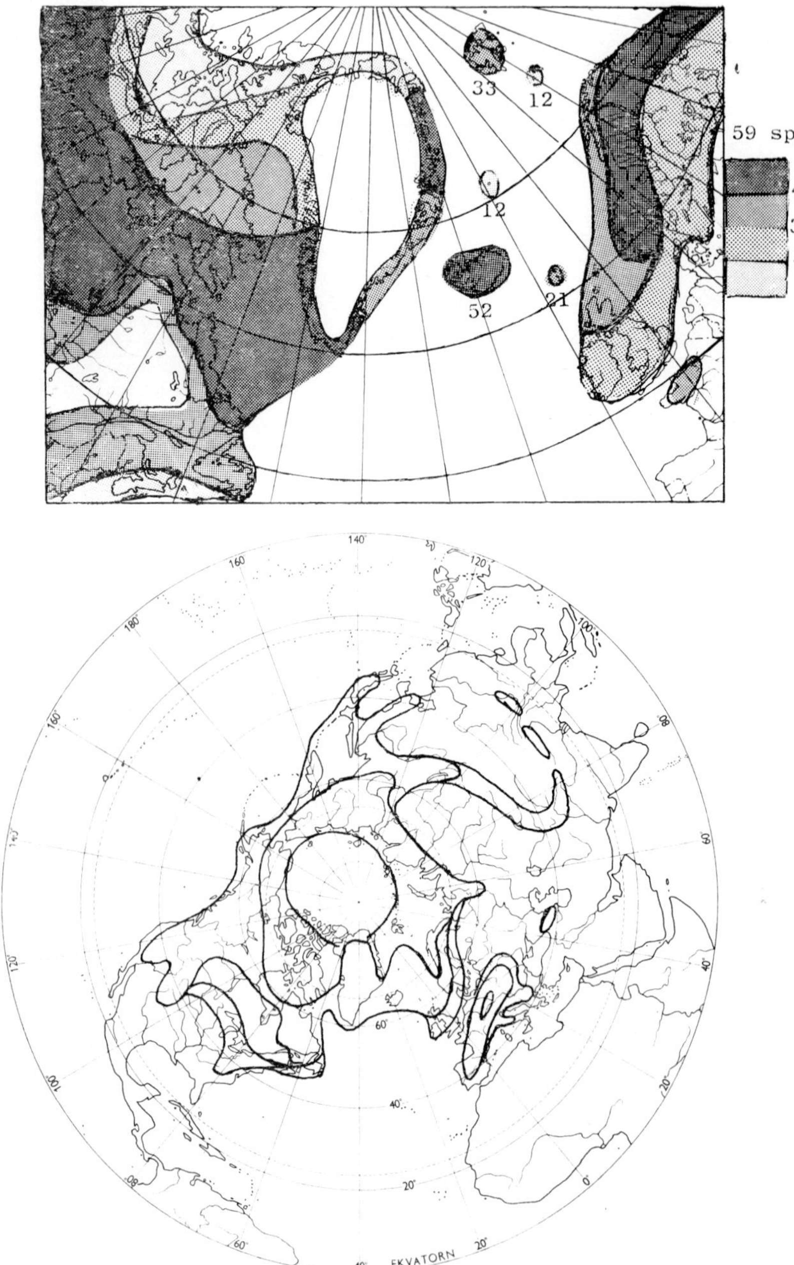

FIG. 4. Circumpolar plants occurring in Greenland and isolated in the mountains of central Europe.

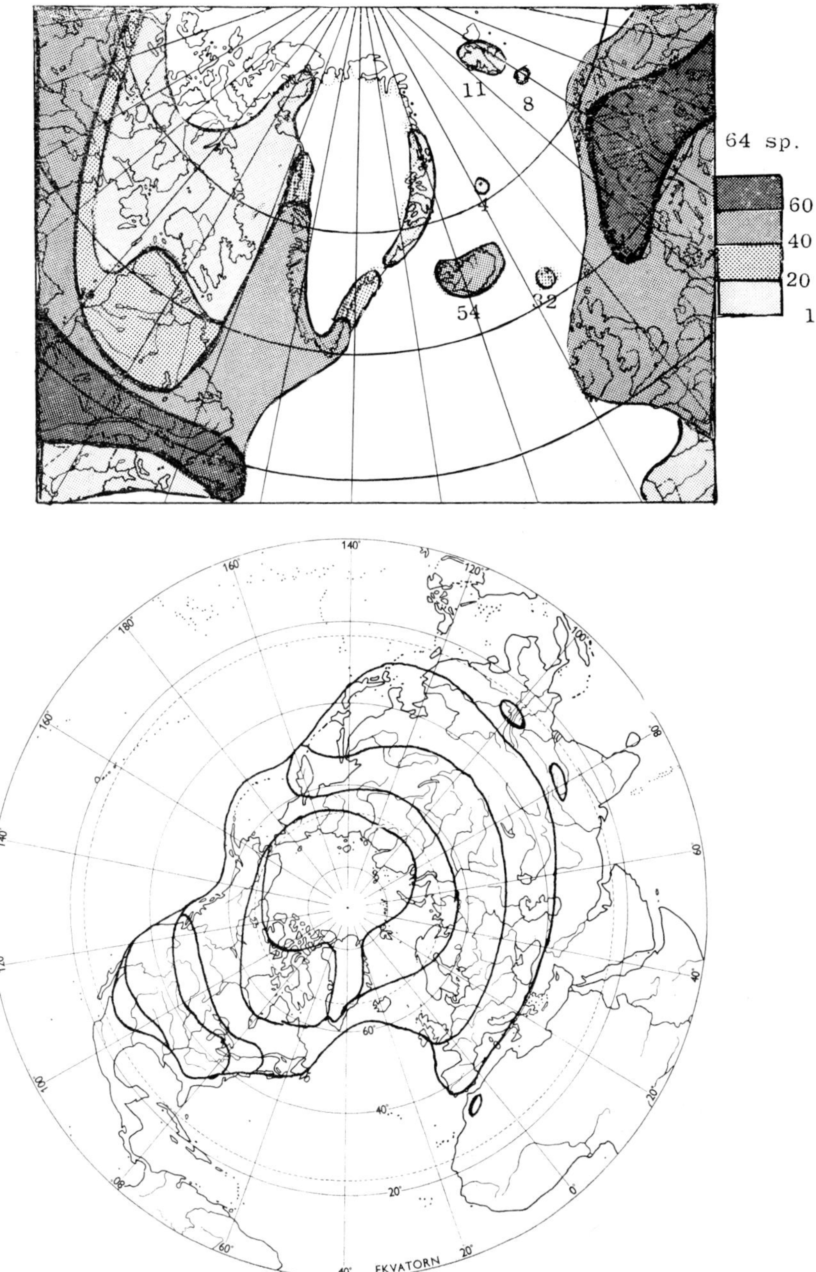

FIG. 5. Circumpolar plants occurring in Greenland and with lowland areas in central Europe.

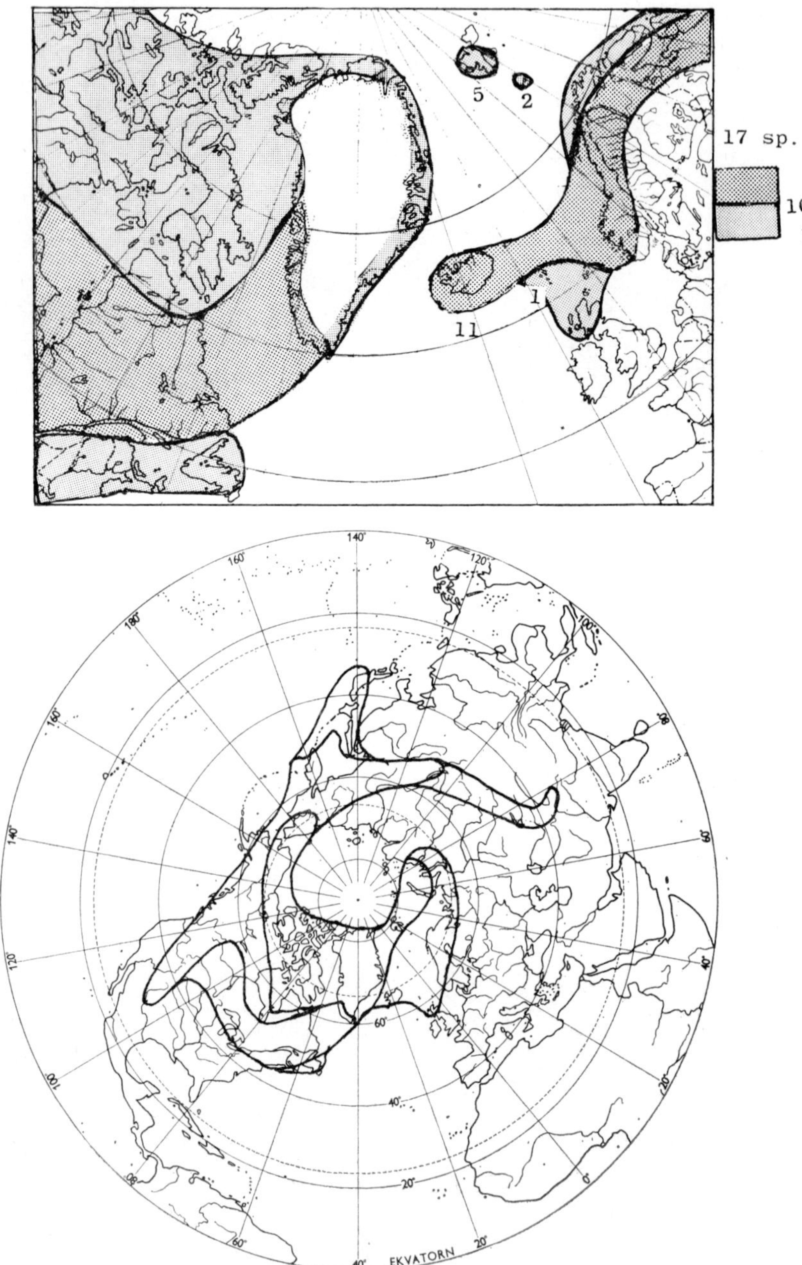

FIG. 6. More or less Circumpolar plants with large gaps in their area in northern Siberia, not occurring in central Europe.

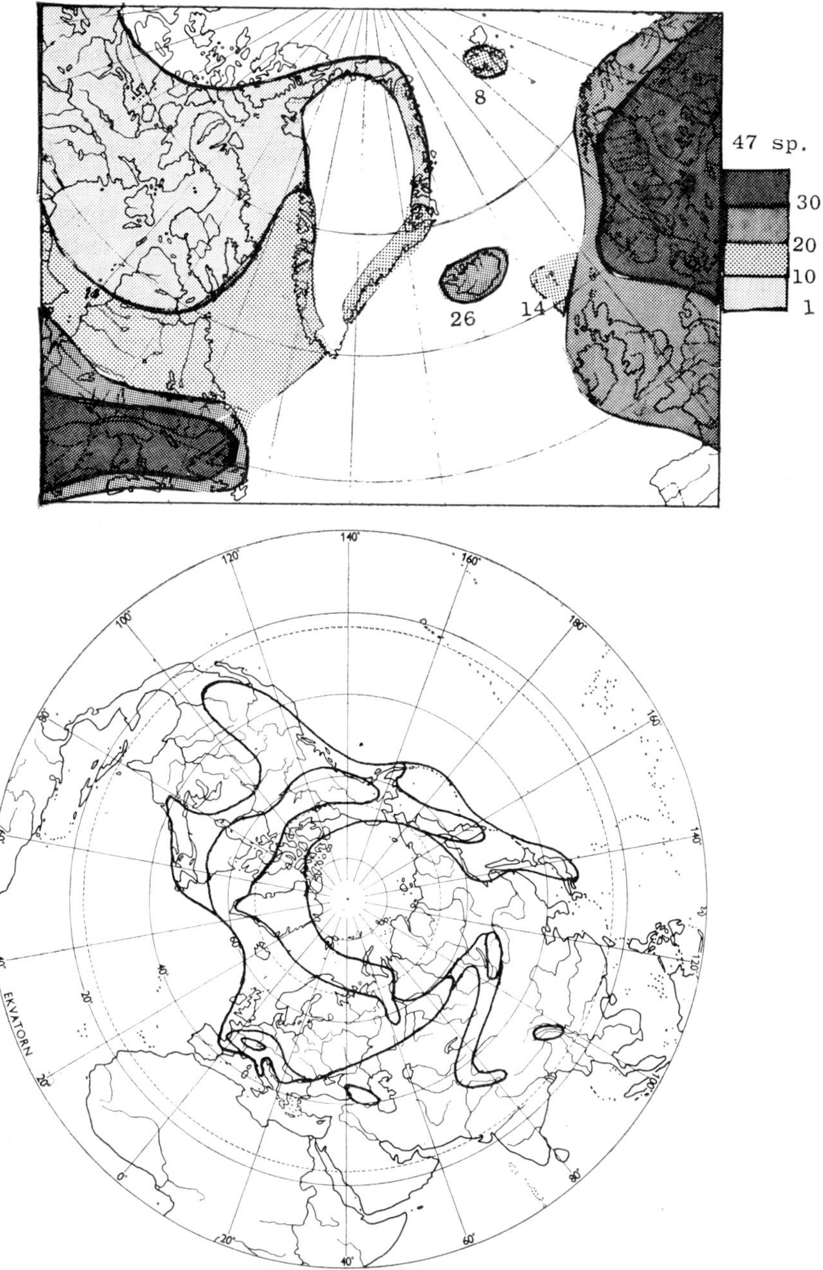

FIG. 7. More or less Circumpolar plants with large gaps in their area in northern Siberia, also occurring in central Europe.

Atlantic point of view they might as well have been included in other Circumpolar groups.

In Figs. 8, 9, and 10 are treated plants which have a more or less Circumpolar area with gaps frequently occurring in different places, but, contrary to the plants of the preceding groups, they appear as different races or as corresponding, slightly differing species on both sides of the Atlantic. There are altogether 107 of these taxa.

Figure 8 includes 76 species not occurring on Iceland or in Greenland, while Fig. 9 includes cases where the European type reaches Iceland or Greenland: in all 21 species. Figure 10 represents American species reaching Greenland and Iceland: 10 species. It is remarkable that all plants with such different races on both sides of the Atlantic are comparatively southern plants, mostly of the Boreal type. Their Atlantic connections are very feeble.

Figures 11 to 14 deal with the so-called Amphi-Atlantic plants. As they are of special interest in this connection, they have been subdivided into smaller groups. Thus, species not occurring in central Europe have been divided into the two groups: namely one having a northern distribution in Greenland, and another with a southern area there. Species found in central Europe have also been divided into two groups: one that reaches Iceland and Greenland, and one that does not.

The sketches illustrating the corresponding total areas indicate that species occurring on Iceland and in Greenland are Arctic or Arctic-montane types, whereas those lacking there are of a Boreal, lowland type. All form a chain of species with the largest part of their ranges in the Atlantic sector, but with gaps in the Pacific sector. In my opinion they are remnants of earlier continuously Circumpolar plants which have lost part of their area due to pressure of changing conditions, but are not remnants of plants which once inhabited a land-bridge in the Atlantic. They comprise 71 species of which 25 occur on Spitsbergen, 7 on Bear Island, 6 on Jan Mayen, 41 on Iceland, and 26 on the Faeroe Islands. Their Atlantic connections are thus not very strong. This is, however, perhaps of less importance, as it must be assumed that their areas became much reduced when the continental climate that must once have existed in what is now the North Atlantic changed to a coastal one when the land-bridge disappeared. Their total areas do not indicate that they are truly continental plants; on the contrary, their ranges even now are reduced in the interior of the continents.

Figure 15 shows the distribution of American or American–eastern Asiatic plants which do not reach Greenland or the Atlantic islands, and Fig. 16 indicates the corresponding European plants which do not extend out into the Atlantic. Both contain a great number of species. Their approximate numbers in different places have been indicated on the map in order to stress the great difference in the flora of the Atlantic shores in Europe and in America.

Figures 17 and 18 show the areas of American plants (with variable ranges

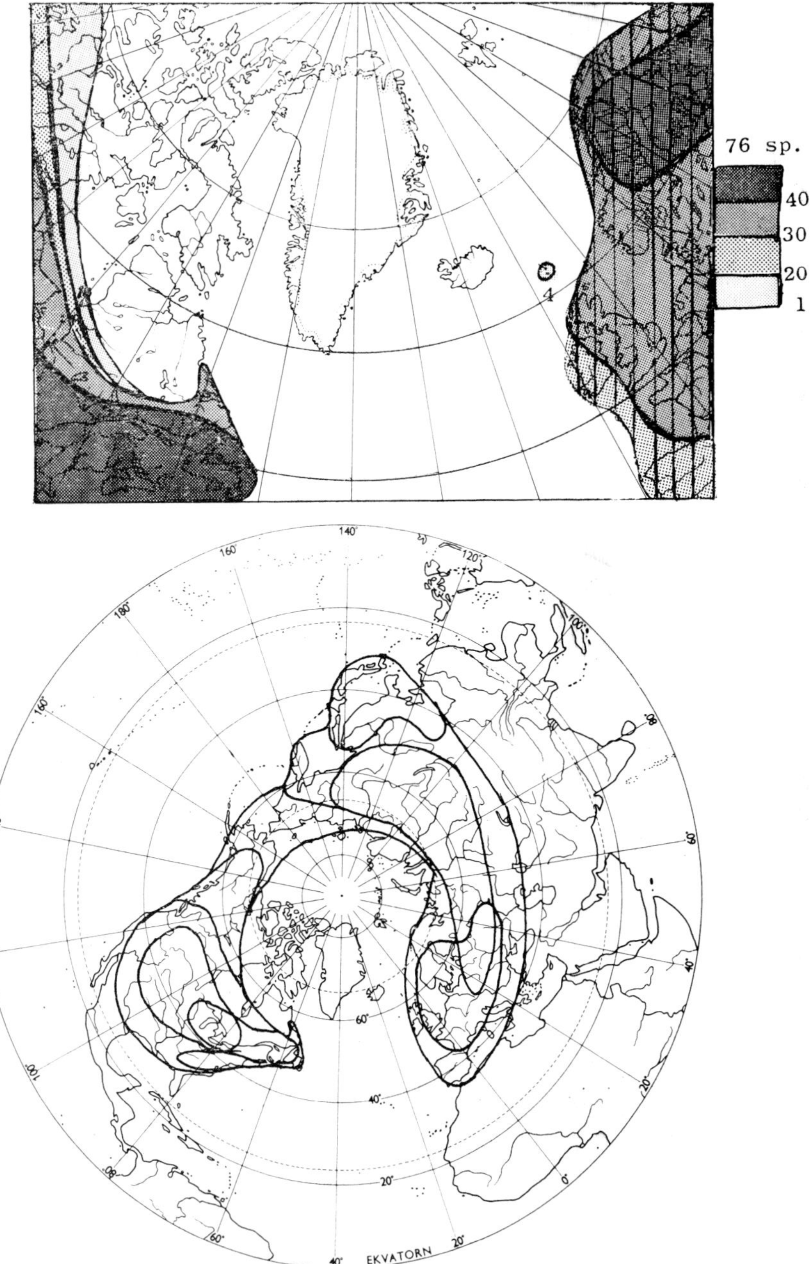

Fig. 8. Plants with different races or corresponding species on both sides of the Atlantic, not occurring in Greenland or Iceland.

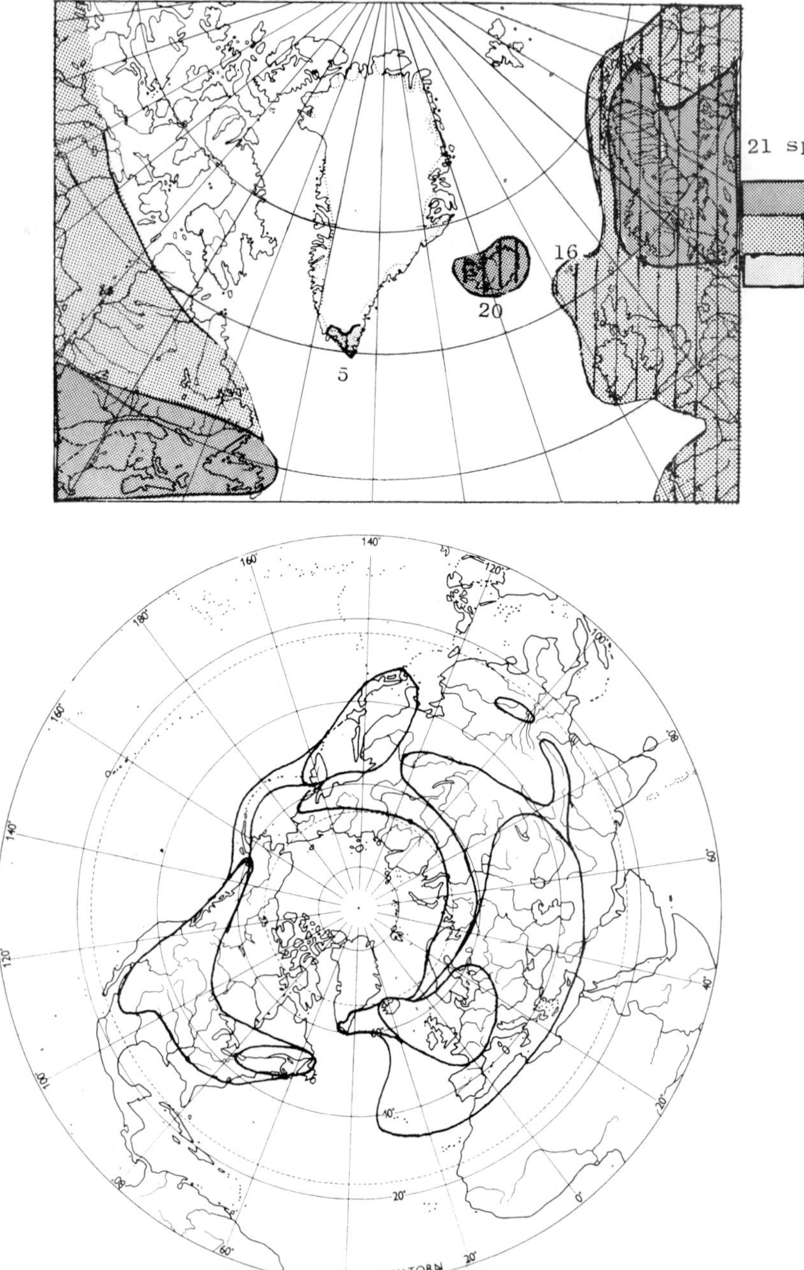

FIG. 9. Plants with different races or corresponding species on both sides of the Atlantic. The European type reaching Iceland–Greenland.

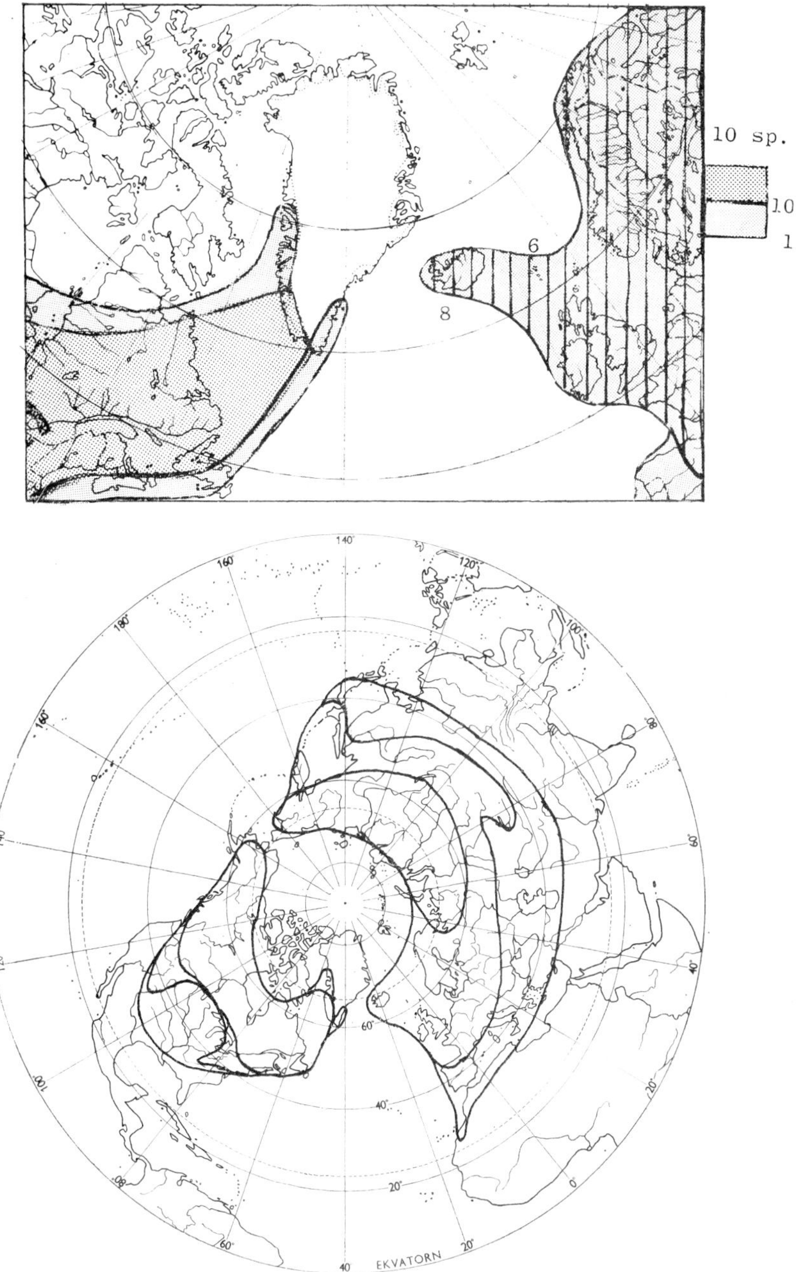

FIG. 10. Plants with different races or corresponding species on both sides of the Atlantic. The American type reaching Greenland–Iceland.

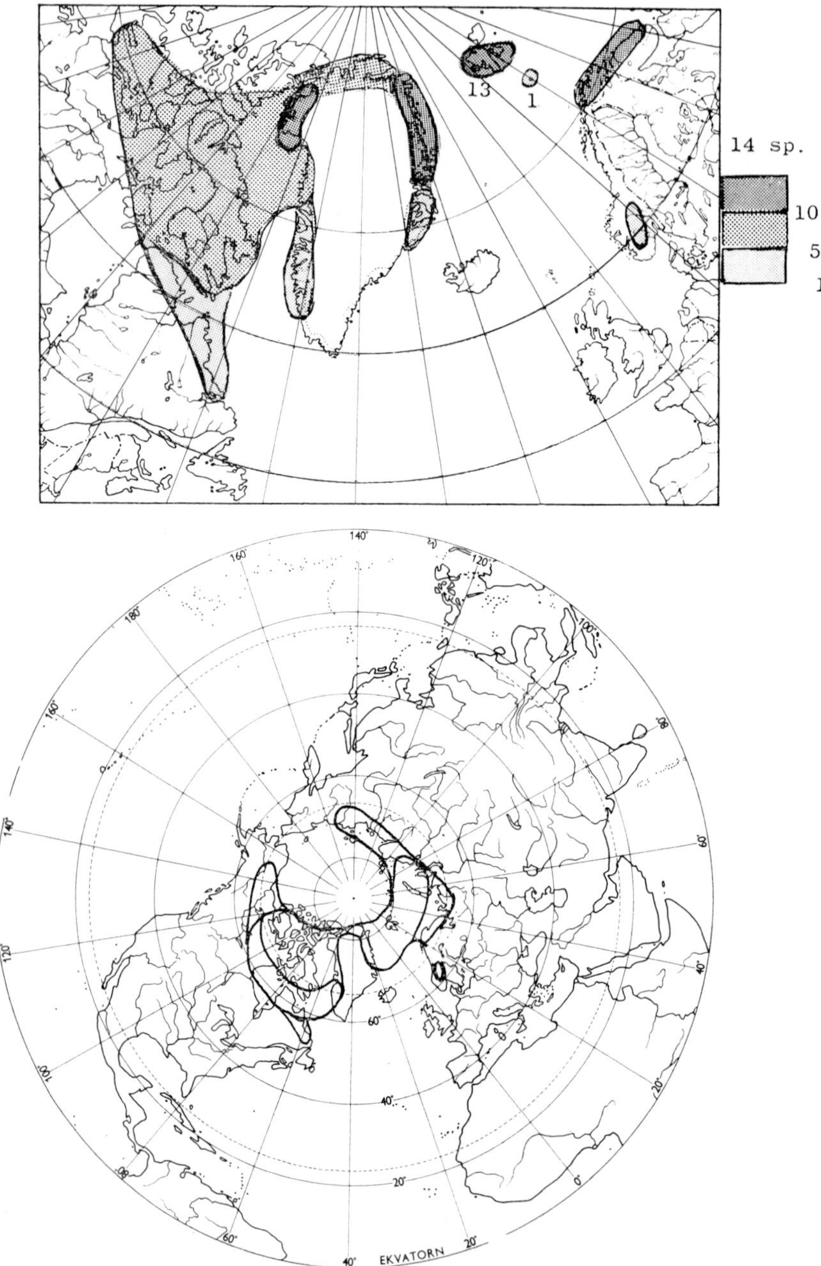

FIG. 11. Amphi-Atlantic plants lacking in central Europe with a northern area in Greenland.

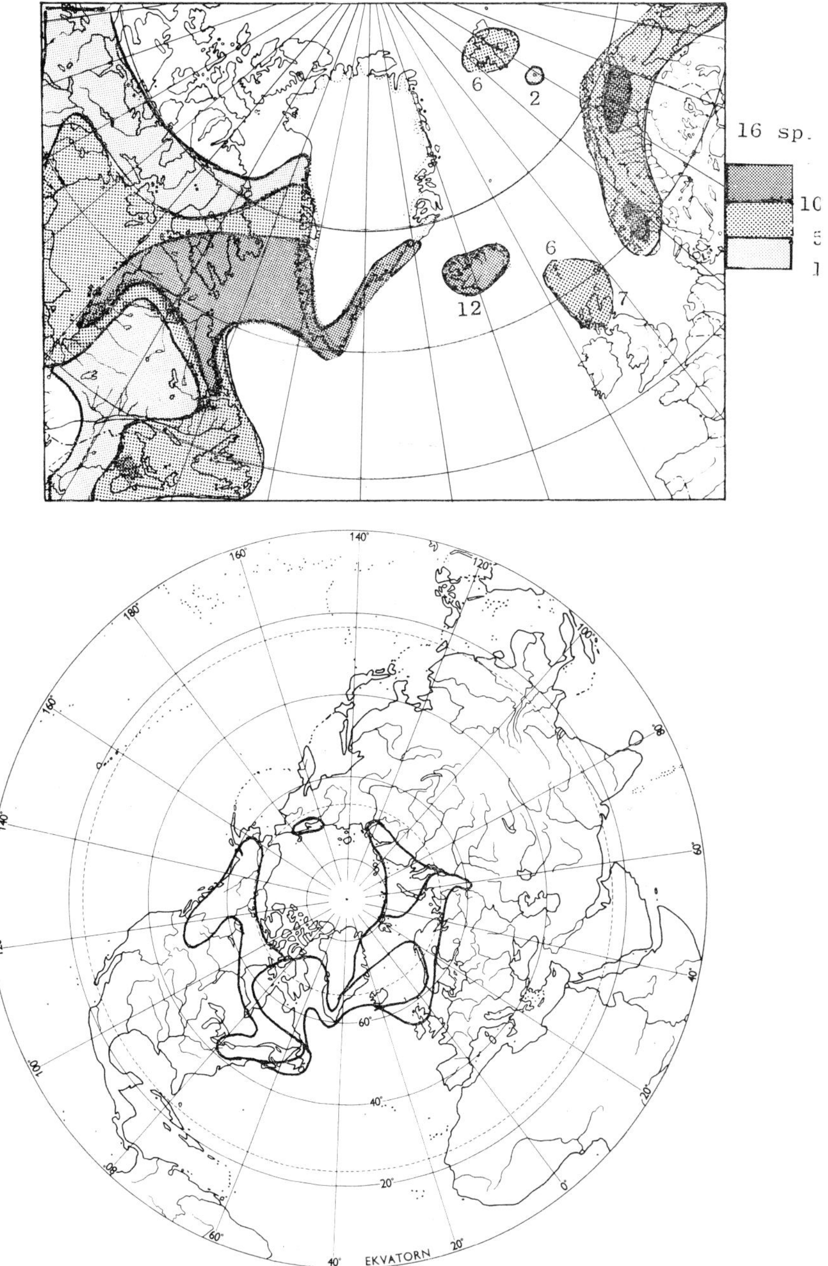

FIG. 12. Amphi-Atlantic plants lacking in central Europe with a southern area in Greenland.

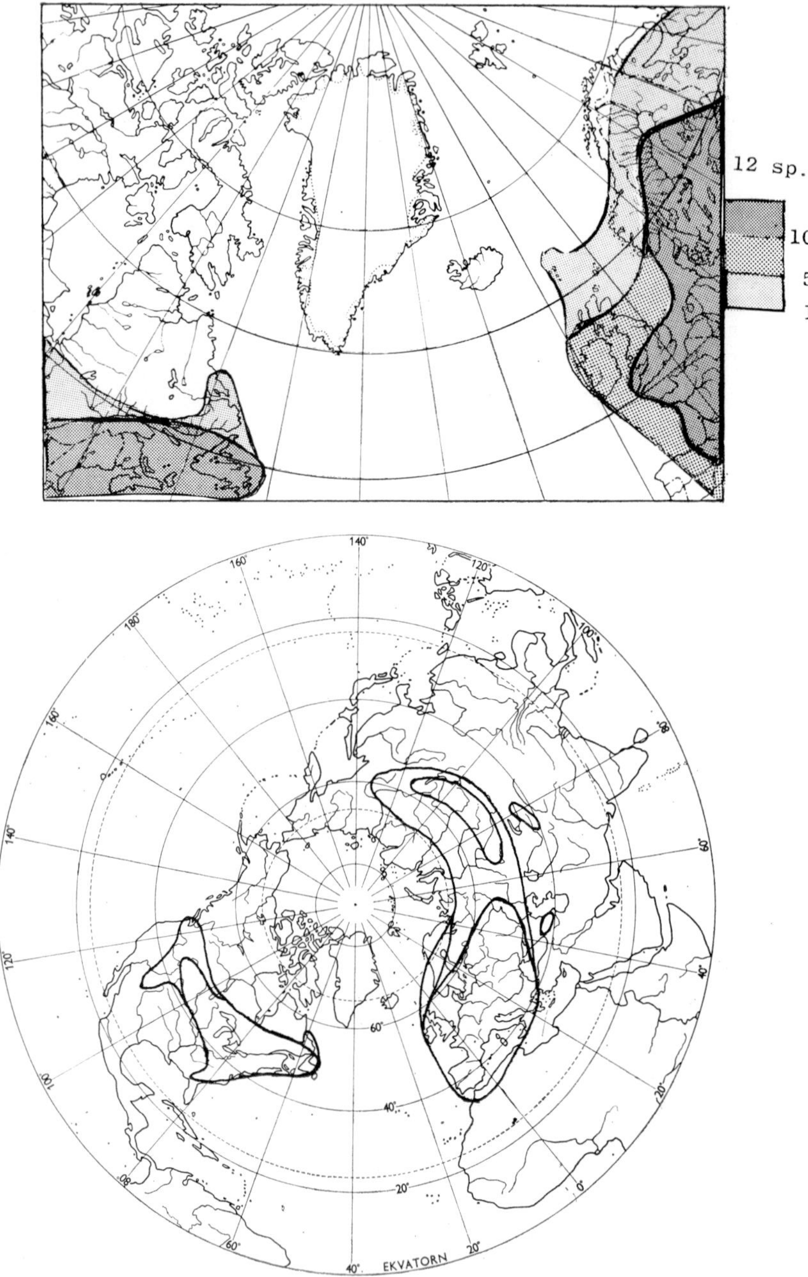

FIG. 13. Amphi-Atlantic plants lacking in Greenland but occurring in central Europe.

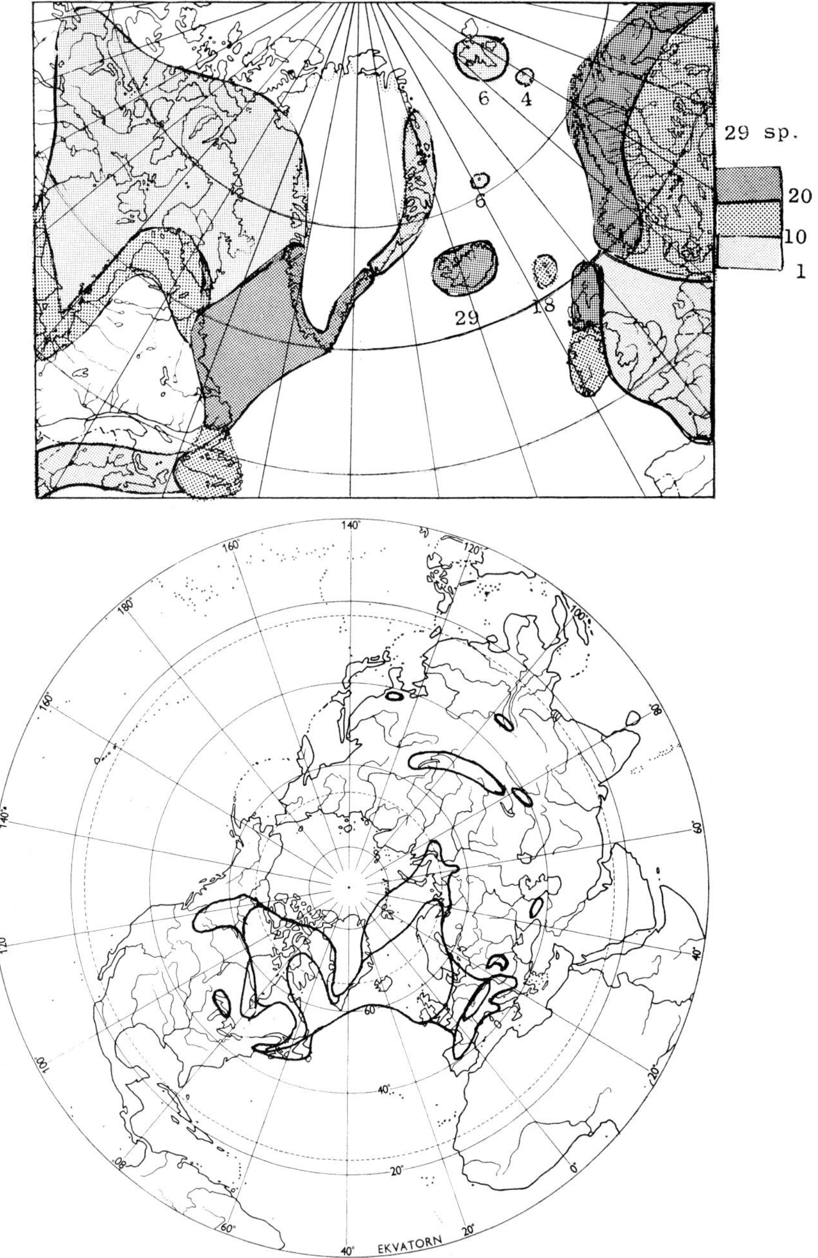

FIG. 14. Amphi-Atlantic plants occurring in Greenland and also in central Europe.

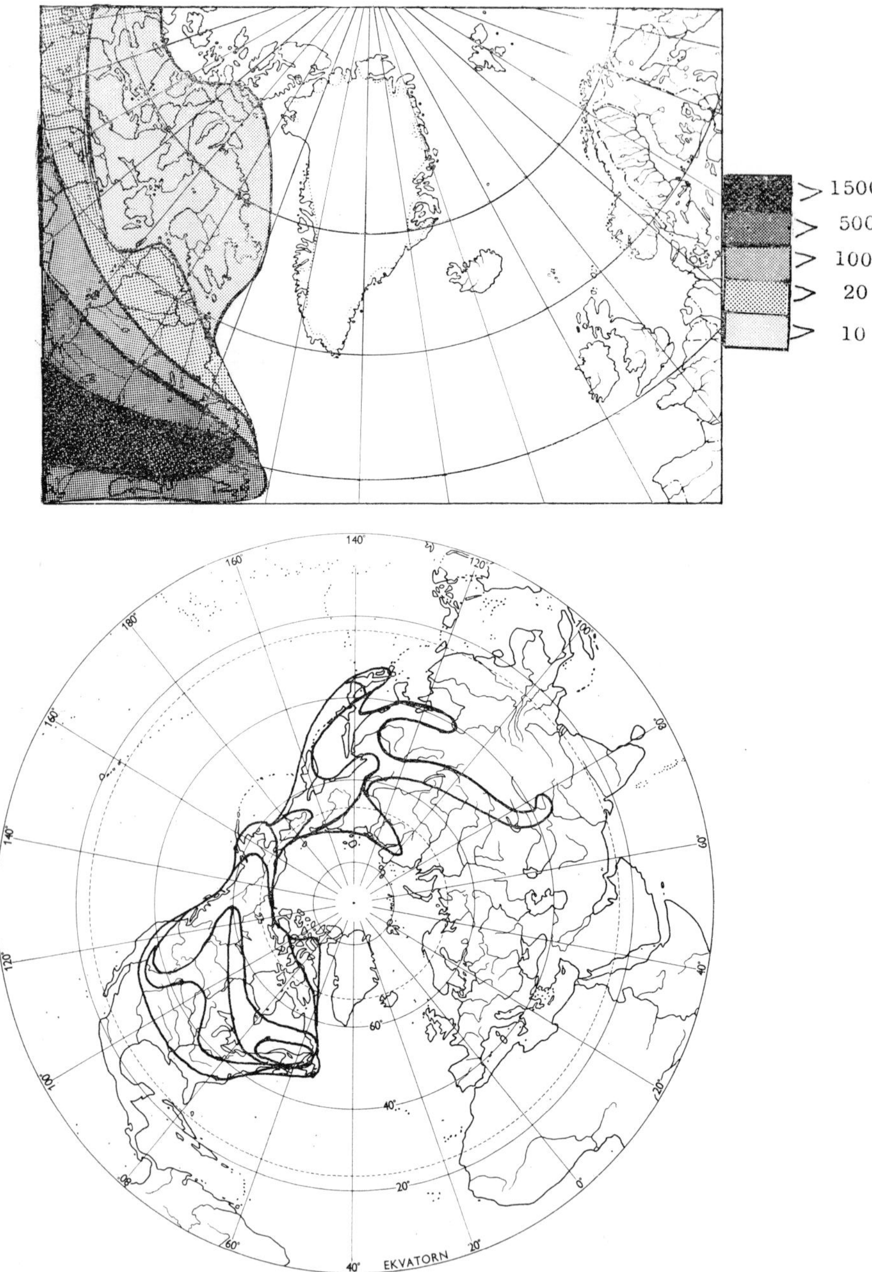

FIG. 15. American plants lacking in Greenland.

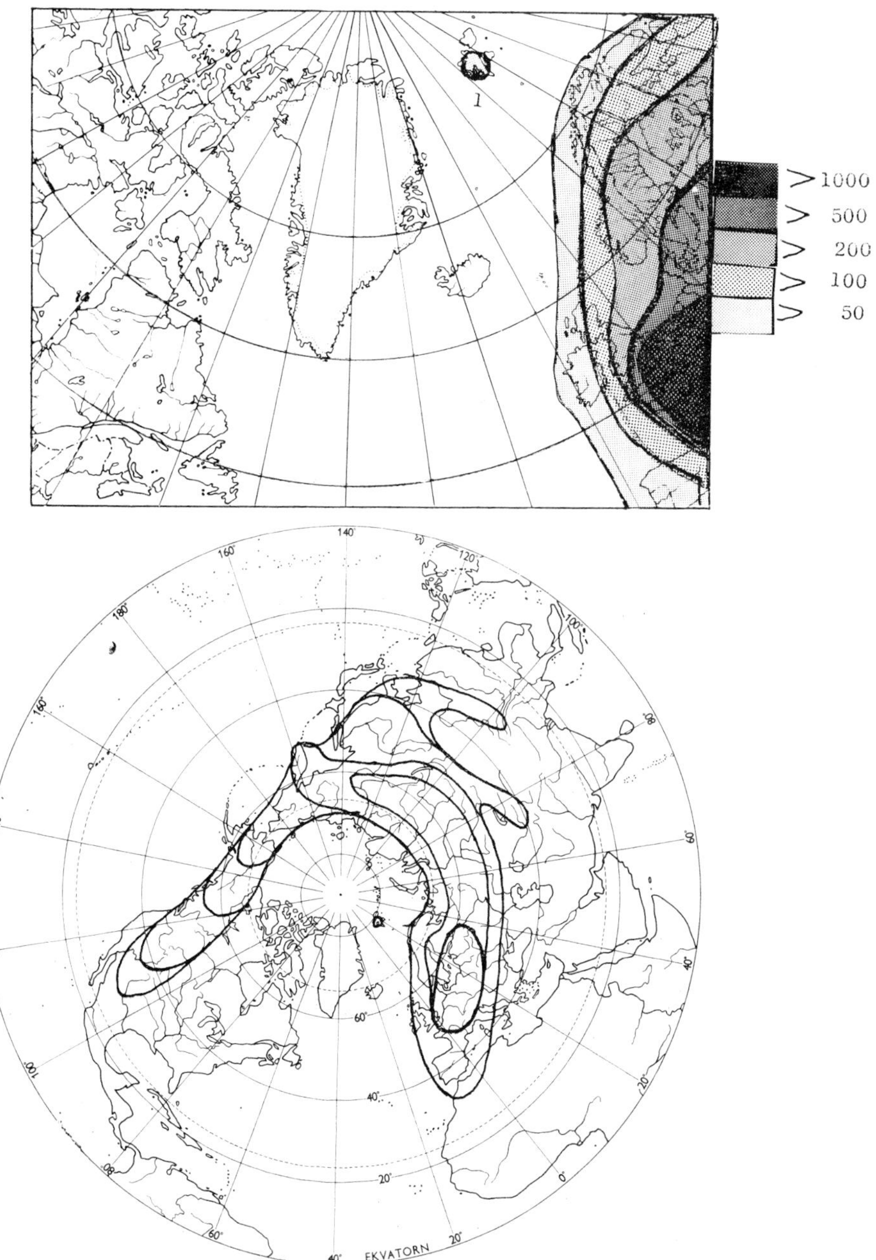

Fig. 16. European plants lacking in Iceland, Greenland and E. America.

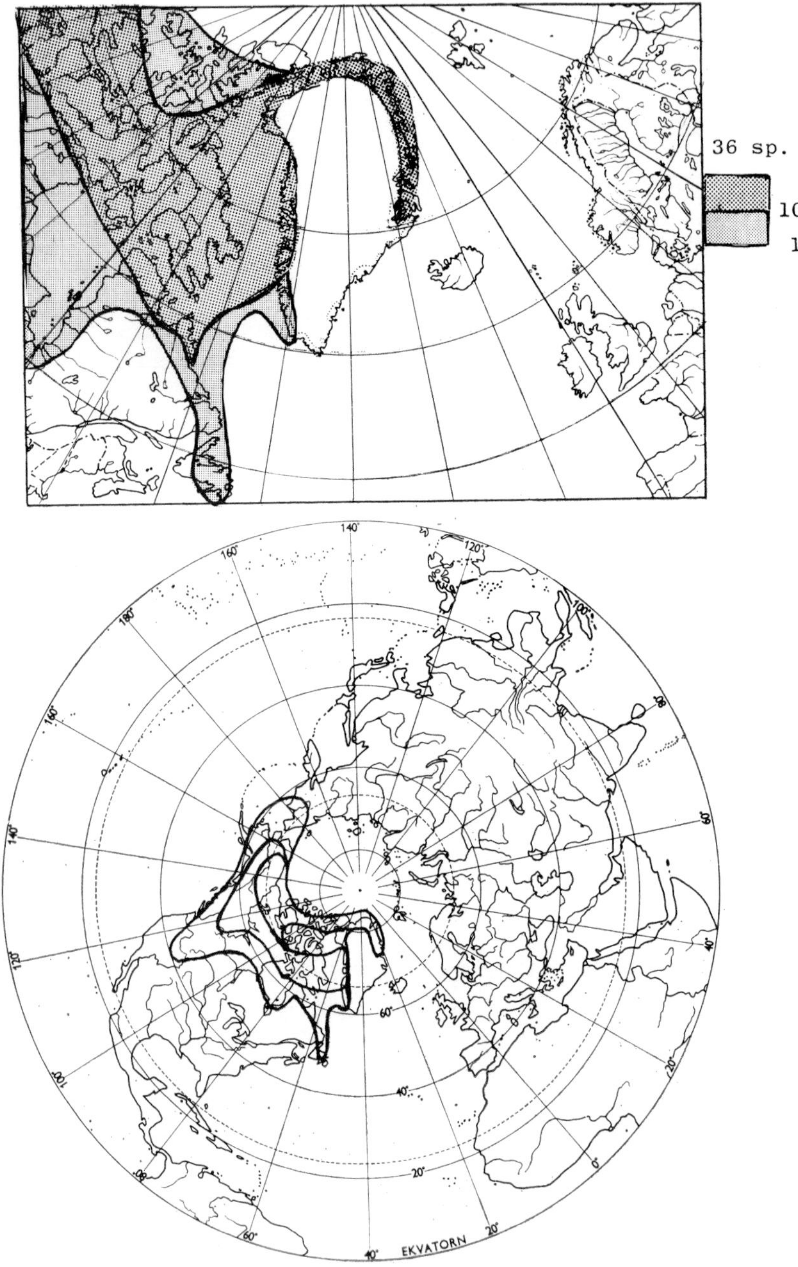

FIG. 17. American plants reaching northern Greenland.

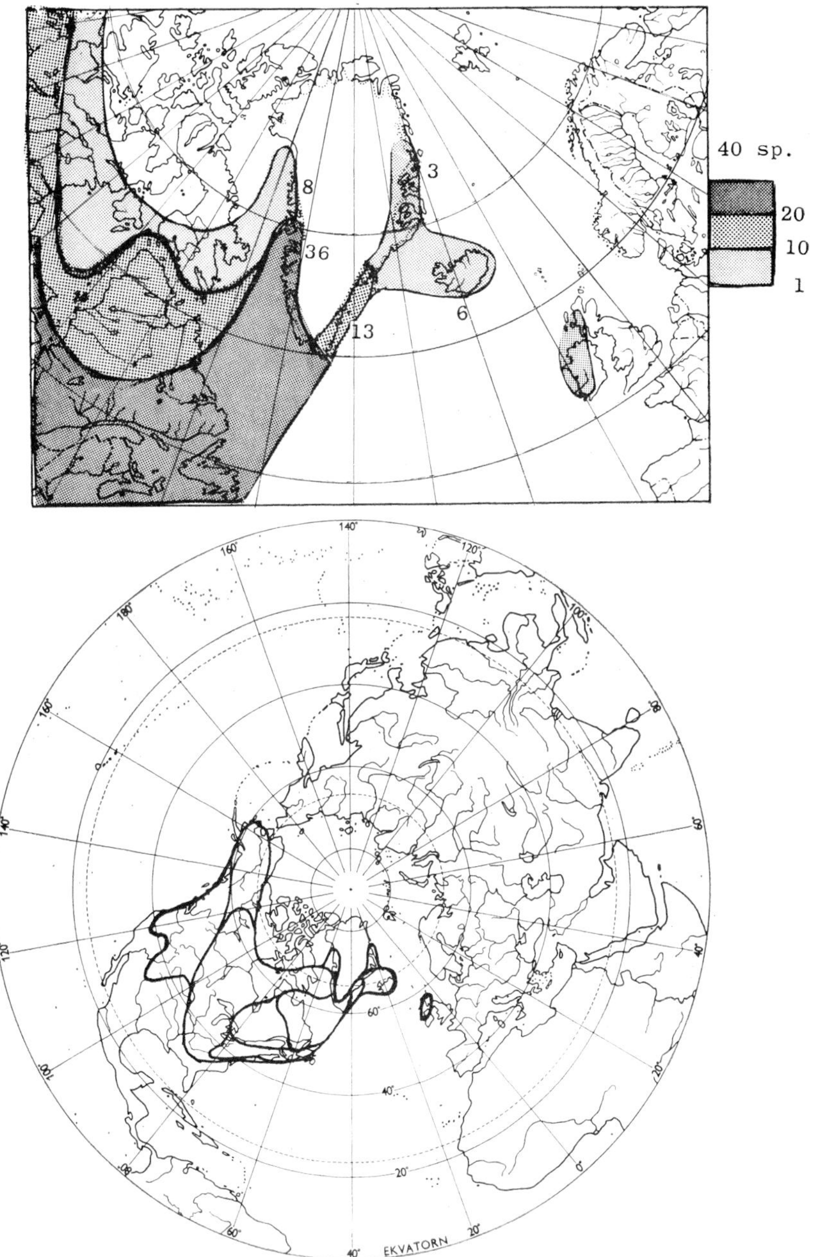

FIG. 18. American plants reaching southern Greenland–Iceland–Europe.

on that continent) which reach respectively northern and southern Greenland, and comprise altogether 74 species. Only 6 of them have extended as far as Iceland, and 4, *Spiranthes Romanzoffiana*, *Potamogeton epihydrus*, *Eriocaulon septentrionale*, and *Sisyrinchium* sp., to the British Isles. A strong connection between America and Greenland is thus demonstrated.

Figures 19 and 20 represent the corresponding European or Eurasiatic elements penetrating out into the Atlantic. The plants in Fig. 19 reach Iceland or Greenland but not America, and those in Fig. 20 extend also to America.

It is especially in these groups that the question about native or introduced species is particularly important. In my opinion, many plants occurring in Iceland have been introduced to that island, because the composition of the group seems to indicate that it consists to a large extent of plants favored by human activity. On the other hand, a few certainly do not belong to an introduced flora, for instance, *Saxifraga hypnoides*, *Vaccinium Myrtillus*, *Salix lanata*, *Orchis maculata*, *Paris quadrifolia*, *Saxifraga Cotyledon*, *Hydrocotyle vulgaris*, *Gentiana aurea*, *Gentiana detonsa*, *Veronica fruticans*, *Geranium silvaticum*, and a few others.

Figure 20 includes those European species which occur in eastern America and are considered by Fernald in his Manual to be native there. It seems to me that most, if not all, of them probably have been introduced into America; those which have the best chance to be of native origin are *Pedicularis silvatica*, *Juncus capitatus*, *J. bulbosus*, *J. subnodulosus*, and *Ranunculus hederaceus*.

In Figs. 21 and 22, respectively, are considered Atlantic Circumpolar and coastbound plants. It seems preferable to treat coastbound species separately because their distribution does not always conform to that of other plants. Several of these species have large inland areas on salt soil in the center of the continents. A few have a fairly unbroken connection from the Atlantic to the Pacific along the shores of the Arctic Ocean, whereas others show large gaps there. This indicates that during a warmer period the latter may have had such an unbroken connection which was later broken up by the deterioration of the climate.

Figures 23 and 24 represent endemics in Greenland or on Iceland–Faeroes. They are all very weak neo-endemics, mostly of critical genera, and cannot support a land-bridge theory.

A few plants have unique areas and could not be placed in any of the above-mentioned groups; thus, *Potentilla stipularis* and *Draba sibirica* have their main ranges in northern Asia with only single outpost localities in Greenland, whereas *Cakile edentula* occurs on the American coast with different types in different places. It has reached Iceland, and furthermore it has also extended to the Azores, apparently by means of sea currents.

Summarizing the above, the following can be stated concerning the phytogeographical connections of the North Atlantic: Very many species

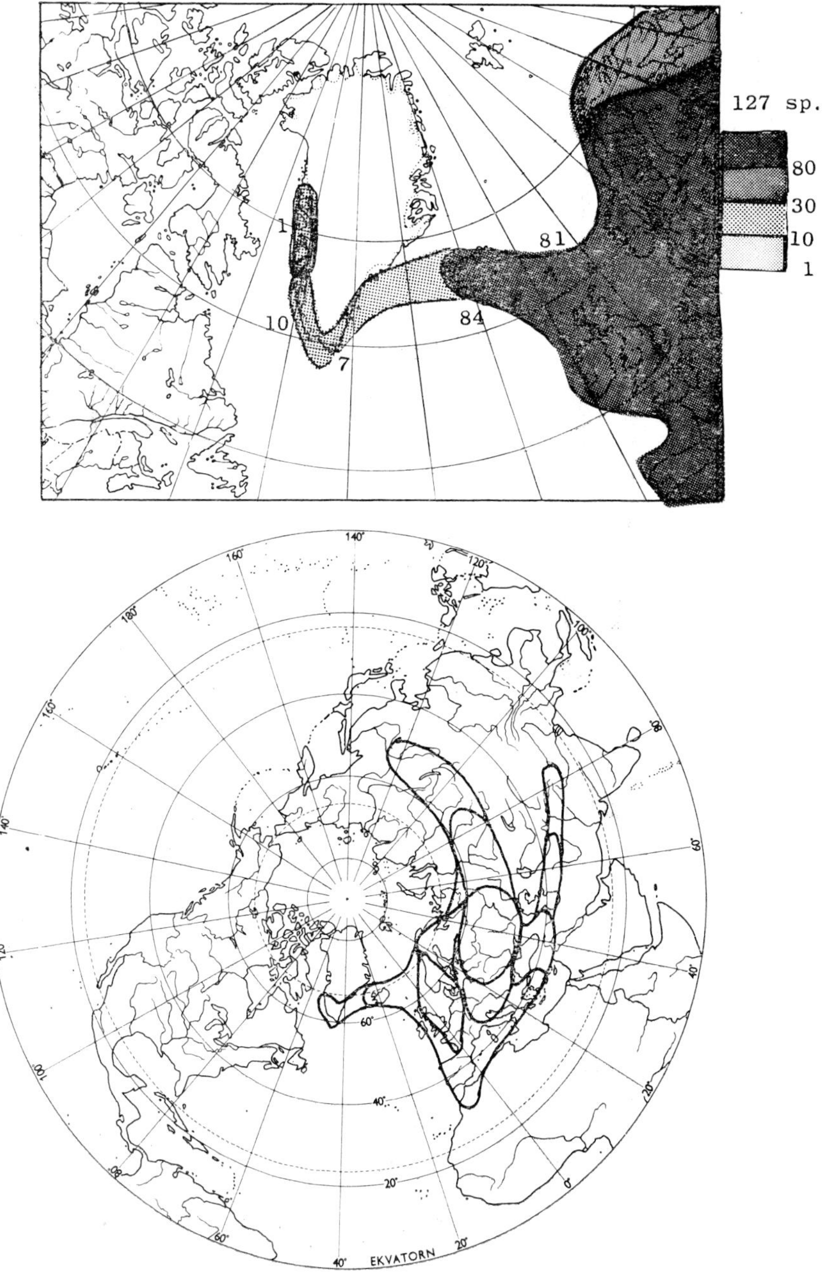

FIG. 19. European plants reaching Iceland–Greenland.

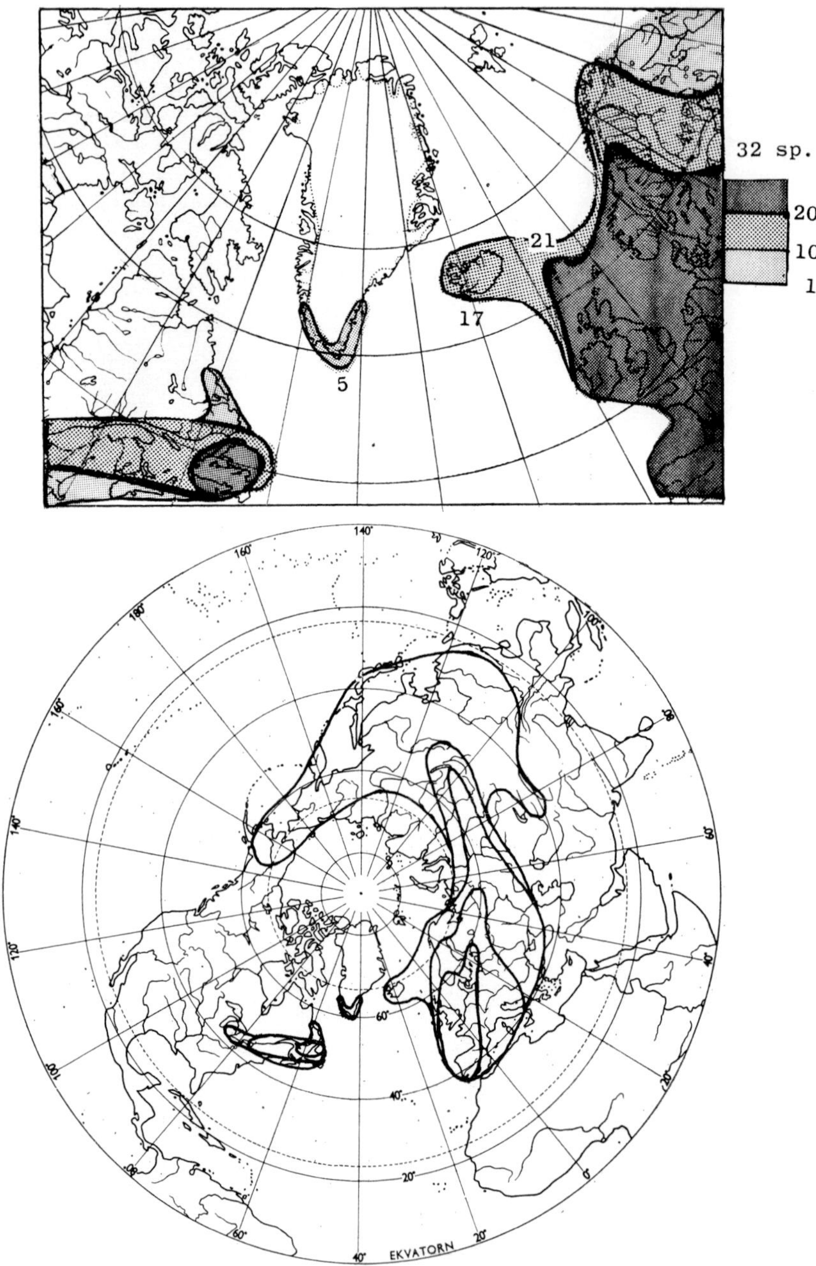

FIG. 20. European plants reaching easternmost America.

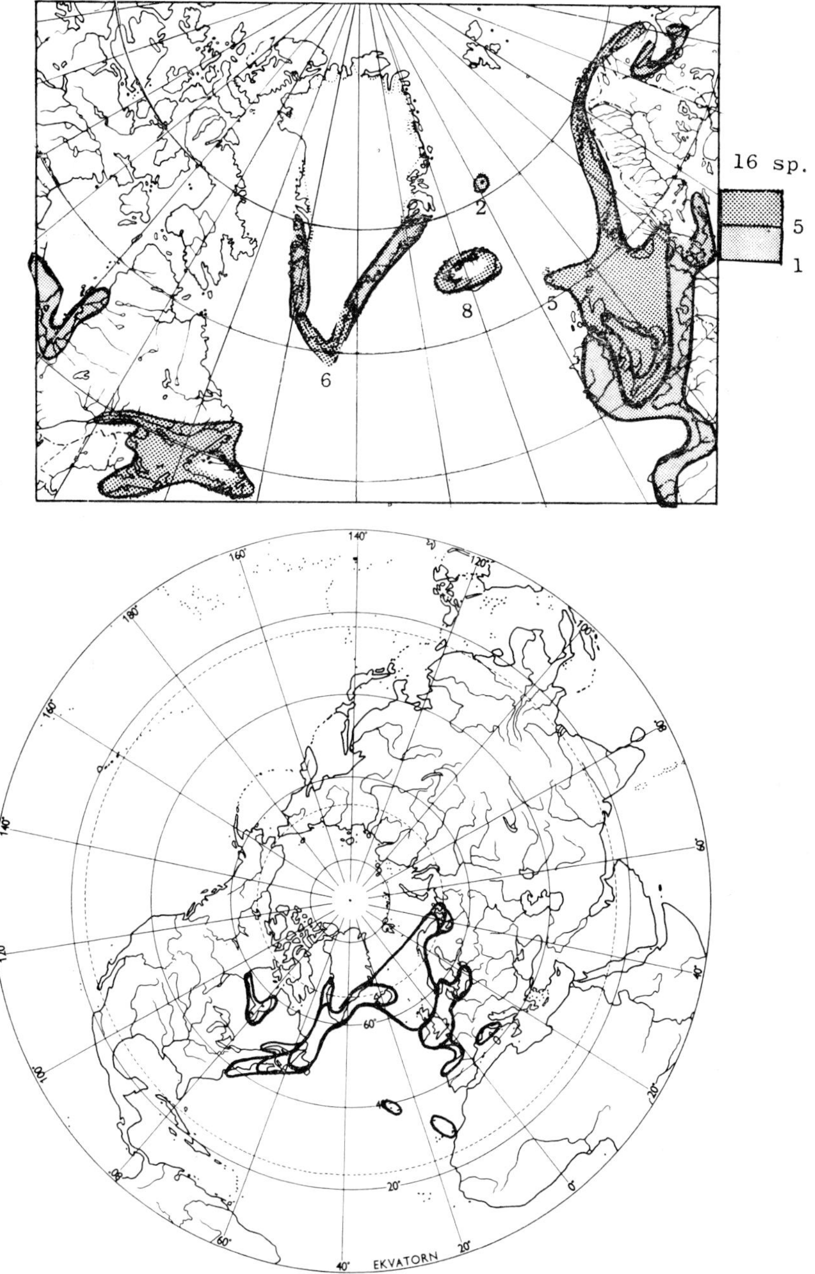

FIG. 21. Atlantic coastbound plants.

FIG. 22. Circumpolar coastbound plants.

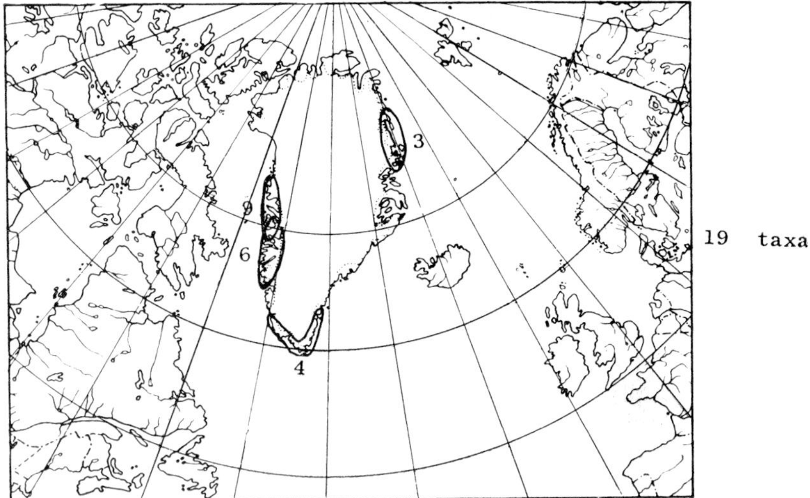

FIG. 23. Endemics in Greenland.

that do not occur in Europe attain the shores of the Atlantic in America, and similarly, many European plants reaching the Atlantic shores do not occur in America. A high number of Circumpolar plants with a Boreal area of a usually somewhat continental type have different races in eastern America and in Europe. Many other species are represented by corresponding, but different, counterparts on both sides of the Atlantic. The differences are thus large and

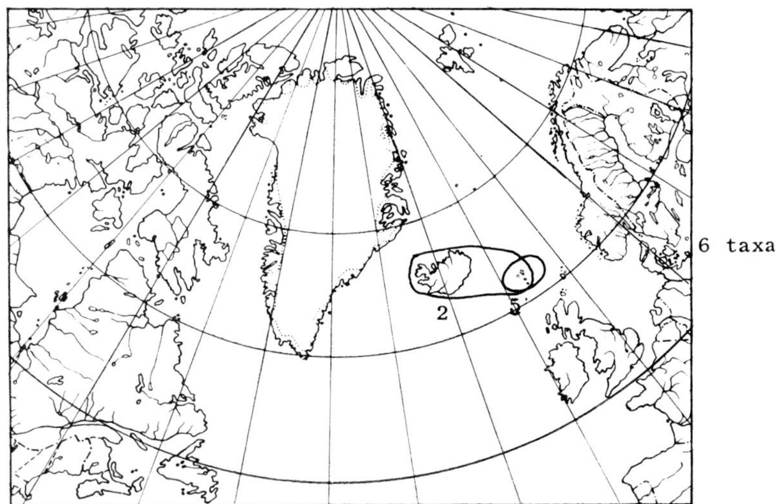

FIG. 24. Endemics in Iceland–Faeroe Islands.

certainly old. That diverse types have developed to such a large extent indicates that a very long time has been at their disposal.

The plants which show the most obvious connections over the Atlantic are those with a more or less Circumpolar area, at present having a northern boundary line fairly far to the north. The distance between the American and European continents is smallest in the north where the connection is strongest. Plants like *Potentilla stipularis* and *Draba sibirica* show that occasional introductions are possible over long distances there. It seems probable that the Circumpolar flora may have been spread by the wind blowing over the frozen Polar Sea or by floating on ice. We know that nowadays on the large floating Ice Islands in the Arctic Sea, living, well developed, flowering plants occur, drifting around the Polar Basin.

As the flora around the Polar Basin apparently is an old one only a few introductions are necessary in every century to account for a fairly even distribution.

The strongest botanical argument for a land-bridge over the North Atlantic is the Amphi-Atlantic plants although only little of the supposed connection is to be seen today, even in this group. Many species are missing in Greenland, on Iceland, and on the other Atlantic islands. The present ranges, however, could be interpreted as centering around the Atlantic, thus indicating that they once spread from a center there. But they may also be explained as reductions of former Circumpolar ranges caused by changing climatical conditions.

The endemics occurring in the Atlantic sector are very weak indicators of a previous connection.

The phytogeographical conditions around the North Atlantic thus, give poor support for a land-bridge that could have existed in Quaternary or Late Tertiary times.

THE PROBLEM OF LATE LAND CONNECTIONS IN THE NORTH ATLANTIC AREA

CARL H. LINDROTH

Zoological Institute, University of Lund, Lund, Sweden

THE idea of an earlier land connection between Europe and North America first occurred to biogeographers who wished to explain the striking similarity of the flora and fauna of the two continents. It found its most ardent supporter in R. F. Scharff (1907, 1909, 1911) and according to Th. Arldt (1917, p. 83) the Tertiary North Atlantic land-bridge constituted "eine der am sichersten feststehenden palaeogeographischen Tatsachen". The latest to express his acceptance of this hypothesis was the Norwegian botanist E. Dahl (1958). An Early Tertiary trans-Atlantic land connection has also been assumed on paleontological evidence (cf. Simpson, 1940, p. 149; 1947, pp. 658, 666).

An analysis of the animal species common to Europe and North America (Lindroth, 1957) has shown, however, that the majority of these belong to either of two about equally large groups: one, whose present distribution is a result of unintentional transport by man, mainly in the direction from Europe to North America; another, having a more or less complete circumpolar area, where the migration between the two continents went through a "back door", via Siberia and the Beringian land-bridge. This bridge is now considered by geologists as well as biogeographers almost unanimously to have functioned as a continuous land connection during each of the Pleistocene glaciations.

Exceptions from the rule that the faunal and floral exchange between Europe and North America took place by the way of Asia may be expected in the group of Amphi-Atlantic species (cf. Hultén, 1958)—provided the plants and animals are indigenous in both continents. This is an important restriction since several examples of Amphi-Atlantic distribution, such as that of the common garden snail, *Cepea hortensis* L., used as arguments in favor of a Eur-American connection, are now supposed to be the results of introductions into North America.

However, originally Amphi-Atlantic species do no doubt exist among animals as well as plants though they are not numerous. It is our task to explain their history and to decide whether an earlier continuous land connection between the two continents can be regarded as responsible for their present distribution. If so, the islands of the North Atlantic, as remnants of a supposed "bridge", would be the most suitable starting-point and we should begin the discussion with an analysis of their faunas and floras.

The Faeroes and Iceland are inhabited by almost purely European biota. The few undisputable cases of Nearctic elements on the islands are listed in Table 1.

TABLE 1. NEARCTIC ELEMENTS IN THE FLORA AND FAUNA OF ICELAND AND THE FAEROES
(lacking on the European mainland)

	Faeroes	Iceland	Greenland
Vascular plants*			
Leucorchis straminea (Fern.) Löve	+	+	+
Habenaria hyperborea L.	—	+	+
Epilobium latifolium L.	—	+	+
Spongiae			
Heteromeyenia ryderi Potts	+	—	—
Copepoda			
Diaptomus minutus Liljeb.	—	+	+
Coleoptera			
Colymbetes dolabratus Payk., sbsp.	—	+	+
Lepidoptera			
Crino sommeri Laf.	+	+	+
Crymodes exulis Laf.	+	+	+
Rhyacia quadrangula Zett.	—	+	+
Diptera			
Simulium vittatum Zett.	—	+	+
Aves (breeding)			
Gavia immer Brünn.	—	+	+
Bucephala islandica Gm.	—	+	+
Histrionicus histrionicus L.	—	+	+

* The number of Nearctic vascular plants may actually be higher in Iceland (Löve and Löve, 1956, p. 171). At least *Salix glauca callicarpaea* (Trautv.) and *Galium brevipes* Fern. & Wieg. (*Brandegei* auct. p.p.) should perhaps be considered; the former is accepted by Hultén (1958, p. 186). On the other hand, I have included *Leucorchis straminea* above, though it is not kept separate from *albida* L. by Hultén (*loc. cit.* p. 116), Böcher, Holmen and Jakobsen (1957), and others. Also, *Carex Lyngbyei* Hornem., occurring on Iceland and the Faeroes, seems to be Nearctic (Huttén, *loc. cit.*, p. 292).

On the Faeroes, they consist of four species: one Orchid with extremely minute seeds; two Noctuid moths with excellent flying ability; finally, the freshwater sponge *Heteromeyenia ryderi*, not found on Iceland but known from Ireland and the Isle of Mull in the Inner Hebrides. It has been suggested (Arndt, 1928, p. 159; Lindroth, 1957, p. 245) that the occurrence on the Faeroes, at least, is the result of bird transport of the resistant "gemmulae" of this sponge.

Iceland possesses a somewhat larger American element (Table 1): three vascular plants (at least); one freshwater crustacean of the genus *Diaptomus*; the eight remaining species being flying animals, insects and birds. The

Diaptomus species are able to produce thick-walled winter eggs, very resistant to desiccation (Wesenberg-Lund, 1937, p. 523, etc.). Considering the geographical position of Iceland, much closer to Greenland (*ca.* 300 km) than to the European mainland (Norway *ca.* 950 km) and the British Isles (*ca.* 800 km), the extremely poor representation of a Nearctic element is indeed surprising. Furthermore, it seems to consist exclusively of species with above average ability of dispersal. There is little doubt that the Nearctic animals and plants of Iceland were able to invade the island by active flight or by passive, "non-human" transport during present-day conditions.

TABLE 2. REPRESENTATIVE GROUPS OF THE TERRESTRIAL GREENLAND FAUNA

Indigenous species and subspecies. Endemic subspecies of birds are distributed among the three geographical groups according to their taxonomic relation to other subspecies (from Lindroth, 1957).

	Total	Holarctic	Palearctic	Nearctic and endemic
Aves (Salomonsen and Gitz, 1950)	68	37 = 45%	12 = 10%	19 = 28%
Macro-Lepidoptera (Henriksen, 1939)	26	14 = 53%	3 = 12%	9 = 35%
Coleoptera (Lindroth, 1957)	24	7 = 29%	11 = 46%	6 = 25%
Collembola (Hammer, 1953)	46	27 = 59%	13 = 28%	6 = 13%
Araneae (Brændegaard, 1946; Holm, pers. comm.)	50	21 = 42%	11 = 22%	18 = 36%
Together	214	106 = 50%	50 = 23%	58 = 27%

The fauna of Greenland, if distributed among geographical groups (Table 2), is a veritable "mixture". Roughly counted, it consists of one-half Circumpolar taxa, and about one-quarter each of Nearctic and Palearctic forms, respectively.

However, it is easily observed that different animal groups behave differently in this respect. The highest percentages of Palearctic forms are found among Coleoptera and Collembola; among Nearctic forms the highest frequency occurs in Araneae, Lepidoptera, and Aves. This is, of course, a biological and not a taxonomical feature. It is an expression for differences in dispersal ability: The Nearctic element of the Greenlandic fauna consists of a high proportion of easily dispersed animals, able to traverse at least moderate distances over the sea by active flight or by passive, aerial transport. The Palearctic element includes many soil-bound species not easily dispersed by these or other methods.

A closer examination of the entire Coleopterous fauna of the North Atlantic islands provides a clearer picture (Fig. 1). The purely Palearctic character of the fauna of the Faeroes and Iceland is strongly manifest and, what is more important, the species concerned are to a great extent flightless and thus not easily spread. In principle, this applies also to the Coleoptera of Greenland. There, the Nearctic element contains a single flightless beetle, the Staphylinid *Micralymma brevilingue* Schiö., fit for hydrochorous dispersal in salt water.

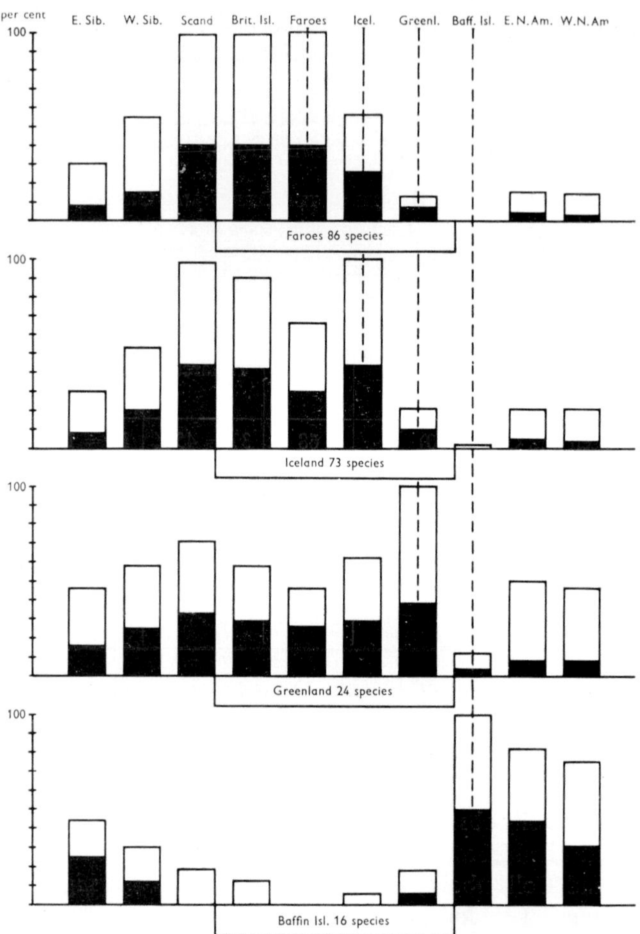

FIG. 1. Species and subspecies of indigenous Coleoptera of the North Atlantic islands and their occurrence in selected regions of the Holarctic.
White = flying; black = flightless. (From Lindroth, 1957.)

Essentially different is the fauna of Baffin Island, separated from Greenland by a strait only 350 km at its narrowest (that is, approximately the same distance as from Iceland, *ca.* 300 km). The Coleoptera of Baffin Island are truly Nearctic having one (Circumpolar) species in common with Iceland, none with the Faeroes, and, respectively, two and three with the British Isles and Scandinavia. All of them are flying forms. Actually, the fauna of Baffin Island shows much more relationship to east Siberia than to Greenland!

As far as the Coleoptera of Iceland, Greenland, and Baffin Island are concerned, the situation may be illustrated, somewhat roughly, in the form of a map (see Fig. 2). It demonstrates the blocking effect west of Greenland by Davis Strait, which may be regarded as *the most effective faunal barrier of the entire Circumpolar area* (Lindroth, 1957, p. 264).

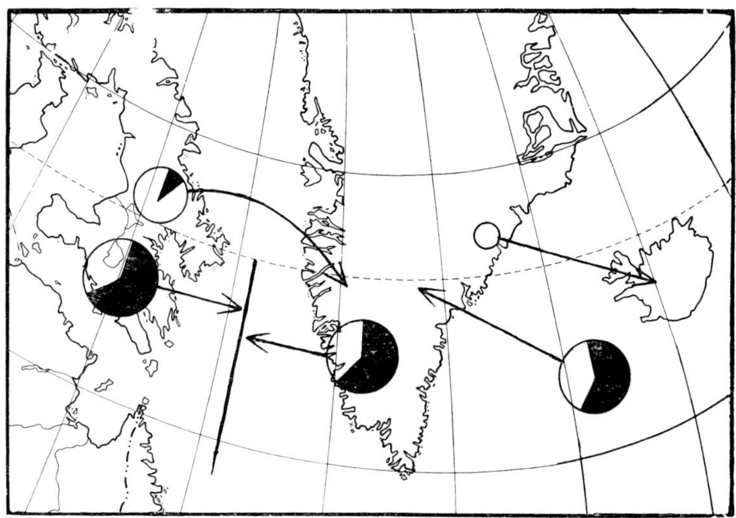

FIG. 2. The Palaearctic and Nearctic elements of indigenous Coleoptera in Greenland and adjacent areas. Black sectors = flightless forms. Size of circles in proportion to number of taxa (from 1 to 11). (Data from Lindroth, 1957.)

The distribution in the same area of Nearctic and Palearctic elements of vascular plants (Fig. 3) gives less evidence because most plants are apparently better suited than soil-animals to passive long-distance dispersal (Lindroth, 1960). But the principle remains the same: plants with low ability of dispersal are to a considerable degree blocked by Davis Strait; the Palearctic element of Greenland includes proportionally more forms not adapted to long-distance dispersal than does the Nearctic element of that island.

This is, indeed, surprising, considering the geographical position of Greenland. It is tempting to resort to the strong pressure of conventional thinking and suppose that if Greenland had belonged to North America politically and not only geographically, everybody would have noticed the strange composition of its fauna and flora.

What ought to be expected is, indeed, that the long distance from Europe—against prevailing winds!—could have been successfully conquered only by organisms with extraordinary means of dispersal, whereas an immigration from Baffin Island and the North American mainland should have been much easier to accomplish. Thus, the actual situation is contrary to all calculations.

Either of two explanations seems possible:

1. The influence of man has been underestimated. The Palearctic element of plants and animals in Greenland is largely a result of introduction by the old Norsemen (and the same would apply to Iceland).

2. A considerable part, notably the Palearctic element, of the flora and fauna of Greenland (and Iceland) has immigrated during a period of geographical conditions fundamentally different from those of the present time. This is the so-called "Land-bridge Theory".

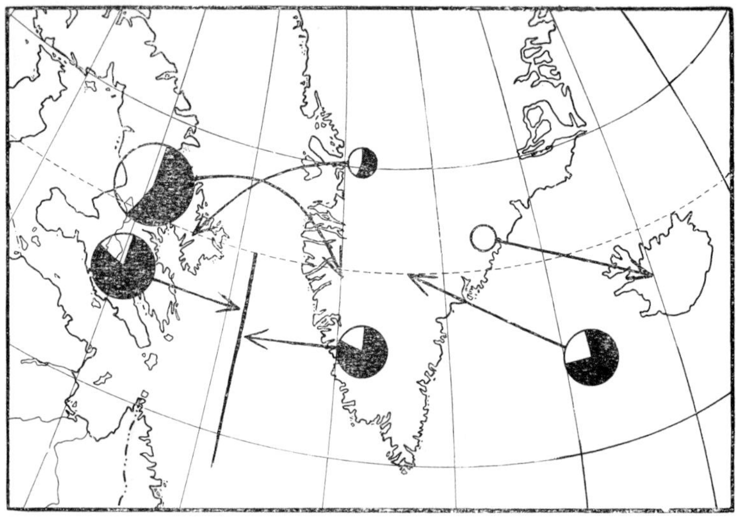

FIG. 3. The Palearctic and Nearctic elements of indigenous vascular plants in Greenland and adjacent areas. Black sectors = species without adaptation to long-distance dispersal. Size of circles in proportion to number of taxa (from 3 to 55). (Data from Lindroth, 1960.)

Commenting on point (1), it should be remembered that the Palearctic plant species of Greenland have been thoroughly scrutinized by M. P. Porsild (1932), considering the possibilities of introduction by man from Europe. Similar calculations on the insect fauna have been made by myself for Iceland (Lindroth, 1931, p. 516) and for Greenland (Lindroth, 1957, p. 268). The conclusions drawn are that both islands possess an old and indigenous Palearctic element. Among other arguments, it is impossible to accept that a haphazard dispersal by anthropochorous transport could result in the rather homogeneous fauna of Greenland, Iceland, and the Faeroes, that have so many flightless species in common.

We have reached our main problem here and I would like to declare my position at once: The fauna and flora of the North Atlantic islands, notably of

Iceland and Greenland, claim decidedly a continuous land connection with Europe.

This is, it should be observed, not the continuous Eur-American land-bridge postulated by Scharff (1907, 1909, 1911), and others. As here proposed, it includes Greenland but does not extend beyond Davis Strait.

The bottom configuration of the North Atlantic Ocean seems rather favorable for the appearance of a land-bridge (Fig. 4). A positive displacement

FIG. 4. The bottom configuration of the North Atlantic. (From Lindroth, 1957.)

of the shore-line amounting to less than 600 m would connect the Faeroes, Iceland, and Greenland with Europe along the present Wyville-Thompson ridge ("the Greenland–Scotland ridge"). Now, 600 m would seem like a modest depth in comparison with ordinary deep-sea values exceeding 2000 m even within short distance and on both sides of the Wyville-Thompson ridge. But it is nevertheless considerably more than the changes in sea level regarded as acceptable in late geological times, at least during the Pleistocene.

The *eustatic* depression of the sea level, due to storage of the precipitation in form of ice on the continents, has been calculated as hardly exceeding 100 m during each of the last two (and possibly earlier) Pleistocene glaciations. There is no reason to believe that similar events have occurred in Tertiary time. Pliocene, or earlier, glaciations (if a reality; cf. Schwarzbach and Pflug, 1957, p. 295) were under all circumstances less extensive.

No *isostatic* movements of the Earth-crust, caused by ice depression and simultaneous upheaval of marginal areas, can have exerted any noticeable effect on the now submerged parts of the Wyville-Thompson ridge.

There is also a special biological reason for denying the importance of iso- and/or eustatic movements effecting positively the rise of a North Atlantic land connection: The Palearctic element of the Greenland–Iceland biota, the history of which we are here trying to trace, is not Arctic, not even Sub-Arctic; the insects, at least, are members of a Boreo-Temperate fauna. Therefore, they must have immigrated, not during a Glacial, but an Interglacial period, possibly in Preglacial time.

Since iso- and eustatic changes of the sea level fail to explain the assumed land connection, the remaining possibility is that it was created by *tectonic* movements within the area, or—more adequately expressed—that continuous land once existed but was broken down by tectonic processes.

This is perhaps more than a mere hypothesis. From northern Ireland and western Scotland over the Faeroes, Iceland, and Greenland west to Disko Island in Davis Strait runs a chain of volcanic rock-occurrences, mainly basalt, formed in Tertiary time (Fig. 5). Whether these are remnants of a

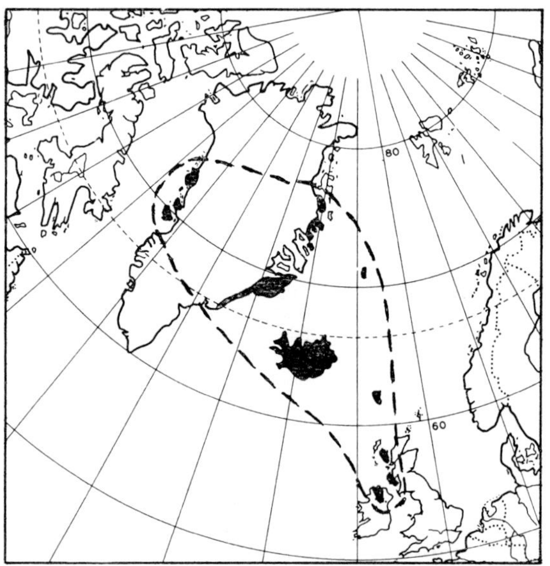

FIG. 5. Tertiary volcanic rock (mainly basalt) of approximately similar age in the North Atlantic area. (Compiled from different sources.)

continuous land area occupying large parts of the present North Atlantic region, is still a matter of dispute (Einarsson, 1961), but some geologists (e.g. Schwarzbach, 1959, pp. 32, 36) think it is probably so.

The crucial question from the point of view of a biogeographer is how long the assumed land connection existed. To geologists, this question is of subordinate interest and only few of them have tried to provide an answer. Schwarzbach and Pflug (1957, p. 296) do not think that connection between Iceland and the British Isles was probably after Eocene, and later, Schwarzbach (1959) seems inclined to remove a possible Eur-American "bridge" to Pre-Tertiary time.

Unfortunately, we do not know even approximately how old the animal species are that now inhabit the Earth. The rate of evolution has been of quite different magnitude in different groups as well as within different genera of the same group. In spite of this, some idea of the minimum of time required for the formation of a "new species" would be extremely valuable for the dating of zoogeographical events.

As far as insects are concerned it is safe to say that no evidence for species formation in Pleistocene time has been brought forth. The fossils from Interglacial or Interstadial deposits so far investigated (from Scandinavia, Great Britain, and central Europe) seem in no case to be different from now living representatives of the species.

On the other hand, the insect fauna of Late Eocene, as amply illustrated by thousands of very well-preserved fossils in the Baltic Amber, was quite distinct on the species level. Most genera were identical with those of the present time but very few are regarded as belonging to the same species (e.g. among the Coleoptera, only one or two).

Thus, species formation among insects in general seems to have taken place after the Baltic Amber time, but before the Pleistocene, i.e. during a period of between 40 and 1 million years ago.

If the postulated North Atlantic bridge with its biota lasted only during Early Tertiary and was broken down before the Oligocene period, and if part of the present fauna and flora had survived from that remote time, then there is no doubt at all that they would have contained a considerable number of taxonomically well distinguished endemic species. For comparison we need only refer to the numerous endemic insect species which survived, often restricted to single mountain peaks, throughout the Pleistocene within the *massifs de refuge* in the European Alps.

Several biogeographers (e.g. Löve and Löve, 1956, p. 235, etc.; Larsson, 1959, p. 36, etc.; Einarsson, 1961, p. 46) have assumed that the land-bridge persisted into Late Tertiary time with subsequent survival of the biota through all Pleistocene glaciations. As far as I can see, however, old Tertiary faunal and floral elements would have been left on Iceland and Greenland also in case the bridge lasted into Pliocene time, with a peculiar flora in Iceland, rather different from that of contemporary Europe (Jónsson, 1954; Schwarzbach and Pflug, 1957, p. 289, etc.).

It is also noteworthy that the shallow and narrow sound between Greenland and Ellesmere Land in the High North was not used as a by-pass for the Icelandic–Greenlandic Palearctic elements. This is easily understood if it is assumed that the species in question immigrated from Europe as far as Greenland during the Pleistocene, when the climate was never much warmer than now. But it is much harder to realize that this northern connection would not have been biologically effective, if the trans-Atlantic land connection is removed entirely to Tertiary, Early Tertiary, or even to Cretaceous time, i.e. to periods with a warm-temperate climate also on the North Atlantic islands (Schwarzbach, 1955, p. 101, etc.).

The most satisfactory explanation of present faunal and floral conditions in Iceland (and Greenland) would be to assume that the Tertiary biota were destroyed and followed by a new invasion from Europe. It is difficult to imagine such a total destruction by any other agency than a glaciation.

According to this hypothesis, the land connection Greenland–Iceland–Scotland persisted (or was re-established) in at least one of the Interglacial periods, offering an immigration route for Boreo-Temperate biota from Europe. It is known from plant fossils that the climate of Iceland was slightly warmer than now during at least one Interglacial period (with *Pinus* and *Picea* in deposits). It was with some hesitation referred to the "Günz–Mindel" by Áskelsson (1960). *Alnus* appeared in the "Mindel–Riss" Interglacial (Thórarinsson, 1958). During the last Interglacial, the "Riss–Würm", at least *Betula* trees grew on the island (Thorkelsson, 1935).

I am perfectly well aware that the hypothesis here emphasized (and maintained also earlier: Lindroth, 1931, p. 551; 1957, p. 253, etc.) is against the opinion of almost all geologists. It would be interesting to live long enough to see how close to the truth it may be!

Since every idea of a North Atlantic land-bridge in Post-glacial time, previously assumed by some older authors (e.g. Simmons, 1905), is a geological impossiblity, the hypothesis stressed above implies that the main part of the indigenous fauna and flora of the North Atlantic islands survived at least one glaciation *in situ*. In this respect, conditions in Iceland are more easily understood than in Greenland and have been treated by many biogeographers.

As usually, only the effect of the Last Glaciation (Würm) can be reconstructed with some claim of reliability. I would like to add one more reason to those proposed by several specialists in favor of a "Würm-hibernation" in Iceland: A deposit is known at Ellidavogur (near Reykjavík) from the "Riss–Würm" Interglacial (Thorkelsson, 1935). It contains fragments of seven beetle species, six of which are members of the present indigenous fauna of the island; the remaining one is a species of flying water-beetles, genus *Hydroporus*, unidentifiable as to species, but apparently not identical with the single present representative of this genus in Iceland, *H. nigrita* F. Of the six species in common with the present fauna, three are flightless, i.e. *Nebria gyllenhali* Schnh., *Pterostichus diligens* Sturm, and *Tachinus corticinus* Gr. Is it really within the limits of probability to assume that the Riss–Würm Interglacial fauna of Iceland was exterminated to be substituted later, in Post-glacial time, by oversea immigration by the very same, in part flightless, species? To accept this would, for me, be a clear underestimation of the random character of long-distance dispersal.

The locating of the Icelandic Würm-refugia has been a matter of some controversy. Botanists (e.g. Steindórsson, 1954) have paid most attention to the isolated occurrences of certain Arctic–Subarctic plants in the northern parts of the island and, consequently, placed most of the refugia there. This seems to be supported also by geological data (cf. map by Einarsson, 1961, p. 44). The terrestrial fauna, however, shows a clear concentration of flightless

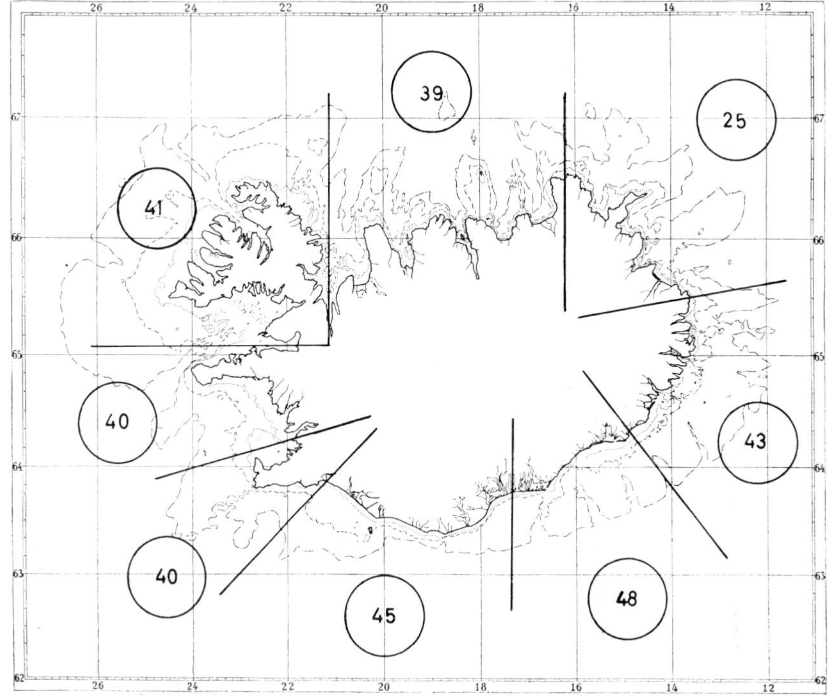

FIG. 6. Percentage of indigenous flightless Coleoptera in different parts of Iceland. Dimorphic species counted, if occurring in the short-winged form. Three species, found isolated in the north, are omitted since regarded as transported by man: *Trechus obtusus* Er., *Othius melanocephalus* Gr., *Apion cruentatum* Walt.

or otherwise not easily dispersed forms in the south and the southeast. For that reason, I have earlier (Lindroth, 1931, p. 481, etc.) tried to locate the two main faunal Würm-refugia to the surroundings of Eyjafjallajökull and Hornafjördur, respectively.

The distribution of flightless Coleoptera in different districts of Iceland is illustrated here (Fig. 6). The two main features are: (1) the high proportion of the said element in the south and, as could be expected, notably in the southeast; and (2) the very low figure for the northeast. This is remarkable, since botanists have claimed several refugia in this area (Einarsson, 1961). It seems to be another proof of the fact that the "botanical refugia" in the north were of quite subordinate importance as far as the land fauna is concerned. Judging from its present distribution on the island, a single beetle species (*Notiophilus aquaticus* L.; a wing-dimorphic Carabid and the only, entirely or partly, short-winged beetle of the Icelandic fauna that in Scandinavia reaches the *regio alpina superior*) may be suggested as a hibernator in the north.

At least during the Last Glaciation, there were apparently two different kinds of refugia in Iceland: (1) northern refugia, both on the coast and in isolated nunatak areas with Arctic and Subarctic conditions; (2) coastal refugia in the south and southeast inhabited mainly by Boreo-Temperate biota.

It is quite possible that conditions have been similar during the Riss Glaciation, but this cannot be inferred from the present species distribution. Thus, from a purely biogeographical standpoint, the most satisfactory explanation of the character of the biota on Iceland as well as on the other North Atlantic islands would be: (1) a land connection that persisted into Early Pleistocene; (2) survival of the main part of the now existing floras and faunas on the isolated islands through the Riss and Würm Glacials.

Finally, I would like to summarize what has been said above:

1. Conditions of faunal and floral distribution in the North Atlantic area are extraordinary, with European biota predominating in Iceland and reaching Greenland, but completely blocked by Davis Strait.

2. An extraordinary explanation is therefore called for: a former land connection from the European mainland to Greenland.

3. The fauna of the Atlantic islands gives the impression of youth since it does not include any endemic species. It can hardly be regarded as directly descended from Tertiary time, but it is thought to have immigrated in one of the Interglacials and thereafter to have survived at least one Glaciation, probably more, *in situ* on coastal refugia in Iceland, Greenland, and probably also in the Faeroe Islands.

REFERENCES

ARLDT, T. (1917). *Handbuch der Palaeographie*. I, 1–3. Leipzig.

ARNDT, W. (1928). Der Süsswasserschwamm *Heteromeyenia ryderi* Potts, &c. *Zool. Anzeiger* **77**, 156–166.

ÁSKELSSON, J. (1960). Pliocene and Pleistocene fossiliferous deposits. Int. Geol. Congr. Exc. Guide A2 (Iceland), 28–32.

BÖCHER, T. W., HOLMEN, K. and JAKOBSEN, K. (1957). *Grönlands flora*. Copenhagen.

DAHL, E. (1958). Amfiatlantiske planter. Problems of amphiatlantic plant distribution. *Blyttia* **16**, 93–121.

EINARSSON, Th. (1961). Pollenanalytische Untersuchungen zur spät- und postglazialen Klimageschichte Islands. *Sonderveröff. Geol. Inst. Univ. Köln* **6**, 1–52.

HULTÉN, E. (1958). The amphiatlantic plants and their phytogeographical connections. *Kgl. Svenska Vetensk. Akad. Handl.* IV, 7 (1), 1–340.

JÓNSSON, J. (1954). Outlines of the geolcgy of the Hornafjördur region. *Geogr. Ann.* **36**, 146–161.

LARSSON, S. G. (1959). Coleoptera 2. General remarks. *Zool. of Icel.* III, 46b, 1–85.

LINDROTH, C. H. (1931). Die Insektenfauna Islands und ihre Probleme. *Zool. Bidr. fr. Uppsala* **13**, 105–589.

LINDROTH, C. H. (1957). *The Faunal Connections between Europe and North America.* Stockholm and New York.

LINDROTH, C. H. (1960). Is Davis Strait—between Greenland and Baffin Island—a floristic barrier? *Bot. Notiser* **113**, 129–140.

LÖVE, Á. and LÖVE, D. (1956). Cytotaxonomical conspectus of the Icelandic flora. *Acta Horti Gotob.* **20**, 65–291.

PORSILD, M. P. (1932). Alien plants and apophytes of Greenland. *Medd. om Grönl.* **92** (1), 1–85.

SCHARFF, R. F. (1907). *European Animals: Their Geological History and Geographical Distribution.* London.

SCHARFF, R. F. (1909). On the evidence of a former land-bridge between northern Europe and North America. *Proc. Irish Acad.* **28B**, 1–28.

SCHARFF, R. F. (1911). *Distribution and Origin of Life in America.* London.

SCHWARZBACH, M. (1955). Allgemeiner Überblick der Klimageschichte Islands. *Neues Jahrb. Geol. Paläontol.* Mh. 97–130.

SCHWARZBACH, M. (1956). Das Vulkangebiet von Hredavatn (West-Island). *Neues Jahrb. Geol. Paläontol.* **104**, 1–29.

SCHWARZBACH, M. (1959). Die Beziehungen zwischen Europa und Amerika als geologisches Problem. *Kölner Univ.-Reden* **23**, 1–39.

SCHWARZBACH, M. and PFLUG, H. D. (1957). Das Klima des jüngeren Tertiärs in Island. *Neues Jahrb. Geol. Paläontol.* **104**, 279–298.

SIMMONS, H. G. (1905). Har en landbrygga öfver Nordtatleanten funnits i postglacial tid? *Ymer* **25**, 150–155.

SIMPSON, G. G. (1940). Mammals and land bridges. *J. Wash. Acad. Sci.* **30**, 137–163.

SIMPSON, G. G. (1947). Holarctic mammalian faunas and continental relationships during the Cenozoic. *Bull. Geol. Soc. Amer.* **58**, 613–687.

STEINDÓRSSON, S. (1954). Um aldur og innflutning íslenzku flórunnar. *Ársrit Ræktunarfél. Nordurl.* **51**, 3–23, 53–72, 101–115.

THÓRARINSSON, S. (1958). The Öræfajökull eruption of 1362. *Acta Nat. Isl.* **2** (2), 1–99.

THORKELSSON, TH. (1935). A fossiliferous interglacial layer at Ellidaárvogur, Reykjavík. *Soc. Scient. Isl., Greinar* **1** (1), 1–14.

WESENBERG-LUND, C. (1937). *Ferskvandsfaunaen, biologisk belyst.* 2. Udgave. Copenhagen.

TAXONOMIC DIFFERENTIATION AS AN INDICATOR OF THE MIGRATORY HISTORY OF THE NORTH ATLANTIC FLORA WITH ESPECIAL REGARD TO THE SCANDES

J. A. NANNFELDT

Institute of Systematic Botany, University of Uppsala, Uppsala, Sweden

IN this everchanging world the distribution of a taxon is determined not only by the sum of all its ecological demands and reproductive properties but also by historical factors. The environment is changing and so is also the genetical constitution of every taxon, but it is only rarely that the changes in distribution can be proved by direct observations.

To keep to the area and era closest to us, the North Atlantic area and the Quaternary era, we know a good deal about, for example, our trees and their immigration after the last glaciation from pollen-analysis and other fossil remains. We know also a good deal about the first plants to invade south Scandinavia after the retreat of the last ice-sheet. Already Nathorst and his contemporaries found *Dryas octopetala*, *Salix herbacea* and other high-mountain species, now growing in the Scandes. Iversen and Erdtman have recently, by pollen-analytical methods, found a rich, very early steppe flora. At least one of its species, *Ephedra distachya*, has long ago disappeared again from Scandinavia. For at least one of the other steppe species, *Centaurea Cyanus*, it seems very improbable, to say the least, that the present-day population of Scandinavia has any genealogical connection with that early Post-glacial population. Also, as for *Dryas* and the other mountain plants now growing in the Scandes, there are no proofs or even indications that there are direct genealogical connections between those early populations of south Scandinavia and the present-day populations of the Scandes. In the opinion of numerous students, amongst them myself, there are none.

About most of our species we know, in fact, nothing of that kind.

One of the first distributional problems in the Scandes to attract the interest of scientists was the presence of what has become known as a "West Arctic Element" in the flora. These plants cannot reasonably have reached their present areas from the south or the east. Neither can their occurrence in the Scandes be explained by chance dispersal from a remote west. The possibility and importance of such long-distance dispersal should of course not to be denied. Is there any better explanation for *Dryopteris fragrans* in Utsjoki (northernmost Finland) or for *Oxytropis deflexa* in Kautokeino (northernmost Norway) or for the short visit of *Arctostaphylos alpina* to a spot in west Jutland?

The "West Arctic Element", however, cannot be explained in that way. The number of species is too large, and they do not occur haphazardly but are restricted to special areas which are inhabited also by other species possessing restricted and disjunct part-areas. A theory explaining the occurrence of the "West Arctic" species is not acceptable, if it does not at the same time explain also the occurrence of these other species. In the mind of numerous phytogeographers, including myself, the only possible explanation is the existence during the Last Glaciation of ice-free refugia west, and perhaps even north, of the ice-sheet, not too far from the areas where these plants grow nowadays. How they survived the previous glaciations is impossible to know, but I feel sure that they, or at least most of them, did survive in north-west Europe. I feel sure that the Scandinavian mountain plants have a long history with us and that few, if any, species have reached us from the south as late as during or after the Würm Glaciation. Possible exceptions are such species as *Campanula barbata*, *Gentiana purpurea* and *Ranunculus platanifolius*. These are far from High-Alpine and are restricted to the south part of the Scandes, except for a most isolated locality in Finnmark for the *Ranunculus* (chance dispersal ? ?). Several species have certainly perished from the severe vicissitudes during the glaciations, and a new glaciation would certainly impoverish our flora still more. This is the only explanation of the absence from the Scandes of such species as *Alopecurus alpinus*, *Chamaenerium latifolium* and *Lomatogonium rotatum*.

Taxonomists and phytogeographers often plead for a broad species concept, lest the general survey and the understanding of the natural connections should be lost. It is true that a species concept such as used by numerous Russian authors who give specific rank to almost every geographically isolated population, leads to a loss of the understanding of the phylogenetical connections. The treatment of all agamospecies as normal "full" species may have the same effect, especially if the agamospecies of, for example, the *Ranunculus auricomus*-complex were treated on the same level as the species within the larger, sexual part of the genus. But the scope of the species is in itself of little importance, if only the lower recognizable units are not neglected, for these smaller units give often important, in many cases perhaps the most important, clues to the migratory history of a species. I shall here give some few examples from the North Atlantic area, especially relating to the flora of the Scandes. My first examples aim at showing the closer floristic connections of the Scandes with Iceland and Scotland than with the Alps and other central and south European mountains.

The *Poa laxa* group or *Poa* sect. *Oreinos* forms an excellent example. This group has its centre in central Europe and has certainly originated there. It is totally absent from the Arctic. To be sure, *Poa laxa* has repeatedly been reported from Greenland and Arctic America, but in so far as I have seen the voucher specimens they have been misnamed. Hultén (1942) claims that closely related plants occur in Alaska and Kamtchatka but as far as I understand they have nothing to do with sect. *Oreinos*. Now, some 25 years ago I (Nannfeldt, 1935) was able to show that the populations of Scandinavia, Iceland and Scotland are very homogeneous both *intra* and *inter se* and that they show sharp though small differences from the populations of the Alps and the other southern mountains. Some years later, Nygren (1950, 1955) showed that the northern taxon (*Poa flexuosa* or *P. laxa* subsp. *flexuosa*) is hexaploid ($2n = 42$) in contrast to the true southern *P. laxa*, which is tetraploid ($2n = 28$) and perhaps also diploid. A very isolated population occurs in eastern North America. I found it to represent a distinct taxon (*Poa fernaldiana* or *P. laxa* subsp. *fernaldiana*) and Nygren (1955) to be hexaploid. All these facts seem to indicate that the northern populations have been isolated from the southern for a very long time, and this conclusion is strengthened by *Poa jemtlandica* (Nannfeldt, 1937; Nygren, 1950). This viviparous taxon has certainly arisen as a hybrid between *P. flexuosa* and *P. alpina* and is so uniform in all morphological characteristics that it must be of monophyletic origin. It propagates exclusively by vivipary. It occurs in Scandinavia and Scotland but is unknown from Iceland. Its Scandinavian (Figs. 1 and 2) and Scottish part-areas are smaller than those of *P. flexuosa* but fall completely within them. Its present distribution affords thus an additional proof of a connection between Scotland and the Scandes and is strongly indicative both of its own high age and of the high age of *P. flexuosa* in the North Atlantic area.

Trisetum spicatum is a grass with an unusually large, almost world-wide Arctic-montane distribution. This species is certainly very old. Hultén (1959a) has recently treated its racial differentiation, distinguishing no less than 14 subspecies. For my purpose it is sufficient to mention that the type subspecies has an Arctic–Subarctic distribution reaching farther south in the central Asiatic mountains and in the western American mountains, whereas the Pyrenees, the Alps and the Caucasus are inhabited by a separate taxon, subsp. *ovatipaniculatum*. It may further be mentioned that Iceland and south Greenland are reached by a northeast American taxon, subsp. *pilosiglume*. The cytological features of this complex are still very imperfectly known. The subsp. *ovatipaniculatum* is unknown cytologically. The type subspecies is tetraploid, and a hexaploid is known from Greenland.

Several additional examples could be given even if those just discussed are the most instructive. It should not be concealed that there are species, in which, at least so far, no significant morphological differences have been found between the populations of Scandinavia and the Alps. Such is the case

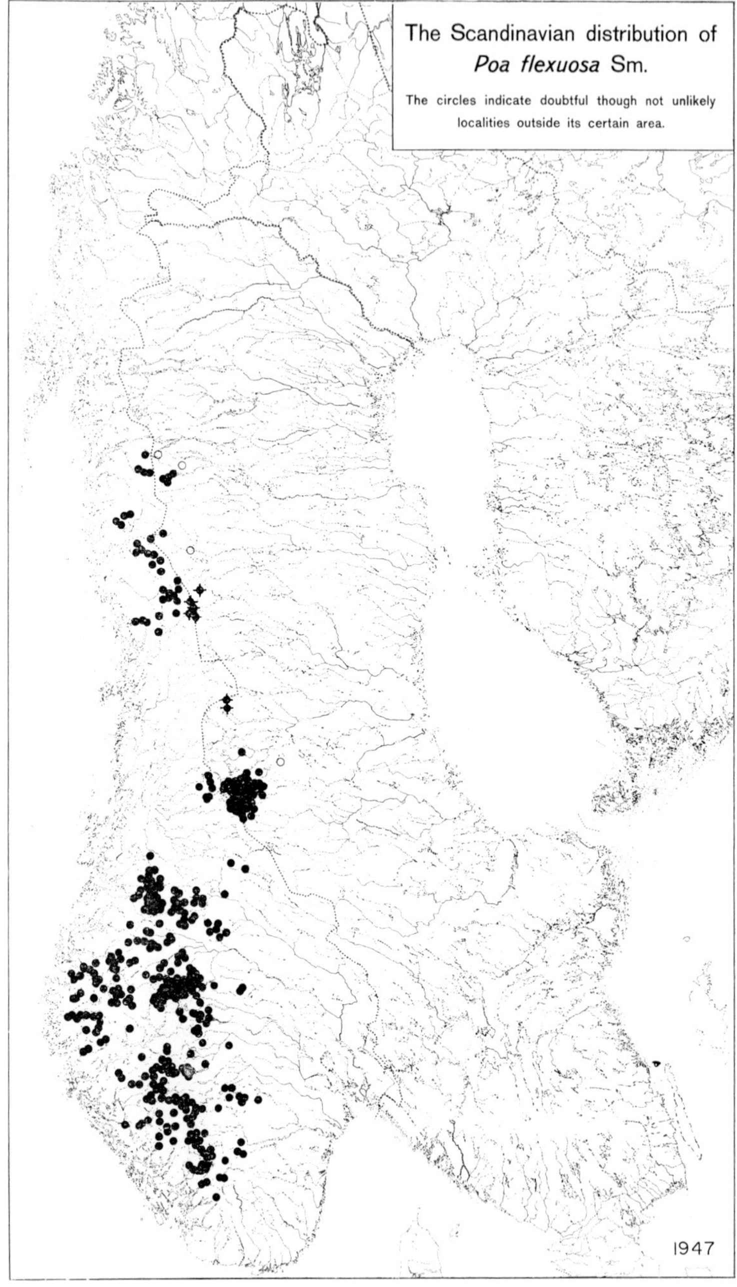

FIG. 1. The Scandinavian distribution of *Poa flexuosa*. (Mainly after Nannfeldt, 1935.)

with *Dryas octopetala*, also recently studied by Hultén (1959b). But nobody can predict the results of detailed and careful cyto-taxonomic studies.

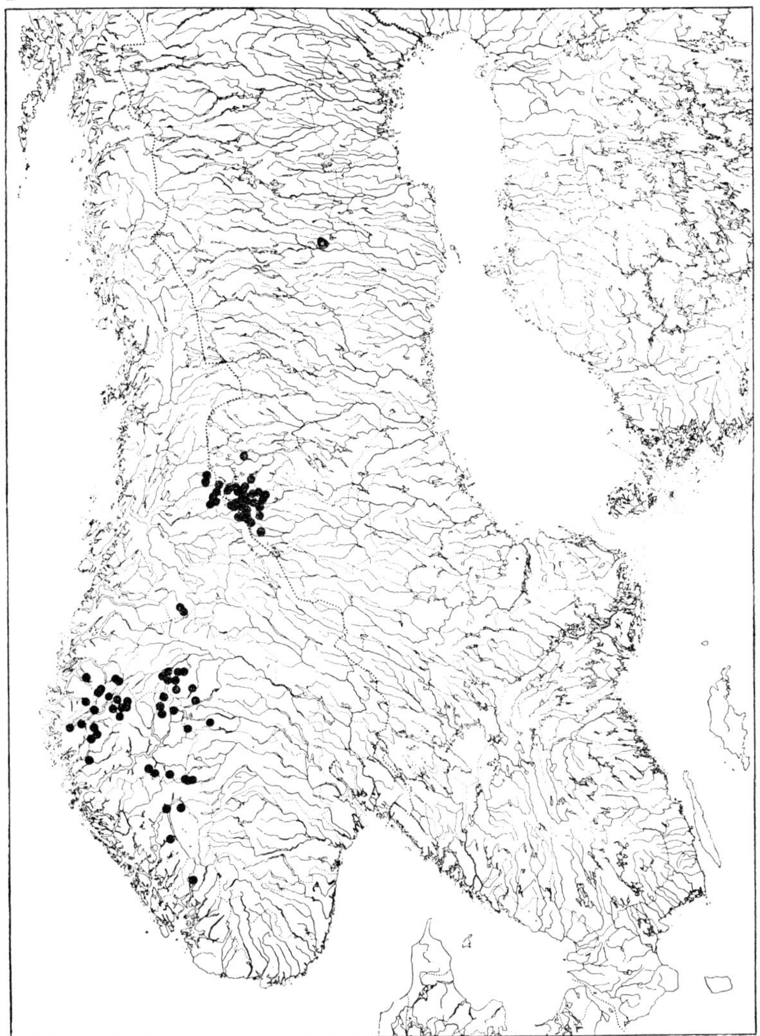

FIG. 2. The Scandinavian distribution of *Poa jemtlandica* (Almqu.) Richt. (After Nannfeldt, 1937.)

I turn now to the problem whether the taxonomic differentiation between populations in different parts of the Scandes can give clues to an understanding of their migratory history. The now classical example is the mountain poppies, studied by Nordhagen (e.g. 1931) from the late twenties onwards and then given a detailed cyto-taxonomical treatment by Gunvor Knaben (1958, 1959 a and b). Löve (1955, 1962) has studied these poppies in other part-areas.

It must first be pointed out that all North Atlantic mountain poppies are widely different from those of the Alps, the latter all being diploids ($2n = 14$), whereas those in the north are octoploids, decaploids and dodecaploids.

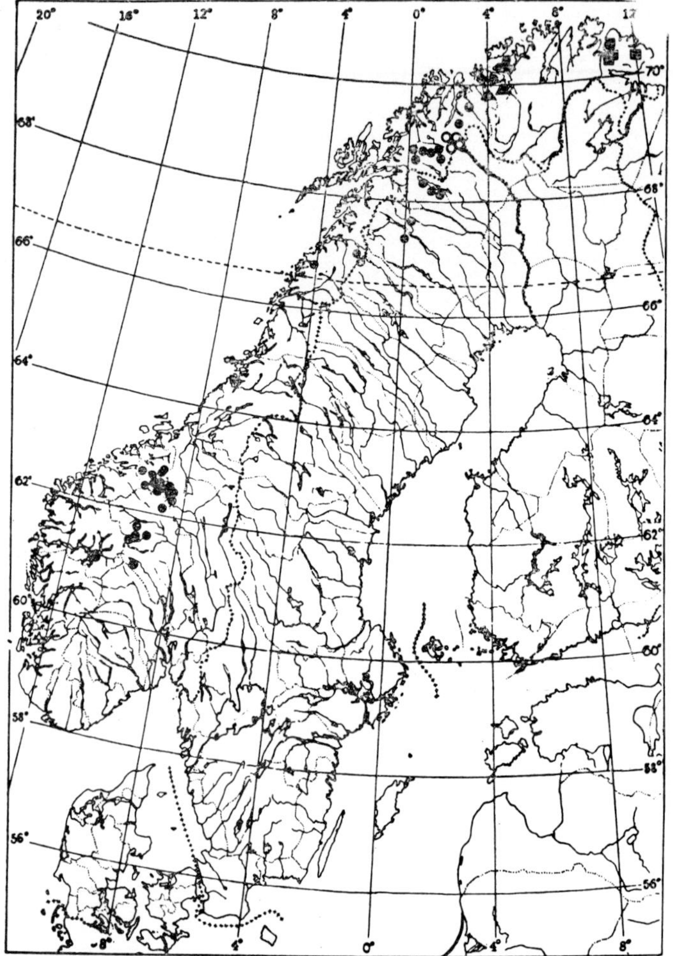

FIG. 3. The total distribution of the mountain poppies in Scandinavia (After Knaben, 1959a).

● *Papaver radicatum* sensu Nordhagen and Knaben.
■ *P. dahlianum.* ○ *P. lapponicum* ssp. *laestadianum.*
▲ *P. lapponicum* ssp. *scandinavicum.*

The populations growing in Scandinavia (Fig. 3) can be grouped into three polymorphous species, one is octoploid, viz. *P. lapponicum* (incl. *P. laestadianum*). Löve (1952) claims that the name *P. radicatum* should be transferred to this species. The two other Scandinavian species are decaploids. One is

P. dahlianum, and the third is the species that Nordhagen and Knaben consider to be the true *P. radicatum* but for which Löve (1955) has coined the new name *P. nordhagenianum*. If Löve's views on the typification of *P. radicatum* are correct and if *P. nordhagenianum* is taken in the broad sense that Knaben and Löve now take it, its correct name seems to be *P. relictum*.

The last-named species has a total distribution comparable to that of *Poa flexuosa*, except that it does not grow in Scotland, instead the Faeroe Islands is an additional area. Its distribution in the Scandes differs from that of the *Poa*, as the poppy is bicentric and the *Poa* southern. Moreover, the poppy is very polymorphous and split up in a number of races with limited distribution. With the more detailed and refined studies their number has increased to ten, six in the southern part-area (Fig. 4) and four in the northern.

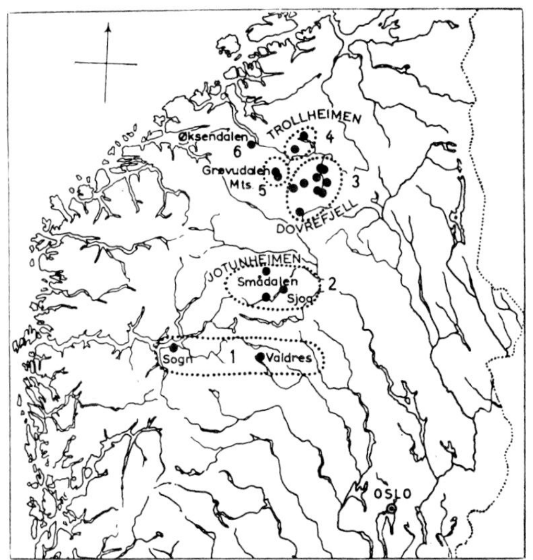

FIG. 4. Distribution areas of the six south Norwegian subspecies of *Papaver radicatum* (After Knaben 1959). 1. *relictum*. 2. *intermedium*. 3. *ovatilobum*. 4. *Gjaerevolli* 5. *groevudalense* 6. *oeksendalense*

But it is not sufficient with this splitting-up. The poppies are very rare plants. They inhabit very restricted localities, and the individuals in each locality are very few. These local populations are very homogeneous in themselves but differ markedly from the populations of even the most adjacent localities, although the differences manifest themselves very little in the physiognomy of the plants but almost exclusively in their chromosome structure. The differences between the races mentioned above and equipped with taxonomic names are of a higher class of magnitude, they manifest themselves clearly in the physiognomy and also the differences in chromosome structure are much larger. At least five of the six southern races show a distinct affinity to each other and contrast markedly to the four northern which show a similar affinity *inter se*. Dr. Knaben's conclusion is that each of the ten taxonomically recognized races survived the Last Glaciation in a refuge of its own and that the lesser differences between the local populations have arisen on the spots where they now grow. This theory is very suggestive but sounds perhaps too good to be true in every detail. It is impossible to calculate even roughly how long these two stages of differentiation have taken, but it is now known that in very small populations differences in chromosome structure may arise in a surprisingly short time. Nevertheless, her establishing of the two stages of differentiation is a most important discovery. The only possible explanation to this remarkable fact is that it is connected with the migratory history of the poppies. The additional fact that the northern races group themselves into one group and the southern races (or at least five of the six) into another, is most tempting to try to explain by historical reasons as well. Also the two other species of Scandinavian mountain poppies behave in a similar way, although they are not bicentric but northern. Our knowledge of the three species outside Scandinavia is not as detailed but their behavior there seems to be modified, i.a. by the circumstance that the populations are often much larger and not so isolated from each other.

Another group showing differentiation within the Scandes is the polymorphous *Poa arctica*-complex, studied by me some 20 years ago (Nannfeldt, 1940) from a taxonomic point of view and then submitted to a cytological study by Nygren (1950). This complex is totally absent from the Alps and the other southern mountains of Europe, and in the Scandes it is typically bicentric (Fig. 5). In the southern part there occur three very distinct and uniform taxa, viz. subsp. *depauperata*, subsp. *elongata* and subsp. *stricta*, whereas in the northern part the polymorphy is more continuous, only a minority of the specimens being referable to distinct lower taxa. The explanation of this difference is given by Nygren's cytological studies. One of the southern taxa, subsp. *stricta*, is viviparous and has a very small area. It has the lowest chromosome number ($2n = 39$) known in the whole complex and forms its embryo-sacs sexually. Due to its vivipary no seeds are ever formed and it propagates exclusively by bulbils. Morphology, chromosome number and lack of aposporous embryo-sacs suggest a very isolated and probably very old type. The two other taxa are non-viviparous and propagate thus exclusively by seeds. Their areas are small but much larger than that of subsp. *stricta*, and one of them, subsp. *depauperata*, has been found on Iceland by Löve (1947), which affords still another example of a close connection between the Scandes and Iceland. Nygren has found that in both the embryo-sac mother-cells always degenerate very early and are substituted by aposporous embryo-sacs in which the egg-cell divides so early that chance fertilization becomes impossible. All embryos are thus formed asexually.

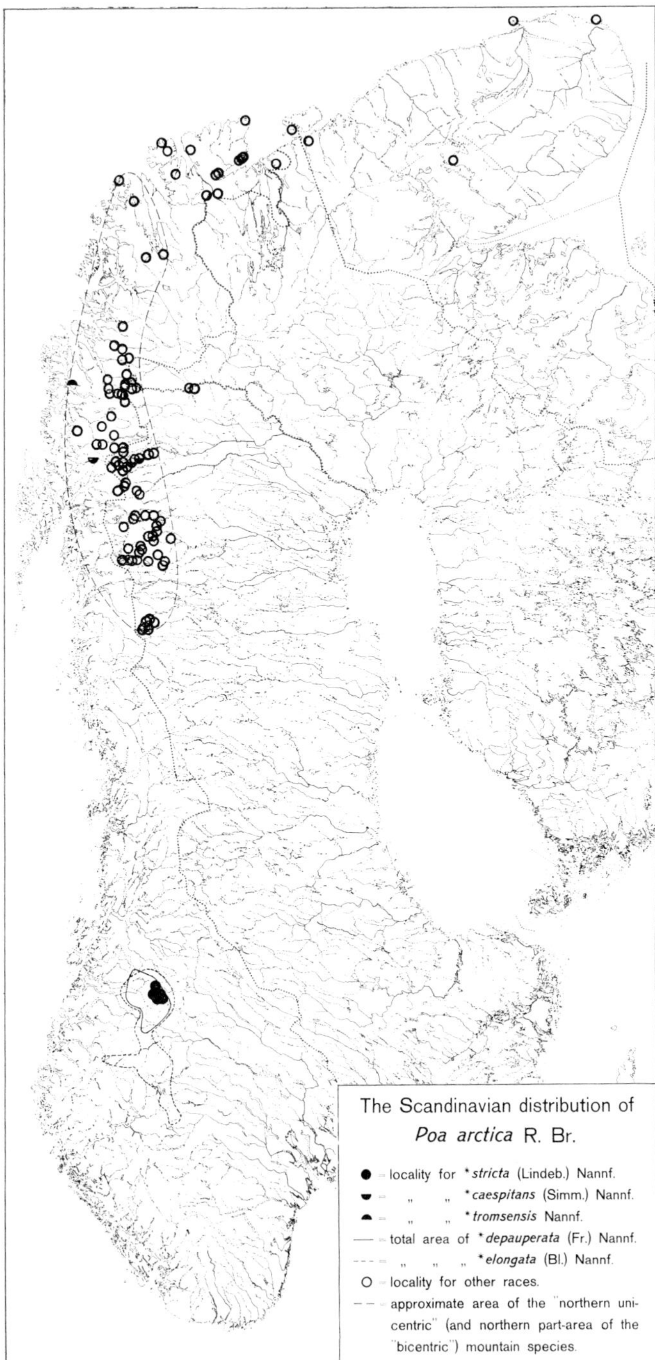

FIG. 5. The Scandinavian distribution of *Poa arctica* and its subordinate taxa. (After Nannfeldt, 1940.)

In the northern population the reproductive features are different. Besides the aposporous embryo-sacs there may now and then—though rarely—be formed sexual embryo-sacs, and even the egg-cells of aposporous embryo-sacs may occasionally become fertilized.

One of the recognizable northern taxa, subsp. *caespitans*, is most outstanding morphologically, i.a. by the always empty anthers. It has very few localities in Scandinavia, and grows there together with other very rare plants, but it has a wide West Arctic distribution and seems to be common in part of its area. Both normal and aposporous embryo-sacs are formed, and the latter are able to form both embryo and endosperm without fertilization. Otherwise the apomictic types, are as a rule, pseudogamous. The subsp. *caespitans* is thus able to breed true and—in spite of its empty anthers—to propagate even in areas where there grows no other type that can supply serviceable pollen. This seems to be the situation in, for example, Ellesmereland. In, for example, Scandinavia the situation is different, for there both normal and aposporous embryo-sacs may become fertilized. Nygren has in one of the Swedish localities found specimens similar to, but not identical with, *caespitans* and having a somatic chromosome number of 86–88. Such specimens have probably arisen from *caespitans* by fertilization of aposporous embryo-sacs by alien pollen.

It seems clear that the populations of the south and the north of the Scandes are both old and have developed independently for a long time, and that the wide West Arctic distribution of *caespitans* proves a high age of that taxon just as the occurrence of *depauperata* in Iceland proves a high age of that taxon.

These examples are selected from plants intensely studied, in the cases of *Papaver* and *Poa* both taxonomically and cytologically, in the case of *Papaver* also genetically.

There are a number of species awaiting similar studies, and I am sure that most of our mountain plants will repay generously the labour devoted to them. It is especially important that the work is not too much concentrated upon the rarest species with widely isolated, very small populations, for in those we run the risk that the special features of "small populations" may overshadow more general trends. Such described taxa as *Artemisia norvegica* var. *scotica*, *Stellaria crassipes* var. *dovrensis* and *Oxytropis deflexa* subsp. *norvegica* exemplify certainly the evolution within such small populations. In several cases, the distinguishing marks of such isolated populations have been found to break down, when the variability within the main area has been studied more in detail. I shall take an example from another part of Scandinavia. When *Orchis Spitzelii* was found on the Swedish island of Gotland this population was described as a var. *gotlandica*, but later Bengt Pettersson (1958, pp. 77–82) could show that closely corresponding individuals occur also in the south of Europe. Also in other species such described local races may meet the same fate, but their describing has not been useless, as it has stimulated further research.

When all or at least most of our mountain species have been studied carefully and in detail we shall certainly be able to draw more certain conclusions about the history of our flora.

REFERENCES

(Only a few recent papers and papers specially referred to are cited here. The problems relating to the mountain flora of Scandinavia have been discussed so often that the pertinent literature is easily found.)

HULTÉN, E. (1942). Flora of Alaska and Yukon. II. *Acta Univ. Lund. N.F.* II, **37,** 1, 131–412.

HULTÉN, E. (1958). The Amphi-Atlantic plants and their phytogeographical connections. *Kungl. Sv. Vet.-Akad. Handl.* **4**, 7, 1.

HULTÉN, E. (1959a). The *Trisetum spicatum* complex. *Trisetum spicatum* (L.) Richt., an Arctic-montane species with world-wide range. *Sv. Bot. Tidskr.* **53**, 203–228.

HULTÉN, E. (1959b). Studies in the genus *Dryas*. *Sv. Bot. Tidskr.* **53**, 507–542.

KNABEN, G. (1958). *Papaver*-studier, med et forsvar for *P. radicatum* ROTTB. som en islandsk-skandinavisk art. *Blyttia* **16**, 61–80.

KNABEN, G. (1959a) On the evolution of the *radicatum*-group of the *Scapiflora* Papavers as studied in 70 and 56 chromosome species. Part A. Cytotaxonomical aspects. *Op. Bot. (Lund)* **2**, 3.

KNABEN, G. (1959b) On the evolution of the *radicatum*-group of the *Scapiflora* Papavers as studied in 70 and 56 chromosome species. Part B. Experimental studies. *Op. Bot. (Lund)* **3**, 3

LÖVE, Á. (1947). Heimskautasveifgras (*Poa arctica*) R. Br.) fundid á Hornströndum. *Náttúrufr.* **17,** 17–21.

LÖVE, Á. (1955). Cytotaxonomical notes on the Icelandic *Papaver*. *Nytt Magas. f. Bot.* **4,** 5–18.

LÖVE, Á. (1962). Typification of *Papaver radicatum*—a nomenclatural detective story. *Bot. Notiser* **115,** 113–136.

LÖVE, Á. and D. (1961). Chromosome numbers of Central and Northwest European plant species. *Op. Bot. (Lund)* **5.**

NANNFELDT, J. A. (1935). Taxonomical and plant geographical studies in the *Poa laxa* group. *Symb. Bot. Ups.* [**1**], 5.

NANNFELDT, J. A. (1937). On *Poa jemtlandica* (Almqu.) Richt., its distribution and possible origin. A criticism of the theory of hybridization as the cause of vivipary. *Bot. Not.* 1937, pp. 1–27.

NANNFELDT, J. A. (1940). On the polymorphy of *Poa arctica* R.Br., with special reference to its Scandinavian forms. *Symb. Bot. Ups.* **4**, 4.

NORDHAGEN, R. (1931). Studien über die skandinavischen Rassen der *Papaver radicatum* Rottb., sowie einige mit derselben verwechselte neue Arten. Vorläufige Mitteilung. *Berg. Mus. Årb., Naturv. r. 2.*

NYGREN, A. (1950). Cytological and embryological studies in Arctic *Poae*. *Symb. Bot. Ups.* **10**, 4.

NYGREN, A. (1955). Chromosome studies in the *Poa laxa* group. *Ann. Roy. Agric. Coll. Sweden* **22**, 359–369.

PETTERSSON, BENGT (1958). Dynamik och konstans i Gotlands flora och vegetation. *Acta Phytogeogr. Suec.* **40**.

PHYTOGEOGRAPHICAL PROBLEMS IN SVALBARD

Olaf I. Rönning

The Royal Norwegian Society of Sciences, Botanical Department, Trondheim, Norway

The Norwegian name Svalbard is a collective appelation given to all the islands situated in the Arctic Ocean between 10° and 35° E. Long. and between 74° and 81° N. Lat. It includes Bear Island in the south, the Spitsbergen Archipelago, and several other smaller groups of islands around Spitsbergen, i.e. King Charles Land, Hope Island, Northeast Land, etc., with a total area of about 62,000 km².

Svalbard belongs to the High Arctic region, but has a climate influenced by the Gulf Stream. One of the branches flows along the western coast of Spitsbergen and keeps the water open in summer farther north than anywhere else on the Globe. Cold, Arctic streams run especially on the east, south and north sides and on the west side between the Gulf Stream and the land.

The mean temperature from 1912 to 1930 (Grönfjorden, 78° 30′ N.) was −7.6°C for the whole year, the average for July being +5.4°C and for March −19.0°C. The precipitation is very low, with an average of 287 mm per annum, but both temperature and precipitation vary greatly from one part of the area to another.

Looking at the Svalbard flora as a whole, we find between 155 and 160 indigenous vascular plants, according to the concept of species now most commonly accepted. This means that in spite of the latitude and the severe climatic conditions, the flora is rather rich. In the south it is related to that of northern Scandinavia or the Scandinavian mountain areas, in the west to the flora of east Greenland. To the east we find many plants common to Svalbard and the Novaya Zemlya islands, but farther east the relationship is not so pronounced.

About 120 of the *ca.* 160 species reported from Svalbard are found also on the neighbouring European mainland, i.e. northern Scandinavia. The rest, about 35 species, have a pronounced High Arctic distribution and do not occur in northern Scandinavia. Among them are: *Alopecurus alpinus*, *Dupontia fisheri*, *Festuca baffinensis*, *F. brachyphylla*, *Pleuropogon sabinei*, *Poa abbreviata*, *Puccinellia angustata*, *Carex ursina*, *Cerastium regelii*, *Minuartia rossii*, *Draba subcapitata*, *Saxifraga flagellaris*, *Taraxacum arcticum*, and others.

A considerable number of the remaining species belong to the group of plants with a centric distribution in Scandinavia, which means that they are mainly within one limited area in southern or northern Scandinavia. In the

Svalbard flora about 12 species belong to the group called bicentric in the sense of Scandinavian botanists, i.e. they occur in both of the above-mentioned areas. Here we mention only: *Luzula arctica, Carex parallela, Sagina caespitosa, Draba nivalis, Saxifraga hieraciifolia, Campanula uniflora,* and others. Plants distributed only within the northern one of the two Scandinavian areas are represented in Svalbard by a larger number, i.e. about 20 species; *Cassiope tetragona, Hierochloë alpina, Papaver dahlianum, Erigeron unalaschkense* and others are examples belonging to this group.

The plants mentioned above have gaps in their distribution areas either from southern to northern Scandinavia and then to Svalbard or from northern Scandinavia to Svalbard. We have, however, among the Arctic–Alpine plants one small, but distinct, group comprising only three species, *Draba gredinii, Kobresia simpliciuscula,* and *Phippsia concinna,* which have an even larger gap in their distribution, stretching from southern Scandinavia to Svalbard. In a way, these latter might also be called bicentric, but with a gap between their areas 600–800 km larger than that of the other group of bicentric plants. The distance between their centers is about 1600–1800 km. One of the three species, viz. *Phippsia concinna,* is also known from Bear Island. We may therefore say that we know three groups of Arctic–Alpine plants which are (a) common to southern Scandinavia and Svalbard, (b) common to northern Scandinavia and Svalbard, and (c) common to both southern and northern Scandinavia and Svalbard, but with a gap between each center. For a fourth group we may place the ubiquitous Scandinavian species, common also in Svalbard.

On the whole, we may say that the Scandinavian centric species constitute the phytogeographically most important group in Svalbard as well, and it should be noted that it comprises a great part of the flora there. If these plants survived the last glaciations in Scandinavia, we are led to the assumption that there must have been chances for a third center farther north in the Arctic, with conditions suitable for a possible survival of plants. This leads us also to conclude that a possible connection between the flora of Svalbard and Scandinavia must have existed before the Last Glaciation or even in Early Pleistocene.

Within the flora of Svalbard proper, plants can be grouped according to their distribution. The southernmost part of Svalbard, Bear Island, has a few plants known from northern Scandinavia, but not occurring farther north in Svalbard. They are: *Cerastium cerastoides, Hippuris vulgaris, Luzula arcuata,* and *Stellaria calycantha.*

In the southernmost parts of the island of West Spitsbergen in the Spitsbergen Archipelago are found two species which are isolated in this area. They are: *Salix herbacea* and *Ranunculus glacialis,* and are known only from a few isolated localities. One of them, viz. *Salix herbacea,* occurs also on Bear Island. According to my opinion, this southernmost area of the Spitsbergen

Archipelago is concomitant with the occurrence of the plants mentioned from Bear Island. Southwest Spitsbergen and Bear Island are now separated only be a rather shallow sea with depths between 10 and 100 m. The plants may be regarded either as southern remnants of a previously continuous Arctic vegetation, or as northern outposts of a flora connected with the Scandinavian mainland.

About half of the Svalbard plants are more or less ubiquitous species and are distributed over the greater part of the Archipelago. But there are about 35 species with a more limited distribution, confined mostly to the inner fjord districts, especially between Van Mijenfjord and Isfjord, including the innermost branches of Wijdefjord on the island of West Spitsbergen (Fig. 1). In this area are distributed the greater part of the most interesting plants

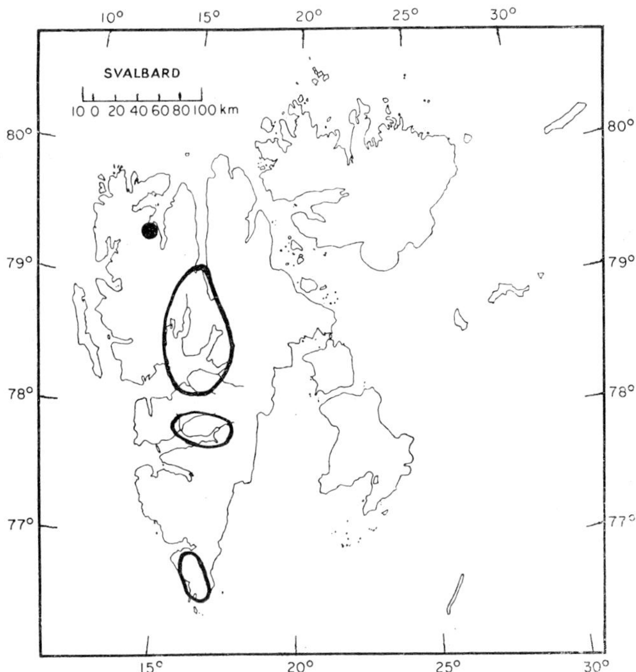

FIG. 1. Areas in Spitsbergen with an especially rich occurrence of plants. Dot indicates locality with hot springs. Bear Island is not indicated on the map.

within the flora of Svalbard, e.g. *Arctagrostis latifolia, Hierochloë alpina, Eriophorum triste, Kobresia simpliciuscula, Juncus arcticus, J. castaneus, Luzula wahlenbergii, Potentilla crantzii, Empetrum hermaphroditum, Cassiope hypnoides, Polemonium boreale, Campanula uniflora,* etc.

The concentration of plants in these areas is due not only to better ecological conditions. Suitable substrata and climate no doubt exist also in other regions of Svalbard, but there is on the whole a striking difference between the floras of these fjord districts and other parts of Svalbard, e.g. the fjords farther south, Hornsound, etc., and the north and east coasts where the floras are much poorer in species. Hadač (1944) found a total of 114 species in the Sassen area of the inner fjord districts. In my opinion the reason for this peculiar distribution must be sought within the historical factors, as these areas must have provided possibilities for a survival of plants during the glaciation. If a migration from the south had taken place recently, we should expect the plants instead to be distributed especially in the southern parts of the Archipelago or scattered all over the area where suitable substrata occur.

ISOLATED SPECIES

A remarkable, isolated occurrence is characteristic of the three species, *Carex capillaris*, *Euphrasia arctica* and *Sibbaldia procumbens*. During an expedition in 1960, I visited some small hot springs situated near the head of the Bockfjorden on the north coast of Spitsbergen. Here, the only locality for these three species was close to the springs and nowhere outside the limited area influenced by the heat from the soil.

The occurrence of these three species, of which *Euphrasia arctica* is one of only two annuals in the flora of Svalbard (the other being *Koenigia islandica*), represents a phytogeographical problem of its own. The nearest localities of the three species are in northern Norway, and a dispersal to that region by long-distance transport of seeds cannot be accepted.

In my opinion, the only way to explain the occurrence of these three species is to regard them as remnants of a previously larger vegetation distributed all over Spitsbergen. But as the climate deteriorated, these species survived within the area influenced by the heat from the hot springs. This explanation is supported by the fact that one of the species, *Euphrasia arctica*, is an annual, and that the hot springs are situated not far from the area previously outlined as a center of rare plants in Spitsbergen, i.e. the inner fjord districts north and south of the large Isfjord. If we presume that this area in a previous epoch with a lesser degree of glaciation had a much richer flora than today, and that the three plant species mentioned also occupied that area, it will be easier to understand how they still can occur in such an isolated locality. The deterioration of the climatic conditions caused other less hardy plants to die out, but a few species succeeded in surviving in this limited area.

From the same point of view it will be possible to consider the existence on Bear Island of the few plants mentioned as occurring there, but nowhere else in Svalbard, viz. *Cerastium cerastoides*, *Hippuris vulgaris* and *Stellaria calycantha*. These plants also must be regarded as remnants of a previous flora extending continuously northwards to the Spitsbergen Archipelago. At least two of them, viz. *Hippuris vulgaris* and *Stellaria calycantha*, are not truly Arctic species, and are confined to more temperate or Low Alpine regions, e.g. in Scandinavia. This greater demand for a mild climate could be the reason why they occur today in Svalbard only on Bear Island.

ENDEMIC SPECIES

It is generally assumed that the frequency of endemic plants within a flora is an indicator of its age and of a long-time isolation. If the flora of Svalbard has been isolated for a considerable length of time, the occurrence of endemic species within the Svalbard area must be expected. During the last years, in the course of my investigations concerning the flora of Svalbard, I have discovered, as far as I can see, that such an endemic element exists, comprising plants ranking both as species and as taxa of lower rank such as varieties. It is in this respect first necessary to look upon the Svalbard flora separately. Here we have two species endemic to that area, viz. *Puccinellia svalbardensis* Rönning and *Ranunculus spitsbergensis* Hadač. Besides there are two endemic varieties, viz. *Puccinellia angustata* var. *decumbens* and *Colpodium vahlianum* var. *pallida*.

However, the two groups of islands, Svalbard and Novaya Zemlya, are closely related both geographically and floristically. Many plants are common to the two areas, but Novaya Zemlya, especially in the southern part, has a greater number of eastern plants than Svalbard. Their phytogeographical connection is further emphasized by the fact that within Novaya Zemlya and Svalbard taken as one unit, there are some endemic plants: *Pedicularis dasyantha*, *Colpodium vacillans* and *Puccinellia phryganodes* of the Spitsbergen type (in the sense of Sörensen, 1953, and Rönning, 1962) are examples of such species, endemic to this larger area.

It is thus possible to separate two areas, the larger comprising both Svalbard and Novaya Zemlya, and the smaller one only the Spitsbergen Archipelago. It is not possible to say exactly how the isolation has taken place, but the endemic plants mentioned give a true indication that these areas once did exist. It is also very likely that even more endemic plants, ranking either as species, subspecies, or varieties, will appear as the investigation of the Svalbard flora continues. This is even more probable since such taxonomically difficult genera as *Draba*, *Potentilla*, and *Poa* have not yet been thoroughly worked out, and some of their varieties may turn out to be endemic to the area in question.

THE CONNECTION BETWEEN THE FLORA OF NORTHERN SCANDINAVIA AND THE ADJACENT ARCTIC REGIONS

The greater part of the plants common to Svalbard and northern Scandinavia have a wide distribution and must be regarded as ubiquitous in Svalbard or at least in the Spitsbergen area. Examples of such plants are *Equisetum variegatum*, *Deschampsia alpina*, *Salix polaris*, *Oxyria digyna*,

Ranunculus pygmaeus, *Saxifraga cernua*, *S. oppositifolia*, *S. groenlandica*, and many others.

Among the ubiquitous species in Svalbard are also many that in Scandinavia belong to the centric species mentioned above.

Another group of plants of a striking importance in Scandinavia is distributed mostly along the coast, or not far from the coast, and is common also to the adjacent Arctic islands and northern Scandinavia. The most important members are *Arctagrostis latifolia*, *Arenaria pseudofrigida*, *Chrysosplenium tetrandrum*, *Braya purpurascens*, *Papaver dahlianum*, and *Stellaria humifusa*. Though some of them can be found at a distance from the coast or fjord areas in northern Scandinavia, they must all be regarded as lowland plants, and as such they represent taxa with a strikingly different ecology. They are also found farther east in northern Europe reaching as far as the Kola peninsula and Vaygach, but not much farther. In my opinion, also these plants point sometimes to a close connection between the floras of northern Scandinavia and the neighbouring Arctic, and show that this connection includes not only Alpine plants, but also lowland or sea shore plants with an ecology different from that of the Alpine ones.

To summarize the phytogeographical features of the Svalbard region we may state that:

1. The number of indigenous species of Svalbard is between 155 and 160, according to the species concept commonly accepted.
2. Among the species, about 35 have a distinct High Arctic distribution and do not occur on the European mainland, i.e. northern Scandinavia.
3. Many of the species common in Svalbard are plants having a centric distribution in Scandinavia. They occur either in both southern and northern Scandinavia and Svalbard, or only in northern Scandinavia and Svalbard, or, only in southern Scandinavia and Svalbard.
4. Groups of species with isolated occurrences in Svalbard are found: (a) in Bear Island, (b) in southernmost Spitsbergen, (c) especially in the inner fjord districts (a larger group with a lower degree of isolation); (d) around the hot springs at the head of Bockfjorden. The existence of this last isolated group is contingent upon the heat of the soil.
5. Distinct groups of endemic species are found, one endemic to the Spitsbergen Archipelago only, and one endemic to both Spitsbergen and Novaya Zemlya.
6. A group of plants, not strictly Alpine in northern Scandinavia, also shows a close connection between the floras of the two areas, Svalbard and Scandinavia.

From the facts presented above it is evident that within the flora of Svalbard distinct groups of plants exist, and that they show a close connection to the flora of the European mainland, i.e. northern Scandinavia.

The problem of how and when this connection has taken place is still a matter of dispute and only a little can be contributed to help solve it. It seems to me that time is the only factor that can give a satisfactory explanation of these problems.

As early as 1933, Lynge, on the basis of the distribution of some Arctic lichens, concluded that ice-free refugia had existed on the north coast of Spitsbergen (Lynge, 1939). He accordingly supposed that the lichens were relic plants of a very high age. Another interesting fact concerning these north coast lichens is that when occurring in Scandinavian mountains, they are not at all High Alpine, but more or less continental Subalpine. Lynge (*loc. cit.*) found no other explanation than "that the area, or a part of it, should have been ice-free refugia during the last glaciation, perhaps all through the time subsequent to the Tertiary age, and that these lichens should be relics which persisted, at least, from the last Interglacial down to the present time".

In 1869 Fries had already launched the hypothesis that some of the Svalbard plants were of a relic nature, and several later authors, among them Nordhagen (1935), have discussed the possible migration tracks for the Scandinavian West Arctic plants. In my opinion, the close relationship shown between the floras of the two areas makes it most likely that in an earlier geological epoch there existed a connection between northern Scandinavia and the islands of the European Arctic. Later geological conditions have split up this continuous area into several isolated ones. The question as to when this happened remains still unsolved, but is of special importance from a phytogeographical point of view.

Nansen (1920) suggested that the Barents Sea area of the Late Tertiary period was situated 400–500 meters higher than today. Orvin (1940, p. 54) says: "From the presence of large submarine valleys in the Barents Sea we may conclude that this area in comparatively recent times has been at a level about 500 meters above the present. This happened probably in the latter part of the Tertiary."

Horn and Orvin (1928, p. 44) also agree with Nansen that the elevation mentioned could have existed in the Tertiary period. However, one important feature concerning the Bear Island needs emphasizing: during the Pleistocene glaciations this island was more or less covered with an ice sheet and was partly submerged. But although the island was covered with ice during the deepest submergence, the mountains in its southern part protruded above the glacier (Horn and Orvin, *loc. cit.*, p. 53 and Fig. 44).

Today the Barents Sea (Fig. 2) is a shallow body of water with large areas less than 200 m deep, especially to the east. Perhaps a continuous area of land once stretched from northernmost western Europe over the Barents Sea east to Novaya Zemlya and west to the other Arctic islands around the Spitsbergen Archipelago. This land area must have offered possibilities for plant migration from south to north and vice versa. It is also possible that such a land mass was invaded by plants from both east and west. Most probably this occurred in the Late Tertiary.

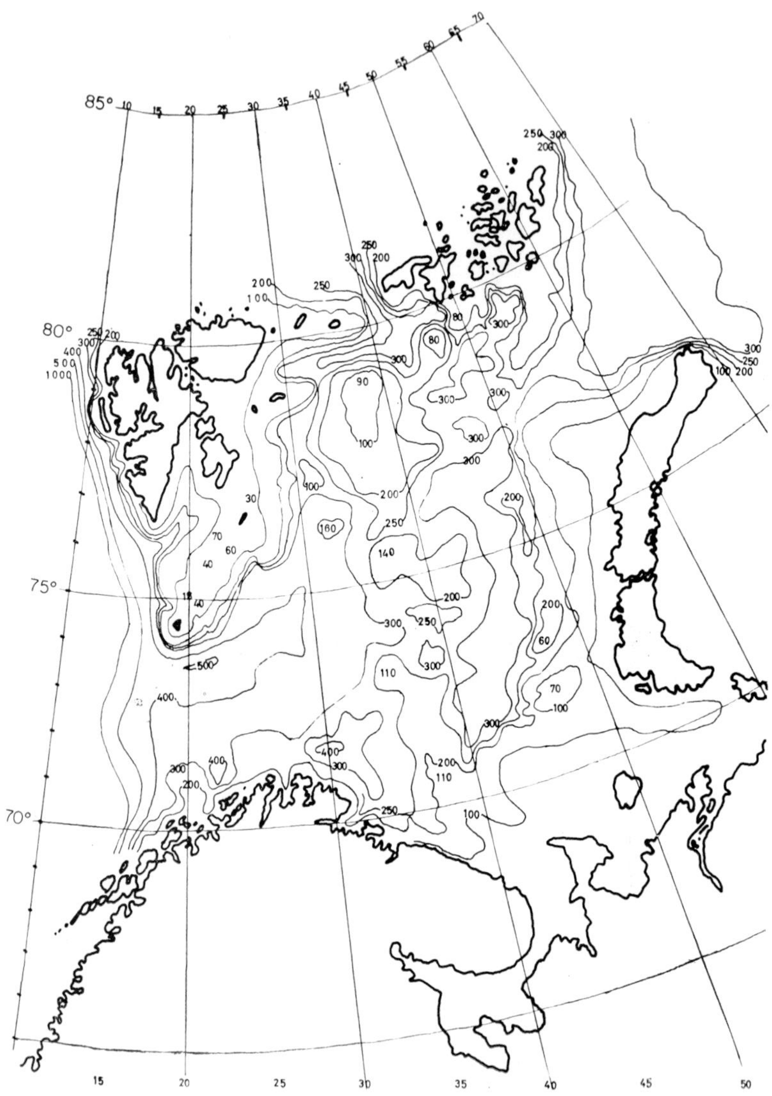

FIG. 2. Barents Sea with depth contour lines.

Later, geological events such as submergence of the land and glaciation during the Pleistocene led to the splitting-up of the flora. Part of the flora from then on has survived the glaciations in refugia most probably where, or close by where, they occur today. This leads us, for example, to the conclusion that there have been conditions for plant life both in refugia along the coast and on nunataks in the inner fjord districts. The plants common to the total area are probably of a very great age but the endemic species mentioned above must be the result of an evolution after the Tertiary.

REFERENCES

FRIES, T. M. (1869). Tillägg till Spetsbergens fanerogam-flora. *Kgl. Sv. Vetensk. Akad.* Förhand **26**, 121–144.

HADAČ, E. (1944). Die Gefässpflanzen des "Sassengebietes", Vest-Spitsbergen. *Norges Svalbard og Ishavsundersökelser*, Skrifter No. 87, 1–71.

HADAČ, E. (1946). The plant-communities of Sassen Quarter, Vest-Spitsbergen. *Studia Botanica Chechoslovaka*, **7**, 127–164.

HORN, G. and ORVIN, A. K. (1928). Geology of Bear Island. *Skr. om Svalbard og Ishavet* **15**, 1–152.

LYNGE, B. (1939). On the survival of plants in the Arctic. *Norsk Geografisk Tidsskrift* **7**, 489–497.

NANSEN, F. (1920). *En ferd til Spitsbergen*. Kristiania.

NATHORST, A. G. (1883). Nya bidrag till kännedomen om Spetsbergens kärlväxter, och dess växtgeografiska förhållanden. *Kgl. Svenska Vetensk.—Akad. Handl.* NF **20** (6), 1–88.

NORDHAGEN, R. (1935). Om Arenaria humifusa Wg. og dens betydning for utforskningen av Skandinaviens eldste floraelement. *Bergens Museums Årbok 1935, Naturv. Rekke* No. 1, 1–185.

ORVIN, A. K. (1940). Outline of the geological history of Spitsbergen. *Skr. om Svalbard og Ishavet* **78**, 1–.

RÖNNING, O. I. (1959). The vascular flora of Bear Island. *Acta Borealia A. Scientia* No 15, 1–62.

RÖNNING, O. I. (1960). The vegetation and flora north of the Arctic Circle. *Norway North of 65°*. Oslo, 1960, pp. 50–72.

RÖNNING, O. I. (1961). Some new contributions to the flora of Svalbard. *Norsk Polarinstitutt Skrifter* **124**, 1–20.

RÖNNING, O. I. (1962). The Spitzbergen species of *Colpodium* Trin., *Pleuropogon* R. Br. and *Puccinellia* Parl. *Det. Kgl. Norske Vidensk. Selsk. Skrifter* 1961, No. 4, 1–50.

SÖRENSEN, TH. (1953). A revision of the Greenland species of *Puccinellia* Parl. *Medd. om Groenl.* **136** (3), 1–179.

AMPHI-ATLANTIC ZONATION, NEMORAL TO ARCTIC

HUGO SJÖRS

Institute of Plant Ecology, University of Uppsala, Uppsala, Sweden

WHEREAS in Canada a book called *North of 55°* (Wilson, 1954) tells the story of a still almost uninhabited country, in Europe about 70 million people live and work above this parallel. The difference in the northward extension of natural ranges and vegetational zones is not quite so evident as the difference in distribution of human population. Still, a considerable disparity also exists between the two continents with respect to climatic conditions and natural resources from a biogeographer's point of view.

On the other hand, the two continents show very similar situations regarding regional zonation. The European zonation is a mirror image of the American one, much displaced toward the north, but Europe's Oceanic West has no counterpart in North America (the "Maritime Provinces" of Canada are far less oceanic).

Broadly speaking, the southern Great Lakes area, extending northward into the Niagara Peninsula of Ontario, has its European equivalent in south-central Europe, as far north as southern Germany. The Canadian provinces of Quebec and Ontario correspond to east-central Europe and the Baltic–Scandinavian area as far north as Finland and northern European Russia. The "Prairie Provinces" and northwestern Canada are better compared to central and eastern European Russia and western Siberia.

It seems of basic importance for any kind of detailed comparison that those points, lines, and zones which correspond most closely to each other biogeographically should be determined on each side of the Atlantic Ocean. If this were possible, much more of the experience from one side could be readily used on the other, not only in pure biogeographical and ecological science but also in practical management of arable land, pasture and forest.

There is a serious obstacle against the direct use of climatic figures in this respect. Northeastern America, except for a narrow zone confined mostly to the "Maritime Provinces", is rather continental as to temperature but has everywhere an adequate rainfall. In Eurasia we must go far east to obtain the same degree of continental temperature, but then summer rainfall becomes scanty.

BIOTIC REGIONS, ZONES, AND BELTS

Individual elements of climate thus fail to give the same pairs of corresponding points. But vegetation, being an integration of climatic as well as other factors, may show the total effect of climatic impact on life better than single variables do.

The vegetational unit most suitable for such a comparison is the *regional* (*vegetation*) *complex* (term by Du Rietz, in mimeographed lectures) which occupies a *vegetation region*, in the sense used by many phytogeographers, notably those of Scandinavia (cf. Du Rietz, 1930, pp. 497–502). If we include animal life and environment, and thus refer to the whole ecosystem—a heterogeneous ecosystem covering vast expanses of land— we may speak of a *biotic region* (Sjörs, 1955, p. 163). Biotic regions situated in different longitudinal sectors of the globe may occupy corresponding positions as to zonation in latitudinal direction. They are regarded as parts of the same *biotic zone* (cf. Rousseau, 1952, p. 437). In mountainous countries, biotic regions homologous in their altitudinal position constitute a *biotic belt* (cf. Du Rietz, 1930, p. 499). There are cases when mountain biotic belts correspond to, or even gradually merge into, biotic zones of the lowland farther north (or south, in the Southern Hemisphere).

In forested biotic regions, forests are usually more important than other kinds of vegetation. Leading tree species become significant for the delimitation of these regions. Usually the dominance, although only partial, of a tree species is more important for this purpose than a scattered occurrence. However, sub-regions within the Boreal coniferous zone (see below) must often be determined from the areas of subordinate species, because the dominant conifers are the same. Also, criteria taken from the physiognomy and total composition of vegetation may be adduced for similar purposes (Kujala, 1936; Hare, 1950, 1954, 1959; Kalela, 1958, 1961; Ahti, 1961).

THE NEMORAL ZONE

Following Regel (1950, 1952) the author prefers to designate as *Nemoral* the three great parts of the Northern Hemisphere where temperate deciduous trees are prevalent. According to Regel (1952, p. 38) the term "Nemoral" was introduced by Russian authors. Regel includes the Boreo-nemoral zone in the Nemoral zone as a special sub-zone. The frequently used term "deciduous forest zone" is open to some criticism. Thus, considerable coniferous forests (pines, etc.) occur within this zone, particularly in North America and Japan. There exist also deciduous forests of quite different types, e.g. those in the Sub-tropics and the seasonally moist Tropics. Nor should the deciduous birchwoods of Sub-Alpine Fennoscandia and Kamchatka be included. Strictly speaking, also *Larix* is deciduous. The word Nemoral is free from such objection, and emphasizes the adaptation of the vegetation and flora to mild-temperate, fairly moist conditions, and the formation of a humus layer of the mull type and a brown forest soil profile, as is typical of most stands of genera such as *Fraxinus*, *Acer*, *Ulmus*, *Tilia*, *Fagus*, and certain sections of *Quercus*.

The Nemoral zone is discontinuous (since Quaternary time) but its three parts, in eastern North America, Europe and the Far East, are remarkably similar in spite of considerable climatic difference. Each of the three parts shows a south–north subdivision into two or more biotic regions, but these conditions, although indicated on the maps, Figs. 2 and 3, are not dealt with further in this paper.

With reduced rainfall and increased continentality, the Nemoral regions change into Steppe or Prairie regions. The usually quite extensive ecotones include the warmer parts of the Woodland Steppe regions (European Russia, and the Middle West of the U.S.A.).

THE BOREO-NEMORAL ZONE

Between the three parts of the Nemoral zone and the true Boreal zone, transitional biotic regions occur, here called Boreo-nemoral. They occupy a considerable width in Europe and in the Far East (Manchuria and Amur districts) but the American Boreo-nemoral region is quite narrow. As this part of the zonation is frequently misunderstood, it is desirable to state more precisely what areas belong here and thus correspond on both sides of the Atlantic.

Because of earlier abundance of white pine (*Pinus strobus*) and the occurrence of other conifers (*P. resinosa*, *Tsuga canadensis*, *Thuja occidentalis*), the Great Lakes–St. Lawrence area has sometimes been regarded as representing this zone in America, but this is only partly correct. The above-mentioned conifers are essentially non-Boreal, and (except *Thuja*) do not reach much farther into the Boreal zone than do several of the Nemoral hardwoods (e.g. *Fraxinus nigra*, *Ulmus americana*, *Populus grandidentata*, *Betula lutea*).

The Boreo-nemoral zone is met with a short distance north of the St. Lawrence and Ottawa Rivers, e.g. at St. Donat and Maniwake. In Quebec the change is abrupt due to the rise in level from the Paleozoic Ottawa–St. Lawrence valley to the uplands of the Pre-Cambrian Shield. The difference in bedrock and Quaternary deposits greatly amplifies the combined effects of latitude and altitude on vegetation. The shift of dominance from exacting, mainly deciduous trees to hardy, less demanding Boreal conifers is thus comparatively abrupt and was evidently still more impressive before so much of the latter were cut.

Farther west the Boreo-nemoral zone is broader, extending also south of the Ottawa River (Petawawa, Algonquin Park), and crossing Lake Superior to reappear in southeastern Manitoba and northeastern Minnesota.

The Boreo-nemoral region in America is a tract of land where Boreal conifers (*Picea glauca, P. mariana, Abies balsamea*) are well distributed and frequently tend to be predominant, even if now largely replaced by secondary hardwood forests. The latter are extensively formed by trembling aspen (*Populus tremuloides*) which, like the white birch (*Betula papyrifera*), is a "neutral" tree of little zonal importance. Also some southern hardwoods have expanded considerably into the widespread secondary forests, notably sugar maple (*Acer saccharum*). Other southern tree species common in most of the Boreo-nemoral region are *Quercus borealis, Tilia americana, Populus grandidentata, Betula lutea, Fraxinus nigra, Ulmus americana,* and the conifers *Pinus strobus, P. resinosa,* and *Tsuga canadensis.* Some of these even reach quite a distance into the Boreal region farther north (see below).

Most of the "Acadian Forest Region" (Rowe, 1959) in the Maritime Provinces of Canada can be classed as part of the Boreo-nemoral zone. It is rich in hardwoods in the lower hills, whereas conifer forests are often predominant on the coast, in the valleys, and in the interior upland. Red spruce (*Picea rubens*), a non-Boreal species, is often dominant.

The spruce-fir forests of the northeastern U.S.A. are found at increasingly higher elevation towards the south (Shantz and Zon, 1924) and are here mapped as Montane (Fig. 2). They merge into the Boreo-nemoral zone towards the north and are not truly Boreal. *Picea rubens* is one of the chief species.

In Europe, conditions are simpler. The European vicariants of *Pinus strobus* (i.e. *P. peuce*), and *P. resinosa* (i.e. *P. nigra*) are confined to the south for historical (not climatic) reasons and do not interfere. *P. silvestris* occurs, chiefly on sandy soils, even in some parts in the Nemoral zone, but in the rest of the Nemoral area, the forests were deciduous almost everywhere before conifers were planted. Passing into the Boreo-nemoral zone, there is a very sudden shift to predominant Boreal conifers: Norway spruce (*Picea abies*) and Scots pine (*Pinus silvestris*). Hornbeam (*Carpinus betulus*), beech (*Fagus silvatica*) and durmast oak (*Quercus petraea*) occur only in small western parts of the Boreo-nemoral. Most of the other southern hardwoods continue their distribution farther north (or rather northeast). The Boreo-nemoral region in Europe, contains much *Quercus robur, Fraxinus excelsior, Ulmus glabra, Tilia cordata, Acer platanoides* (not *A. pseudoplatanus*), *Corylus avellana*, etc. Although generally subordinate, these southern hardwoods may be of great local importance, particularly on calcareous soils (e.g. on the island of Öland, Sweden, which is crossed by the borderline between the Nemoral and Boreo-nemoral regions).

The Boreo-nemoral region in Europe is narrow in the west and the east but quite broad in the central part. It reaches from southernmost Norway over most of the southern third of Sweden (the southwestern and southern coastal parts belong in the Nemoral zone). The southwestern corner of Finland belongs in the Boreo-nemoral (Jalas, 1957), which further comprises the former Baltic States, northeastern Poland, and large parts of western and central European Russia east to the Urals. The northern limit of *Quercus robur* is generally considered as its boundary towards the Boreal zone proper, but in Russia the latter boundary is drawn some distance farther south (Lavrenko and Sochava, 1954).

From Manitoba westward, and east of the Urals, the Nemoral zone is absent, being replaced by prairies (steppes). The Boreo-nemoral zone in turn is replaced by a transition zone between the Boreal coniferous forest zones and the steppes, a zone where both most Boreal conifers and Nemoral hardwoods are absent or scarce. *Betula* and *Populus* remain, and aspen groves are particularly characteristic (*P. tremuloides* and *P. tremula*, respectively). In the Canadian Prairie provinces this zone is represented by the Aspen-Oak Section (with *Quercus macrocarpa*, *Ulmus americana*, *Acer negundo*, etc.) and the Aspen Grove Section of Rowe (1959). The west Siberian counterpart is divided into a northern region of "parvifoliate forest" (Lavrenko and Sochava, 1954) and a Woodland Steppe region between this and the treeless Steppe.

THE BOREAL ZONE

Encircling the globe south of the Arctic there is a Boreal zone (Hare, 1954) where forests are usually formed by a very limited number of species belonging to a few coniferous and hardwood genera: *Picea*, *Larix*, *Pinus*, *Abies*, *Betula*, *Populus*, *Alnus*. In addition, species of *Salix*, *Sorbus* (*aucuparia* type), and *Prunus* (*padus* type) reach tree size. Only very few of the species of these large genera are actually Boreal, as emphasized by Hare (*loc. cit.*). Some of these, e.g. the *Populus* species, extend much farther south; others are prevailingly Boreal, but all of them extend south at least into the Boreo-nemoral zone. This is true also of many Boreal species of smaller size.

As expressly stated by Hare (*loc. cit.*) a large part of the conifer forests of the world should not be included in the Boreal (or Boreo-nemoral). This is true of the Pacific forests, and of the pinewoods occurring in the Nemoral and still warmer zones. More related to Boreal forests are some Montane or Sub-Alpine forests at the middle latitudes (e.g. in the Rockies, the Alps, Altai, etc.), and the oceanic pinewoods of Scotland and westernmost Norway, but they are kept separate in this paper.

The Boreal forests, after having reached maturity, are usually made up of conifers, but some areas belonging here are permanently covered by birchwoods, alderwoods, or groves of poplar. The Boreal zone is also very rich in bogs and fens. It comprises by far the largest part of the peatland areas of the world (Fig. 1, from Sjörs, 1961b).

The Boreal zone may be subdivided into three or more east–west sectors with different floras. Some species of small size, but not trees, occur in all sectors. *Alnus rugosa* var. *americana* and *Sorbus decora* of northern Canada, for example, are more similar to the Eurasian *A. incana* and *Sorbus aucuparia* than admitted by leading present-day dendrologists, and probably would have been regarded as conspecific if they had been small plants. However important from the point of view of historical plant geography, this longitudinal subdivision is less important than the latitudinal zonation ecologically and also for economic forestry. Such a zonal subdivision of the Boreal zone has been independently proposed in most Boreal countries.

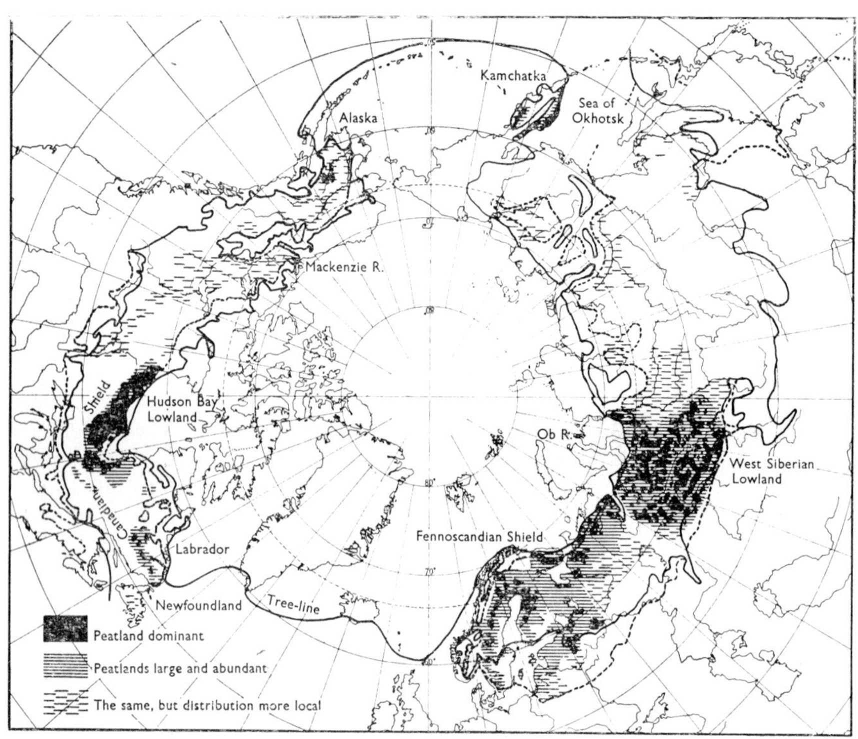

FIG. 1. Extension of the Boreal zone (between the full lines). South of, or below, the tree-line, woodland-tundra or Sub-Alpine areas extend to the northern broken line. South of the Boreal zone, Boreo-nemoral and Aspen–Birch Woodland regions reach to the southern broken line. The abundance of peatland is indicated on the figure. Most lowland in Iceland and the Shetlands is south of the tree-line.

Boreal of North America

In Canada propositions regarding a subdivision of the Boreal have been advanced by Halliday (1937), Hustich (1949, 1951), Rousseau (1952), Hare (1950, 1954, 1959), Ritchie (1956, 1959, 1960), Rowe (1959), and others. The approach and the terms of these authors differ widely but nevertheless there is a fairly close similarity in the results arrived at, as far as strictly zonal divisions are considered. Space does not allow a discussion, but references may be given to Hare (1959, p. 34). Three sub-zones are more or less generally accepted, but the first of these is further sub-divided in the present paper.

(a) *The southern Boreal sub-zone.* Here several of the species mentioned for the Nemoral and Boreo-nemoral zones occur, usually in low frequency: *Pinus strobus, P. resinosa, Acer saccharum, Betula lutea, Fraxinus nigra, Ulmus americana,* etc. The dominant conifers are *Picea mariana, P. glauca,* and *Abies balsamea,* with *Pinus Banksiana* on rocks and sandy soils and on disturbed sites; birch and particularly aspen are prominent in secondary growth. The sub-zone is typically developed east of Lake Superior. North and northwest of the latter it is virtually absent, only *Pinus strobus, P. resinosa, Populus grandidentata, Ulmus americana,* and *Fraxinus nigra* sparsely representing the southern tree species here. In Manitoba the sub-zone reoccurs, although the southern species are largely different: *Acer negundo, Quercus macrocarpa, Ulmus americana,* and *Fraxinus pennsylvanica* var. *subintegerrima.* This sub-zone is again lacking in Alberta and most of Saskatchewan.

(b) *The Main Boreal sub-zone.* As the preceding sub-zone, the Main Boreal is characterized by closed-canopy coniferous forests except on burned sites and bogs and fens. The Boreal conifer species are the same. *Abies balsamea* is an important forest tree mainly in the east. There is often a complete dominance of the two spruces, with *Picea mariana* on poor soils and *P. glauca* on the better soils which are more widespread on the sedimentary rocks of the western interior. In some areas *Pinus banksiana* prevails, and in the westernmost parts *Pinus contorta* var. *latifolia* is abundant. The southern species are lacking or represented by very few outposts, mainly of *Fraxinus nigra* and *Ulmus americana;* only *Thuja occidentalis* and *Acer spicatum* are still fairly common in some parts. Conditions for forest growth are quite satisfactory within this sub-zone which extends across Canada from Newfoundland to the upper Mackenzie and the Liard valleys, and possibly even to some of the deep valleys in the mountainous Yukon Territory.

(c) *The Sub-Arctic sub-zone.* This is characterized by open, parklike stands usually formed by low black spruce (*Picea mariana*) with a *Cladonia* undergrowth. These stands are regarded as woodland, but not as true (commercially valuable) forests, although pulpwood size is usually reached. On more favourable sites white spruce (*P. glauca*) is found, and the undergrowth is often richer in species. Boggy sites are extremely common, both wooded ("black spruce muskegs") and treeless. *Larix laricina* is frequent on peat, especially in wooded fens. Along rivers grows balsam poplar (*Populus balsamifera*). All four tree species occur throughout the Boreal (and Boreo-nemoral) zones. The other Boreal trees are confined to certain parts of the Sub-Arctic, not reaching its northern outskirts everywhere. The sub-zone

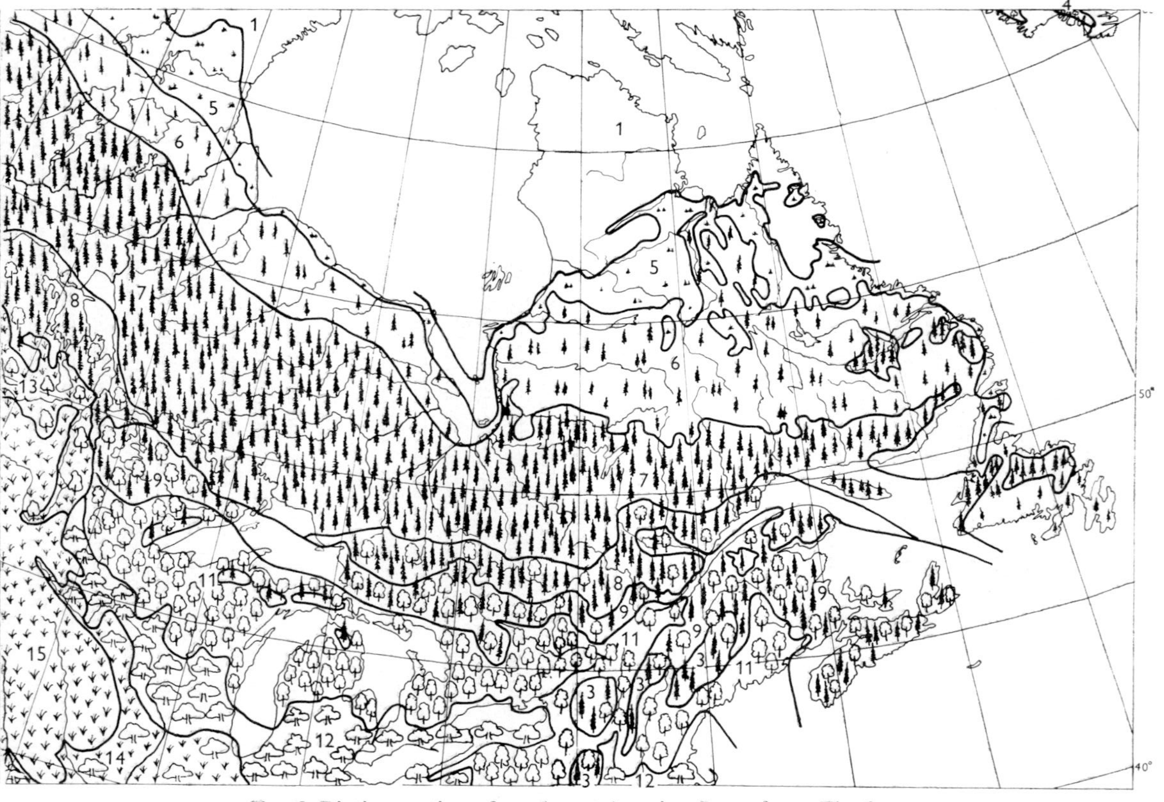

FIG. 2. Biotic zonation of north-east America. Legend, see Fig. 3.

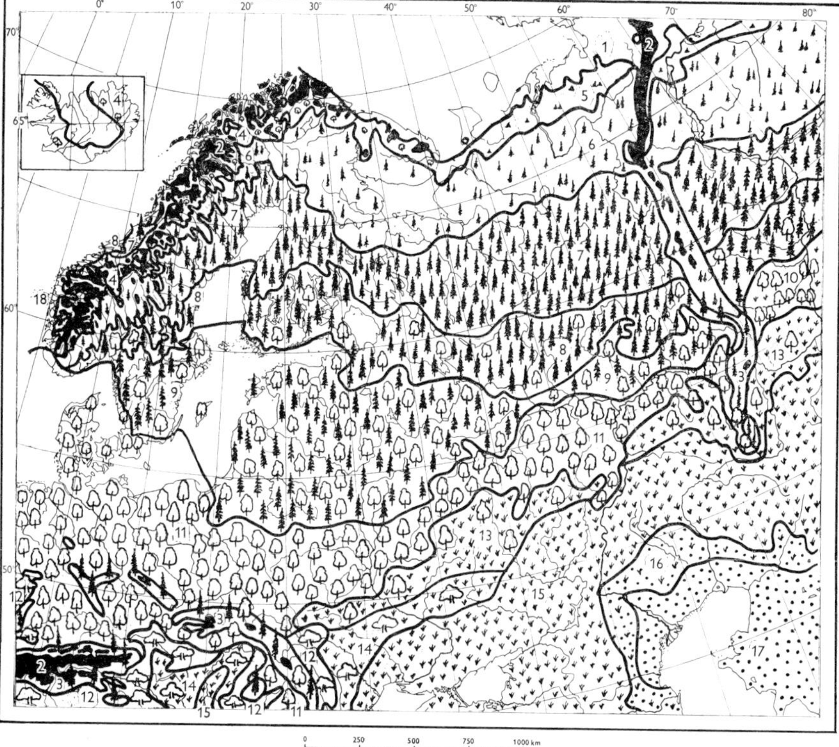

FIG. 3. Biotic zonation of north, central and east Europe.

1. Arctic zone.
2. Alpine belts.
3. Sub-Alpine and Montane belts of non-Boreal mountains.

4–8. Boreal zone:
   4. Sub-Alpine Birch Woodland belt of Fennoscandia.
   5. Woodland-tundra sub-zone.
   6. Sub-Arctic and Boreo-montane sub-zone.
   7. Main Boreal zone.
   8. Southern Boreal sub-zone.

9. Boreo-nemoral zone.
10. Birch–Aspen Woodland region of west Siberia.

11–12. Nemoral zone:
   11. Northern sub-zone.
   12. Central sub-zone. In North America: *Quercus-Carya* and *Castanea - Quercus - Liriodendron*; in Europe: *Quercus pubescens*, *Juglans*, cultivation of grapes, etc. (sub-Mediterranean).

13–14. Woodland Steppe zone:
   13. Northern sub-zone. In North America: Pine, aspen, birch and a few southern species, e.g. *Acer negundo*, *Quercus macrocarpa*, etc.; in Europe: *Quercus robur*; in Europe and west Siberia: *Tilia cordata*. The North American region equates both regions (10) and (13) of Siberia.
   14. Southern sub-zone. In North America: Oak–hickory groves; Europe: oak and pine with sub-Mediterranean species.

15. Steppe (Prairie) zone.
16. Steppe Desert zone.
17. Desert Scrub zone.
18. North Atlantic Pine–Birch Woodland and Heath region (with *Quercus*, *Taxus*, *Hedera*, *Ilex* in Scotland and west Norway).

extends from the east coastal parts and the uplands of Newfoundland and Labrador to Alaska.

Rowe (1959) and Hare (1959) disagree in the mapping of easternmost Labrador. The "coastal tundra" is probably caused here by high winds and lack of soil, and has only partly been mapped as Woodland-Tundra sub-zone on Fig. 2. The woodland farther inland is largely regarded as Sub-Arctic, even if fairly dense, because of low stature. The Hudson Bay Lowland is divided between the Main Boreal and Sub-Arctic (Sjörs, 1959, 1961a and in prep.), and is not as entirely Sub-Arctic as one may believe (Hustich, 1957; Rowe, 1959).

(d) *The Hemi-Arctic* (Rousseau, 1952) or *Woodland-tundra sub-zone*. Here tree growth is reduced to scattered clumps and low, shrubby stands in sheltered localities, e.g. along riversides. Nearly or totally treeless barrens occur between these outposts. Near the tree-line, the tundra areas become predominant and only a small percentage is actually covered by the woodland. Any of the four species mentioned for the Sub-Arctic may form the actual tree-line (or rather the outposts of potentially tree-forming species), but the white spruce (*Picea glauca*) is the most common, particularly close to the sea shore.

The typical woodland-tundra is a feature of flat country, either continental or adjacent to Arctic coasts. However, Rowe (1959) describes an "Alpine Forest-Tundra Section" on the slopes west of the lower Mackenzie Valley, and similar sites occur near the tree-line in interior Yukon Territory (Porsild, 1951), both areas being extremely continental as to climate. In mountainous or hilly districts the altitudinal tree-line tends to be sharper than the latitudinal tree-line in flat country, but some of the tree species develop a shrubby appearance; what actually corresponds to the woodland tundra is often a belt of stunted woods and, on exposed localities, even shrubs. Porsild (1951, pp. 27–28) describes the dense shrub of alpine fir (*Abies lasiocarpa*) near the tree-line in southeast Yukon. The *Picea mariana* and *Abies balsamea* woodlands of coastal eastern Labrador and some parts of Newfoundland are described as often very dense but dwarfed, and interspersed with barren heaths, due to a wet, cool and windy climate (Hustich, 1939, 1949, p. 12; Rowe, 1959; Ahti, 1959, p. 2).

Russian Boreal, or Taiga

As east Siberia is very aberrant, only west Siberia and European Russia are considered here. Russian authors (cf. Lavrenko and Sochava, 1954; Sotchava, 1954; Tikhomirov, 1960) subdivide the Boreal zone, which they call the Taiga, into the *southern*, *central*, and *northern Taiga*, in addition to which comes the *Lyeso-tundra* (Sylvo-tundra, forest- or woodland-tundra). This subdivision corresponds very well to the Canadian one, but the southern Taiga is a more extensive sub-zone than the Canadian counterpart (a) mentioned above, whereas the central Taiga, in Siberia, may be less wide than the Main Boreal (b) of the Canadian West.

The conifer trees of the Taiga (except east Siberia) are only five. *Picea* is mainly represented by *P. obovata*, which is better regarded as a sub-species of *P. abies*. The two "species" of *Larix* (*L. Sukatchewii* in Europe, *L. sibirica* in west and central Siberia) are probably also conspecific races. *Pinus sibirica* is very close to the central European *P. cembra*. The other two trees are *Pinus silvestris* and *Abies sibirica*. *Picea* and *Larix* reach the woodland-tundra. In northwest Russia (Kola Peninsula and Karelia) *Abies* is absent and *Larix* and *Pinus sibirica* are extremely rare. For geological and phytogeographical reasons this area is better included in Fennoscandia (as is always done by western botanists). *Pinus silvestris* is prevalent in most of the Russian Fennoscandia, except on eastern Kola where *Picea* reaches farther coastward, but both are ultimately superseded on Kola by the mountain birch (*Betula pubescens* ssp. *tortuosa*). Elsewhere in Russia, birch only exceptionally forms the northern tree-line.

The northern limit of the woodland-tundra in Fig. 3 was taken from a sketch-map by Andreyev (1956; reproduced in Tikhomirov, 1961). It is somewhat more northern than on the vegetation map by Lavrenko and Sochava (1954).

Boreal Fennoscandia

Zonal problems in northern Fennoscandia are simplified by the low number of coniferous trees, only *Pinus silvestris* and *Picea abies* occurring there. Otherwise, the situation is quite complicated.

Two vegetation regions are generally accepted for the Fennoscandian part of the Boreal zone, viz. the "Northern coniferous forest region (without oak)" and the "Sub-alpine birch woodland region". Only Hustich (1960) gives a slightly different treatment. The former region has been subdivided both in Finland and Sweden (Kalela, 1958, 1961; Du Rietz, 1950, 1952; Sjörs, 1950, 1956), but unfortunately the proposed sub-regions agree neither in extent nor in number; probably none of them corresponds exactly to any of the above-mentioned Canadian and Russian sub-zones.

The Boreal sub-zonation in Fennoscandia is largely due to other factors than latitude. In Norway and Sweden altitude is apparently more effective than latitude, and the influence of the altitude is also evident on recent Finnish maps (Kalela, 1958, 1961). Moreover, the absence of spruce in several western and northern parts of the Scandinavian Peninsula has often been considered of regional importance.

Both in Norway and in Sweden as well as in Finland, a transitional *Southern Boreal sub-zone* has some scattered occurrences of Nemoral species, particularly *Tilia cordata*, *Acer platanoides*, and the scrub *Corylus avellana*. The upper and northern limit of this sub-zone is very ill-defined in Norway and Sweden, due to the broken topography. The wide occurrence of *Tilia* in Finland makes it broader there.

The *Main Boreal sub-zone* corresponds, in Sweden, both to the upper part of the area where *Myrica gale* still occurs, and to the central Norrland or middle sub-region which lacks *Myrica* and a number of other southern species. The nearest Finnish equivalent is the sub-region of Ostrobottnia (Pohjanmaa), according to Kalela (1958, 1961). It borders the central Taiga towards the east, but seems to be somewhat more northern in latitudinal position.

In northern Sweden, open pine-lichen woodlands of *Sub-Arctic* type are closely confined to coarse, sandy and gravelly soils, and thus do not form a regionally characteristic feature. According to Ahti (1961), they occur also on other soils in northernmost Finland, but lichen woodlands are not so widespread as in more continental parts of the Sub-Arctic areas. However, even forests of a more mesic appearance tend to be widely spaced in northern and high upland parts of Boreal Fennoscandia. The spacing of the forest ought to be used as a phytogeographical regional criterion. Its importance in Swedish forestry has only recently been duly emphasized (Ebeling, 1962). Stature and rate of growth have long been considered important for site classification (edaphical as well as climatic).

Thus the uppermost and northernmost coniferous woodlands in Fennoscandia are of Sub-Arctic type with regard to the wide spacing, slow growth and low stature of the conifers. In Sweden, the "Pre-Alpine conifer forest sub-region" (sensu Du Rietz, 1950, p. 7; Swedish = *fjällbarrskogsregionen*, Du Rietz, 1942b, 1952 or "upper sub-region of the northern coniferous forest region", Sjörs, 1950, p. 177; 1956, p. 202) is largely identical with the area above the economic limit for artificial regeneration (Swedish = *skogsodlingsgränsen*) in the State forests of Sweden, as drawn by Höjer (1954). It seems likely that some more areas in the high uplands (outside the mountainous district proper) should be included in the area equivalent to the Sub-Arctic, with respect to the poor growth of the forest. Du Rietz (1952, p. 7) gives the lower limit at about 350 m in the north and 600 m in Härjedalen. In Finland, according to Ahti (1961), both the coniferous woodland area of Lappland and that of "Peräpohjola" (farther south; terms by Kalela, 1958) as well as some of the birchwoods (see below) belong in the Sub-Arctic (or northern Taiga) sub-zone.

Practically everywhere in Fennoscandia (also the Russian parts, i.e. Kola Peninsula), birchwoods (*Betula pubescens* ssp. *tortuosa*) extend beyond the limit of coniferous trees. The vertical extension of this zone, which is commonly regarded as *Sub-Alpine*, is very variable, from almost none to several hundred meters, a fact showing that it is hardly a zone of equal significance in all parts. If a *Woodland-tundra sub-zone* exists in Fennoscandia, it is located in the upper part of the birch belt (and near the Polar coast) where birches are often interspersed by barren areas, and are in any case low and nearly shrubby.

This uppermost Sub-Alpine sub-zone (or rather "Hemi-Alpine" ecotone because the open patches are outposts of Alpine plant communities) is usually of narrow vertical extension in the Scandes (Scandinavian mountains) proper but is more extensive on the elevated plateaux of northeasternmost Fennoscandia. This type of vegetation even goes down to sea-level on the Polar coasts of Norway and the Kola Peninsula.

The lower parts of the birchwoods are continuous with the birches usually of small tree size, reaching as much as 10 m or more in sheltered valleys and slopes with rich, moist soils. These lower parts are better regarded as equivalent to the Sub-Arctic.

In a recent work Hustich (1960) regards most of northernmost Fennoscandia, with woodlands formed by birch and some pine, as a Sub-Arctic region which he considers different from the Sub-Alpine region and equivalent to the woodland-tundra farther east. This seems to be an underestimation. In some of his earlier papers (e.g. 1949, p. 52) on Canadian phytogeography, Hustich used the rather ambivalent term "Sub-Arctic" expressly in the meaning "Woodland-tundra". However, in 1957, he included some more "southerly" and even Main Boreal vegetation under the heading of Sub-Arctic.

The Sub-Alpine–Sub-Arctic birchwoods are a feature of cool, oceanic areas. Outliers of them are found on southwest Greenland and on Iceland. The impact of severe over-grazing has probably caused them to disappear from the Shetland Islands (Spence, 1960), and much of the Scottish Highlands. However, there is no definite evidence that a birch belt has existed above the pinewoods of Scotland, except in the extreme north and west (McVean and Ratcliffe, 1962). Birchwoods are also locally present, usually near river estuaries and deltas, within the Siberian woodland-tundra, where the latter comes close to the Arctic Sea (Lavrenko and Sochava, 1954). *Betula Ermanii* birchwoods also grow in Kamchatka and some of the Kuriles together with Sub-Alpine alder thickets.

ARCTIC AND ALPINE ZONES

The zonal subdivision of the Arctic is far from clear. It is evident that altitude and maritimity influence Arctic vegetation as much as latitude, and thus regional subdivision cannot result in regularly consecutive zones on a small-scale map except on flat continents or very large islands. Polunin (1951) has proposed a subdivision into three zones (Low Arctic, Middle Arctic, and High Arctic), but it is not known exactly how these zones are distributed. A more detailed subdivision has been carried out and mapped for the Russian Arctic (Lavrenko and Sochava, 1954; Sotchava, 1954; Tikhomirov, 1960).

For the Alpine barrens, a subdivision into three regions or belts is now unanimously accepted in Scandinavia (e.g. Du Rietz, 1928, 1930, 1942a and b, 1950; Nordhagen, 1936, 1943). Each of the Low Alpine, Middle Alpine, and High Alpine belts has a phytogeographical significance about equal to one of the zones of the forested country. Similar belts are expected to occur in other northern mountains, and also in high mountains at somewhat lower latitude, e.g. the Alps (see a comparison by Du Rietz, 1930). A detailed comparison of the Arctic and Alpine zonations must be left to the botanists of the future.

CONCLUSIONS

Ecological conclusion

On comparing the two maps, Figs. 2 and 3, the general similarity is striking. A closer analysis reveals two interesting features.

1. All zones bend southward when near cold seas. The effects of Hudson Bay (incl. James Bay), the Atlantic off Labrador and Newfoundland, and the White Sea are evident. The Woodland-tundra in these sectors (and even the Sub-Arctic near James Bay) is extraordinarily narrow due to this depression. The Baltic, although cool in spring, has an opposite effect, presumably because of comparatively long-lasting autumnal warmth.

2. When not influenced by the cold sea effect, the width of the zones and sub-zones is dependent on slope. If the general slope is southern, they tend to be narrow (Boreo-nemoral of Quebec, sub-zones of the Boreal in Sweden). Great width is often related to a northward slope (Main Boreal of Canada west of Quebec, Sub-Arctic of Labrador Peninsula, Russian Main Boreal and Sub-Arctic). This, of course, is an effect of altitude, and shows that such an effect is present not only in mountainous areas. Even moderate elevation has considerable impact on vegetation, an impact that has not always been duly appreciated.

It would require too long a report to discuss the climatic factors by which the zonations are conditioned. It should only be mentioned that at least for the Boreal sub-zonation the length of the growth period appears to be highly important. It is defined as duration of the period when mean temperature is above $+5.5°$ or $6°$. A lower temperature limit makes cool oceanic areas seem more favourable than they are. Summer heat seems to be more important near and above the tree-line. Winter cold is hardly of any general importance, and there is little relation to the distribution of permafrost (Brown, 1960).

Historical conclusion

The present zonation of the northern vegetation is young. It was practically non-existent as late as 9000 years ago; only 4000 and even 3000 years ago it was considerably different from modern conditions. Even if some of the species probably are very old, their re-combination into plant communities thus is comparatively recent. The elements of the Boreal or Taiga zone, for instance, must have survived the latest Glacial Epoch in several widely separated refugia where ecological conditions and types of vegetation were necessarily different in various respects from those prevailing in the present Taiga. It is astonishing that the products of the re-combination of these elements is so uniform, and that such a great zonal parallelism exists in areas as much as 8000 miles apart in longitudinal direction.

The history of the vegetation is the evident starting-point of ecology. On the other hand, the ecological requirements of both single taxa and whole plant communities, as reflected in their present zonal distribution, put down limits which historical deduction should not overstep without very strong reasons. Therefore, this somewhat lengthy exposure of largely well-known facts may be of some value as a background for the historical discussions of these problems.

REFERENCES

AHTI, T. (1959). Studies on the caribou lichen stands of Newfoundland. *Ann. Bot. Soc. Vanamo* **30** (4), 1–44.

AHTI, T. (1961). The open Boreal woodland sub-zone and its relation to reindeer husbandry. *Arch. Soc. Vanamo* **16** (suppl), 91–93.

ANDREYEV, V. N. (1956). Zaselenie tundry lyesom v sovremennuyu epokhyu (Penetration of forest into the tundra in the present epoch). In *Rastitel'nost Kraynevo Severa S.S.S.R. i yeyo osvoynie* (*The vegetation of the Far North of the U.S.S.R. and its utilisation*)

BROWN, R. J. E. (1960). The distribution of permafrost and its relation to air temperature in Canada and the U.S.S.R. *Arctic* **13**, 163–177.

DU RIETZ, G. E. (1928). Fjällens växtregioner. *Naturens liv i ord och bild* II, 800–811.

DU RIETZ, G. E. (1930). Classification and nomenclature of vegetation. *Sv. Bot. Tidskr.* **24**, 489–503.

DU RIETZ, G. E. (1942a). Rishedsförband i Torneträskområdets lågfjällbälte. *Sv. Bot. Tidskr.* **36**, 124–146.

DU RIETZ, G. E. (1942b). De svenska fjällens växtvärld. *Ymer* **1942**, 169–190.

DU RIETZ, G. E. (1950). Phytogeographical excursion to the surroundings of Lake Torneträsk in Torne Lappmark (Northern Sweden). Seventh Int. Bot. Congr. Stockholm 1950, Exc. Guid. C III c, 1–19.

DU RIETZ, G. E. (1952). Vegetations- och odlingsregioner som uttryck för klimat och jordmån. In *Trädgårdskonst I. Växtmaterial och anläggningsteknik*. Stockholm.

DU RIETZ, G. E. (mimeographed): *Växtgeografiens grunder*. Uppsala, finished 1961.

EBELING, F. (1962). Beståndsbehandling i norrländskt storskogsbruk. In *Skogen och Skogsbruket*. Stockholm.

HALLIDAY, W. E. D. (1937). A forest classification for Canada. *Canada Dept. Res. and Developm., Forest Res. Div. Bull.* **89**, 1–50.

HARE, F. K. (1950). Climate and zonal divisions of the Boreal forest formations in eastern Canada. *Geogr. Rev.* **40**, 615–635.

HARE, F. K. (1954). The Boreal conifer zone. *Geogr. Studies* **1**, 4–18.

HARE, F. K. (1959). A photo-reconnaissance survey of Labrador–Ungava. *Canada Dept. Mines and Techn. Surv., Geogr. Branch, Mem.* **6**, 1–64.

HÖJER, E. W. (1954). Skogsodlingsgränsen på kronoparkerna i Norrland. *Norrl. Skogsvårdsförb. Tidskr.* 1954, 233–253.

HUSTICH, I. (1939). Notes on the coniferous forest and tree limit on the east coast of Newfoundland–Labrador. *Acta Geogr.* **7** (1), 1–77.

HUSTICH, I. (1949). On the forest geography of the Labrador peninsula. A preliminary synthesis. *Acta Geogr.* **10** (2), 1–63.

HUSTICH, I. (1951). The lichen woodlands in Labrador and their importance as winter pastures for domesticated reindeer. *Acta Geogr.* **12** (1), 1–48.

HUSTICH, I. (1952). Barrträdsarternas polara gräns på norra halvklotet. *Comm. Inst. Forest. Fenn.* **40**, 29, 1–20.

HUSTICH, I. (1957). On the phytogeography of the Subarctic Hudson Bay Lowland. *Acta Geogr.* **16** (1), 1–48.

HUSTICH, I. (1960). Plant geographical regions. In *A Geography of Norden.* Oslo.

JALAS, J. (1957). Die geobotanische Nordostgrenze der sog. Eichenzone Südwestfinnlands. *Ann. Bot. Soc. Vanamo* **29** (5), 1–32.

KALELA, A. (1958). Über die Waldvegetationszonen Finnlands. *Bot. Notiser* **111**, 353–368.

KALELA, A. (1961). Waldvegetationszonen Finnlands und ihre klimatischen Paralleltypen. *Arch. Soc. Vanamo* **16** (suppl.), 65–83.

KUJALA, V. (1936). Tutkimuksia Keski- ja Pohjois-Suomen välisestä kasvillisuusrajasta. *Comm. Inst. Forest. Fenn.* **13**.

LAVRENKO, E. M. and SOCHAVA, V. B. (ed.) (1954). Geobotanicheskaya karta SSSR, scale 1:4,000,000. *Akad. Nauk Moskva-Leningrad.*

MCVEAN, D. N. and RATCLIFFE, D. A. (1962). Plant communities of the Scottish Highlands. *Monogr. Nat. Conservancy* **1**.

NORDHAGEN, R. (1936). Versuch einer neuen Einteilung der subalpinen–alpinen Vegetation Norwegens. *Bergens Mus. Årb. 1936, Naturv. Rekke* 7, 1–88.

NORDHAGEN, R. (1943). Sikilsdalen og Norges fjellbeiter. *Bergens Mus. Skr.* **22**, 1–607.

POLUNIN, N. (1951). The Real Arctic: suggestions for its delimitation, subdivision and characterization. *J. Ecol.* **39**, 308–315.

PORSILD, A. E. (1951). Botany of southeastern Yukon adjacent to the Canol Road. *Nat. Mus. Canada Bull.* **121**, 1–400.

REGEL, C. (1950). Dynamik von Klima und Pflanzendecke in Nordeuropa. *Ber. Geobot. Forsch.-Inst. Rübel 1949*, 11–23.

REGEL, C. (1952). Botanische Betrachtungen auf einer Reise in Schweden. *Ber. Geobot. Forsch.-Inst. Rübel 1951*, 35–55.

RITCHIE, J. C. (1956). The vegetation of northern Manitoba. I. Studies in the southern spruce forest zone. *Canad. J. Bot.* **34**, 523–561.

RITCHIE, J. C. (1959). The vegetation of northern Manitoba. III. Studies in the Subarctic. *Arct. Inst. N. Am. Techn. Paper* **3**, 1–56.

RITCHIE, J. C. (1960). The vegetation of northern Manitoba. V. Establishing the major zonation. *Arctic* **13**, 210–229.

ROUSSEAU, J. (1952). Les zones biologiques de la péninsule Québec–Labrador et l'hémi-arctique. *Canad. J. Bot.* **30**, 436–474.

ROWE, J. S. (1959). Forest regions of Canada. *Canada Dept. North. Aff. and Nat. Resourc., Forest. Branch Bull.* **123**, 1–71, map: Forest classification of Canada 1957.

SHANTZ, H. L. and ZON, R. (1924). The natural vegetation of the United States. *Atlas of Am. Agric.* **I. E.**

SJÖRS, H. (1950). Regional studies in north Swedish mire vegetation. *Bot. Notiser 1950*, 173–222.

SJÖRS, H. (1955). Remarks on ecosystems. *Svensk Bot. Tidskr.* **49**, 155–169.

SJÖRS, H. (1956). *Nordisk växtgeografi.* Stockholm.

SJÖRS, H. (1959). Bogs and fens in the Hudson Bay lowlands. *Arctic* **12**, 2–19.

SJÖRS, H. (1961a). Forest and peatland at Hawley Lake, northern Ontario. *Nat. Mus. Canada Bull.* **171**, 1–31.

SJÖRS, H. (1961b). Surface patterns in Boreal peatland. *Endeavour* **20**, 217–224.

SJÖRS, H. (in prep.): Bogs and fens on Attawapiskat River, northern Ontario. *Nat. Mus. Canada Bull.*

SOTCHAVA, V. B. (1954). Les principes et les problèmes de la cartographie géobotanique. *Essais de Botanique I*, 273–288.

SPENCE, D. H. N. (1960). Studies on the vegetation of Shetland. III. Scrub in Shetland and in South Uist, Outer Hebrides. *J. Ecol.* **48**, 73–95.

TIKHOMIROV, B. A. (1960). Plantgeographical investigations of the tundra vegetation in the Soviet Union. *Canad. J. Bot.* **38**, 815–832.

TIKHOMIROV, B. A. (1961). The changes in biogeographical boundaries in the north of U.S.S.R. as related with climatic fluctuations and activity of man. *Bot. Tidsskr.* **56**, 285–292.

WILSON, C. (ed.) (1954). *North of 55°*. Toronto.

DISTRIBUTION OF THE TERRICOLOUS OLIGOCHAETES ON THE TWO SHORES OF THE ATLANTIC

P. Omodeo

Institute of Biology and General Zoology, University of Siena, Italy

In order to describe the distribution of the terricolous Oligochaetes that populate the two coasts of the Atlantic, I think the best system is to list the forms that populate the various faunistic districts of America and to describe, case by case, their relationships with those found on the other side of the Atlantic.

To carry out this review I shall follow Wallace's zoogeographic classification, which lends itself splendidly to our purpose.

I shall begin with the Nearctic region (map, Fig. 1), which can be most clearly and briefly dealt with because of its extraordinary poverty. In this region there are 27 species of the Holarctic family Lumbricidae; one species for each of the genera *Criodrilus* and *Sparganophilus*, of uncertain systematic position but undoubtedly related to the Lumbricidae; about 20 species of *Diplocardia* (fam. Acanthodrilidae, subfam. Acanthodrilinae); four species of *Ilyogenia* (fam. Acanthodrilidae, subfam. Ocnerodrilinae); five species of *Plutellus* (Megascolecidae). Only the genus *Diplocardia* is endemic in the Nearctic region.

These animals are not uniformly distributed: in the Canadian subregion we find only a few earthworms belonging to European species, whereas in the more southern Alleghany subregion, which is richest in forms, we find, in addition to the European species, which are always predominant, many endemic species: eight of the family *Lumbricidae*, twenty of the genus *Diplocardia*, and one of the genus *Sparganophilus*.

Very few of these forms (*Sparganophilus eiseni* and four species of *Diplocardia* reach the nearby subregion of the Rocky Mountains, where they occupy several stations on the mainland of Mexico and in Lower California; in Lower California we also find four endemic species of the genus *Ilyogenia*, particular to the Neotropical region and equatorial Africa. Apart from these infiltrations, which concern only the southern districts, the better part of the fauna of the subregion of the Rocky Mountains is made up of European species.

The Oligochaete fauna of the Californian subregion is also made up of

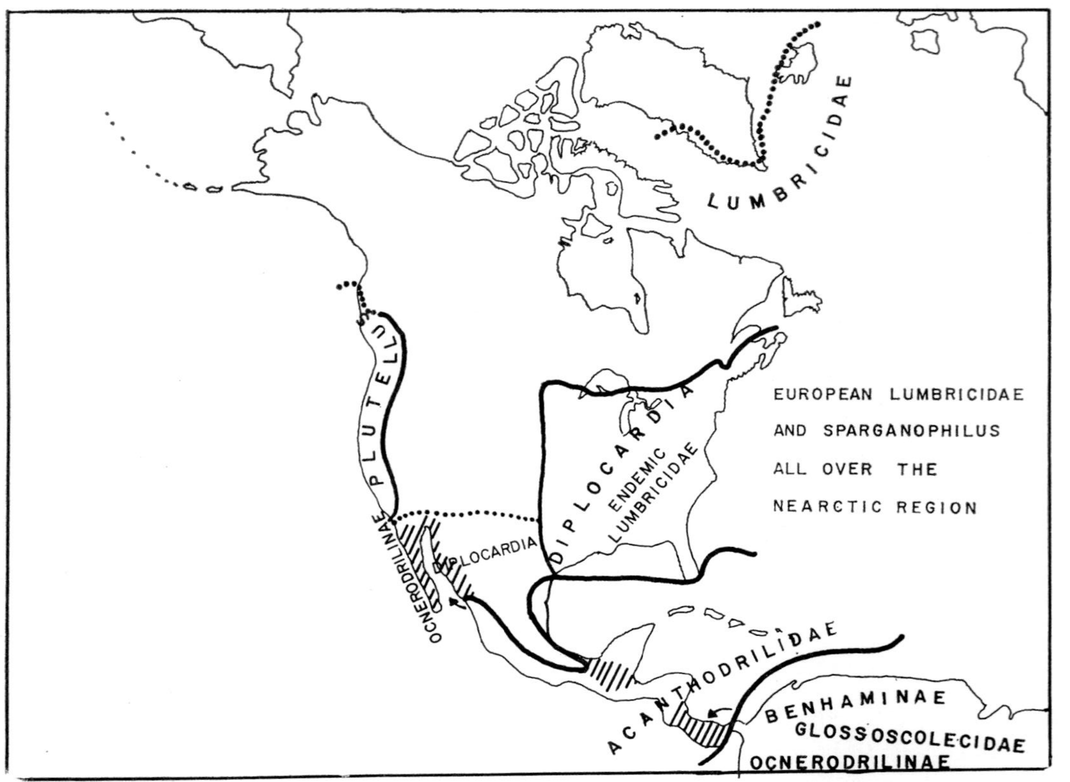

FIG. 1. Earthworm faunas of the Nearctic region; the dotted lines do not coincide with the boundaries of Wallace's subregions. The hatched areas contain a mixed fauna.

European earthworms, but—a very curious fact— there we find five endemic species of the genus *Plutellus*, of which genus the other endemic species are found principally in Australia, Tasmania, and New Caledonia. The northernmost species, which is also the only one endemic in Canada, is found on Queen Charlotte Island. It is important to note that the genus *Plutellus* is one of the very few that include forms that tolerate brackish and salt water.

The earthworm fauna of the Neotropical region follows the classical subdivisions quite well, with the difference, however, that the border line between the Brazilian fauna and that of Chile–Patagonia runs farther south than shown on maps drawn by most biogeographers (map, Fig. 2). It is worth noting that along the same line the distribution of certain groups of freshwater teleostei, amphibians, and terricolous molluscs comes to a halt.

The peculiarity of the Neotropical Oligochaete fauna lies in this fact: the differences from subregion to subregion are very clear cut and do not correspond to any existing geographical barriers. Nevertheless, whoever is familiar with the biogeography of the Oligochaetes will not be surprised, because a similar state of affairs occurs in many parts of the world.

The Brazilian subregion is the one that has the most typical fauna, represented by an endemic family, Glossoscolecidae, and by members of two subfamilies of the Acanthodrilidae.

The family Glossoscolecidae is made up of about 160 species belonging to 22 genera. The two most important centers of endemism of this family are found in the high basin of the Amazon and in the low basin of the Paranà/Uruguay. To the north the Glossoscolecidae extend into Mexican and Antillean subregions, but it is important to note that there exist no endemic genera, and the only two endemic species are found in Costa Rica and on the Island of Barbados (the latter usually not included in the Antillean region). Some Glossoscolecidae extend into the northwestern corner of the Chilean subregion, formed by the Peruvian and Equadorian Andes: there the endemic species are numerous. No species of Glossoscolecidae has ever been found south of the line that joins Bahia Blanca with Antofagasta.

The Ocnerodrilinae are represented in the Brazilian subregion by four genera of which five are endemic (*Haplodrilus*, *Kerriona*, *Quechuona*, *Paulistus*, *Liodrilus*) and one is found also in Lower California. However, the taxonomy of this genus (*Eukerria*) needs some amendment (cf. Gates, 1957), which may lead to the two Californian species being separated. We find other genera of this subfamily in central America.

Another genus endemic in the Brazilian subregion is the aquatic *Drilocrius*, of uncertain systematic position, but undoubtedly closely related to the African genus *Alma*: the northernmost species, found in Costa Rica, (*D. alfari* Cognetti) has a morphology such that, if it had been found in Africa, it would certainly have been ascribed to the genus *Alma*.

The last Oligochaete group of the Brazilian subregion belongs to the

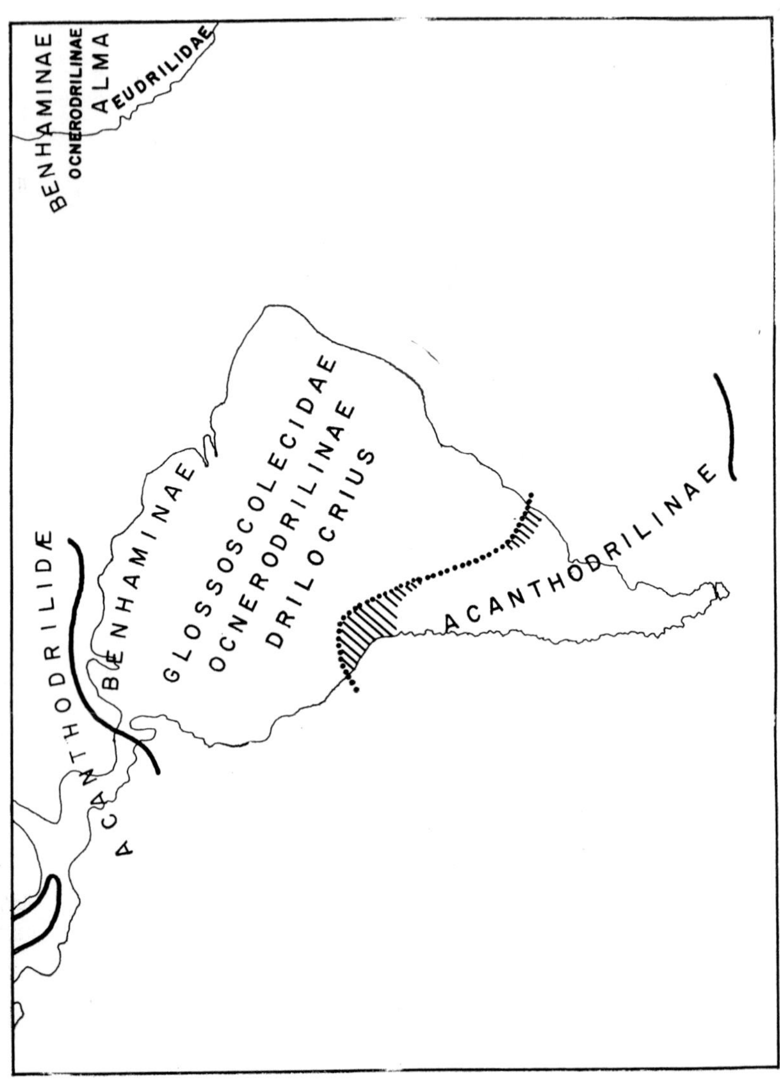

FIG. 2. The earthworm faunas of the Neotropical region.

subfamily Benhaminae and consists of two species of the genus *Neogaster* and three of the genus *Wegeneriella*. These five species are found along the Atlantic coast from Darien to the mouth of the Amazon River. The other four species of these two genera are distributed along the Atlantic coast of Africa from Cameroon up to Guinea. The American species of *Neogaster* are extremely similar to the African ones; there are however, differences of subgeneric rank between the species of *Wegeneriella* of the two opposite shores. But one can say about these animals too, that the taxonomic distinction would not have developed if the species had been gathered on the same continent: other genera of the subfamily are more heterogeneous than *Wegeneriella*, and no one has bothered to subdivide them.

Facts regarding the Oligochaetes of the Brazilian subregion can be summarized in these words: the fauna has a very high degree of endemism, has nothing in common with the Chilean–Patagonian subregion, and very little relationship with the fauna of the Mexican and Antillean subregions; the latter is probably due to relatively recent migrations. A certain relationship between the earthworm fauna of the Brazilian subregion and the Palaeotropical fauna is shown by the two genera *Wegeneriella* and *Neogaster*, common to both, and the close resemblance between the American genus *Drilocrius* and the African genus *Alma*.

In the Chilean–Patagonian subregion, excluding the corner north of Antofagasta and the region around the River Plata estuary, the Glossoscolecidae, Ocnerodrilinae, Benhaminae, and the genus *Criodrilus* disappear; that is, all the taxonomic groups represented in the Brazilian subregion disappear, whereas a new family appears, the Acanthodrilidae.

The Chilean–Patagonian Acanthodrilidae include more than fifty species belonging to five genera. The genus *Yagansia* is endemic, and its fifteen species are distributed from the Tierra del Fuego up to Titicaca; two other genera (*Chilota* and *Parachilota*) occur from Chile to South Africa over the islands between the two continents: in the southern part of South America, on the Falklands and in South Georgia, twenty-two species of *Chilota* and one of *Parachilota* are endemic. The genus *Microscolex* has a similar but much more extensive distribution, reaching the islands of Crozet and Kerguelen south of Africa, and the islands of Macquarie, Auckland and Campbell south of New Zealand; ten species of *Microscolex* are endemic to the southern point of America. On the adjacent islands, no less than three are endemic on the small island of Possession in the Crozet group (maps Figs. 3–5).

The last genus, primitive as its name *Eodrilus* indicates, has a still greater distribution and reaches Madagascar, New Zealand and Australia. Four species of *Eodrilus* are endemic to the Chilean–Patagonian subregion.

Thus, the tip of South America has four genera out of five in common with South Africa; on the other hand, it does not have any genus, not even a subfamily in common with the Brazilian subregion. I can add that the subregion of Cape of Good Hope shares with the Chilean–Patagonian subregion four out of seven genera, but has no genus and only one of its two subfamilies in common with the rest of the African continent. Because of this, an oligochaetologist could mistake a collection from Patagonia for one from the Cape of Good Hope, but he could never confuse a collection of Chilean earthworms with one from Brazil.

To complete the picture, I want to add some information regarding the biogeography of an austral family of limicolous Oligochaeta, the Phreodrilidae, sub-divided into four genera, *Hesperodrilus, Phreodrilus, Gondwanaedrilus*, and *Phreodriloides*. The first genus has endemic species spread through Chile, the Tierra del Fuego, the islands of South Georgia, Crozet, Kerguelen, and Campbell, New South Wales, and Ceylon. The genus *Phreodrilus* has endemic species in New Zealand, South Africa, the Tierra del Fuego, and the Falklands. *Gondwanaedrilus* and *Phreodrilus* are endemic, respectively, in South Africa and New South Wales (map, Fig. 6). It is notable that two families of fish, Haphochitonidae and Galaxidae, and one family of crayfish, Parastacidae, have distributions almost identical with those of the Phreodrilidae and the Acanthodrilinae (cf. Joleaud, 1939).

To summarize: the Austral fauna of Oligochaetes extending from Chile and Patagonia to South Africa across the Falkland islands and New Georgia, and from South Africa to New Zealand across the Crozet, Kerguelen, Macquarie and Campbell islands is one of the most uniform and typical despite its great geographical splitting.

The situation in the Mexican and Antillean subregions is much more singular than in the rest of America and also a bit more difficult to unravel because of the disorder that remains in some of the taxonomic categories, whereas, it must be stated, the systematics of the South American and South African Oligochaetes revised in the two large monographs by Michaelsen (1917) and Pickford (1937) are in perfect order.

The Oligochaetes of these central American subregions (which will be dealt with together because they are essentially alike) belong to one family only, the Acanthodrilidae. The recent infiltrations from the South, which reach up to Costa Rica and the island of Barbados, and the admixtures from the north, which have come as far as Guatemala, are of course not counted. They make up a negligible part of the fauna and, except in a couple of cases, do not involve endemic species.

The four subfamilies of the Acanthodrilidae are represented in central America as follows: there are about a dozen endemic species of Acanthodrilinae, most of which are usually attributed to the genus *Eodrilus*, but which, in my opinion, would be better placed in a separate genus. There are twenty-two endemic species of Benhaminae belonging to the genus *Dichogaster* found also in equatorial Africa (map, Fig. 7). The Ocnerodrilinae are represented by the genus *Nematogenia*, which lives exclusively in central

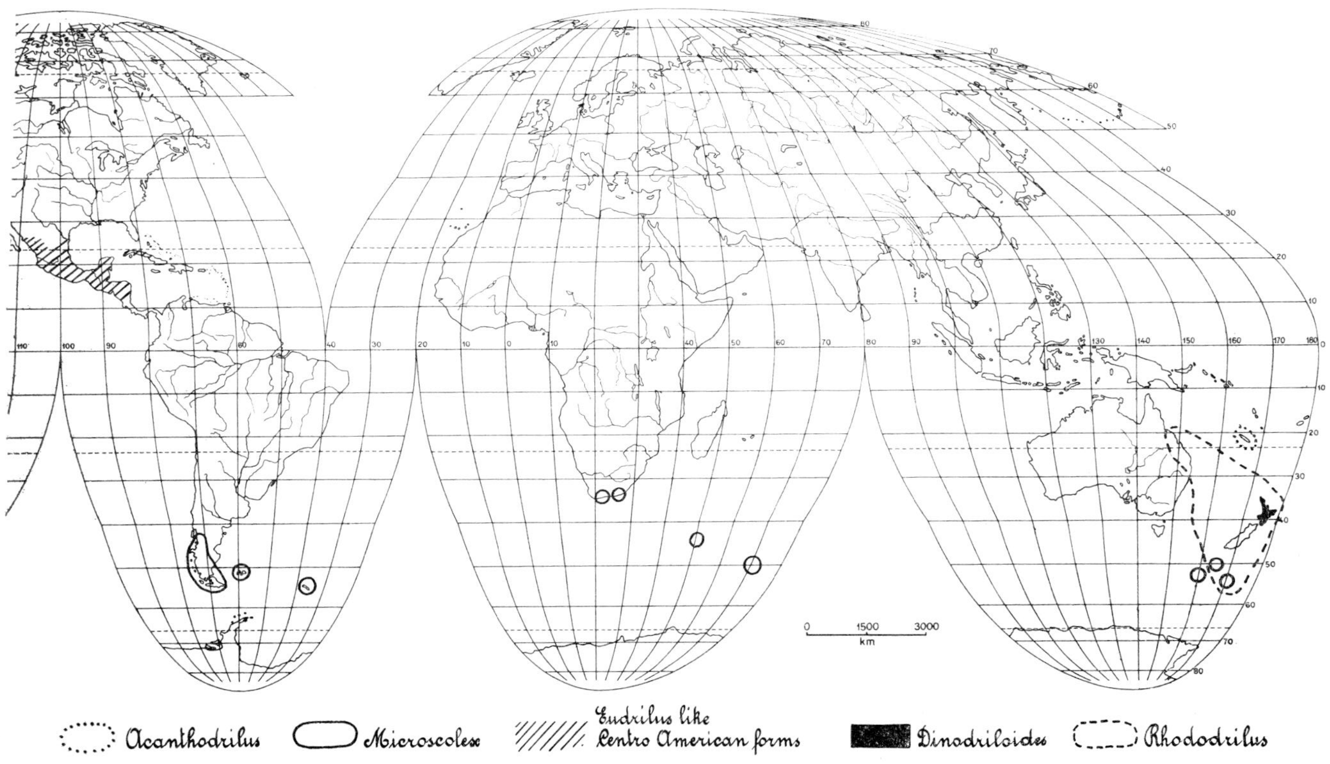

FIG. 3. Geographical distribution of the Acanthodrilinae (1).

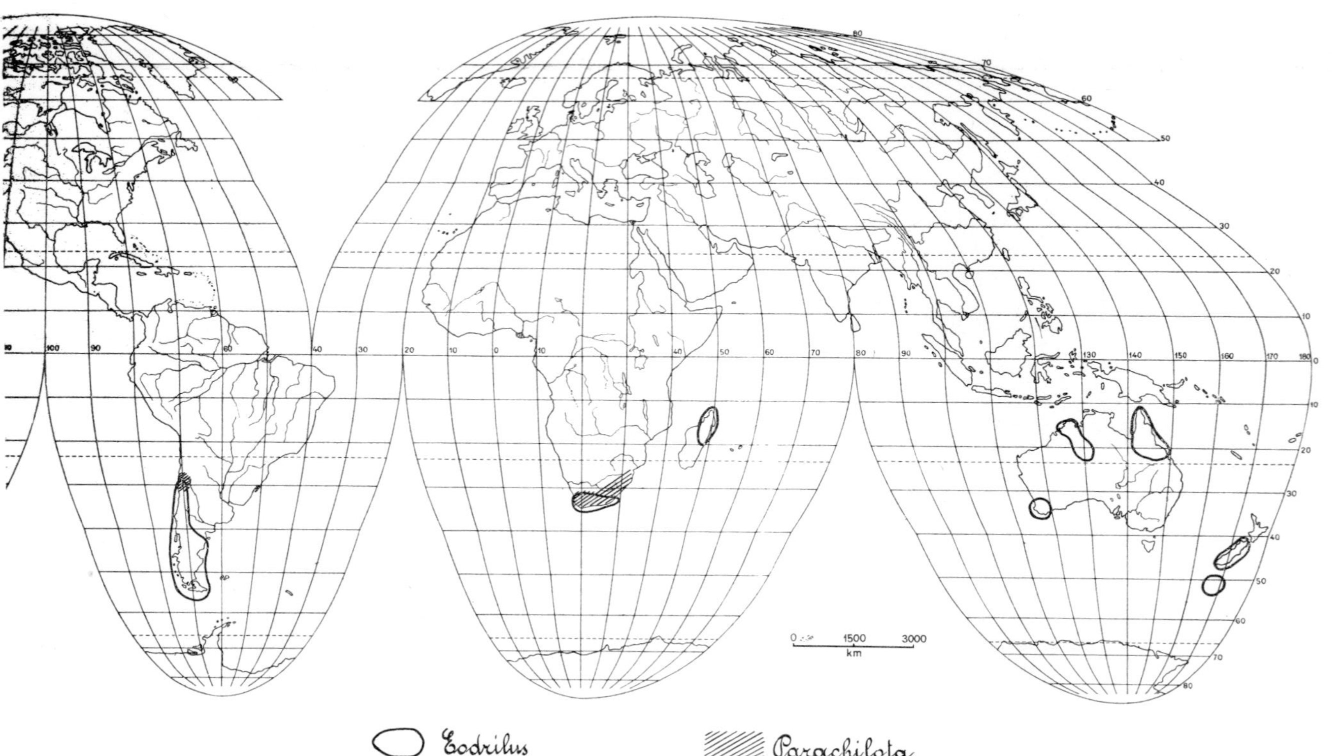

FIG. 4. Geographical distribution of the Acanthodrilinae (2).

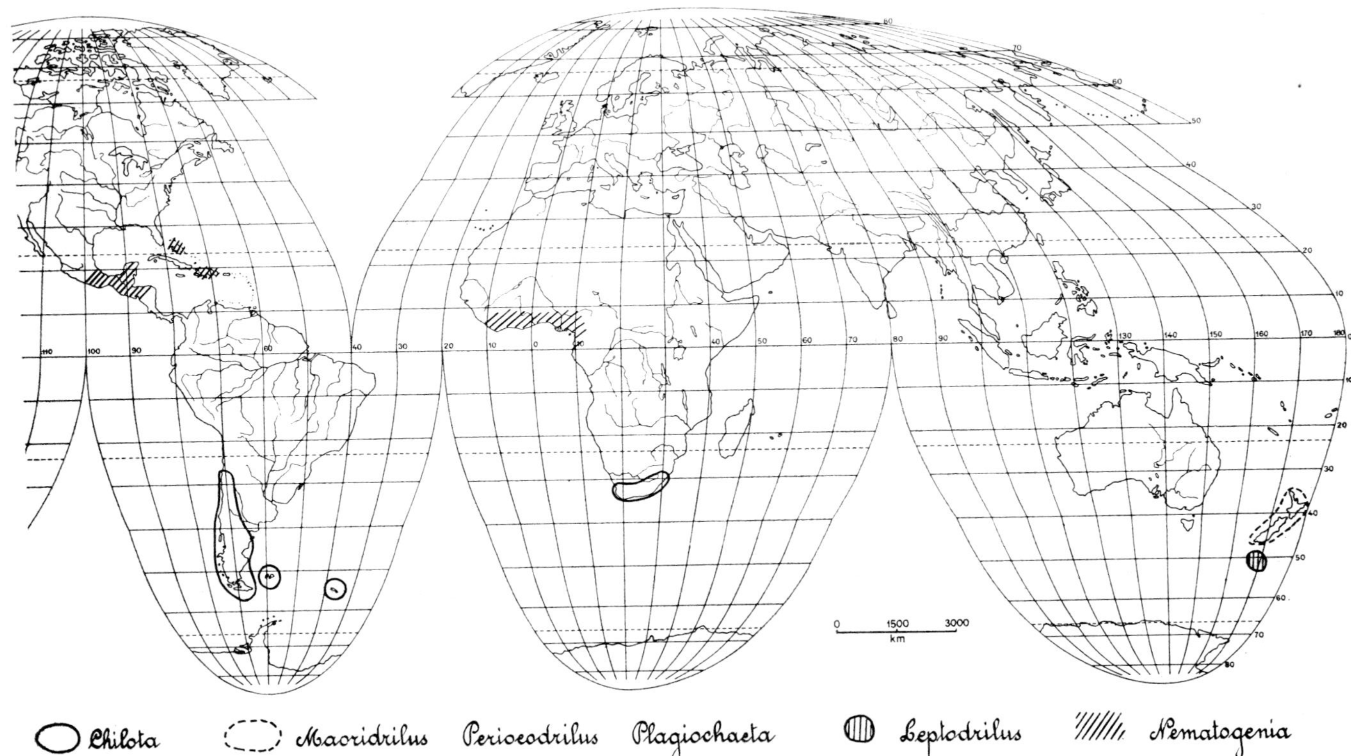

FIG. 5. Geographical distribution of the Acanthodrilinae (3), and of the Ocnerodrilinae genus *Nematogenia*.

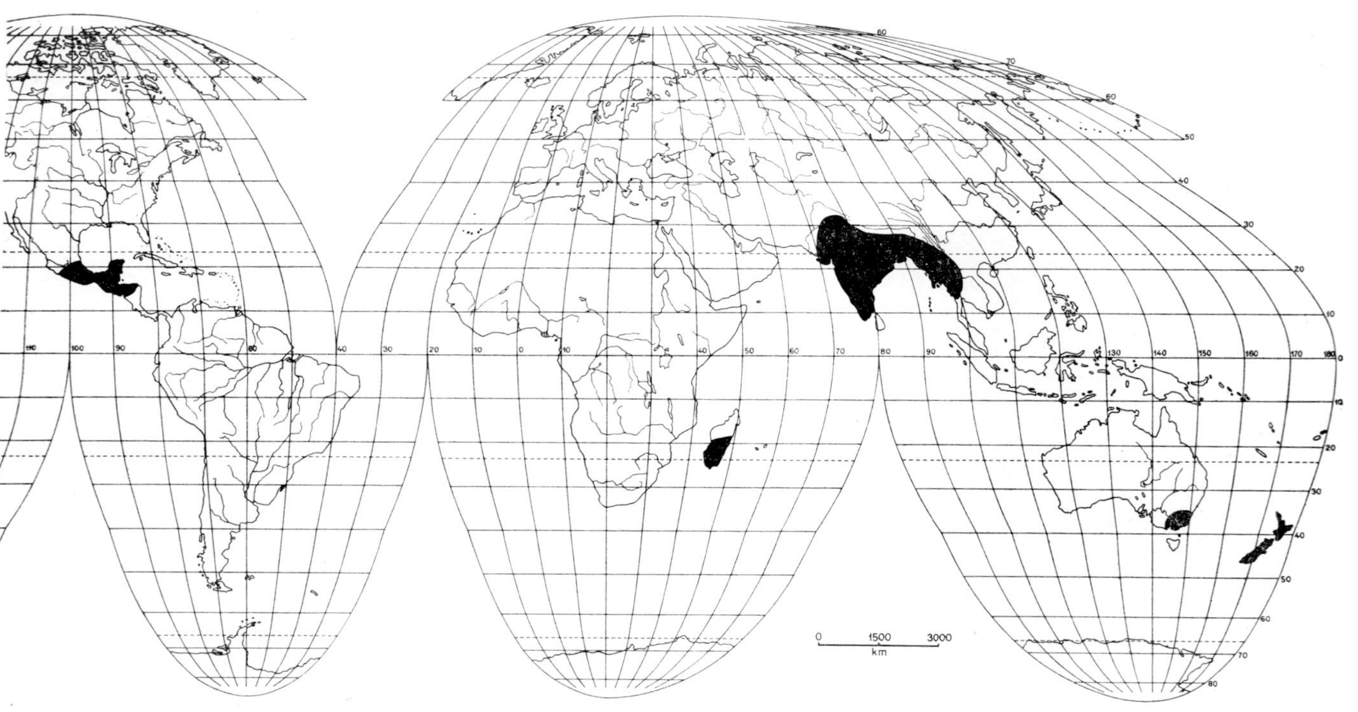

FIG. 6. Geographical distribution of the Octochaetinae.

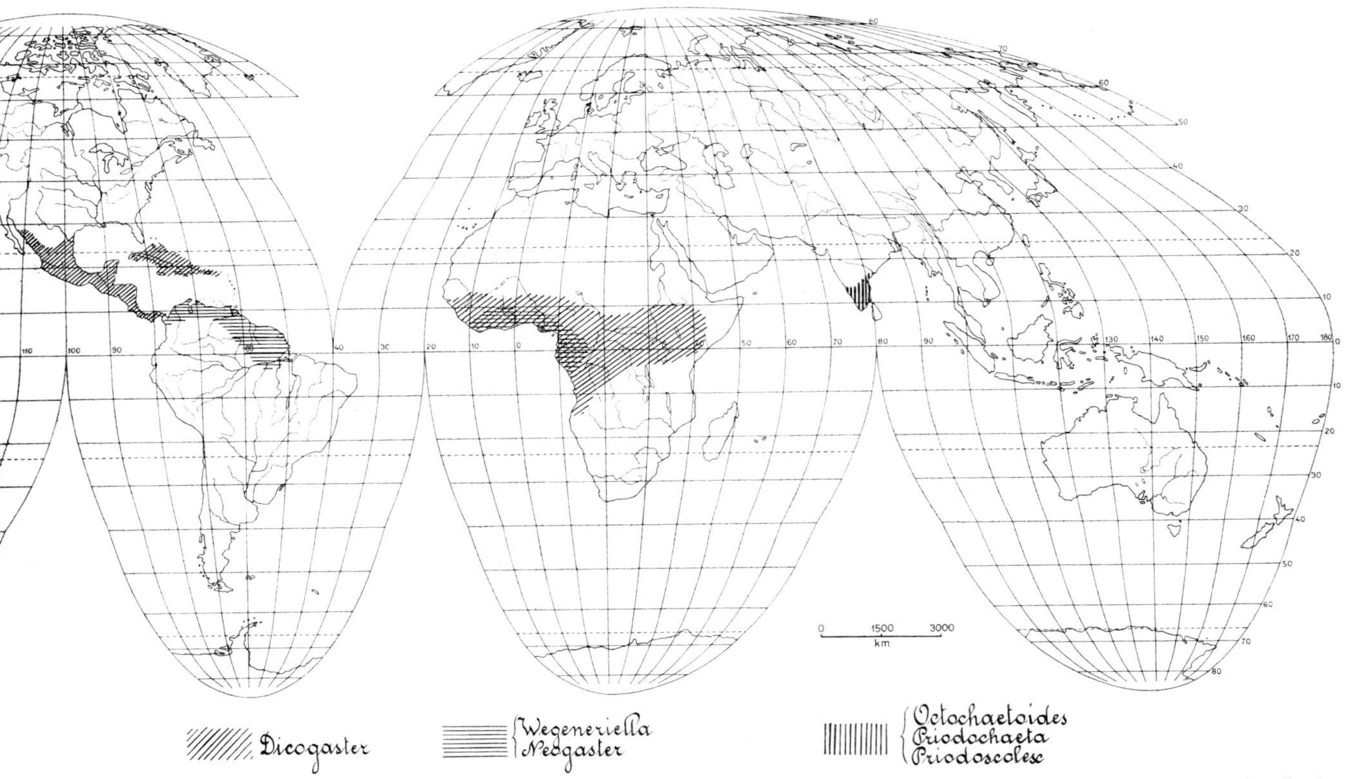

FIG. 7. Geographical distribution of the Benhaminae; the remaining genera *Benhamia*, *Millsonia* and *Pickfordia* have the same distribution as the African *Wegeneriella* and *Neogaster*.

America and western Africa (map, Fig. 5) and by the genera *Ilyogenia* (Fig. 10), *Ocnerodrilus*, and *Gordiodrilus*, which live throughout tropical Africa also. Lastly there are six to eight species of Octochaetinae. Some of these have been attributed to the Indo-Malagasy genus *Howascolex* and one to the Indian genus *Ramiella*. It seems to me that they should be placed together in a genus of their own; at any rate their relationship with the Malagasy and Indian forms is certain.

To conclude, in central America and the Antilles we find fauna similar to that of Africa with Indo-Malagasy elements as well as elements related to that of the Chilean–Patagonian subregion wedged in between a commonplace Holarctic fauna and a Neotropical fauna with a high degree of endemism.

I should like to emphasize the relationship with the African fauna which concerns five genera out of eight. We find that these five genera are abundant precisely on the western coast of Africa from Guinea to Angola. Apart from the representatives of the family Eudrilidae, confined to the equatorial strip of the Paleotropical region, there were represented in some West African collections that I have had an opportunity to study, eleven genera of which five were common to Africa and central America and two to the northeastern coasts of South America and Africa.

To show the particular situation of the central American Oligochaetes more clearly, I shall momentarily modify the method of exposition that I have been following and instead of listing the faunas of each region and their relationship, I shall here describe the distribution of the family Acanthodrilidae (cf. Table 1). This family, as mentioned above, is divided into the subfamily Acanthodrilinae (the most primitive), Ocnerodrilinae (generally specialized for limicolous life), Octochaetinae, and Benhaminae. The Acanthodrilinae are distributed in the southern countries, from Chile to New Caledonia, and have in addition several genera in central and northern America: the Diplocardiacea section is endemic to this latter area. The Ocnerodrilinae occupy all of central America, the Brazilian subregion, Africa, Madagascar, and the Oriental region. Contrarily, the Octochaetinae are peculiar to New Zealand, the Oriental region, Madagascar, and are missing on the African continent but reappear in central America. The Benhaminae have the same distribution as the Ocnerodrilinae but they are very scarce in South America (map, Fig. 7).

Only in central America are found all four subfamilies of Acanthodrilidae: following an old rule of biogeography, one should conclude that this district was the center of origin and diffusion of the entire group. This is possible but there remain some doubts because of the great gap between the central American and austral Acanthodrilinae and between the central American and Indo-Malagasian Octochetinae. However, it must be kept in mind that out of all the families of earthworms the one of which we are speaking here has the widest distribution and includes forms with the most

TABLE 1

GEOGRAPHICAL DISTRIBUTION OF THE ACANTHODRILIDAE

(S = endemic section; G = endemic genus; + = endemic species)

Region	NEOTROPICAL						AETHIOPIAN							
Subregion		Mexican Antillean	Brazilian	Chilean				West African	East African	South African			Malagasy	
District					Falkland	Georgia					Kerguelen	Crozet		Seychelles
ACANTHODRILIDAE	G	G	G	G	+	+	G	G	+	G	+	+	G	G
Acanthodrilinae	G	G		G	+	+	G			G	+	+	+	
Acanthodrilacea	G	G		+	+	+	+			+	+	+	+	
Chilotacea	G			G	+	+	G			G				
Maoridrilacea														
Diplocardiacea	G	G												
Benhaminae	+	+	+				G	G	+					
Ocnerodrilinae	G	+	G				G	+	+				G	G
Octochaetinae	G	G					+						+	

Region	ORIENTAL					AUSTRALIAN						
Subregion		Ceylon	Indian	Indo-Chin.	Indo-Malayan		Austral.	New Zealand				Polynesian
District									Macq.	Auckl.	Campb.	New Caledonia
ACANTHODRILIDAE	G	G	G	+		S	+	S	+	+	+	G
Acanthodrilinae						S	+	S	+	+	+	G
Acanthodrilacea						G	+	G	+	+	+	G
Chilotacea												
Maoridrilacea						S		S	+	+	+	
Diplocardiacea												
Benhaminae	G	G										
Ocnerodrilinae	G	G	G	+								
Octochaetinae	G	G	G	+		G		G				

simple morphology; therefore it is probably very ancient. That makes the point more clear because it is known that other more or less ancient systematic groups (reptiles, fresh water fish and amphibians) have a similar discontinuous distribution in central America and Madagascar since they have found conditions suitable for their survival only in these rather isolated districts.

At this point we can begin trying to reconstruct the genesis of the profound and undeniable relationship responsible for the fauna of Guinea being more similar to the American fauna than to that of East Africa, and for the Patagonian fauna being almost identical to that of the Cape area but entirely different from that of Paraguay.

The explanations proposed for problems of this sort can be classified in two categories, which we will call static and dynamic. The static explanations presume that in the past the continents had more or less the same configuration and relative position as they do now; the dynamic ones presume that there have been substantial modifications in the configurations of the continents and especially of their relative positions.

If one admits the stability of the continents, the Amphi-Atlantic relationship of the terricolous Oligochaetes can be explained either by the hypothesis of passive transport across the ocean, or by Matthew's (1915) theory according to which certain systematic groups reached their present centers by radiating from Arctic Circumpolar regions; the subsequent extinction of the northern taxa would have lead to the present discontinuity.

On other occasions (Omodeo, 1955, 1957) I have maintained that similar interpretations cannot be applied to the earthworms. I am still of the same opinion, but now I am disposed to grant a minimal margin of probability to these interpretations.

If Simpson (1952) is right in believing that highly improbable events become almost certain given a very long period of time, it is also true that if the probability of an event is nil, eternity will not be enough to make it come true. It is a fact that earthworms, with the exceptions of very few species, have no possibility of crossing the ocean haphazardly since they do not tolerate immersion in salt water. If they get bathed in it, they die immediately and the same happens to their eggs.

Their transport across the ocean on rafts or logs is therefore unthinkable, and even if, for the sake of argument, we would accept it as possible, we would still have to explain how they could have crossed the beaches or the wave-beaten rocks on which they were stranded.

Earthworms and their eggs dwell underground and they do not have any chance of getting stuck to the feet of some birds, and what is more, if they are exposed to the air, they dehydrate and die in a few minutes, or even faster if the air is moving. Thus their transport from one continent to another by aid of birds appears decidedly impossible, and even more so since no case of bird migration across the middle of the Atlantic is known.

It is well known that the Oligochaetes are exclusively terricolous or fresh-water taxa and everything that is known about their phylogenesis leads us to assume that they have evolved exclusively in such habitats. Only a few forms of limicolous Oligochaetes and two genera of Megascolecidae have acquired secondarily a certain tolerance of brackish and even salt water. The two genera of Megascolecidae which tolerate sea water are *Pontodrilus* (the name is significant) and *Plutellus*, often considered as one. Only for these forms is the passage from one continent to another thinkable, but mainly by means of slow displacement along the shores: the presence of five endemic species of *Plutellus* in the Californian subregion can be explained by postulating the arrival of an ancestor from the eastern coasts of Asia. This is the only case where I consider it permissible to suppose than an earthworm was able to move, if not across the sea, then at least along its shores, to reach America.

I want to add one last objection before moving on to other points: if we admit that the relationship between the earthworms of the two Atlantic coasts is due to passive transport of some ancient forms across this ocean, how do we justify the great differences existing between the earthworm faunas of Madagascar and the African mainland, which are separated by a body of water so much narrower than the Atlantic?

The hypothesis that the principal zoological groups of the two coasts of the Atlantic came from the north—a hypothesis which has found its most authoritative defender in Matthew (1915) and has recently been supported by Darlington (1957)—does not offer as serious theoretical difficulties as the preceding idea. Nevertheless, it raises myriads of doubts and problems calling for very complicated, additional hypotheses.

To explain the presence of the Acanthodrilinae in South Africa and in the Chilean–Patagonian region, intentionally ignoring their presence in New Zealand and other lesser southern islands and admitting that they started from the northern continents, we must explain also why they have disappeared from immense continental areas where once they must have been common. If we assume that the environmental conditions became hostile to them in these zones and that the appearance of new zoological groups has completely replaced them, we must ask ourselves why it is that two species of Acanthodrilinae, *Microscolex phosphoreus* and *M. dubius*, recently have been able to invade Europe, North America, and many tropical countries where they now flourish and compete successfully with indigenous forms.

Certain facts regarding the biology of earthworms, which it would be well to make clear immediately, make the application of Matthew's (1915) theory to our case difficult. Earthworm species have often a latitude of adaptation unparalleled by any other invertebrate: *Dendrobaena rubida* lives on the island of Disko off Greenland, on the Himalayas and throughout the tropical

Malayan peninsula; the African species *Eudrilus eugeniae*, dispersed voluntarily and involuntarily by man, colonizes much of the United States, whereas its original environment is the equatorial forest. Such an extraordinary adaptability makes it hard to imagine a climatic modification capable of totally destroying the populations of a genus or a family of earthworms living on a continent: it is almost certain, as we shall see, that the Lumbricidae of Greenland and Iceland have survived *in situ* all of the Last Glacial and maybe the entire Quaternary.

The competition among these saprophagous species is very slight: in an area of a few square meters, in Africa as well as in Europe, it is possible to collect individuals belonging to 15–20 different species and also to two or more families. In any Tuscan garden it is normal to find living together species of Lumbricidae, Microchaetidae and Acanthodrilidae (the latter introduced). This being the situation, the substitution of an entire family of earthworms by another over a whole continent does not appear probable. In this connection, I think it is worth while to recall the case of the family Phreorictidae (or Haplotaxidae)—certainly very ancient and primitive and probably the ancestor of all living families of earthworms—containing endemic species belonging to two or three genera in all corners of the world: from Europe to New Zealand, from Sumatra to Japan, from the Cape to Guinea. In colder climates these species take shelter in phreatic waters, in hotter climates they occupy surface as well as subterranean waters; in any case they always have been found wherever an accurate investigation of the fauna has been carried out.

Summing up, we can say that although Matthew's (1915) theory appears plausible for an explanation of the discontinuity of the neotropical Acanthodrilinae or the absence of the Octochaetinae in equatorial Africa, it is completely inadequate to justify the principal pattern of earthworm zoogeography.

It remains to consider the theories that suggest major modifications of the continental areas and of their reciprocal relationship through the geological eras: the theory of the intercontinental land bridges, and that of continental drift.

Only geophysicists and geologists can decide which of the two theories is correct or at least preferable; however, while waiting for them to come to an agreement on this point, I shall state my point of view.

Personally I prefer a certain eclecticism and would tend to explain the genesis of the earthworm fauna of the central and southern countries facing each other on both sides of the Atlantic Ocean on the basis of Wegener's theory and the genesis of the fauna of the North Atlantic countries on the basis of the land-bridge theory.

A glance at the present distribution of earthworms superimposed on Wegener's paleogeographic maps (maps, Figs. 8–10) is more satisfactory than a long discussion. It demonstrates how simply and completely can be

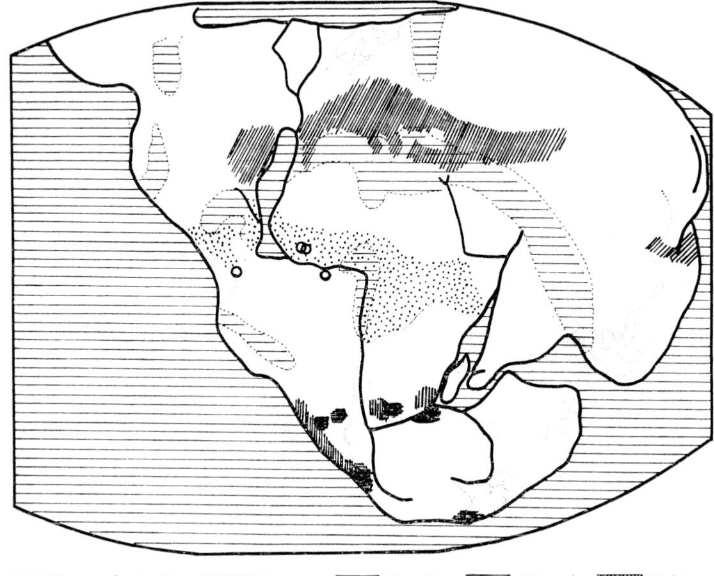

FIG. 8. Distribution of the endemic species of the Lumbricidae, of the Acanthodrilinae genera *Microscolex* and *Chilota*, and of the Benhaminae genera *Neogaster* and *Dichogaster*, on Wegener's Mesozoic map.

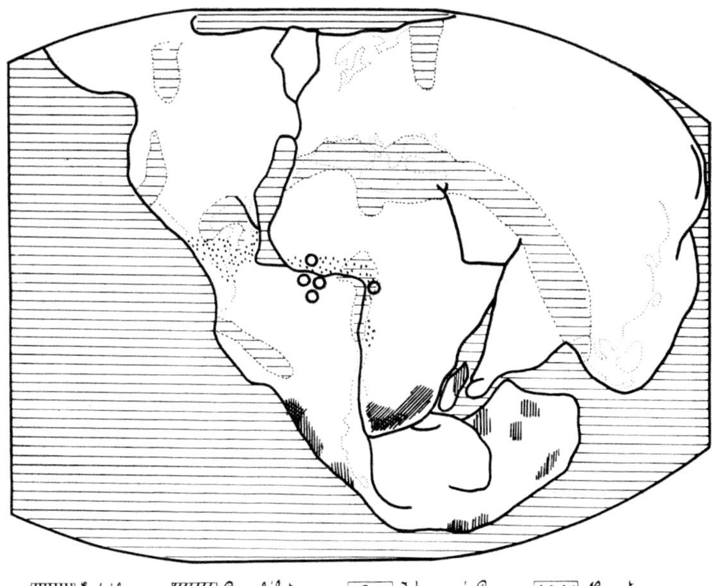

FIG. 9. Distribution of the Acanthodrilinae genera *Eodrilus* and *Parachilota*, of the Benhaminae genus *Wegeneriella*, and of the Ocnerodrilinae *Nematogenia*, on Wegener's Mesozoic map.

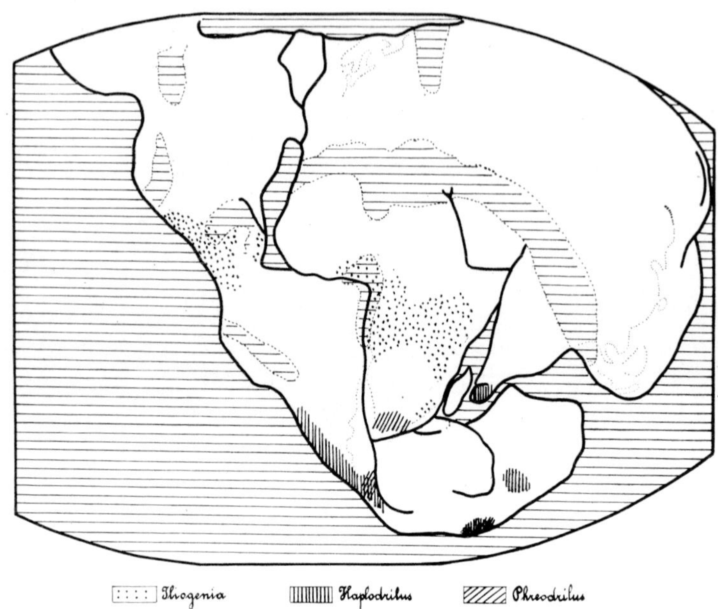

FIG. 10. Distribution of the Ocnerodrilinae genus *Ilyogenia* and of two genera of Phreodrilidae (freshwater Oligochaeta), on Wegener's Mesozoic map.

solved what Michaelsen (1911) called the great puzzle of earthworm biogeography. Naturally, the explanation based on Wegener's theory does raise important collateral problems, and this has often been reiterated. The main objection is that, if the continental drift theory is correct, there should be a greater uniformity in the distribution of the zoological groups, especially in the Southern Hemisphere.

This objection can be answered by stating that the genera of earthworms are extremely ancient and have evolved very slowly, whereas other systematic groups have become so greatly differentiated that the ancient resemblance of the faunas has become almost obsolete.

The great tardiness in the evolution of terricolous Oligochaetes is documented by innumerable circumstances. One of these, I think, must be apparent to whoever has followed me up to now: the distribution of single genera of earthworms corresponds generally to the distribution of superior taxonomic categories, families and superfamilies, of vertebrates or arthropods. Other indirect data on the antiquity of the Oligochaetes can be gathered from the study of various fossil types of soil. It is a fact that no fossil remains of earthworms are known but fossil remains of soil types produced by the work of earthworms are well known: gyttja and mull. We know also that these soil types evolved during the Mesozoic in correspondence with the evolution of the modern Spermatophyta.

Critical analyses of these phenomena have been carried out satisfactorily by Wilcke (1955) but it must be remembered that some of the Oligochaetes dwell in peat or moor soil, which was certainly the first environment that they occupied; even now the Phreorictidae—presumed ancestral group of all the living families of terricolous Oligochaetes—live in this environment; other, more modern groups, e.g. the Ocnerodrilinae, the genera *Alma* and *Drilocrius*, etc., have invaded this important ecological niche secondarily, but without doubt this occurred in a very ancient time while other parallel groups were specializing themselves in their present habitats.

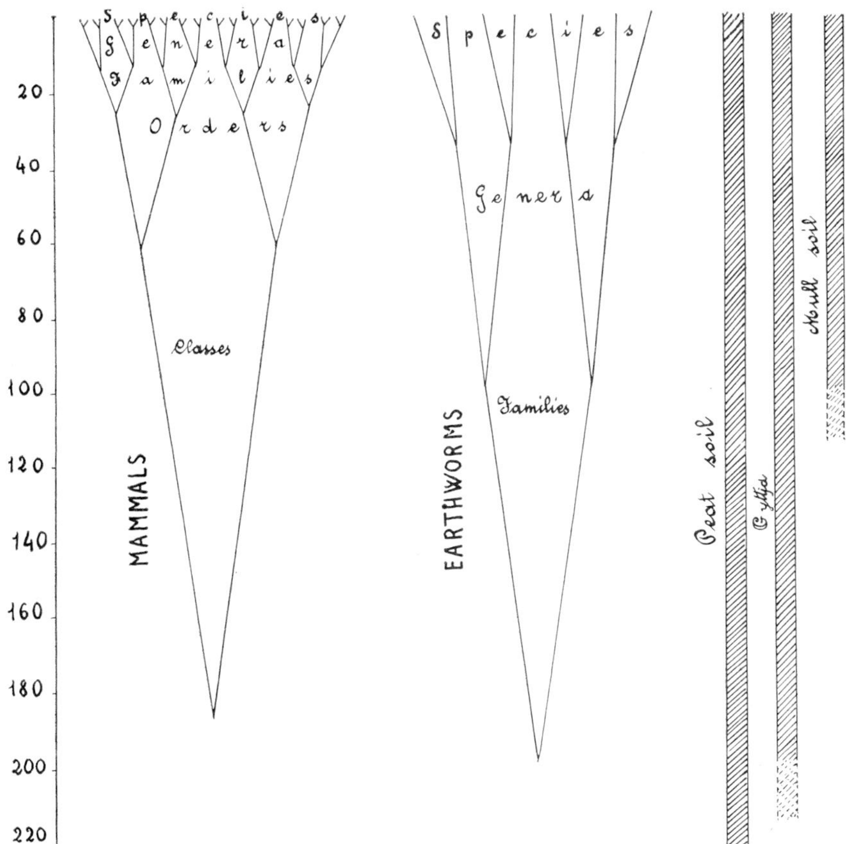

FIG. 11. Chronology of Mammals, of Terrestrial Oligochaeta, and of three types of soil in millions of years. The data for Mammals after Rensch (1954), the data of soil types after Wilcke (1955).

The diagram in Fig. 11 establishes the parallel between the chronology of the Mammal evolution as schematized by Rensch (1954), and the chronology of the Oligochaete evolution as it can be reconstructed from their geographical

TABLE 2

DISTRIBUTION OF SOME HOLARCTIC AND EURO-AMERICAN EARTHWORM SPECIES

	Californian subregion	Rocky Mts. subregion	Alleghany subregion	Eastern Canada	Newfound-land	Greenland	Iceland	Faeroes	British Isles	France	Italian peninsula	Sardinia
HOLARCTIC SPECIES												
Allolobophora rosea	+	+	+	+	—	—	+	—	+	+	+	+
A. caliginosa	+	+	+	+	+	—	+	+	+	+	+	+
Eiseniella tetraedra	+	+	+	+	—	—	+	+	+	+	+	+
Dendrobaena rubida	+	+	+	+	+	+	+	+	+	+	+	+
Octolasium lacteum	+	+	+	—	—	—	—	—	+	+	+	—
O. cyaneum	—	—	+	—	—	—	+	+	+	+	—	—
Eisenia foetida	+	+	+	—	—	—	+	+	+	+	+	(1)
EURO-AMERICAN SPECIES												
Lumbricus terrestris	+	+	+	+	+	—	+	—	+	+	—	—
L. rubellus	+	+	+	+	+	+	+	+	+	+	+	—
L. castaneus	—	—	+	+	—	—	+	+	+	+	+	—
L. festivus	—	—	+	+	—	—	—	—	+	+	—	—
Dendrobaena octaedra	+	+	+	+	+	+	+	+	+	+	—	—
D. hortensis	+	—	+	—	—	—	—	—	+	—	+	—
Allolobophora chlorotica	+	+	+	+	—	+	—	—	+	+	+	—
A. limicola	—	—	+	—	—	—	—	—				
A. longa	—	—	+	+	—	—	—	—	+	+	—	—
Bimastus muldali	—	—	+	—	—	—	—	—	+	—	—	—
Dendrobaena mammalis	—	—	+	—	—	—	—	—	+	+	—	—
Sparganophilus	+	+	+	+	—	—	—	—	+	+	—	—

(1) found only in a botanic garden.

distribution, and the ancient history of soil types as summarized by Wilcke (1955, 1960).

As I have already mentioned, the validity of the Wegenerian hypothesis can be confirmed only by geophysicists but it seems reasonable for me to underline the extreme simplicity and completeness with which it resolves certain zoogeographical problems, something which other Oligochaetologists, Michaelsen (1922, 1928) and Černosvitov (1936), have already done with greater authority.

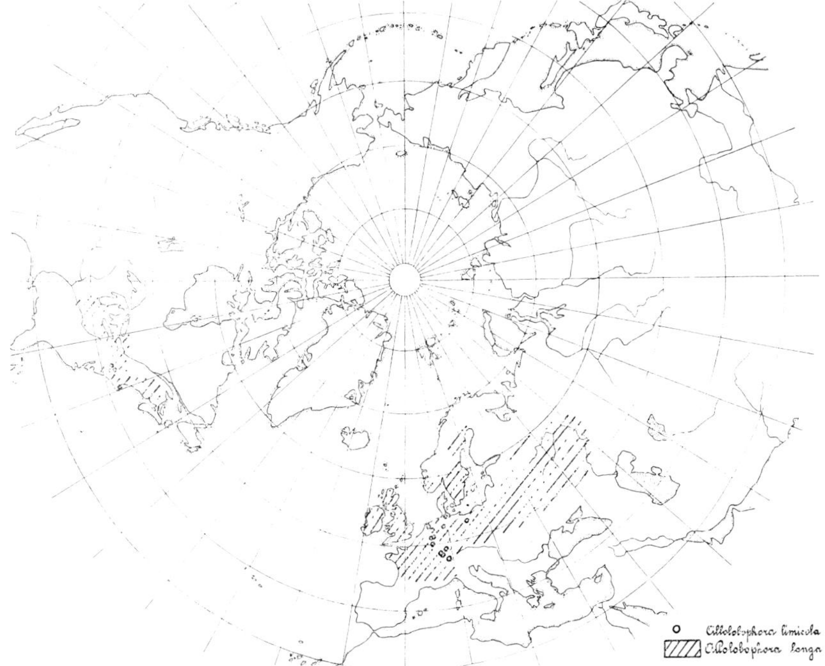

FIG. 12. Distribution of *Allolobophora longa* and *A. limicola*.

But putting aside these purely conjectural solutions, let us return to the first zoogeographical problem: the sameness of north European and North American earthworm faunas. Gates (1929, 1959) thought he had solved the questions by stating that all European species in North America were introduced by European settlers during the last two centuries; Lindroth (1957) accepts this point of view without reservations.

I am very skeptical of this solution and feel obliged to ask: is it possible that a whole continent was almost entirely devoid of earthworms up till 200 years ago? Or, is it possible that the European Lumbricidae annihilated the autochton taxa almost everywhere in North America?

To the first question the answer is: no. Any pedologist would refuse to accept that the soil of the North American grass and forest land was produced differently from that of other continents. Nor would it be possible to justify the presence in North America of certain higher animals, such as moles, whose diet is made up almost exclusively of earthworms, if none were there.

To the second question the answer is another: no. More than 200 years ago European earthworms were introduced into central and South America, where they have competed successfully with the indigenous fauna, however, without ever replacing them, even in limited areas.

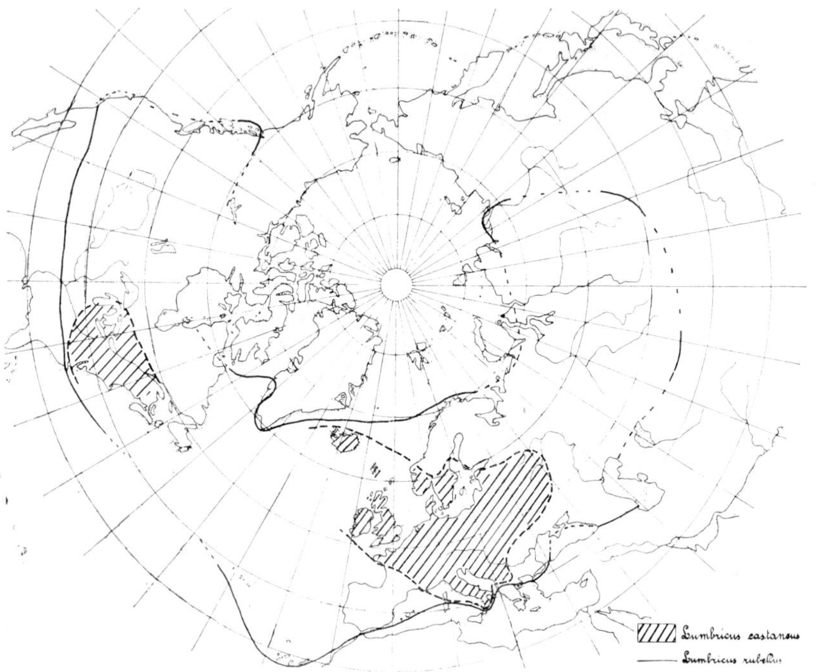

FIG. 13. Distribution of *Lumbricus castaneus* and *L. rubellus*.

On the other hand, the European species present in North America do not have the random distribution that would be expected if they had been introduced exclusively by the European settlers: they all occur in the northern part of Europe and many do not go beyond the northeastern part of North America (maps, Figs. 12–15). Of course, most of the traffic went on precisely between the northern countries of Europe and New England, but this is not enough to explain the massive presence of these animals in northern localities where farming is very recent. It must be remembered that traffic has been going on between Italy and Sardinia for two millenia and has not yet resulted in the introduction into Sardinia of species that are common on the Italian mainland (and found also in Canada). Table 2 eloquently sums up the situation.

Usually, the species of Lumbricidae have a very wide distribution and therefore the Palearctic earthworm fauna is very uniform. For example, the earthworms of Afghanistan (cf. Omodeo, 1959) belong to species, all but one of which are found also in Italy; most of the Manchurian earthworms belong to species that we find in Caucasia as well as in the Urals; etc. Therefore, all premises exist for considering the North American populations of European earthworm taxa an integral part of the Holarctic, ancient fauna.

FIG. 14. Distribution of *Lumbricus festivus* and *L. terrestris.*

In addition to indirect proofs and merely inductive arguments, there exist also very convincing direct proofs: *Allolobophora caliginosa*, a very common earthworm throughout the Palearctic, is represented in the United States by two types, *molita* and *arnoldi* (Gates, 1952), which have already evolved to a subspecific or maybe even specific rank. We also have the case of the North American genus *Sparganophilus*, represented in England and France by an endemic species. Finally we have, scattered all over the arc from the Faeroes over Iceland to Greenland, a large number of stations of Euro-American species. The biometric and caryological studies of the populations of Iceland and Greenland permit us to state that they are not as similar as would be expected had they developed recently from introduced material. Instead, they differ significantly both in morphology and in degree of ploidy (cf. Omodeo, 1957).

In my opinion, the sum of these arguments points to only one explanation for the type of distribution we are dealing with, the existence of a land-bridge

FIG. 15. Distribution of *Dendrobaena octaedra* and *Sparganophilus*.

across the North Atlantic along which the earthworm fauna of Europe moved to North America, and a few rare American species went in the opposite direction, in a relatively ancient age, but not so ancient as to permit specific differentiation of most of the Lumbricidae.

REFERENCES

ČERNOSVITOV, I. (1936). Notes sur la distribution mondiale de quelques Oligochètes. *Mem. Soc. Zool. Tchechosl.* **3**, 16–19.

DARLINGTON, P. J. (1957). *Zoogeography*. New York.

GATES, G. E. (1929). Earthworms of North America. *J. Wash. Acad. Sci.* **19**, 339–347.

GATES, G. E. (1952). New species of earthworms from Arnold Arboretum, Boston. *Breviora Mus. Comp. Zool. Cambr.* **9**, 1–3.

GATES, G. E. (1957). Contribution to a revision of the earthworm family Ocnerodrilinae. The genus *Nematogenia*. *Bull. Mus. Comp. Zool. Cambr.* **117**, 427–445.

JOLEAUD, L. (1939). *Atlas de paléobiogéographie*. Paris.

LINDROTH, C. H. (1957). *The Faunal Connections between Europe and North America*. Stockholm.

MATTHEW, W. D. (1915). Climate and evolution. *Ann. N.Y. Acad. Sci.* **24**, 171–318.

MICHAELSEN, W. (1911). Die Oligochäten des inneren Ostafrika und ihre geographischen Beziehung. *Wiss. Erg. Deutsch Zentral Afrika Exp.* **3**, 1–60.

MICHAELSEN, W. (1917). Die Lumbriciden mit besonderer Berücksichtigung der bisher als Familie Glossoscolecidae zusammengefassten Unterfamilien. *Zool. Jahrb.* (*Syst.*) **41**, 1–398.

MICHAELSEN, W. (1922). Die Verbreitung der Oligochaeten im Lichte der Wegener'schen Theorie der Kontinental-Verschiebung, etc. *Verh. Naturwiss. Ver. Hamburg*, **29**, 1–37.

MICHAELSEN, W. (1928). Oligochaeta. Kükenthal: *Handb. d. Zoologie*. Berlin u. Leipzig.

MICHAELSEN, W. (1933). Die Oligochaetenfauna Surinames mit Erörterung der verwandtschaftlichen Beziehungen der Octochätinen. *Tijdschr. Ned. Dierk. Vereen.* **3**, 112–131.

OMODEO, P. (1955). Nuove specie dei generi a distribuzione anfiatlantica *Wegeneriella* e *Neogaster*. *Ann .Ist. Mus. Zool. Univ. Napoli*, **7** (3), 1–29.

OMODEO, P. (1957). Lumbricidae and Lumbriculidae of Greenland. *Medd. om Groenl.* **124** (6), 1–27.

OMODEO, P. (1959). Oligocheti dell'Afghanistan. *Boll. di. Zool.* **26**, 1–20.

PICKFORD, G. E. (1937). *A monograph of the Acanthodrilinae earthworms of South Africa.* Cambridge.

RENSCH, B. (1954). *Neuere Probleme der Abstammungslehre. Die transspezifische Evolution.* Stuttgart.

SIMPSON, G. G. (1952). Probabilities of dispersal in geologic time. *Bull. Amer. Mus. Nat Hist.* **99**, 163–176.

WILCKE, D. E. (1955), Bemerkungen zum Problem des erdzeitlichen Alters der Regenwürmer (Oligochaeta opisthopora). *Zool. Anz.* **154**, 149–156.

WILCKE, D. E. (1960). Fossile Lebensspuren von Regenwürmern. *Decheniana* **112**, 255–269.

HISTORICAL AND TAXONOMICAL ASPECTS OF THE LAND GASTROPODA IN THE NORTH ATLANTIC REGION

HENRIK W. WALDÉN
Museum of Natural History, Gothenburg, Sweden

A ZOOGEOGRAPHICAL division with respect to land Gastropoda rather markedly differs from the conventional one, which is based mainly on the distribution of vertebrates (cf. Darlington, 1957). However, more thorough studies of the differences show that an essential causal consistency exists. Somewhat schematically, the terrestrial Gastropoda can be characterized as a conservative group, whose actual distribution and taxonomy to a rather remarkable degree reflect the past. On the contrary, they less obviously react to short-term changes. The rich paleontological evidence offers substantial basis for speculations concerning the faunal development.

For an understanding of the recent distribution of the gastropod fauna on both sides of the North Atlantic it is necessary to follow its development since the late Mesozoic. At that time a terrestrial gastropod fauna, with obvious points in common with the present one, appears for the first time.

At this era the gastropod faunas in Europe and North America are already thoroughly distinct from each other, and they have largely remained so till the present time. However, this does not imply a parallel development—on the contrary, very marked differences in the trends of development exist. These differences are of importance to the recent distribution of the land Gastropoda.

Owing to the presence of modern, comprehensive literature, it is easier to demonstrate how the gastropod fauna has been formed in North America than in Europe. The European literature in the field no doubt is much richer than the American, but for obvious reasons it is highly diverse from the point of language as well as quality. These circumstances should be kept in mind in the following discussion.

Taxonomy, distributional and paleontological data mainly follow the fundamental works of Wenz (1961–2), and Wenz and Zilch (1959–60), in addition to which Pilsbry (1939–48), and Henderson (1935), constitute the main sources concerning North American Gastropoda. Certain modification, especially concerning fossil records, has been undertaken in accordance with Hibbard and Taylor (1960); Licharev and Rammelmeyer (1952); and Taylor (1954).

It may also be pointed out that, diverging from Wenz and Zilch, the subgenus *Calidivitrina* has been placed under *Vitrina* (cf. information given by Hubendick, 1953). Consequently *Semilimax* has been regarded as an endemic European genus. *Lehmannia* has been classified as a subgenus of *Limax* (cf. Waldén, 1961). Finally, the records assigned to the highly problematic genus *Brachyspira* have been disregarded.

As it seems still to be current in the literature, attention is drawn here to an old opinion that the early European gastropod fauna has much in common with the recent American (cf. Ehrmann, 1914, and authors mentioned by him). It was based on superficial shell resemblances, but its ground has nowadays been radically demolished by the gradually deepened taxonomical knowledge. It is not excluded that future taxonomical revision will correspondingly modify the conception of some further taxa, whose common presence on both sides of the Atlantic today seems rather enigmatic.

THE NORTH AMERICAN LAND GASTROPOD FAUNA AND ITS DEVELOPMENT

In all, more than 750 terrestrial gastropod species are known from North America. Of these, about 50 have been introduced by man in historical time. The occurrence of this element has been so exhaustively elucidated by different authors (see Lindroth, 1957; Pilsbry, 1939–48; and Quick, 1952) that it can be disregarded in the present account. The remaining more than 700 species are dispersed through 107 genera.

The North American land Gastropoda are dominated by two pronouncedly endemic groups, which together comprise about 80 per cent of the indigenous species. In relation to the European Gastropoda the endemism occurs largely on the family level.—The first group is eastern, with the Appalachians as its center, and comprises about 250 species. Among these the members of the autochtonous family Polygyridae dominate. Only a minor fraction of the endemic species, about 50 in all, have Old World relatives. In most instances, however, those belong to different genera or subgenera.

The other, West American group, comprises about 300 endemic species, localized on the Pacific coast and in the Rocky Mountains. This group is dominated by two families of very old, autochtonous development, viz. the Helminthoglyptidae and the Camaenidae. The latter is represented by other genera in Australia and East Asia. Holarctic genera are less well represented in western North America than in eastern. On the contrary, the influx of central or South American genera is much richer in the southwest as a consequence of the land connection there.

Figure 1 illustrates the development of the terrestrial gastropod fauna in

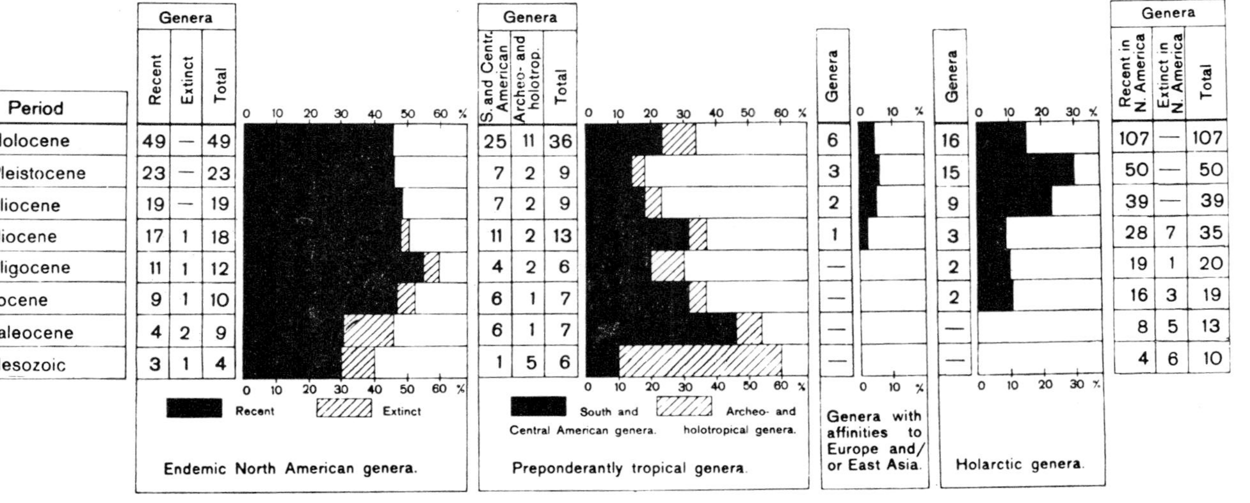

Period	Endemic N. Am. genera: Recent	Extinct	Total	Tropical genera: S. and Centr. American	Archeo- and holotrop.	Total	Genera with affinities to Europe and/or East Asia	Holarctic genera	Genera: Recent in N. America	Extinct in N. America	Total
Holocene	49	—	49	25	11	36	6	16	107	—	107
Pleistocene	23	—	23	7	2	9	3	15	50	—	50
Pliocene	19	—	19	7	2	9	2	9	39	—	39
Miocene	17	1	18	11	2	13	1	3	28	7	35
Oligocene	11	1	12	4	2	6	—	2	19	1	20
Eocene	9	1	10	6	1	7	—	2	16	3	19
Paleocene	4	2	9	6	1	7	—	—	8	5	13
Mesozoic	3	1	4	1	5	6	—	—	4	6	10

FIG. 1. The development of the North American land gastropod fauna since late Mesozoic.

A classification like the present must always to some extent be conditional. Genera may fit more or less well into zoogeographical groups. Taxonomy has its limitations, especially concerning fossil material. However, readers with experience in this field certainly are familiar with shortcomings of this kind, and they need not be discussed further. On the other hand, attention is drawn to the fact that it has proved necessary to undertake some generalizations to make the material manageable. Thus, a genus has been regarded as present in the area during all periods, from the earliest to the latest record, also when not known from all intervening strata. However, with few exceptions this assumption certainly corresponds to reality, and does not appreciably influence the validity of the diagram. When regarding the figures it shall be kept in mind that those from Holocene are not entirely comparable with those from earlier periods, because certain groups necessarily are under-represented in the fossil record. This pertains to forms which are more or less devoid of shells, or have a very limited distribution, with consequently poor chances of fossilification. For specific details, see notes to Table 1.

North America. From its early beginning it seems to be entirely distinct from the Palearctic one. At the end of the Mesozoic, tropical genera dominate, which seem to be purely American. Already some early representatives of the two major endemic groups appear. These increase rapidly, whereas the Tropical genera decrease correspondingly. Soon, in the Eocene, the proportions between endemic North American and essentially Tropical genera are near those of the recent period. At the same time the first representatives of the Holarctic genera appear in the strata.

In addition to these trends in the development it is striking that the number of now extinct genera has always formed a minor fraction. The recent fauna, essentially, is composed of direct descendants of the early Tertiary fauna, which have been able to adapt themselves from the original, almost tropical, conditions to the present temperate ones.

Henderson (1931) suggests as the basic reason for the American endemic pattern the probably profound separation of land masses in the Cretaceous. The largely remaining differences between the eastern and western gastropod groups have been maintained by unfavorable conditions in a broad area, east of the Rocky Mountains, which seem to have existed rather continuously since the Eocene. The principal exchange of land Gastropoda has taken place from the east to the west. The forcing of the Rocky Mountains by some eastern genera had largely come to an end in the Miocene, resulting in a today partially highly endemic offshoot from the eastern group. The effect of the interchange between the two major endemic groups never reached beyond the North American continent.

Table 1 gives an account of the extracontinental relations on the generic level for the North American land Gastropoda. As the biogeographical boundary of North America the border of Mexico has been used, in accordance with Pilsbry (1939–48). Only six of the essentially endemic North American genera exceed this border.

The dispersal of the tropical American element falls beyond the present theme, and will not be discussed further. It comprises about 50 species, most of them in the extreme south of North America. The Tertiary Tropical gastropod fauna was composed largely of species closely related to the recent ones, but the latter are late invaders, probably mainly Post-glacial. The signs of endemism are weak, or non-existent.

For the remaining non-endemic element three possible ways of dispersal must be considered:

(1) The North Pacific route.
(2) The North Atlantic route.
(3) Across the subtropical or tropical parts of the Atlantic.

The Holarctic genera comprise somewhat over 100 species in North America. These represent all stages from morphological identity in the New

TABLE 1

Distribution type \ Number of genera	Extinct in N. America	Recent in N. America	Total
Holarctic	—	16	16
Archeo- or holotropical*	6	11	17
Central or South American	9	25	34
Mainly North American and East Asiatic†	1	4	5
European	—	2	2
Endemic North American‡	4	49	53

* In the Archeo- and Holotropical group, marine littoral genera play a major role. This refers to four extinct and six recent genera. They are useful as climate-dependent indicators in faunal development, but do not tell much about the ways of dispersal of the land fauna proper. Apparently, their often very wide distribution is a consequence of the fact that they are far better adapted to the possibilities of passive dispersal offered, e.g by ocean currents, than the other, truly terrestrial genera. In fact, some littoral species are rather amphibious than terrestrial. Two of the strictly terrestrial genera are regarded here as Archeotropical, viz. *Pseudocolumna* and *Protornatellina*, Paleocene and Cretaceous respectively. To the Holotropical group are assigned *Pupoides*, *Pupisoma*, *Cecilioides*, *Lamellaxis* and *Opeas*. Of these, *Pupoides* appears in the Eocene, the others in N. America, are known from the Holocene only.

† In the North American–East Asiatic group the record of *Rhiostoma*, from Oregon Miocene, must be regarded as somewhat problematic. *Catinella*, with a Pacific center, has been included in this group. The remaining genera are *Hendersonia*, *Strobilops* and *Gastrocopta*. The last two have a wider distribution and a complicated history, briefly discussed in the text.

‡ Some of the endemic North American genera show significant extra-continental relations. *Philomycus*, *Anadenulus* and *Prophysaon* have their closest relatives in East or Central Asia. Concerning the relations to certain European genera of *Gastrodonta* and *Euglandina* (the latter assigned to the Central and South American group), see text.

Cf. also the caption to Fig. 1.

and the Old World to distinct species and subgenera. Apparently their dispersal must have proceeded during a very long time, a statement which is verified by paleontological evidence. A remarkable feature in the distribution of the Holarctic genera is their dominance in the gastropod fauna north of 47° N. Lat., thus largely within the area of the Pleistocene glaciations.

However, not only in the Holarctic element, but also in the Tropical and East Asiatic, affinities to Europe are evident. These are partly of a highly intricate nature. But before the routes of dispersal can be discussed, the European gastropod fauna and its history must be regarded.

THE EUROPEAN LAND GASTROPOD FAUNA AND ITS DEVELOPMENT

The history of the European land gastropod fauna shows a pattern which is very different from that of the North American. In detail it is much more complicated in Europe; this is reflected in the markedly richer taxonomical differentiation. In recent times, 229 genera are indigenous to Europe. For the number of species, however, no actual, reliable figures exist, but they may be estimated as more than double those of North America. On an average, however, the geographical splitting of taxa takes place on a lower taxonomical level than in North America. The major causal background—the highly complicated history of the European mountain upfoldings and seashore dislocations—has led to isolation processes which were richly varied, but only moderately persistent. However, the details are of infra-European interest only, and consequently they can be largely ignored here.

The principal traits in the development of the European land Gastropoda is demonstrated by Fig. 2.

As already pointed out in the preceding paragraph, the land gastropod fauna which appears in Europe in the Late Mesozoic had no points in common with the contemporaneous North American fauna. But, in addition, it has very little in common with the recent European. Except for some unimportant, very specialized remnants, the Mesozoic genera today are quite absent from Europe. In 88.5 per cent (24 of 27 genera), the connections were Tropical, either with the recent South Asiatic and African gastropod fauna, or, for the greater part, representing an Archeotropical element which is difficult to evaluate taxonomically.

Some authors have made the fascinating, though very hypothetical suggestion that this Archeotropical element partly represents an old "Gondwana" fauna.

However, from the Paleocene onwards the recent European genera appear. At first, such genera, which today are Holarctic, form a relatively large fraction. Later, more and more endemic European genera are added. The Archeotropical element rapidly disappears, whereas still in the Eocene that which has connections to South Asia and Africa constitutes nearly 40 per cent of the land gastropod fauna. Then it continuously decreases, a process which no doubt reflects the climatic development during the Tertiary. In this respect the trend entirely parallels that of the marine Mollusca (Davies, 1934), and of the flora (Reid, 1935).

Up to and including the Miocene nearly half the endemic European element is constituted by subsequently extinct genera. After this period, however, their number rapidly decreases. Also this process probably should be considered against the background of the climatic development. In the Pliocene, the European land gastropod fauna has essentially its recent character; 87 per cent of the genera of this period still live in Europe. From the Pleistocene only recent genera are known, if the very doubtful record of *Archaeoxesta* in Germany is disregarded. This record may be due to redeposition from Tertiary strata.

To conclude, the European land gastropod fauna has kept less of its earlier

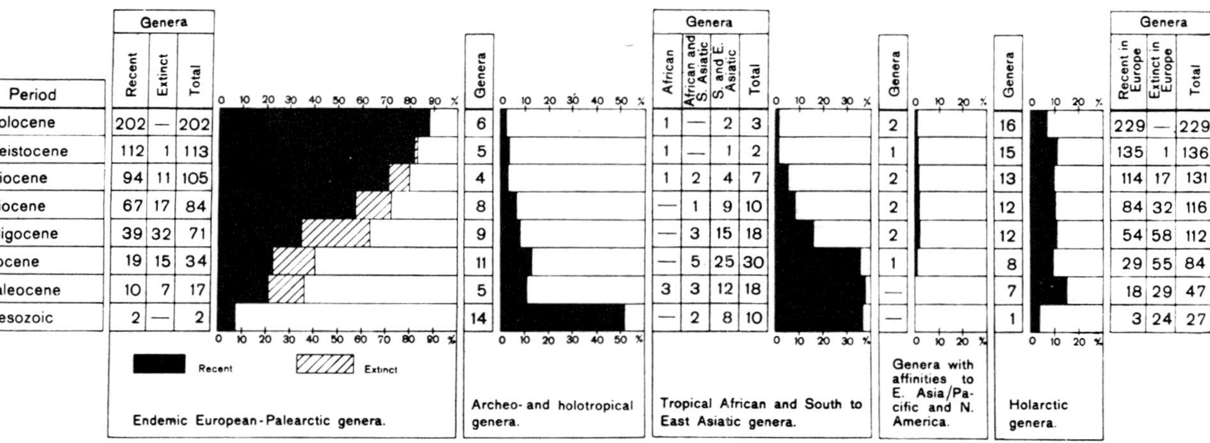

Period	Endemic European-Palearctic: Recent	Extinct	Total	Archeo- and holotropical: Genera	Tropical African etc.: African	African and S. Asiatic	S. and E. Asiatic	Total	Affinities to E. Asia/Pacific and N. America: Genera	Holarctic: Genera	Recent in Europe	Extinct in Europe	Total
Holocene	202	—	202	6	1	—	2	3	2	16	229	—	229
Pleistocene	112	1	113	5	1	—	1	2	1	15	135	1	136
Pliocene	94	11	105	4	1	2	4	7	2	13	114	17	131
Miocene	67	17	84	8	—	1	9	10	2	12	84	32	116
Oligocene	39	32	71	9	—	3	15	18	2	12	54	58	112
Eocene	19	15	34	11	—	5	25	30	1	8	29	55	84
Paleocene	10	7	17	5	3	3	12	18	—	7	18	29	47
Mesozoic	2	—	2	14	—	2	8	10	—	1	3	24	27

FIG. 2. The development of the European land gastropod fauna since late Mesozoic.

Compare the notes to Fig. 1 and Table 2.—*Catinella* (in the Pacific E. Asiatic-America group) here has been regarded as known from the Holocene only, but it has been reported from strata, which may possibly be of Interglacial age (Sparks, 1957).

character than has the North American. But in spite of this it is remarkably conservative in comparison with most other animal groups, known by fossil evidence, as well as with the vascular plants. Szafer (1954) stated that the Euro–Asiatic element in the Pliocene constituted only between 6 and 20 per cent of the flora in southern Poland. For the rest, now disappeared American and East Asiatic species dominated.

In Table 2 the extracontinental relations of the European land Gastropoda are elucidated. It may be emphasized that Transcaucasia and Macaronesia (the Azores, Madeira, and the Canary Islands) have been counted with Europe. In this connection it is worth mentioning that the Macaronesian

TABLE 2

Distribution type \ Number of genera	Extinct in Europe	Recent in Europe	Total
Holarctic	—	16	16
Archeo- or holotropical*	24	6	30
African–European	3	1	4
African and South Asiatic	9	—	9
South and East Asiatic†	42	2	44
Mainly North American and East Asiatic‡	1	2	3
Endemic European-Palearctic§	48	202	250

* Marine littoral genera, with their special dispersal ecology, play a certain role also in the European gastropod fauna. Among the Archeo- and Holotropical genera four extinct and four recent ones represent this group. The two recent, strictly terrestrial genera, here classified as Holotropical, *Cecilioides* and *Coilostele*, are discussed in the text.

† The South and East Asiatic group includes nine marine littoral genera, all extinct in Europe.

‡ Concerning the heterogenous group of North American–East Asiatic genera (*Gastrocopta*, *Strobilops* and *Catinella*), cf. second note to Table 1, and the text.

§ Among the recent European–Palearctic genera, 124 are exclusively European, the remaining ones occurring also in NW. Africa and/or the Orient, in a few instances also with adjoining areas in tropical Africa. Six genera have a more or less wide distribution also in temperate Asia. The two genera reaching North America, *Limax* and *Cepaea*, are discussed in the text.

Cf. also the caption to Fig. 1.

gastropod fauna, which is the taxonomically most independent and most isolated partial fauna of the region, is decidedly an offshoot of the early Tertiary Mediterranean and west European fauna. The affinities to other regions are very insignificant.

In a case where an entirely extinct genus shows clear taxonomical affinities to, for example, recent South Asiatic genera, it has been classified as South Asiatic, even if it has only been found in Europe.

Table 2, as well as Fig. 2, particularly well demonstrates the importance of the interchange in a southeastern direction. A long series of Tertiary European genera, or relatively closely related forms, today are met in South and even East Asia. To these is joined a more limited element, which occurs both in South Asia and in Africa, mainly in the eastern parts. From the point of view of principles it is of secondary importance whether the genera are European emigrants, or if they have spread from, for example, an Asiatic center of origin to Europe, and later become extinct there.

An exclusive African affinity, which does not seem possible to connect to the South Asiatic route of dispersal, is shown by very few genera only. Except for three Paleocene genera which, indeed, are rather difficult to delimit from the previously regarded Archeotropical element, only the recent genus *Lauria* belongs to this group. However, as this genus is comprised of small forms well adapted for passive dispersal, for instance, by birds, its distribution is not very significant. In fact, also some Paleo- or Holarctic genera, with similar qualifications for passive dispersal, have adjoining areas in Africa, mainly on high mountains. For one genus, *Truncatellina*, the African distribution is so extensive that an African origin is not excluded.

These conditions in terrestrial Gastropoda are quite compatible with modern conceptions regarding the pattern of evolution of tropical African biota (cf. Moreau, 1952), dominated by the long and efficient isolation.

However, in recent time the European land gastropod fauna is as completely isolated from the South and East Asiatic one as it has been from the African one throughout the Tertiary. The part of the Mediterranean fauna, which has its center in northwestern Africa, has scarcely more points in common with the tropical African one; its affinities are almost exclusively European.

For the Holarctic genera, which will be mentioned later, the dispersal over the Euro–Asiatic territory has been of fundamental importance. These too can be seen as an example of interchange between Europe and Asia, though in a more northerly latitude, and less influenced by climatical and geographical barriers during the Tertiary.

Disregarding the possibility that an interchange of Holarctic taxa has also taken place in the North Atlantic area (though, for several reasons, to a limited degree only), there are no traces whatever of any contributions to the European land gastropod fauna from North America. Likewise, in the opposite direction, there are no incontrovertible examples of dispersal, except the doubtful, and in every case late, instances of *Cepaea* and *Limax* which will be attended to further on.

However, a careful examination makes evident that for some taxa, which are common to the warmer parts of Europe and America, the possibility of a trans-Atlantic dispersal must be considered. But the nature of this dispersal seems enigmatic in the light of the facts that are known at present.

ON THE PRE-QUATERNARY WAYS OF DISPERSAL OF LAND GASTROPODA BETWEEN EUROPE AND NORTH AMERICA

For a correct understanding of the distributional history of the land Gastropoda their means of dispersal must be regarded. Small forms, especially when exposed, e.g. by climbing up into the vegetation, are subject in a considerable degree to passive dispersal, by birds and other higher animals, or even as aerial plankton. In all regions it is mainly the minute forms that exhibit wide distributions. This is pertinent on generic as well as specific levels.

Increasing size limits the chances of passive dispersal, and the animals mainly become dependent on their capacity to actively migrate. It might be superfluous to state that this is rather restricted for land snails. However, the ability to self-fertilize must essentially favor dispersal. Large species may easily be transported passively when juvenile, but if capable of self-fertilization a single specimen can be the origin of a new population. It is known that different species behave differently in this connection, but unfortunately the knowledge is too limited yet to allow a broad application to zoogeographical relationships.

Hydrochorous dispersal, e.g. by drifts, is of great importance in the case of fresh water. But for transport over the oceans it can almost be discounted, partly because of the marked sensibility to NaCl-exposure of most land Gastropoda, partly due to their specialized ecological requirements. The great majority of species definitely avoid sea-shore habitats. Also when the transport (for instance under the bark of a floating log, cf. Kew 1893), may have been successful, the chance of reaching a proper habitat is very low.

The marine littoral species constitute exceptions. As a consequence of the possibilities of dispersal which thus are opened for them, they often are very widely distributed. Being irrelevant to the present subject they will be disregarded here.

All stages between excellent fitness for passive dispersal and an almost absolute dependence upon their own active migration are met among the land Gastropoda.

The Bering Strait route without a doubt has played an important role in the dispersal of land gastropods. Certainly it has been of essential importance for the development of the Holarctic element. The Holarctic genera, 16 in all, are presented in Table 3, with data for their earliest occurrence in European and North American strata respectively.

For at least 12 genera earlier, often considerably earlier, records are present from Europe. It seems justified to assume a preponderantly Palearctic origin for the recent Holarctic element. Also, the indication that already in the Paleocene those genera reached their relative maximum (15 per cent) in the European gastropod fauna, whereas their North American relative maximum (30 per cent) was reached as late as in the Pleistocene, points in the same direction.

Most of the Holarctic genera are characterized by their considerable age; thus in Europe they belong to the oldest persisting element in the gastropod fauna. With some generalization, the hypothetical nature of which may be admitted, the recent Holarctic element can be regarded as a relic Mesozoic to early Tertiary gastropod fauna of northern latitudes. It is probably not accidental that this gastropod element is more or less associated with the plants which characterized the corresponding Arcto–Tertiary flora.

The species which belong to the Holarctic gastropod genera are largely well adapted for passive dispersal. Besides favoring extensive distribution, this

TABLE 3

Genus	Earliest European record	Earliest North American record
Carychium	Jurassic	Pliocene
Cochlicopa	Paleocene	Pleistocene
Columella	Pliocene	Pleistocene
Vertigo	Paleocene	Eocene
Pupilla	Oligocene	Pliocene
Vallonia	Paleocene	Miocene
*Zoogenetes**	—	—
Succinea	Paleocene?	Pliocene
Oxyloma	Eocene?	Pleistocene
Punctum	Oligocene	Pleistocene
Discus	Paleocene?	Eocene, possibly Cretaceous
Vitrina	Oligocene	Pleistocene
Zonitoides	Oligocene	Pliocene
Nesovitrea	Pleistocene	Pliocene
Deroceras	Pleistocene	Pliocene
Euconulus	Paleocene	Pleistocene

* The absence of fossil records of *Zoogenetes* must be seen against the background that its shells, owing to shortage of lime, are not suited for fossilification.

must have counteracted genetic isolation and thereby taxonomical differentiation. Fischer (1960) has argued that the repeated interruption of biotic evolution by climatic disasters in the Circumpolar region tends to keep the biota on an immature, relic level. In fact, this fits very well to the ancient nature of the Holarctic Gastropoda, at the same time as it must be intimately linked with their fitness for passive dispersal, which apparently must be of selective value in regions of violently fluctuating physical conditions.

The recent distribution of Holarctic gastropod taxa must have reached its pattern to such a great extent during the Quaternary that it hardly gives any indications for, or against, a Tertiary dispersal across the North Atlantic. Reasonably, however, the presence of passive dispersal, a characteristic of the group, may have played a role also in the Tertiary.

But it is quite evident that no interchange of the endemic European and North American elements in the North Atlantic region took place during the Tertiary. The profound character of the endemism is elucidated by the fact that it is almost total, also on the family level. Besides the Holarctic group (and the doubtful cases of *Limax* and *Cepaea*) none of the families, which dominate on the respective sides of the North Atlantic are represented on both. As already mentioned this separation has existed throughout the Tertiary; indeed, the initial differences in the late Mesozoic seem to have been even more profound. The few common features which exist, besides the Holarctic group, refer to a more heat-requiring element, for which dispersal via more lengthy routes must be considered.

On the Pacific side, on the contrary, common features are more manifest. For a number of important families there are clear affinities to Australia and tropical East Asia; these, however, fall beyond the present scope. Pertinent in connection with a probable North Pacific dispersal is a group of five genera (cf. the Notes to Table 1), one of which is now extinct. To be correct, the relationship is not very close. The forms on the two sides of the Pacific are placed in different subgenera, or even genera. This indicates that the time for the interchange must be remote, probably in the Early Tertiary. The genera in question belong to the warm–temperate to Subtropical element, and the later apparent checking of the interchange via the Bering Strait bridge certainly must be seen in connection with the Tertiary climatic development. In the Middle and Late Tertiary the climate in the Bering Strait area apparently was too cold to allow passage for other than cold-adapted, or generally hardy animals. This has been very clearly demonstrated for mammals by Simpson (1940).

In relation to the total endemic land Gastropoda, in North America as well as in East Asia, this "Amphi-Pacifi" (in fact the recent occurrence of some of the genera is remote from the Pacific coast) element constitutes an inconsiderable fraction only.

More doubtful is the evidence given by certain other genera which occur in North America and East Asia, though not exclusively. *Strobilops*, which appears in the North American Pliocene, already existed in Europe in the Eocene, though it became extinct there in the Pliocene. Pilsbry (1948, p. 853) suggests an Asiatic center of origin for this genus, from which it has radiated on the one hand to Europe, on the other to East Asia and via the Bering Strait bridge to North America. However, a careful consideration shows that two of the American subgenera occurred also in the European Tertiary, whereas the genus in East Asia is represented by subgenera which do not live in America. Instead, also one of the East Asiatic subgenera is known from the European Tertiary. As a consequence, the reasons for a North Pacific dispersal of *Strobilops* scarcely are convincing, whereas it seems difficult to reject the possibility of a trans-Atlantic dispersal within the warm latitudes, the more so since the subgenera in question occur also in South and Central America. The alternative of a North Atlantic dispersal is certainly out of the question for the essentially warm–temperate to tropical genus *Strobilops*.

A similar distributional pattern and history is also shown by the richly differentiated, preponderantly tropical genus *Gastrocopta* as well as by *Pupoides* whose origin, however, may be American. There are no indications that the latter genus has ever lived in Europe.

Some further genera, which may be characterized as chiefly Pantropical, have a distribution which is difficult to understand without assuming a trans-Atlantic dispersal. As an example, the subterranean-dwelling *Cecilioides* may be mentioned. It is represented by different subgenera in Europe and America, the European one having advanced as far north as the southern Baltic.

However, it must be admitted that all these genera, by their very extensive distribution and their good qualifications for passive dispersal, show rather vague indications of faunal history. Stronger evidence for trans-Atlantic dispersal is given by the American genera *Gastrodonta* and *Euglandina*. The former genus shows affinities to *Janulus* of Madeira and the Canary Islands, which was widely distributed in Europe during the Tertiary. *Euglandina*, along with several tropical American genera, is related to *Poiretia* in the Mediterranean territory. These genera suggest a trans-Atlantic dispersal, but it must have been remote, perhaps in the Mesozoic.

To conclude, there are no facts which unambiguously indicate that the southern element in the land gastropod fauna, which Europe and North America have in common, has followed the North Pacific route. The alternative, a trans-Atlantic dispersal within the warm latitudes is, on the contrary, difficult to reject. But the nature of this dispersal yet seems enigmatic.

The evidence is too scattered to support assumptions of any kind of land bridge. Rather it points to factors facilitating the passive dispersal, e.g., by the presence of interjacent islands. The idea that the Macaronesian archipelago once offered a connecting link can be rejected. When regarding their gastropod fauna it appears to be, as already emphasized, a decided derivative of the Early Tertiary Mediterranean and west European fauna. Probably this has a bearing on the occurrence of *Janulus* too.

The arguments for a connection between tropical Africa and South America, which have been brought forward, can be ignored here. They have no bearing on the actual problem, because the European land gastropod fauna always has been so profoundly isolated from the tropical African one. Besides, South America has relatively few groups in common with Africa, its main affinities being Australian and East Asiatic.

However, these problems will not be discussed further here, as they refer to a faunal element of only peripheral importance in connection with the North Atlantic biota. It has seemed justified to draw attention to them because otherwise there would be the danger of overstressing the importance of the

North Pacific route. The indications given by the land Gastropoda may be kept in mind when discussing other animal groups for which one must depend largely on the recent distribution, in the absence of fossil evidence.

Finally, two further genera, *Catinella* and *Coilostele*, are common to Europe and America. Both have a phylogenetically ancient character. *Catinella* has a Pacific center and is represented by different subgenera in North America and northwestern Europe respectively. *Coilostele* occurs within a series of seemingly isolated areas from southernmost Spain to Timor; in addition there is, according to Pilsbry (1948, p. 1051), a quite isolated occurrence in Mexico.

The distribution of these genera exhibits a pattern so decidedly relic that it seems hardly possible to discuss them in connection with any specific alternative of dispersal.

THE RECENT RELATIONS OF THE LAND GASTROPOD FAUNA IN THE NORTH ATLANTIC REGION

From Figs. 1 and 2 it is obvious that the Pleistocene caused no major changes in the composition of the gastropod fauna, neither in North America, nor in Europe. There occurred no mass extinction of species or radical dislocations of the gastropod faunas during the Glacials. Evidently the local Tertiary faunas largely survived within, or in relative proximity of the recent areas. The idea of radical changes in the distribution of the biotas during the Pleistocene, advocated especially by Deevey (1949), has a very moderate bearing for the terrestrial Gastropoda. However, in the North Atlantic region, in a narrow sense, their distributional pattern has been formed in the Quaternary, perhaps throughout in the Post-glacial time.

Figure 3 illustrates the distribution of the gastropod species in the area. Excluded from the material are all settlements due to anthropochorous dispersal. Sometimes the origin is difficult to determine, and in such instances the occurrence within the territory in question has been indicated by hatching. The diagram is based on information given by Brooks and Brooks (1940), Ellis (1951), Forcart (1955), Lohmander (1938), Mandahl-Barth (1938), Oekland (1925), and Pilsbry (1939–48), in addition to which unpublished material in Scandinavian and American museums has been considered.

The material has been divided into four categories, viz. endemic European, endemic American, and Holarctic species, plus representatives of the Holarctic form complexes, which seem to be specifically distinct on the two sides of the Atlantic. It may be admitted that our present knowledge does not always allow us to draw a sharp border between the last two categories. Furthermore, the question as to whether the genetic connection is continuous within the Euro–Siberian territory is left open. Endemic representatives for Holarctic genera are assigned to the European and the American groups respectively.

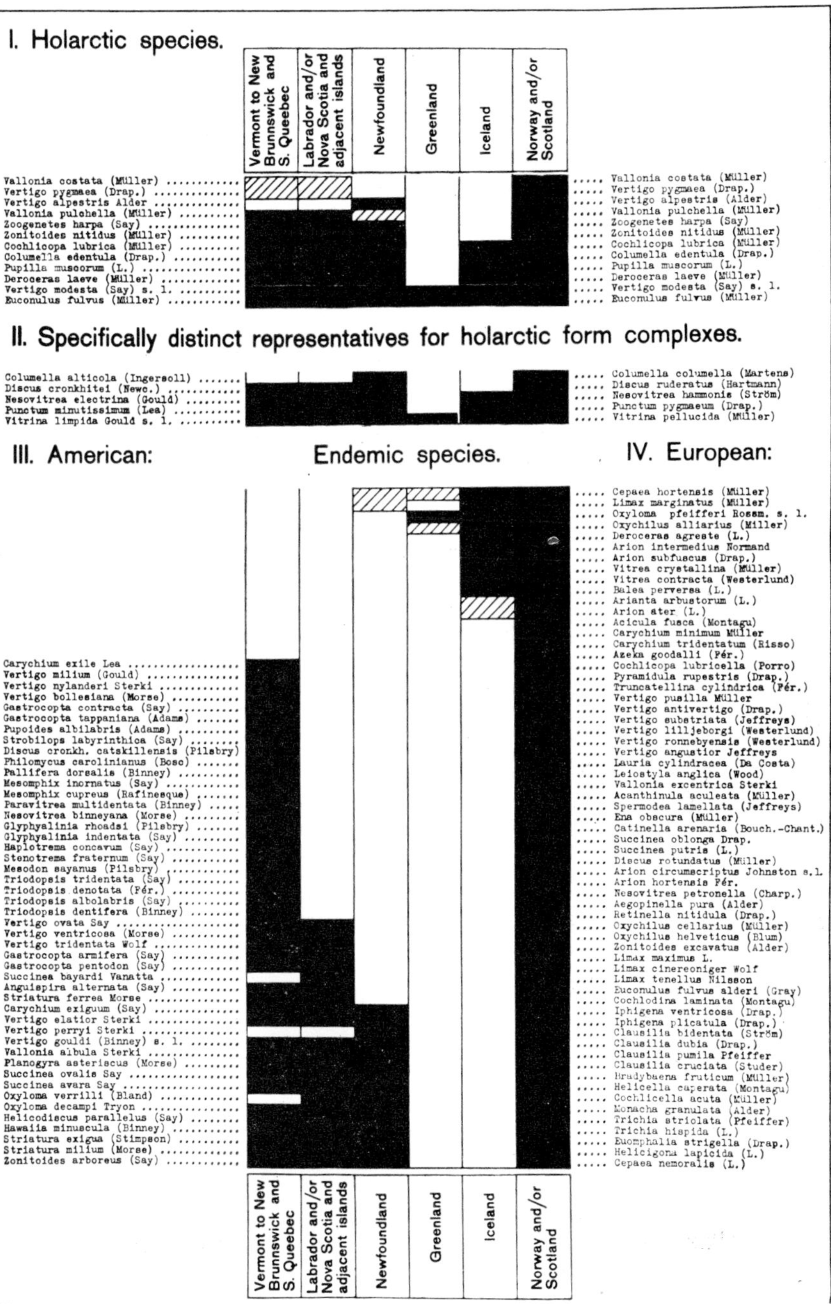

FIG. 3. Terrestrial gastropod species in the North Atlantic region.

Detailed comment on the diagram might be unnecessary. The extensive negative faunal character of Greenland is conspicuous. Obviously this is the consequence of combined climatic and dispersal obstacles. In principle the categories of land Gastropoda show a similar reaction, but most strikingly in the climatically more pretentious endemic groups.

On the American side the Davis Strait forms a nearly absolute barrier. Numerically the decrease in species from Scotland and Norway to Iceland is as striking, but relatively it is less well marked. Then, among the Icelandic species only a minor fraction has spread to Greenland. Among these, two (*Cepaea hortensis* and *Oxychilus alliarius*) have been regarded by modern authors as probably introduced to Greenland.

All definitely indigenous species in Iceland and Greenland must be regarded as well adapted for passive dispersal. For two species in Iceland, *Arion ater* and *Arianta arbustorum*, a spontaneous passive dispersal seems improbable. However, Lohmander (1938), the author who has most thoroughly penetrated the problem of Iceland's gastropod fauna, is of the opinion that for these very species anthropochorous dispersal in historical time is a probable alternative. A random, passive dispersal is also indicated by the absence of certain species, which, as Lohmander assumes, are well able to endure Icelandic conditions. For the idea of a Pleistocene landbridge to Iceland, and subsequent refugia, the land Gastropoda offer no positive evidence. The nearest known periglacial deposit of non-marine Mollusca is that of Lea Valley, England (Kennard and Woodward, 1912), the age of which has recently been dated to 28,000 ± 1500 years, or early main Würm (Godwin and Willis, 1960). It represents a poor fauna, but some of the species are definitely not Arctic (*Pupilla muscorum*, various *Succinea* species, also some of the freshwater forms). If existing, an Icelandic refugial fauna most probably would have been still more depauperated. The presence of some remarkably demanding forms (the *Vitrea* species, and *Arion intermedius*) suggests that the Postglacial Hypsithermal was of outstanding importance for the establishment of the gastropod fauna in Iceland.

Against this general background concerning the distribution of land Gastropoda in the North Atlantic region, the presence of the European *Cepaea hortensis* and *Limax marginatus* in northeastern North America is very puzzling. American authors especially have been inclined to regard them as indigenous. *L. marginatus* seems to be limited to a very narrow strip in Newfoundland, whereas *C. hortensis* has a rather extensive and relatively continuous distribution from Newfoundland to New England. The conclusive arguments have been concentrated in the discussion on the latter species.

The opinion that *C. hortensis* has an indigenous distribution in America in based upon observations by different workers who have studied its occurrence in natural habitats and pointed out that this species, contrary to definitely anthropochorous species, seems to have a continuous, "mature" distribution; to some extent this conclusion is also based on subfossil records (cf. Pilsbry, 1939, p. 8, and references given by him). Lindroth (1957, p. 234, etc.), however, finds the evidence weak and incomplete and suggests an entirely anthropochorous origin. A supposed Pleistocene fossil thus may equally well be of 19th century origin.

There is no doubt that part of the population is of a recent anthropochorous nature. On the other hand, radiocarbon dating shows that the species is definitely of pre-Columbian age in Nova Scotia (Clarke and Erskine, 1961: 700 ± 225 years; later dating 600 ± 45 years B. P., according to a personal communication by Clarke). This may be thought to speak in favor of the old idea of dispersal by aid of the Vikings. That idea, however, is nothing more than an entirely unproven hypothesis and, furthermore, there exists no positive evidence that the Vikings ever visited Nova Scotia. The actual shells of *C. hortensis* were found in the camps of the Micmac Indians. When these matters are considered the statement of their pre-Columbian age evidently is in favor of an old, indigenous occurrence.

With regard to the possibility of passive dispersal, an indigenous American occurrence is not definitely excluded. It is not difficult to raise various hypotheses, regarding the recent area as relic, due to dispersal via Greenland–Labrador during a Post-glacial period, or even an Interglacial one. But owing to lack of really conclusive evidence it is very unproductive. The only way to solve the problem of *C. hortensis*—which would be of certain interest owing to its crucial significance—is new, careful field research, by which special regard must be given to the existing rich experience of the ecological occurrence of *C. hortensis* in Europe.

For land gastropods a solution of problems of this kind evidently is attainable. Owing to the slow rate of establishment, also when highly favored by passive dispersal, introduced gastropods very long maintain an immature pattern of distribution. Practically always, it seems possible to give a definite answer to the question whether or not a species is introduced into an area, if only its distribution on an ecological basis has been accurately clarified.

A field survey would result in a more correct picture)of several further species (*Vallonia pulchella* and *costata*, *Vertigo pygmaea* and *alpestris*, also the above-mentioned *Limax marginatus*) whose faunistic state in northeastern America is yet obscure. Of course, the distribution and history of the endemic American gastropod fauna would also be elucidated.

Surprisingly, the interchange of endemic gastropod species in the North Pacific territories seems to be very limited. The American *Zonitoides arboreus* and *Hawaiia minuscula*, according to Licharev and Rammelmeyer (1952), have an inconsiderable spontaneous distribution in the Far East. The preponderantly Siberian *Succinea strigata* reaches Arctic North America.* It is not

* Pilsbry (1948, p. 811) cites *S. strigata* from Igaliko Fjord, Greenland. However, the actual sample, by revision, has proved to belong to *Succinea pfeifferi* subsp. *groenlandica*.

excluded that forthcoming faunistic and taxonomical research will unveil some further examples within the Holarctic genera, but it will scarcely change much in the picture. The favorable situation for dispersal, due to the narrow separation of the land masses and the late direct connection, apparently has been of limited importance for the Gastropoda when the ecological conditions, mainly climatic, are preventive. Obviously this has a bearing on the situation in the North Atlantic region too.

It must be admitted that the discussion which can be carried out from present knowledge concerning the land Gastropoda within the Arctic and northerly Boreal realm is of rather general character. Few positive conclusions are possible. The key to several problems, which also concern the North Atlantic region, may lie within the immense territories in northern Asia and North America from which extremely little is known about the land Gastropoda (as well as most other animal groups). Data are needed equally concerning distributional patterns, taxonomy on $\pm$ species level, and fossil occurrence. The fact that the Pleistocene refugia, most firmly supported by geological evidence, existed in the Bering Strait region may be especially considered in this connection. Also, for an understanding of prospective North Atlantic refugia, data from those of the Pacific may be beneficial.

It is a matter of course that the detailed field research on the first hand must be concentrated on geographical sectors and habitats which are thought to be especially profitable, as well as on species of outstanding significance. But such research can attain its full value only against the background of a fairly homogeneous knowledge about the whole territory, also including the extensive "less interesting" areas. Strictly speaking, no area in which biota exist is uninteresting to the biologist. It depends upon the problem to which the approach refers.

With the resources of transport available today there are scarcely any technical obstacles to bringing forth an acceptably homogeneous fund of data from the Arctic and northernmost Boreal regions. Thereby it would be possible to adjust a good deal of the obvious imbalance in recent discussions of zoogeography and faunal history.

REFERENCES

BAKER, F. C. (1920). The life of the Pleistocene or Glacial period. *Bull. Univ. Ill.* **17**, 41, 1–476.

BROOKS, S. T. and BROOKS, B. W. (1940). Geographical distribution of the recent Mollusca of Newfoundland. *Ann. Carneg. Mus.* **28**, 53, 53–75.

CLARKE, A. H., and ERSKINE, J. S. (1961). Pre-Columbian *Littorina littorea* in Nova Scotia. *Science* **134**, 393–394.

DARLINGTON, P. J., JR. (1957). *Zoogeography: the geographical distribution of animals.* New York.

DAVIES, A. M. (1934). *Tertiary Faunas.* Vol. II. Guildford.

DEEVEY, E. S., Jr. (1949). Biogeography of the Pleistocene. I. *Bull. Geol. Soc. Amer.* **60**, 9, 1315–1416.

EHRMANN, P. (1914). *Grundzüge einer Entwicklunsgeschichte der Tierwelt Deutschlands.* Lit.-Gesellsch. Neue Bahnen. Leipzig.
ELLIS, A. E. (1951). Census of the distribution of British non-marine Mollusca. *J. Conch.* **23**, 6–7, 171–244.
FISCHER, A. G. (1960). Latitudinal variation in organic diversity. *Evolution* **14**, 1, 64–81.
FORCART, L. (1955). Die nordischen Arten der Gattung *Vitrina. Arch. Molluskenk.* **84**, 4–6, 155–166.
GODWIN, H., and WILLIS, E. H. (1960). Cambridge University natural radiocarbon measurements II. *Amer. J. Sc., Radiocarbon Suppl.* **2**, 62–72.
HENDERSON, J. (1931). Molluscan provinces in the western United States. *Univ. Colo. Stud.* **18**, 4, 177–186.
HENDERSON, J. (1935). Fossil non-marine Mollusca of North America. *Spec. Pap. Geol. Soc. Amer.* 3. Baltimore.
HIBBARD, C. W., and TAYLOR, D. W. (1960). Two late Pleistocene faunas from Southwestern Kansas. *Contrib. Mus. Geol. Univ. Mich.* **16**, 1, 1–223.
HOPPE, G. (1959). Några kritiska kommentarer till diskussionen om isfria refugier. *Stat. Naturvet. Forskningsråds Årsbok.* **12**, 123–134.
HUBENDICK, B. (1953). The relationships of the East African *Vitrinae* with notes on the taxonomy of *Vitrina. Ark. Zool.* Ser. 2, **6**, 51, 83–96.
KENNARD, A. S., and WOODWARD, B. B. (1912). Appendix III.—The Mollusca. In: WARREN, S. H.: On a Late Glacial stage in the valley of the River Lea, subsequent to the epoch of River-Drift Man. *Quart. J. Geol. Soc. London.* **68**, 2, 234–240.
KEW, H. W. (1893). *The dispersal of shells.* Internat. Scient. Ser. **75**. London.
Vidensk. Akad. I. Mat.-Naturv. Kl. 8.
LICHAREV, I. M., and RAMMELMEYER, E. S. (1952). *Nazemnyje Molljuski Fauny SSSR.* Acad. Scient. SSSR. 43. Leningrad.
LINDROTH, C. H. (1957). *The Faunal Connections between Europe and North America.* Uppsala.
LOHMANDER, H. (1938). Landmollusken aus Island gesammelt von Dr. Carl H. Lindroth (1929). *Göteborg Vetensk-Samh. Handl.* Ser. B. **6**, 2, 3–52.
MANDAHL-BARTH, G. (1938). Land and freshwater Mollusca. *The Zoology of Iceland* **4**, 651, 1–31.
MOREAU, R. E. (1952). Africa since the Mesozoic: with particular reference to certain biological problems. *Proc. Zool. Soc.* **121**, 869–913.
OEKLAND, F. (1925). Die Verbreitung der Landgastropoden Norwegens. *Skr. Norske Vidensk-Akad. I. Mat. Naturv Kl.* 8.
PILSBRY, H. A. (1939–48). Land Mollusca of North America (north of Mexico). *Acad. Nat. Sci Monogr.* **3**, I–II. Philadelphia.
QUICK, H. E. (1952). Emigrant British snails. *Proc. Malac. Soc.* **29**, 5, 181–189.
REID, E. M. (1935). British Floras Antecedent to the Great Ice Age. In: Discussion on the Origin and relationship of the British Flora. *Proc. Roy. Soc. London.* Ser. B. 118, 808, 197–202.
SIMPSON, G. G. (1940). Holarctic Mammalian faunas and continental relationships during the Cenozoic. *Bull. Geol. Soc. Amer.* **58**, 7, 613–688.
SPARKS, B. W. (1957). The Tale Gravel near Thriplow, Cambridgeshire. *Geol. Mag.* **94**, 3, 194–200.
SZAFER, W. (1954). Pliocene flora from the vicinity of Czorstyn (West Carpathians) and its relationship to the Pleistocene. *Prace Inst. Geol.* **11**, 1–238.
TAYLOR, D. W. (1954). Nonmarine Mollusks from the Upper Miocene Barstow Formation, California. *Prof. Pap. U.S. Geol. Surv.* No. 254-C. Washington.
WALDÉN, H. W. (1961). On the variation, nomenclature, distribution and taxonomical position of *Limax (Lehmannia) valentianus* Férussac (Gastropoda, Pulmonata). *Ark. Zool.* Ser. 2, **15**, 3, 71–95.
WENZ, W. (1961–2). Gastropoda. Teil 1, Allgemeiner Teil/Prosobranchia. *Handbuch der Paläozoologie* **6**, 1. 2nd edition. Berlin.
WENZ, W., and ZILCH, A. (1959–60) Gastropoda. Teil 2, Euthyneura. *Ibid.* **6**, 2.

PLANT MIGRATIONS ACROSS THE NORTH ATLANTIC OCEAN AND THEIR IMPORTANCE FOR THE PALEOGEOGRAPHY OF THE REGION

EILIF DAHL

Department of Botany, Agricultural College, Vollebekk, Norway

IT IS a striking fact that the Arctic–Alpine floras on both sides of the North Atlantic Ocean are very similar while this similarity does not extend to more Temperate floras. A Scandinavian botanist feels quite at home in south Greenland, whereas a French botanist working in areas of eastern America with a climate corresponding to his homeland probably would recognize most of the native genera but a few of the indigenous species.

Many Arctic–Sub-Arctic species grow on both shores of the North Atlantic Ocean, some being confined to that area while others have large gaps in their distribution in Siberia or in western America. Such plants are said to have an Amphi-Atlantic distribution pattern which has recently been beautifully mapped by Hultén (1958).

From Scandinavia to Scotland, the Faeroes, Iceland, east Greenland, west Greenland, and into Canada, there seems to be a gradual transition from a predominantly European flora in the east to a predominantly American flora in the west. There are also very close phytogeographic connections between Spitsbergen and northeast Greenland. This presents a problem since it suggests that a direct migration has taken place. But the area is split apart by long stretches of water and it is commonly supposed that migration of plants and animals does not easily take place across large sea areas. This problem has been discussed by numerous workers; from earlier times might be mentioned Hooker, Darwin, Warming, Nathorst, Blytt, and Ostenfeld and more recently Fernald, Lynge, Nordhagen, Hultén, Nannfeldt, Böcher, and Löve and Löve. Lindroth (1957) has recently treated the zoological and also some botanical aspects of the problem in a very inspiring manner.

TRANSPORT OF PLANTS BY MAN ACROSS THE ATLANTIC OCEAN

Many plants and animals have been carried across oceans by human traffic. Distribution patterns resulting from this transport should be excluded from consideration in discussing the old phytogeographic connections between

Europe and America. This brings up the question of how to discriminate between native and introduced plants.

This is not a serious question as far as recent dispersal is concerned where often, if not the actual introduction, the subsequent phase of dispersal in the new country has been observed. It is much more difficult if the introduction took place long before any systematic botanical investigations were carried out.

In general more species seem to have been spread from the east towards the west than vice versa and the problem is not very difficult as far as American species introduced to Europe is concerned.

The question of the impact on the flora of the Norse colonists in Greenland and Iceland has been discussed by many authors. Ostenfeld (1926) believed that as much as 14 per cent of the Greenland flora had been introduced this way whereas Porsild (1932) thinks this figure too high, probably not more than 5 per cent. Modern intensive studies in the infra-specific races throw light on these questions since among the anthropochorous species (species following human occupation) some races may be anthropochorous and others not. Also palynological research is of help; e.g. *Angelica archangelica* which has been suspected of being introduced to Greenland by Norse colonists has been identified in pollen deposits considerably older than the Norse colonization (Iversen, 1953). But still, several doubtful cases are known. I have here accepted the evaluation given by Böcher, Holmen and Jakobsen (1957) regarding Greenland, and Löve and Löve (1956) regarding Iceland.

In Newfoundland and adjacent areas a peculiar isolated European element of plants occurs which Fernald (1929) considered a relict, indigenous element. However, Lindroth (1957) has pointed out that many of the species were probably introduced during the period of fishing as early as in the sixteenth century by British, French, and Iberian fishing boats carrying ballast westwards and throwing it ashore and bringing fish back. For this reason, all plants apparently native only in the Newfoundland–Nova Scotia area in America, but common somewhere along the coast from south England to Portugal and taxonomically indistinguishable from the European populations, have been considered here as introduced by man during the early fishing period. This makes a list of about 60 taxa (species and taxonomic entities of a lower rank than species) to be excluded from the number of possible Amphi-Atlantic plants.

THE WESTERN AMPHI-ATLANTIC ELEMENT IN EUROPE AND THE EASTERN AMPHI-ATLANTIC ELEMENT IN AMERICA

A western Amphi-Atlantic element in the flora of Europe can be recognized, consisting of taxa found in eastern America and not occurring east of the River Lena, the Carpathians and the Balkans in the Old World. Altogether 83

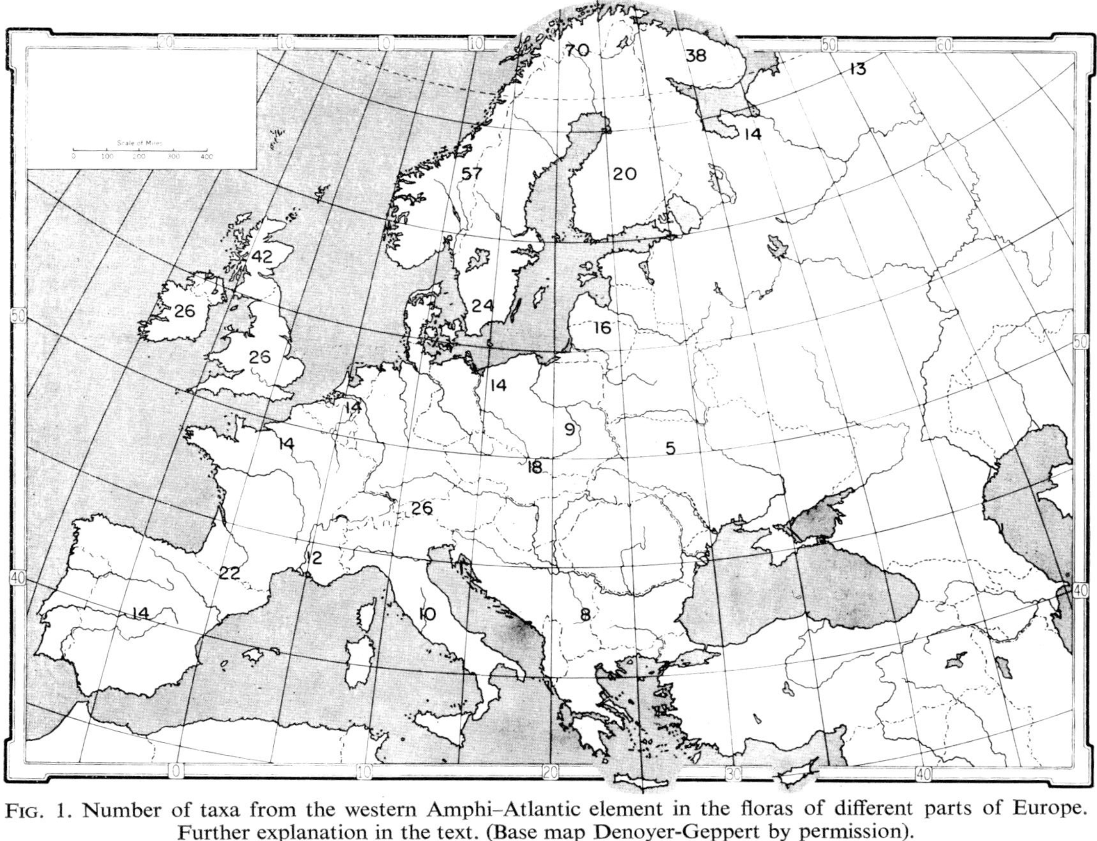

FIG. 1. Number of taxa from the western Amphi–Atlantic element in the floras of different parts of Europe. Further explanation in the text. (Base map Denoyer-Geppert by permission).

taxa belong here and Fig. 1 gives the number of taxa in this element in the different parts of Europe. The highest number is found in north and central Scandinavia, a fair number also in Scotland, whereas the number decreases eastwards and southwards, in the south they are mainly confined to the mountains.

Within the western Amphi-Atlantic element sub-elements with more restricted distribution can be discerned. Four taxa grow only in Spitsbergen east of the Atlantic Ocean. Another sub-element grows in Scandinavia, a few species of it also in Novaya Zemlya and Scotland, but it does not reach Ural or the Alps. This element has been called "West Arctic" by Blytt (1876) and 34 taxa belong to it. Finally there are five species restricted to the British Isles east of the Atlantic Ocean.

Corresponding to the western Amphi-Atlantic element in Europe, there is an eastern Amphi-Atlantic element in America. Its species are native in Europe and also in eastern America, but not farther west than the Great Plains and a line east of the Rocky Mountains from the Great Plains to the mouth of the Mackenzie River. Figure 2 gives the number of members belonging to this element in America. It will be seen that the highest number is found in south Greenland with a fair number also in Newfoundland, and that the number drops westwards and southwards. The number is also relatively low farther north, but this is not pronounced if the element is taken as a percentage of the native flora.

Within the eastern Amphi-Atlantic element in America sub-elements with more restricted distribution can be recognized. Eight taxa are confined to northeast Greenland on the west side of the Atlantic Ocean and an additional 30 taxa do not reach farther west than Greenland. Twelve taxa have a very restricted distribution along the Atlantic seaboard. The three sub-elements mentioned form an American counterpart of the West Arctic element in Europe (see Lindroth, 1957, p. 237). Around the Gulf of St. Lawrence and in Newfoundland a European element of five taxa form a counterpart to the American element in the British Isles.

From the data given it will be evident that the Amphi-Atlantic element essentially is Arctic–Sub-Arctic in character and very few plants from the temperate regions exhibit an Amphi-Atlantic distribution pattern.

THE LONG-DISTANCE DISPERSAL HYPOTHESIS

Different hypotheses may be invoked to explain the present-day distribution patterns of the Amphi-Atlantic plants. One main hypothesis suggests that the Amphi-Atlantic species once migrated across the North Atlantic Ocean, either by long-distance dispersal or across a former land connection between America and Europe. The other main hypothesis suggests that they once migrated across the Bering Strait between Asia and America and subsequently died out in areas other than those which they now occupy. The long-distance dispersal hypothesis will be considered first.

Plants can be spread over long distances in different ways. Anemochorous species are carried by wind and have very light and small seeds or spores (less than 0.2 mm) or have wings or hairs attached to seeds or fruits which

FIG. 2. Number of taxa from the eastern Amphi-Atlantic element in the floras of different parts of America. Further explanation in the text. (Base map Denoyer-Geppert, by permission).

reduce the settling velocity in air. Zoochorous species are transported by animals and have fruits or seeds with either edible, fleshy parts or hooks which attach them to animals passing by. Or, they may be spread by sea currents; it is then important that the seeds or fruits float well in sea water. Unfortunately, not enough data are available for classifying all the plants concerned according to buoyancy of seeds and fruits. But it seems evident that halophilous plants growing on the sea shores in haline environment would have a particular advantage of dispersal in this way since the fruits or seeds would tend to land in an environment favorable for further growth and reproduction.

Lastly, I have considered limnic species growing in fresh water as adapted to long-distance dispersal since there is some evidence that such plants are easily spread by water birds.

If the Amphi-Atlantic plants attained their present area by long-distance dispersal one would expect plants with adaptations to long-distance dispersal to be more numerous within the Amphi-Atlantic elements as compared to other elements which presumably immigrated across more or less continuous land connections. Table 1 gives a breakdown of the Scandinavian Arctic–Alpine flora according to adaptations to distance long-dispersal and phytogeographic elements. A two-way grouping is obtained, a so-called contingency

TABLE 1

COMPARISON OF THE ARCTIC–ALPINE ELEMENTS IN THE FLORA OF FENNO-SCANDIA AS TO PHYTOGEOGRAPHIC ELEMENTS AND ADAPTATIONS TO LONG-DISTANCE DISPERSAL

Taraxacum and *Hieracium* excluded from the enumerations.
[Upper figure = observed, lower figure (in brackets) = statistically expected number of species per element.]

	No adaptations to long-distance dispersal	Anemochorous species	Zoochorous species	Limnic species	Halophilous species	Total
West Arctic species	24 (20.6)	3 (6.6)	0 (0.6)	0 (0.2)	2 (1.0)	29 11.6%
Other western Amphi-Atlantic species	20 (17.7)	4 (5.7)	0 (0.5)	0 (0.2)	1 (0.9)	25 10.0%
Other elements	134 (139.7)	50 (44.7)	5 (3.8)	2 (1.6)	6 (7.0)	197 78.4%
Total	178 70.0%	57 22.7%	5 2.0%	2 0.8%	9 3.6%	251 100%

table, and by standard methods it can be tested whether there is any correlation or contingency between the subdivision in phytogeographic elements and dispersal groups. The figures expected under assumption of no correlation or contingency are given in brackets.

In general the numbers observed agree quite well with those expected, assuming that no contingency and no statistically significant discrepancies occur. There is a slight under-representation of types adapted to long-distance dispersal in the western Amphi-Atlantic element and this observation can be used as an argument against the hypothesis that they immigrated by long-distance dispersal.

Table 2 gives a similar break-down of the flora of Iceland. In the Amphi-Atlantic group are included species belonging either to the western Amphi-Atlantic element in Europe or the eastern Amphi-Atlantic element in America. Some European species reach their westernmost and some American species their easternmost limit in Iceland.

TABLE 2

COMPARISON OF THE DIFFERENT ELEMENTS IN THE FLORA OF ICELAND (BASED ON LÖVE, 1945; LÖVE AND LÖVE, 1956) AS TO ADAPTATIONS TO LONG-DISTANCE DISPERSAL.

Taraxacum and *Hieracium* excluded from the enumerations.

[Upper figure = observed, lower figure (in brackets) = statistically expected number of species per element.]

	No adaptations to long-distance dispersal	Anemochorous species	Zoochorous species	Limnic species	Halophilous species	Total
Amphi-Atlantic species	62 (51.0)	10 (15.5)	1 (3.8)	4 (6.4)	6 (6.4)	83 19.9%
European species	76 (68.2)	17 (20.7)	9 (5.0)	5 (8.5)	4 (8.5)	111 26.6%
American species	3 (5.5)	3 (1.7)	0 (0.4)	0 (0.7)	3 (0.7)	9 2.2%
Other species	116 (132.1)	48 (40.1)	9 (9.8)	23 (16.5)	19 (16.5)	215 51.5%
Total	257 61.5%	78 18.7%	19 4.6%	32 7.7%	32 7.7%	418 100%

The European character of the Icelandic flora is clearly evident; there are about 12 times as many European as American species. The same facts apply to the Icelandic fauna (Lindroth, 1957). There is some over-representation of limnic species in the other flora elements, and a tendency to over-representation of types adapted to long-distance dispersal among the American species, but the numbers are too low to yield any statistical significance. However, considering also taxa of lower rank than species, 16 American taxa are found in Iceland of which only 4 are not adapted to long-distance dispersal. This is certainly significant. Similarly, Lindroth (1957) found that the American animals in Iceland are adapted to long-distance dispersal. In the Amphi-Atlantic and European elements in the Icelandic flora there is an under-representation of types adapted to long-distance dispersal. Thus, there is no evidence that the Amphi-Atlantic and European species reached

TABLE 3

COMPARISON OF THE DIFFERENT ELEMENTS IN THE FLORAS OF GREENLAND (BASED ON BÖCHER, HOLMEN AND JAKOBSEN, 1957); NEWFOUNDLAND AND LABRADOR (MAINLY BASED ON ROULEAU, 1956) AND GASPÉ (MAINLY BASED ON SCOGGAN, 1950) AS TO ADAPTATIONS TO LONG-DISTANCE DISPERSAL.

Polymorphic apomictic groups (*Taraxacum* and *Hieracium* in Greenland, *Oenothera*, *Crataegus* and *Rubus* subg. *Eubatus* in other areas) excluded from the enumerations.

[Upper figure = observed, lower figure (in brackets) = statistically expected number of species per element.]

	No adaptations to long-distance dispersal	Anemochorous species	Zoochorous species	Limnic species	Halophilous species	Total
GREENLAND						
Eastern Amphi-Atlantic element	64 (52.1)	10 (15.5)	1 (2.7)	2 (4.8)	3 (4.9)	80 18.3%
Other elements	221 (232.9)	75 (69.5)	14 (12.3)	24 (21.2)	24 (22.1)	358 81.7%
Total	285 65.1%	85 19.4%	15 3.4%	26 5.9%	27 6.2%	438 100%
LABRADOR						
Eastern Amphi-Atlantic element	35 (23.9)	4 (11.3)	0 (3.6)	1 (2.7)	4 (2.5)	44 7.1%
Other elements	302 (313.1)	156 (148.7)	51 (47.4)	37 (35.3)	31 (32.5)	577 92.9%
Total	337 54.3%	160 25.8%	51 8.2%	38 6.1%	35 5.6%	621 100%
NEWFOUNDLAND						
Eastern Amphi-Atlantic element	29 (20.5)	8 (13.2)	0 (4.0)	1 (3.0)	5 (2.3)	43 4.9%
Other elements	388 (396.5)	260 (254.8)	82 (78.0)	61 (59.0)	42 (44.7)	833 95.1%
Total	417 47.6%	268 30.6%	82 9.4%	62 7.1%	47 5.4%	876 100%
GASPÉ						
Eastern Amphi-Atlantic element	21 (15.2)	7 (9.3)	0 (3.6)	0 (2.0)	4 (1.9)	32 3.3%
Other elements	436 (441.8)	273 (270.7)	108 (104.4)	59 (57.0)	52 (54.1)	928 96.7%
Total	457 47.6%	280 29.2%	108 11.3%	59 6.2%	56 5.8%	960 100%

Iceland by long-distance dispersal, whereas there is evidence that this was the case by the immigration of the American element.

Table 3 gives the breakdown of the floras of Greenland (Böcher, Holmen and Jakobsen, 1957), Labrador and Newfoundland (Rouleau, 1956) as well as Gaspé Peninsula (Scoggan, 1950) in a similar manner. The eastern Amphi-Atlantic elements in all these areas are consistently under-represented in types adapted to long-distance dispersal; in several instances the differences between observed and expected numbers are statistically significant. The percentage of Amphi-Atlantic species in the floras decreases from north towards south. The percentage of anemochorous and zoochorous species increases towards the south while the percentage of species not adapted to long-distance dispersal decreases. This trend also is significant. In part, this may be the reason why the Amphi-Atlantic element, which is essentially an Arctic–Sub-Arctic element, is under-represented in types adapted to long-distance dispersal. But there is no evidence to suggest that the eastern Amphi-Atlantic species reached their present stations by long-distance dispersal.

There appears to exist a discrepancy between the zoogeographical and phytogeographical observations regarding Davis Strait as a biogeographic barrier. According to Lindroth (1957) the Greenland fauna consists of about one half Holarctic species and about one quarter each of Nearctic and Palearctic species. The Palearctic influence is particularly evident in the soil-bound fauna which is not easily spread across the sea, while most of the Nearctic fauna can be more easily dispersed. The fauna of Baffin Island, however, has an almost purely Nearctic character. Lindroth (1960) has also performed an analysis of the botanical aspects of the problem.

I have examined the data presented by Lindroth from a statistical point of view and found their significance doubtful. However, Lindroth treated the flora of Greenland as a whole. Smith Sound between Greenland and Ellesmere Island is hardly an important barrier for Arctic plants. If Davis Strait has been a barrier this should be most clearly evident among more Low Arctic plants. It should also be remembered that during the Post-glacial climatic optimum (the Hypsithermal) many plants could grow in the Smith Sound area, but they are now found only farther south. For this reason, I have made an analysis of the Low Arctic element, here defined as species with a northern limit in Greenland at or south of the Nugssuak Peninsula and on Baffin Island at or south of the Pangnirtung Peninsula. The result of this analysis is presented in Table 4.

From the table it will be seen that no enrichment of types adapted to long-distance dispersal is evident among the eastern Amphi-Atlantic taxa penetrating into America. However, among the western plants penetrating into Greenland and Iceland there is an over-representation of types adapted to long-distance dispersal. Using the entire flora of Greenland as a basis for comparison the difference becomes clearly significant. Taking the entire flora

TABLE 4

COMPARISON OF LOW-ARCTIC ELEMENTS IN THE FLORA OF GREENLAND AND EASTERN NORTH AMERICA AS TO ADAPTATIONS TO LONG-DISTANCE DISPERSAL.

Further explanation in text.

	No adaptations to long-distance dispersal	Anemochorous taxa	Zoochorous taxa	Halophilous taxa	Limnic taxa	Total
Eastern Amphi-Atlantic taxa:						
Reaching east Greenland	3	0	0	0	0	3
Reaching west Greenland	16	5	1	2	1	25
With limited area in eastern America	9	2	0	0	1	12
With wider area but not west of Hudson Bay	11	4	0	0	0	15
Reaching west of Hudson Bay	6	2	0	0	2	10
Total	45	13	1	2	4	65
%	68.2	19.7	1.5	4.6	6.1	
Western taxa reaching Greenland and Iceland	27	17	4	6	6	60
%	45.0	28.3	6.7	10.0	10.0	

of Labrador as a basis for comparison results in some over-representation of types adapted to long-distance dispersal, but the difference is not statistically significant. This is, however, probably due to the higher representation of types adapted to long-distance dispersal within the more temperate elements in the flora of Labrador.

From the data presented the following conclusions can be drawn:

1. The Arctic–Sub-Arctic flora in general and the Amphi-Atlantic elements in particular are under-represented in types adapted to long-distance dispersal.

2. There is evidence of over-representation of types adapted to long-distance dispersal within western Low Arctic elements penetrating to Greenland and Iceland.

From this it can be concluded either that the adaptations recognized as favoring long-distance dispersal are of no biological significance, or that the problem of Amphi-Atlantic plant distribution is not a matter of long-distance dispersal.

The first conclusion is difficult to accept. As to the anemochorous species the reader is referred to the work by Wilhelm Schmidt and others (cf. Geiger, 1961, p. 50 etc.) regarding probable travelling distances of seeds and spores as a function of turbulence and settling velocity in air. These considerations are borne out by finds of numerous far-travelled spores and pollen. Also, the re-colonization of the flora of the island of Krakatoa shows that species apparently adapted to long-distance dispersal had a considerable advantage in colonizing the island after its flora was destroyed by a volcanic eruption in 1883 (cf. Dahl, 1959). Thus, it is concluded that, whatever is the explanation of the Amphi-Atlantic distribution pattern, it is not a matter of long-distance dispersal.

DID THE AMPHI-ATLANTIC PLANTS MIGRATE ACROSS THE BERING SEA?

Only two hypotheses now remain to be considered in order to explain the distribution of the Amphi-Atlantic plants. One is the hypothesis of a former migration across the Bering Sea, and the other concerns migration across a land connection between Europe and America.

The first hypothesis involves very extensive plant dispersals with the result that populations on both sides of the Atlantic Ocean must have been isolated genetically for a long time. Especially in polymorphic groups of species, and in taxa of lower rank than species, one would expect to find a differentiation of the populations on both sides of the North Atlantic Ocean. On the contrary, if plants had dispersed directly across the North Atlantic Ocean one would expect to find closely related taxa on both sides of the Ocean differing from the populations farther east in Asia, in the Pacific area, and in western America.

The Eastern Amphi-Atlantic element in North America can be sub-divided into the following groups, mainly based upon information from Hultén (1958):

1. Amphi-Atlantic taxa of lower rank than species with vicariants in the Pacific area (Alaska and easternmost Asia) — 13 taxa
2. Amphi-Atlantic taxa of lower rank than species with vicariant taxa elsewhere in Europe, Asia, or America but absent in the Pacific area — 8 taxa

3. Amphi-Atlantic species with vicariant taxa of lower rank in eastern America and western Europe — 10 species
4. Species of polymorphic groups with vicariants in the Pacific area — 22 species
5. Species of polymorphic groups with vicariant species elsewhere in Europe, Asia and America but not in the Pacific area — 25 species
6. Other Amphi-Atlantic species — 33 species

Of the groups listed above, only Group 3 can be said to support the hypothesis that the plants dispersed across the Bering Sea, whereas Groups 1 and 2 and, to some extent, also Groups 4 and 5 contradict the hypothesis. It will be seen that the data clearly suggest a direct migration between Europe and America.

Within Group 3, supporting the hypothesis of dispersal across the Bering Sea, are seven temperate plants and only three Arctic–Sub-Arctic ones. As a comparison, in Group 1, supporting the hypothesis of a direct Atlantic dispersal, all except one species (the sea-shore plant *Ligusticum scoticum*) have an Arctic–Sub-Arctic type of distribution. Thus, the hypothesis of migration across the Bering Sea seems more likely concerning temperate than Arctic–Sub-Arctic plants.

The outline given above can be exemplified by numerous individual examples. Here, I shall consider only one example, where more detailed and advanced information is available.

In the *Papaver radicatum* complex studied by Knaben (1959a, b) one species, *P. lapponicum*, is Amphi-Atlantic, as far as is known. In Europe it grows in northern Scandinavia as far east as Kola, whereas in North America it has a wide area including most of Greenland, northern Labrador and the Canadian Arctic Archipelago as far west as Banks Island. Knaben (*loc. cit.*) recognizes one subspecies in northern Norway and three different subspecies west of the Atlantic Ocean. The morphological differences between the American subspecies seem to be about as great as the differences between the Scandinavian and the American subspecies.

More quantitative information on the degree of genetic differentiation is available through crossing and subsequent cytological analysis. When mutations take place the pairing of corresponding chromosomes in meiosis of hybrids is often impaired and the number of bivalents, thus formed, in the meiosis of such hybrids seems to be a fair measure of the degree of genetic differentiation. Knaben has carried out a number of intra-racial and inter-racial crosses, and Table 5 is based on information contained in her work. The maximum number of bivalents is 28. The number of bivalents in intra-racial crosses of ssp. *occidentale* is fairly low, suggesting that it is genetically heterogeneous and may one day be split up into more subspecies. But the

TABLE 5

NUMBER OF BIVALENTS IN INTRARACIAL AND INTERRACIAL CROSSES IN PAPAVER LAPPONICUM (based on Knaben, 1959).

The mean number of bivalents with standard error of the mean given together with number of PMC's counted and number of crosses.

	scandinavicum	*occidentale*	*porsildii*	*labradoricum*
ssp. *scandinavicum* (North Norway)	25.2 ± 0.35 17, 3x	16.5 ± 0.74 21, 5x		14.5 ± 1.55 7, 2x
ssp. *occidentale* (Greenland–Arctic Canada)		19.1 ± 0.79 12, 3x		15.8 ± 1.07 13, 4x
ssp. *porsildii* (Greenland–Arctic Canada)			26.0 ± 0.82 6, 2x	22.3 ± 0.53 15, 5x
ssp. *labradoricum* (South Greenland–Ungava)				

important point is that the genetic differences between ssp. *scandinavicum* and the American ssp. *occidentale* and *labradoricum* is about the same as the genetic difference between ssp. *occidentale* and ssp. *labradoricum* themselves. If *Papaver lapponicum* once dispersed in both directions from the Pacific area, the isolation between ssp. *occidentale* and *labradoricum* must be of a younger date than the isolation between these two subspecies and ssp. *scandinavicum*. This is not borne out by the observations made.

As pointed out above, there is a fairly gradual transition in the flora from Scandinavia across Scotland to Iceland and Greenland, and this applies also to the fauna. This general feature can hardly be explained by the hypothesis that the plants came from the Pacific area. The strength of the hypothesis is that it avoids creating a new land-bridge, but in order to explain, for instance, the European element in the flora of Iceland, it seems necessary to postulate some land connection across the longest stretch of water now separating America and Europe.

THE HYPOTHESIS OF A LAND CONNECTION BETWEEN EUROPE AND AMERICA

By process of elimination, the conclusion is reached that the only hypothesis capable of explaining the Amphi-Atlantic biota is that of a former land connection across the North Atlantic Ocean. Since there is evidence that long-distance dispersal has been of importance in the immigration of the western elements into Iceland and Greenland, it is concluded that the land connection was broken first between Iceland and America, and the strong European influence in the biota of Iceland corroborates this. Consequently, the western Low Arctic elements in Greenland and Iceland must be younger than the Amphi-Atlantic and eastern elements and this is borne out also by the endemics in Iceland, most of which have many close relatives on the European side of the Ocean but only a few on the American side. It is not denied that some species originally might have dispersed across the Bering Sea or have attained their distribution by long-distance dispersal, but for the majority of the biota this explanation does not seem feasible.

It has been emphasized that the Amphi-Atlantic plants are Arctic–Sub-Arctic, whereas very few Temperate plants have this distribution pattern. This implies that the climate on our hypothetical land connection must have been favorable to Arctic–Sub-Arctic plants but not to Temperate plants. The same fact is brought out by an analysis of altitudinal limits in the Scandinavian flora; very few species unable to grow in the birch belt occur west of the Atlantic Ocean. In this element there is a high over-representation of types adapted to long-distance dispersal (Dahl, 1959). It is concluded that the climate on the land-bridge was about the same as is found in the birch belt of Scandinavia or of Iceland today.

This permits us to propose an age for the land connection. In Mid-Tertiary times the climate was warmer than at present and only in later times, during Pliocene and Pleistocene, do we find climatic conditions comparable to the present-day climate. It is therefore concluded that the connection existed at least as late as the Pliocene.

GEOLOGICAL EVIDENCE OF A FORMER LAND CONNECTION BETWEEN EUROPE AND AMERICA

The biogeographic data presented suggest the existence of a former land connection between Europe and America as late as in the Pliocene. However, one cannot conclude from the distribution that the land-bridge existed and then explain the distribution pattern by the means of the land-bridge. This becomes circular reasoning; thus independent support in the form of geological observations is necessary in order to establish the existence of a land connection.

It is tempting to invoke the Wegener hypothesis of continental drift to explain the features, and the data presented above may be taken as support for the hypothesis of continental drift. However, this is a very controversial matter and at present it seems unwise to build too much on the Wegener hypothesis.

There are, however, other indications suggesting the existence of a land connection between Europe and America during Tertiary times. In the Eocene large eruptions took place in an area extending from Scotland to east Greenland and a huge basalt plateau was formed. Fossiliferous deposits between the basalt layers permit its dating. Since no deposits of Mid-Tertiary age are known from this region, it is believed that the plateau existed as a land area. The basalt plateau was later broken up by renewed volcanic activity in Pliocene or Pleistocene times and only some remnants are preserved.

Barth (1941, p. 8) has given this account of the geologic history of Iceland:

> Across Iceland, from the south to the north, there is a broad belt with mountains and plateaus with sharp peaks and jagged crests. The rest of the country to the east and to the west consists of flat-topped mountains made up of layers of solidified lava which came up from the interior of the Earth about 50 million years ago, long before man appeared on Earth. The material making up these mountains was molten lava, stream after stream gushed out, gave off the heat to the Cosmos, and became solid rock; layer upon layer were formed and huge flat plateau mountains built up. In this way the Old Iceland was born, a huge stone plateau which filled almost the whole of the North Atlantic Ocean; Old Iceland was much larger than the Iceland we know today; it stretched northwards and eastwards with a land connection to both Jan Mayen and the Faeroes.
>
> After this, all became quiet for a while; the eruptions stopped and the lava retreated slowly into the interior of the Earth. There it remained for millions of years, until it once again came back up to the surface. As the spring flood breaks the ice so that the floes are broken and raised on end, thus were the plateau mountains of Old Iceland broken up by new volcanic activity and the molten lava pressing upwards; from innumerable cracks and crannies the lava again flowed out over the surface. The foundations of the stone plateau gave way, and, like another Atlantis, Old Iceland sank into the sea. What remains is chiefly the Faeroes and the large island now known as Iceland. This happened less than a million years ago, and volcanic activity has continued with undiminished force ever since. (Translated from the Norwegian.)

As may be seen, Barth's outline, based on geologic evidence, fits well the results obtained by biogeographic reasoning. The idea that a land connection existed between Europe and America as late as the Pliocene or the Pleistocene must be said to rest upon strong foundations.

Many questions remain unanswered, however. The most important concerns the time when the connection was broken. The close relationships in biota between Iceland, Scotland and Scandinavia suggest that this might have happened in relatively recent times. The connection probably did not exist during the Post-glacial climatic optimum (the Hypsithermal). Marine deposits along the coast of Norway from this period contain molluscs of a southern distribution type. If a connection between Iceland and Scotland had existed, the Atlantic warm water could not enter the Polar Basin, and the effect of this should be noticeable in the marine fauna. The connection between eastern America and western Europe was probably not operative during the Glacial Ages since the ice masses on Iceland and Greenland then ought to have formed obstacles to plant and animal migration. It seems unlikely that the connection existed after the Last Glacial Age, but precisely when it was broken remains an open question. The answer is of considerable evolutionary interest, since it could afford us with a means to gauge rates of evolution. Also, the question of where the Amphi-Atlantic plants and animals survived the glacial ages after the connection had been broken is interesting.

The most reasonable method to obtain the information desired seems to be by means of deep sea borings since a connection between Scotland and Iceland and also between Iceland and Greenland must have affected profoundly the oceanographic situation in the seas adjacent to the bridges, and this should be noticeable in the character of the sediments.

Some relevant information might also be obtained by closer study of Icelandic Interglacial peat deposits which have been preserved from subsequent destruction by lava flows. By proper dating and analysis of such deposits more might be learned about the time when the different components of the fauna and flora immigrated to Iceland.

REFERENCES

BARTH, T. F. W. (1941). *Island.* Oslo.

BLYTT, A. (1876). *Essay on the Immigration of the Norwegian Flora during Alternating Dry and Rainy Periods.* Christiania.

BÖCHER, T. W., HOLMEN, K. and JAKOBSEN, K. (1957). *Grönlands Flora.* Köbenhavn.

DAHL, E. (1959). Amfiatlantiske Planter. Problems of Amphi-Atlantic plant distribution. *Blyttia* **16**, 93–121.

FERNALD, M. L. (1929). Some relationships of the floras of the Northern Hemisphere. *Proc. Int. Congr. Plant Sci.* **2**, 1487–1507.

GEIGER, R. (1961). *Das Klima der bodennahen Luftschicht.* Die Wissenschaft **78**, 646 p.

HULTÉN, E. (1958). The Amphi-Atlantic plants and their phytogeographical connection. *Kgl. Svenska Vetensk. Akad. Handl.* Ser. 4, **7**(1), 1–340.

IVERSEN, J. (1953). Origin of the flora of Greenland in the light of pollen analysis. *Oikos* **4**, 85–103.

KNABEN, G. (1959a). On the evolution of the *radicatum*-group of the *Scapiflora Papavers* as studies in 70 and 56 chromosome species. Part A. *Opera Botanica* **2**(3), 1–76.

KNABEN, G. (1959b). On the evolution of the *radicatum*-group of the *Scapiflora Papavers* as studied in 70 and 56 chromosome species. Part B. *Opera Botanica* **3**(3), 1–96.

LINDROTH, C. H. (1957). *The Faunal Connections between Europe and North America.* Stockholm and New York.

LINDROTH, C. H. (1960). Is Davis Strait—between Greenland and Baffin Land—a floristic barrier? *Bot. Notiser* **113**, 130–140.

LÖVE, Á. (1945). *Íslenzkar jurtir.* Copenhagen.

LÖVE, Á. and LÖVE, D. (1956). Cytotaxonomical conspectus of the Icelandic flora. *Acta Horti Gotoburg.* **20**, 69–291.

OSTENFELD, C. H. (1926). The flora of Greenland and its origin. *Biol. Medd. Dansk. Vidensk. Selsk.* **6**(3), 1–71.

PORSILD, M. P. (1932). Alien plants and apophytes of Greenland. *Medd. om Grönl.* **92**(1), 1–85.

ROULEAU, E. (1956). A check-list of the vascular plants of the province of Newfoundland (including the French islands of St. Pierre and Miquelon). *Contr. de l'Inst. Bot. de l'Univ. de Montréal* **69**, 41–105.

SCOGGAN, H. J. (1950). The Flora of Bic and the Gaspé Peninsula, Quebec. *Nat. Mus. Canada Bull.* **115**, 1–399.

DISPERSAL AND SURVIVAL OF PLANTS

Doris Löve

Institut Botanique de l'Université de Montréal, Montréal, Canada

Speed of movement has become an integral part of human life. At present we tend to think of distances as a matter of hours rather than miles. Man is now able to swing around the globe in less than 2 hr, but he really becomes aware of distances only if he has to walk on foot. Still, both man and other animals have the ability of a more or less speedy transfer from one point to another, an ability which can assume life-saving proportions in cases of food-shortage, inclement weather, or other adversities.

It is different with plants. Once they have taken root, it is touch and go. They do not have the choice of deciding where to go next. It is purely a matter of chance as to where the wind will waft the seeds, the water carry them, or how far that animal, to whose feathers or pelt the seed sticks, will travel. Chance alone decides even how far a seed will be conveyed between being consumed and deposited. Furthermore, plant dispersal is a feature of generations of plants, and only a new generation can bring the species a step farther on its way.

The area with which we are concerned here is mainly covered with water. It has been subjected to heavy glaciation over and over again, in parts it is still in the grip of the Last Ice Age. Yet, we find on both sides of the Atlantic, as well as on the islands in its northern parts, several plant species which are practically undifferentiated. In some way, or at some time, these species must have been able to disperse over all this area, even if it consists of landmasses so far apart today that it may seem impossible for plants to bridge the distances between them.

Only a few plant species are actually adapted for long-distance dispersal, having seeds or other reproductive parts which can be carried far away from the immobile mother plant. Many more species are adapted to dispersal over relatively short ranges, from a few meters up to several kilometers, but in our particular area the shortest span between two landmasses is the 11 km gap between the islands in the Spitsbergen chain. The other distances are considerably longer, most of them over 300 km and all the way up to the 1761 km between Jan Mayen and Iceland (cf. Table 1).

Some plants have reproductive parts which seem truly adapted for transport over long distances by wind or water, or by sticking to feathers or pelts.

Quite a number of plants and seeds, if eaten, can be accidentally dispersed over considerable distances.

Considering first the role of animals as a transportation medium, we find that at the present time man is by far the most active plant disperser, even in the northern latitudes with which we are concerned. But his role is of a very late date, seen against the geological time scale, and for our particular purpose it is actually insignificant. I will therefore disregard man-made dispersal.

TABLE 1

EXACT DISTANCES IN MILES AND KILOMETERS BETWEEN THE NEAREST POINTS OF THE LANDMASSES IN THE NORTH ATLANTIC AREA. *Courtesy Dr. J. D. Ives, Geographical Branch, and the Computer Center of the Department of Mines and Natural Resources, Ottawa, Canada.*

From	To	Miles	Km
Scotland (Hebrides, Luchruban)	Iceland (Hornsvik Light)	488.3	785.7
Scotland (Mainland, Cape Wrath)	Faeroes (Akraberg)	199.6	321.2
Scotland (Mainland, Duncansby Head)	Orkney (S. Ronaldsay)	6.2	10.0
Orkney (Westray Island)	Faeroes (Akraberg)	188.0	302.5
Orkney (N. Ronaldsay Island)	Shetland (Scatness)	54.8	88.2
Shetland (Stanshi Head)	Faeroes (Akraberg)	180.1	289.8
Shetland (Unst Island)	Norway (Storöy Island)	181.3	291.7
Faeroes (Mykines Island)	Iceland (Kambar Light)	255.1	410.5
Faeroes (Fugloy Island)	Norway (Bremanger Island)	362.6	583.4
Iceland (Rekjavik Light)	Greenland (Kap Grivel)	182.2	293.2
Iceland (Fontur Light)	Jan Mayen (Kikut)	1094.3	1760.7
Iceland (Einstakafjall Arm)	Norway (Stadlandet)	601.9	968.5
Greenland (Cape Ammen)	Ellesmere Island (Wrangel Bay)	12.2	19.6
Greenland (Inugsugtussoq)	Baffin Land (Cape Dyer)	207.7	334.2
Greenland (Nordostrundningen)	Spitsbergen (Amsterdam Island)	282.4	454.4
Greenland (Rathbone Island)	Jan Mayen (Höybergodden)	275.5	443.3
Jan Mayen (Norkapp)	Spitsbergen (Sörkapp)	587.3	945.0
Jan Mayen (Austkapp)	Bear Island (Cape Duner)	541.3	871.0
Jan Mayen (Söraustkapp)	Norway (Heggelvoer Island)	542.1	872.2
Spitsbergen (Mainland)	Spitsbergen (W. Storöya)	7.0	11.3
Spitsbergen (Storöya E.)	Spitsbergen (Kvitöya W.)	42.4	68.2
Spitsbergen (Kvitöya E.)	Frans Joseph's Land (Mary Hamsworth Cape)	98.6	158.6
Spitsbergen (Sörkapp)	Bear Island	142.5	229.3
Bear Island	Norway (Ingö Island)	246.5	396.6

Among other mammals, polar bears and foxes are the only ones that are occasionally carried by ice between the North Atlantic islands (and even from Greenland to Iceland). But during the time when these animals venture so far from land (and the possibility of eating vegetable matter) that they are caught in the drift ice, they subsist exclusively on animal food. We can therefore safely ignore them as possible plant dispersers.

With birds it is another question. They travel freely between landmasses in our area, and there is no doubt that they are active as transportation media for both ingested and externally carried plant parts. Over short distances their role is unquestionably of very great significance (Samuelsson, 1934; Ridley, 1930). But how important is it, when it comes to long distances? It is necessary to consider not only which birds can act as carriers in our area, but also what they eat and where and how they travel. Due regard must be given to such phenomena as behavior, food intake, rate of metabolism, flight speed, migration dates, etc.

Most of the migratory birds in our area are shore- and waterbirds. Many subsist on a diet of plankton, fish, or other animal matter, augmented only occasionally by a nibble of berries, grain (e.g. from a shipwreck), and garbage (Witherby *et al.*, 1939). But there are also some, which are mainly vegetarian, like swans, geese, and ducks. Smaller, vegetarian landbirds, as well as gulls and terns, which occasionally eat vegetable matter, can be disregarded because their metabolism is too fast in relation to their flight speed to permit them to carry anything internally between our landmasses (Ridley, 1930).

Experiments with captive ducks, geese, and swans have shown that the passage of food in these large birds from the time of ingestion to evacuation takes from 3 or 4 hr up to, in extreme cases, 7 hr (Ridley, 1930). Their flight speed during migration is not too well known. Over land it seems, according to Hochbaum (1955), to be about 80 km/hr at an altitude of 300–1000 m. Over open sea speed as low as 50 km/hr and altitudes of only 50–70 m have been measured by radar (Buss, 1946; Yocom, 1947) for mallards (*Anas platyrhyncha* L.) and pintails (*Anas acuta* L.). If, therefore, one of the large birds consumed a seed just before take off, it is possible that, flying at maximum speed, it could carry the seed as far as 600 km in 7 hr before depositing it. But it is likely that the rate of metabolism is considerably increased during a strenuous flight, and if the flight speed over oceans really is slower than over land (Buss, 1946; Yocom, 1947), the distance covered will be considerably shorter, down to as little as 150 km.

Furthermore, it has been observed that ducks, swans, and geese do not eat immediately prior to taking off on a migratory flight (Ridley, 1930; Hochbaum, 1955). There are even reports that they start on an empty stomach (Andersson in Ridley, 1930).

The question must also be asked whether seeds will pass unharmed through the viscera of these large birds. The action of their crop is very energetic, and most soft seeds will inevitably be crushed although hard-shelled seeds may escape damage. This has been observed in domestic geese (Ridley, 1930). Too little is actually known about the diet of wild swans, geese, and ducks (cf. Table 2; also Ridley, 1930; Schaaning, 1933 a, b; Witherby *et al.*, 1939; Durango, 1953; Löwenskjold, 1954; Hochbaum, 1955; Sladen, 1960) to evaluate the chances for a substantial part of consumed seeds to escape unharmed through the digestive channel of these birds.

TABLE 2

LIST OF BIRDS, WHOSE FLIGHT SPEED AND RATE OF METABOLISM SEEM TO PERMIT THE PASSAGE OF SEEDS INTERNALLY BETWEEN THE LAND-MASSES OF THE NORTH ATLANTIC AREA.

Species of bird	Nest areas	Winter areas	Known food
Cygnus cygnus cygnus (L.) Whooper swan	Br. Isles, Norway, Sweden, Finland	Scotland, England, S. and Centr. Europe	In Iceland: *Batrachium confervoides Eriophorum Scheuchzeri*, grasses, roots and stems of aquatic plants; in Scotland: *Glyceria fluitans*, *Catabrosa aquatica*
Cygnus cygnus islandicus Brehm Icelandic whooper swan	Iceland, E. Greenland, Jan Mayen	Iceland	as above in Iceland
Cygnus cygnus bewickii Yarr. Bewick's swan	Iceland, Finland, Russia (casual in Spitsbergen)	Gr. Britain, S. and Centr. Europe	*Potamogeton*, *Zannichellia*, *Zostera*, *Trifolium repens*
Anser anser anser (L.) Gray Leg goose	Hebrides, Iceland, Scandinavia, Balticum, Russia (casual in the Faeroes)	Gr. Britain, South Europe, North Africa	in Ireland: *Scirpus maritimus;* in Norway: *Rubus Chamaemorus;* in Russia: *Trapa natans*, *Lemna*, *Glyceria fluitans*, *Zostera*
Anser albifrons albifrons (Scop.) White-fronted goose	N. America, West Greenland, NE. Russia (casual in the Faeroes, Iceland)	Hebrides, Gr. Britain	*Equisetum*, *Plantago maritima*, *Sagina subulata*, *Triglochin maritimum*, *Statice maritima*, *Glyceria*, *Trifolium repens*
Anser fabalis brachyrhynchus Baillon Pink-footed goose	E. Greenland, Iceland, Spitsbergen, Frans Joseph's Land ?, (reported from Jan Mayen, Bear Island, Scandinavia, the Faeroes)	Hebrides, Gr. Britain, Denmark	*Cerastium Edmondstonii*, *Saxifraga*, *Equisetum*, *Cochlearia* and grasses, *Salix reticulata*. Young birds in Iceland: *Equisetum variegatum*, *Galium pumilum*, *Juncus trifidus*, *Luzula spicata*, *Carex* sp.
(*Anser hyperboreus hyperboerus* (Pall.) Snow-goose)	North America (casual in Iceland, Norway, North Sweden, W. Europe, but may have been confused with albino white-fronted geese)	U.S.A.	*Scirpus americanus*, *Empetrum*, *Zizania*, aquatic plants
Branta ruficollis (*Pall.*) Red-breasted goose	Yamal–NW. Siberia (casual in Greenland, Novaya Zemlya, Iceland, Gr. Britain, SW. Europe)	Centr. and E. Europe and Asia	Seems to consist mainly of grass and grass-shoots
Branta leucopsis (Bechst.) Barnacle goose	Greenland, Iceland ?, Spitsbergen (passes over Iceland, Jan Mayen, the Faeroes, Scandinavia, Finland)	West and Centr. Europe	Green grasses (*Puccinellia maritima*, *Festuca rubra*, *Poa* sp.), *Bellis perennis*, *Ranunculus repens*, *Caltha palustris*, *Apium nodiflorum*, *Equisetum palustre*, *Hypnum cuspidatum*, *Lophocolea bidentata*
Branta bernicla hrota (L.) Pale-breasted Brent goose	E. and W. Greenland, Iceland ?, Spitsbergen, (passes	West Europe	*Zostera marina*, at least during migration; *Ulva latissima*

It must also be remembered that most migratory flights take place early in the spring, before there is a fresh crop of seeds and berries, and that the birds at this time of the year usually eat the soft, fresh vegetative parts of the plants, like young shoots of grasses, waterplants, etc. Occasionally, however, old seeds from the preceding fall must be consumed, but they do not make up a large part of the diet. In the autumn, when the migration goes from north to south, it starts in many places so early in August that during some years seeds and fruits may not yet be fully ripe. In other years a substantial part must have ripened and then no doubt fruits and seeds make up a considerable bulk of the bird diet.

A number of Arctic seeds, particularly those that ripen early, are able to germinate at once. Others which ripen late need in most cases a rest period and exposure to cold before they can germinate (Bliss, 1958). We do not know what effect the passage through a bird can have on these seeds, but it seems likely that those seeds which need a rest period would have a better chance of survival.

It is worth mentioning in this connection that 45 km to the north of Iceland there is a small island, Grimsey. It supports large colonies of birds (gulls, terns, ducks, ravens, etc.) and many of them fly back and forth to the mainland. In spite of seemingly perfect ecological conditions this island still has no *Empetrum*, though the mainland abounds in this genus and birds are known to greedily devour the fruits in the fall.

It must also be remembered that birds theoretically are able to carry seeds and other plant parts capable of vegetative reproduction externally, attached, for example, to feathers, feet, or beaks. At Delta, Manitoba, Canada, it has been observed that birds had *Lemna* in their feathers when shot down (Hochbaum, pers. comm.). Especially when the birds are suddenly scared away from their feeding grounds, the accidental transport of plants or parts of plants from one pond to another is likely to take place (Samuelsson, 1934; Hochbaum, pers. comm.). Farmyard birds also have been observed with lumps of clay, containing live seeds, sticking to their bodies (Ridley, 1930), but it is a fact that wild birds (as all other wild animals) keep themselves much better groomed than captive ones. Wild birds usually preen themselves meticulously before taking off on a flight, and it seems especially so before a migratory flight (Hochbaum, pers. comm.).

It is therefore highly unlikely that any larger bits of plants are carried by migrating birds. Even if this were the case, these plant parts would have to endure several hours of drying winds, during spring migration often combined with temperatures below freezing. It is hard to guess what effect the wind-chill factor can have on thus exposed plant parts, but most likely it would kill them within few hours. Seeds, on the other hand, would probably survive, and such genera as *Potamogeton*, *Zannichellia*, *Sparganium*, etc., could theoretically have been spread in this manner (Samuelsson, 1934). However, among the North Atlantic islands only the Faeroes and Iceland harbor any of these genera.

A group of plants in Great Britain were believed to have been brought attached to the bodies of the Pink-footed geese from North America via Greenland to Ireland (Heslop-Harrison, 1953). Later, some of these taxa have been shown to consist of different species on both sides of the Ocean (Löve and Löve, 1958): *Sisyrinchium angustifolium*, $2n = 96$ chromosomes, in North America, *S. montanum*, $2n = 32$, in Greenland, *Sisyrinchium hibernicum*, $2n = 64$, in Ireland; *Eriocaulon septangulare*, $2n = 64$, in Europe, *E. Parkeri*, $2n = 32$, and *E. pellucidum*, $2n = 48$, in North America (cf. also Löve and Löve, 1961, and unpubl.), etc. The remaining species still need further investigation in order to clarify their relationship across the water.

It seems thus, when closely considered, that there is a relatively small chance for any large number of plants to have been dispersed by birds over distances as great as the present ones between the North Atlantic islands. The role of the birds as dispensers over shorter distances is no doubt much more significant (Samuelsson, 1934) and they must have had a much more important function if, at some time, these distances were shorter than now (Löve and Löve, 1956; Dahl, 1958; Hadač, 1960).

Based on a native flora of *ca.* 565 species (including ferns and fern-allies, *Juniperus*, and Angiosperms except *Taraxacum* and *Hieracium*) in the Faeroes (Rasmussen, 1952), Iceland (Löve, 1945; Löve and Löve, 1956), Jan Mayen (J.Lid, Oslo, pers. comm.), Bear Island (Rönning, 1959), Spitsbergen (Scholander, 1934; Dahl, 1937; Hadač, 1944; Dahl and Hadač, 1946; Hagen, 1952) and Franz Joseph's Land (Hanssen and Lid, 1932), not more than at most 10 per cent can be referred to a category of plants which in recent (= Post-glacial) time possibly have been dispersed, internally or externally, by birds (cf. also Table 2).

Many plants are said to be dispersed by water, streams, currents, even frozen in ice, etc. In most cases such dispersal takes place in fresh water, which, however, in our area is of considerably limited importance. Except in Iceland, there are virtually no rivers or lake systems which can possibly act as transportation media.

Long-distance dispersal by water in our area is therefore limited to the carrying capacity of sea-currents, and thus at present only to the warm Gulf Stream, and perhaps (though highly unlikely) to the cold currents around Greenland and in the northernmost parts of the North Atlantic and the Polar Sea.

Few land plants have seeds which can stand immersion in salt water for even a short time without losing both their buoyancy and germination ability (cf. Salisbury, 1942), but there are seeds which can float for a long time. *Cakile edentula* has such seeds, and this species has evidently been dispersed by the Gulf Stream from the coast of North America, as late as in Post-glacial and Present time, as far north as Spitsbergen (Löve and Löve, 1947; Hadač, 1960).

Other shore plants which can fit into a similar distribution pattern, but probably one of an older date, belong to genera such as *Cochlearia*, *Honckenya*, *Mertensia* and *Glaux* (Ridley, 1930), of which the first three reach the Arctic part of our area, but *Glaux* so far is found only in Iceland, and not yet in the Faeroes.

The large size and weight of *Honckenya* and *Cakile* seeds (cf. Table 3) indicate that they are well adapted to floating. Those of *Glaux* are smaller, individually, but usually united in a cluster of five and most likely therefore quite buoyant. *Mertensia* seeds are lighter in weight, but of a relatively large size and may possibly float well. *Cochlearia groenlandica* is found as a shore plant throughout our area but it consists of a complex, circumpolar group of subspecies whose areas are not yet well known, and it is somewhat uncertain whether it should actually be included in the group of plants dispersed by sea-currents.

Salt water plants are of course naturally adapted to dispersal in sea-water, and the genus *Zostera* produces seeds (with a corky appendage) and vegetative parts which seem to have the necessary buoyancy for long-distance dispersal by sea-currents. In Iceland (Löve and Löve, 1956) and perhaps also in Greenland (Böcher, Holmen and Jakobsen, 1957; Jörgensen, Sörensen and Westergaard, 1958) the genus is represented by *Z. stenophylla*, an American species. Whether the Faeroes plants are true *Z. marina*, as indicated by the Flora of the Faeroes (Rasmussen, 1952), or are identical with the American one, is not yet known to me. None of these species, however, has reached the Arctic islands of the North Atlantic.

Ruppia spiralis and *Hippuris lanceolata* (= *H. tetraphylla* p.p.) probably belong to this group also, the former so far known only from the Faeroes, Iceland and Greenland in our area. None of the two species is represented on the Arctic islands, but apparently good *H. vulgaris* has been collected on Bear Island (Rönning, 1959). *H. vulgaris*, being a freshwater plant does not belong in this group, but *H. lanceolata* is found in brackish and salt water also along the Arctic coasts of America and Eurasia. No *Hippuris* of any kind is found at or around the Faeroes, Jan Mayen, Spitsbergen and Franz Joseph's land.

The number of plant species dispersed over long distances inside our area by sea-currents, thus, are quite few, at most 1.5 per cent of the total flora (cf. Table 3). It has been impossible, furthermore, for this author to find any evidence whatsoever for transport over the open seas of living plant material frozen in ice. It seems highly unlikely that, even if seeds frozen into the ice of a calving glacier could float around in the North Atlantic or the Polar Sea, they would ever reach shore again (Osborne, 1855; cf also Hultén, 1962).

TABLE 3

LIST OF PLANT SPECIES WHICH MAY BE DISPERSED BY SEA-CURRENTS IN THE NORTH ATLANTIC, THEIR SEED WEIGHTS AND DIMENSIONS, AND THEIR PRESENTLY KNOWN DISTRIBUTION.

Species	Seed dimensions in mm	Seed weight in mg‡	Faeroe Islands	Iceland	Jan Mayen	Bear Island	Spits-bergen	Franz Joseph's Land
Ruppia spiralis	0.8 × 1.6 × 3.0*	—	×	×	—	—	—	—
Zostera stenophylla	—	—	—	×	—	—	—	—
Zostera marina	2.0 × 2.0 × 4.2 + cork*	—	×	—	—	—	—	—
Honkenya diffusa	2.6 × 3.8†	11.4 — 13.9	×	×	×	—	×	—
Glaux maritima	(1.0 × 1.0 × 1.5) × 5*	—	—	×	—	—	—	—
Cakile edentula	—	10.9	—	×	—	—	×	—
Cakile maritima	1.5 × 2.3 × 5.2*	—	×	—	—	—	—	—
Cochlearia groenlandica	0.9 × 1.1 — 1.3†	0.2 — 0.5	×	×	×	×	×	×
Hippuris lanceolata	—	—	—	×	—	—§	—	—
Mertensia maritima	2.1 × 4.0†	1.4 — 1.9	×	×	×	—	×	—

* Beijerinck, 1947. for *R. maritima.*
† Porsild, 1920.
‡ After Porsild, 1920.
§ *Hippuris vulgaris*, not sea-current dispersed.

TABLE 4

NATURAL DISPERSAL LIMITS OF FRUITS, POLLEN, AND SPORES (AFTER GEIGER, 1950).

Substance	Settling rate in cm/sec at 6 m.p.h. wind	Average dispersal limits in km
Fraxinus excelsior fruits	200.0	0.03
Abies pectinata fruits	106.0	0.09
Picea excelsa fruits	57.0	0.3
Betula verrucosa fruits	25.0	1.6
Taraxacum officinale fruits	10.0	10.0
Pinus silvestris pollen	5.3	40.0
Lycopodium spores	1.76	330.0
Polytrichum spores	0.23	19 000.0
Lycoperdon spores	0.047	460 000.0

Then, seeds blown over sea-ice by the wind would seem to have a better chance, but this will be considered below

The role of the wind as a long-distance dispenser of plant material is perhaps the most important one (Ridley, 1930; Salisbury, 1942, etc.). It is well known that very many plants are equipped for wind-dispersal, and a lot of seeds and fruits have extra appendages making this sort of dispersal especially feasible.

There is, however, a substantial difference between wind-dispersal over moderate distances and dispersal over such long ones as we deal with here. Fruits and seeds equipped with plumes, wings, and similar arrangements may not fly long distances at all, because their settling rate, which is dependent on the weight and dimensions of the seeds, is too fast (Ridley, 1930; Geiger, 1950). The only particles which actually can serve as a sort of "air-plankton" and be carried very far from the mother plants are spores, pollen, and similar microscopical bodies (cf. Tables 4 and 5). But even these do not go very far if the wind dispersing them is faint or occurs in stratified layers as is not seldom the

TABLE 5

EXPERIMENTAL DISPERSAL LIMITS OF *Papaver* SEEDS (AFTER SALISBURY 1942). THE SEEDS WERE DISSEMINATED FROM THE CAPSULES BY AID OF WIND, DELIBERATELY MADE TURBULENT, BY AN ELECTRICAL FAN. THE GERMINATION CAPACITY OF THE THUS DISSEMINATED SEEDS WAS TESTED.

Distance in cm	Number of viable seeds which would be furnished by one plant		
	P. dubium	*P. argemone*	*P. hybridum*
176–325	155.0	63	25
326–375	3.2	0	0
over 375	1.6	0	0

TABLE 6.

LIST OF PLANT SPECIES WITH SEEDS WHICH MAY QUALIFY FOR WIND-DISPERSAL IN THE NORTH ATLANTIC AREA, THEIR SEED DIMENSIONS, SEED WEIGHTS, AND PRESENTLY KNOWN DISTRIBUTION.

Species	Seed dimensions in mm	Seed weight in mg.	Faeroes	Iceland	Jan Mayen	Bear Island	Spits-bergen	Franz Joseph's Land
37 spore plants	microscopical	—	22	32	3	3	6	0
Juncus bufonius	0.3 × 0.3 × 0.5*	0.015†	×	×	—	—	—	—
Juncus biglumis	0.3 × 0.8†	0.04	×	×	—	×	×	×
Juncus triglumis	0.23 × 0.7†	0.02	×	×	—	—	×	—
Juncus articulatus	0.3 × 0.3 × 0.6*	—	×	×	—	—	—	—
Orchis mascula	0.1 × 0.15 × 0.15 (incl. app. 0.2 × 0.4)*	—	×	—	—	—	—	—
Dactylorchis maculata	0.15 × 0.25 × 0.5 (incl. app. 0.2 × 0.7)*	—	×	×	—	—	—	—
Dactylorchis purpurella	0.05 × 0.15 × 0.15 (incl. app. 0.2 × 0.7)*	—	×	×	—	—	—	—
Coeloglossum viride	0.1 × 0.2 × 0.2 (incl. app. 0.25 × 0.5)*	—	×	×	—	—	—	—
Platanthera hyperborea	—	0.01	—	×	—	—	—	—
Listera ovata	0.10 × 0.12 × 0.12 (incl. app. 0.25 × 0.8)*	—	—	×	—	—	—	—
Corallorhiza trifida	0.1 × 0.15 × 0.15 (incl. app. 0.3 × 0.9)*	—	—	×	—	—	—	—

Tofieldia palustris	0.36 × 0. 7†	0.03	—	×	×	—	×	—
Sagina procumbens	0.2 × 0.2 × 0.25*	0.01	×	×	—	—	—	—
Minuartia verna	0.5 × 0.6†	0.05	×	—	—	—	—	×
Ranunculus pygmaeus	—	0.06	—	×	×	×	×	—
Draba nivalis	0.65 × 1.0	0.04	—	×	×	—	×	—
Drosera rotundifolia	0.1 × 0.1 × 0.2* (incl. app. 2.0)	—	×	×	—	—	—	—
Sedum villosum	0.3 × 0.6†	0.02	×	×	—	—	—	—
Saxifraga rivularis	0.4 × 0.6†	0.03	×	×	—	—	—	—
Saxifraga nivalis	0.3–0.4 × 0.6 × 0.9†	0.04	×	×	×	×	×	×
Saxifraga groenlandica	0.3–0.4 × 0.6–0.8†	0.05	—	×	—	×	×	×
Saxifraga aizoides	—	0.04	—	×	—	×	×	—
Pyrola minor	0.1 × 0.2 (incl. app. 0.6)*	0.0007	×	×	—	—	—	—
Pyrola grandiflora	microscopical†	0.0002	—	×	—	—	—	—
Orthilia secunda	0.1 × 0.2 (incl. app. 0.6)*	—	—	×	—	—	—	—
Phyllodoce coerulea	microscopical†	0.0001	—	×	—	—	—	—
Loiseleuria procumbens	microscopical†	0.01	×	×	—	—	—	—
Harrimanella hypnoides	—	0.01	—	×	—	—	—	—
Veronica Wormskjoldii	0.5 × 0.6	0.04	×	×	—	—	×	—
Campanula (dubia?)	0.25 × 0.65†	0.06	×	×	×	—	—	—
Gnaphalium norvegicum	—	0.08	—	×	—	—	—	—

* Beijerinck, 1947. † Porsild 1920.

case on a quiet, warm day (Geiger, 1950). On the other hand, if there is a high degree of turbulence in the air near the ground, even light seeds can eventually be lifted to sufficient height for a long-distance dispersal to take place (Ridley, 1930; Dahl, 1958).

It seems that such seeds must have approximately the same properties as loess or very fine sand, i.e. no diameter in any direction over 0.2 mm (Dahl, 1958), or a density of not more than 2.6 gr/cm^3 with a largest diameter below 0.6 mm (J. Elson, Montreal, pers. comm.). Very few plant species have seeds which come inside these narrow limits, and in our area only species of Orchidaceae and certain *Juncus*, *Sagina*, *Drosera*, *Pyrola*, *Phyllodoce*, *Loiseleuria*, and *Harrimanella* seem to qualify outright (cf. Table 6).

Air turbulence is often created by thunderstorms in lower latitudes, but the violent hurricanes in the North Atlantic area certainly create enough turbulence in the ground layers of the atmosphere to move dust-seeds out of their capsules and up to a sufficient altitude for long-distance dispersal (cf. also Sverdrup, 1957).

The quantity of spores (of ferns, clubmosses, horsetails, mosses, and lichens, etc.) no doubt exceeds in relative amounts the mass of airborn seeds, including dust-seeds (Ridley, 1930). Some must be regarded as ever-present "air-plankton" (e.g. *Lycoperdon*, cf. Table 4, and Geiger, 1950), but ecological and climatological factors certainly limit the areas where both spores and dust-seeds can develop into mature plants (Salisbury, 1942). Though some species of, for example, Orchidaceae, *Lycopodium*, *Equisetum*, and various ferns reach very high latitudes, the bulk of them belong to more southern areas.

It cannot be denied, however, that there are a number of species which could have spread over our area very easily if the distances between the landmasses at some time in the past were shorter than now (Löve and Löve, 1956; Dahl, 1958; Hadač, 1960). Under such circumstances it would be much easier to account for the present distribution of species whose seeds are carried moderate distances from the mother plant by the wind, and it would explain, for instance, why we have a dominance of windspread species in the western element of this flora (Dahl, 1958). The winds in the North Atlantic are predominantly westerly, although occasionally easterly winds of carrying capacity blow for short intervals (Orvig, Montreal, pers. comm.).

But wind-dispersal does not consist only of material blown through the air, it also includes heavier particles blown over the surface of the ground. It is self-evident that open water limits this form of dispersal in most of our area, but in the far north the continuous ice-cover over the Polar Sea might provide means for ground dispersal of seeds over relatively long distances. Thus, some Russian scientists (Tikhomirov, 1951; Aleksandrova, 1960) believe that all the present flora of Novaya Zemlya has blown in from the mainland over the Kara Sea and Strait in Post-glacial time. Whether this form of distribution is able to convey seeds from, for example, Greenland to Spitsbergen, and from there on to Franz Joseph's Land or vice versa cannot be definitely established, but the possibility should not be totally excluded.

It must be remembered, however, that the sea-ice provides a far from smooth surface over which seeds can slide as easily as over lake-ice. Sea-ice is very rugged, full of relief, ridges, etc. (Sverdrup, 1957), that will easily trap the seeds. It is, furthermore, a rough surface even on a minute scale and would act as an abrasive on the material being pushed over it. Thus, probably only seeds with heavy coats will be able to withstand this treatment for a sustained period of time.

Not being able to estimate the number of plants dispersed by blowing over the polar ice, we can calculate that at most 10 per cent of the species in our area are able to spread over long distances by air.

Considering the three media for long-distance dispersal of plants and seeds, it is evident that only a fraction of the present day distribution of plants in the North Atlantic area can be explained as a result of Post-glacial wind-, water-, or animal-dispersal over the present distances. Those plants, which cannot have made use of any of the above-mentioned transportation media, or which have not been brought around by man during very recent times, must therefore have come to the Atlantic islands over land-connections, or, over a system of landmasses at considerably shorter distances from each other than at present. This author does not doubt that such conditions did exist in some form or another at some time or another, but probably so early that it has been necessary for the main part of the present, native flora to survive all or at least part of the Pleistocene Ice Age in the area.

That this survival has resulted in the loss of a great deal of a previous flora is beyond question; it is more surprising that so much has managed to survive.

In our area it can be said that the Ice Age still reigns in certain parts, as in Greenland, Spitsbergen, and Franz Joseph's Land. Some authors doubt that the climate in the Arctic was as severe as at present during the time when there were continental ice sheets in Eurasia and North America, and it has been designated as an area for possible plant refugia during the Ice Age by, for example, Fernald (1925), Hultén (1937), Marie-Victorin (1938), Ewing and Donn (1956), to mention only a few. Voices to the contrary have of course also been heard (Flint, 1947; Savile, 1961).

When an area is studied the average temperature is often used as an indicator to the rigor of its climate, but the annual average is a poor figure so long as the amplitude of the temperature variations is not given. If the plants have any frost tolerance at all, it does not seem to matter so much how deep the temperature dips. Three species of cacti easily survive winter temperatures down to −45°C in Manitoba, Canada. Summer temperature, duration of vegetative season, and precipitation are factors that largely determine distribution areas (Jeffre, 1960). Even the average air temperature of the summer months may not give a full answer to the tolerance of a given species. Under conditions which may seem forbidding to a human, a microclimate may exist that is very tolerable for a plant (Monteith, 1960). Floras, from a dozen to well over a hundred species, exist today in areas where the temperatures at meteorological stations indicate averages only slightly above the freezing point throughout the growing season (cf. Fristrup, 1952, for Peary Land, Greenland: June 2.6°, July 6.3°, Aug. 3.6°C; Aleksandrova, 1961, for Great Lyakhovsky Island, N. of Siberia: June 0.2°, July 3.5°, Aug. 2.5°C; Savile, 1961, for Isachsen, Queen Elizabeth Islands, Canada: June 0.38°, July 3.5°, Aug. 1.25°C).

Aleksandrova's (1961) detailed analysis of the phenology of Great Lyakhovsky Island in the Novosibirsk Archipelago in the summer of 1956 demonstrates the close relationship between temperature at ground level and plant development, and shows that even in this rigorous climate a rhythmic and seasonal development of the flora takes place. During the short vegetative season, thus, both *Ranunculus sulphureus* and *R. Sabinei* had two different flowering periods, a spring anthesis 23 June to 25 July and a fall anthesis 8 Aug. to 20 Aug., both apparently temperature-regulated. She noticed a difference also in the rhythmic development and length of the vegetation periods between various plant communities. The ones on the quickly thawing and warming polygon-tundra were richest in species, first to start growth, and first to reach a fall aspect, whereas communities in depressions with a long-lasting snow-cover, in spite of starting vegetative development under the snow, were slower in maturing and had shorter, more compressed seasons, as well as a lesser number of species.

Tikhomirov, Shamurin and Shtepa (1960) have recently used micro-thermo-couples to measure the temperature in various parts (buds, leaves, stems, roots, etc.) of Arctic plants (e.g. *Sieversia glacialis* in E. Siberia), and found their temperature to be up to several degrees (Centigrade) higher than the surrounding air temperature. The differences were most marked on clear, quiet days, but noticeable also on overcast and windy days. It is interesting that the roots, too, had higher temperatures than the soil around them.

At high altitudes in the Himalayas (Swan, 1961) it has been demonstrated that a favorable microclimate and access to some water will permit wind-dispersed plant species to take hold, even where the success seems bleak indeed, judged by human standards.

A high degree of adaptation against climatic rigors: polster-growth, much hairiness, dark buds, characters which we regard as "protective measures", are of course often found among plants thriving in our area. But there are also several plants which lack these qualities and still survive well (cf. Böcher, 1938; Sörensen, 1933).

It is, however, easily forgotten that these same plant species, subjected to such cold treatment, have also had to go through a period of considerably higher temperatures than at present, the Hypsithermal. It may be said that the plants have had their tolerances tried to the utmost.

That many species, which we regard as confined to cold climates, do have an almost incredible tolerance, has been demonstrated to me by some wild plants at present cultivated in our greenhouse at the Montreal Botanical Garden. These plants were brought down from the top of Mt. Washington, New Hampshire, U.S.A., from an altitude of 1918 m and a climate with a yearly average temperature of −2.8°C (July 9.5°C, extremes Jan. −43.9°C, July 21.7°C). They have been able to survive three years of maltreatment in small pots, scorched by summer temperatures of over 50°C, erratically over- and under-watered, occasionally frozen, subjected to extraordinary variations in air-moisture, and still they go on existing, growing, and even flowering and fruiting. Among them are such species as *Silene acaulis*, *Saxifraga hyperborea*, *Campanula dubia*, *Bistorta vivipara*, *Juncus trifidus*, *Hierochloë orthantha*, all normally considered as requiring Arctic, or at least High Alpine, conditions for their existence.

If one dares to judge from the few examples given above, the tolerance of many of the species which grow in the North Atlantic area is very wide indeed. Most likely it is the result of strong selection over a very long period of time.

The fact that we have a high percentage of polyploids in this flora may also be an indication of its genetical amplitude for varying conditions at the same time as it may possibly indicate its old age (Löve and Löve, 1943, 1949; Löve, 1959).

In the opinion of this author it seems therefore that, dispersal and survival conditions considered particularly, there are very strong indications that the present native flora in the North Atlantic area is old, well established, and in the majority of cases a relict from a time preceding the Pleistocene Ice Age or at least its latest phases.

REFERENCES

ALEKSANDROVA, V. D. (1960). Some regularities in the distribution of the vegetation in the Arctic tundra. *Arctic* **13**, 147–163.

ALEKSANDROVA, V. D. (1961). Seasonal dynamics of plant associations in the Arctic (in Russian). *Problem i Severa* **4**, 59–24. Acad. Sci. U.S.S.R.

BEIJERINK, W. (1947). *Zadenatlas der Nederlandschen Flora*. Veenman & zonen, Waageningen.

BLISS, L. C. (1958). Seed germination in Arctic and Alpine species. *Arctic* **11**, 180–189.

BÖCHER, T. W. (1938). Biological distributional types in the flora of Greenland. *Medd. om Groenl.* **106**, 1–339.

BÖCHER, T. W., HOLMEN, K. and JAKOBSEN, K. (1957). *Grönlands flora*. P. Haase & Söns Forlag, Copenhagen.

BUSS, I.O. (1946). Bird detection by radar. *The Auk* **63**, 315–318.

DAHL, E. (1937). On the vascular plants of Eastern Svalbard. *Norges Svalbard og Ishavsundersökelser. Skr. Svalbard og Ishavet* **75**, 1–50.

DAHL, E. (1958). Amfiatlantiske planter. Problems of Amphiatlantic plant distribution. *Blyttia* **16**, 93–121.

DAHL, E. and HADAČ, E. (1946). Et bidrag til Spitsbergens flora. *Norges Svalbard og Ishavsundersökelser. Medd.* **63**, 1–15.

DURANGO, S. (1953). *Fåglarna i färg.* 2nd ed. Almquist & Wiksell, Stockholm.

EWING, M. and DONN, W. L. (1956). A theory of Ice Ages. *Science* **123**, 1061–1066.

FERNALD, M. L. (1925). Persistence of plants in unglaciated areas of boreal America. *Mem. Amer. Acad. Arts & Sci.* **15**, 241–342.

FLINT, R. F. (1947). *Glacial geology and the Pleistocene epoch.* John Wiley, New York.

FRISTRUP, B. (1952). Physical geography of Peary Land. *Medd. om Groenl.* **127**, 1–143.

GEIGER, R. (1950). *The Climate near the Ground.* Harvard Univ. Press.

HADAČ, E. (1944). Die Gefässpflanzen des "Sassengebietes" Vestspitzbergen. *Norges Svalbard og Ishavsundersökelser. Skr. Svalbard og Ishavet* **87**, 1–71.

HADAČ, E. (1960). The history of the flora of Spitzbergen and Bear Island and the age of some Arctic plant species. *Preslia* **32**, 225–253.

HAGEN, A. (1952). Plants collected in Vestspitzbergen in the summer of 1933. *Norsk Polarinstitutt Medd.* **70**, 1–13.

HANSSEN, O., and LID. J. (1932). Flowering plants of Franz Josefs Land. *Norges Svalbard og Ishavsundersökelser. Skr. Svalbard og Ishavet* **39**, 1–42.

HESLOP-HARRISON, J. (1953). The North American and Lusitanian elements in the flora of the British Isles. In J. E. LOUSLEY (ed.): *The Changing Flora in Britain*, 105–123.

HOCHBAUM, H. A. (1955). *Travels and Traditions of Waterfowl.* Univ. of Minnesota Press.

HULTÉN, E. (1937). *Outline of the History of Arctic and Boreal Biota during the Quaternary Period.* Stockholm.

HULTÈN, E. (1962). Plants of the floating Ice-island "Arlis II" *Svensk Bot. Tidolir* **56** 362–367.

JEFFRE, E. P. (1960). A climatic pattern between latitudes 40° and 70° and its probable influence on biological distribution. *Proc. Linn. Soc. London* **171**, 89–121.

JÖRGENSEN, C. A., SÖRENSEN, T., and WESTERGAARD, M. (1958). The flowering plants of Greenland. A taxonomical and cytological survey. *Dansk Vidensk. Selsk. Biol. Skr.* **9**, 1–172.

LÖVE, Á. (1945). *Islenzkar jurtir.* Einar Munksgaard, Copenhagen.

LÖVE, Á. (1959). Origin of the Arctic flora. *McGill. Univ. Mus, Publ.* **1**, 82–95.

LÖVE, Á., and LÖVE, D. (1943). The significance of differences in distribution of diploids and polyploids. *Hereditas* **29**, 145–163.

LÖVE, Á. and LÖVE, D. (1947). Studies on the origin of the Icelandic flora I. Cyto-ecological investigations on *Cakile. Icel. Univ. Inst. Appl. Sci. Dept. of Agric. Rep.* **B,2**, 1–29.

LÖVE, Á. and LÖVE, D. (1949). Geobotanical significance of polyploidy. I. Polyploidy and latitude. *Portug. Acta Biol.* (*A*). R. B. Goldschmidt Vol, 273–352.

LÖVE, Á. and LÖVE, D. (1956). Cytotaxonomical conspectus of the Icelandic Flora. *Acta Horti Gotoburg.* **20**, 65–291.

LÖVE, Á. and LÖVE, D. (1958). The American element in the flora of the British Isles. *Bot. Notiser 1958*, 376–388.

LÖVE, Á. and LÖVE, D. (1961). Chromosome numbers of central and northwest European plant species. *Opera Botanica* **5**, I–VIII, 1–581.

LÖWENSKJOLD, H. L. (1954). Studies on the avifauna of Spitzbergen. *Norsk Polarinstitutt Skrifter* **103**, 1–131.

MARIE-VICTORIN, FRÈRE (1938). Phytogeographical problems of eastern Canada. *Amer. Midl. Nat.* **19**, 489–558.

MONTEITH, J. L. (1960). Micrometeorology in relation to plant and animal life. *Proc. Linn. Soc. London* **171**, 71–82.

OSBORNE, S. (1855). Mirgration of plants on ice *Journ. of H. M. Sledge.*

PORSILD, A. E. (1920). Sur le poids et les dimensions des graines arctiques. *Rèv. Gen. Botanique* **32**, 97–120.

RASMUSSEN, R. (1952). *Föroya flora.* 2nd ed. Torshavn, the Faeroes.

RIDLEY, H. N. (1930). *The Dispersal of Plants throughout the World.* L. Reeve & Co. Ltd., Ashford, England.

RÖNNING, O. I. (1959). The vascular flora of Bear Island. *Acta Borealia A. Scientia* **15**, 1–53.

SALISBURY, E. J. (1942). *The Reproductive Capacity of Plants.* G. Bell, London.

SAMUELSSON, G. (1934). Die Verbreitung der höheren Wasserpflanzen in Nord-Europa. *Acta Phytogeogr. Suec.* **6**, 1–211.

SAVILE, D. B. O. (1961). The Botany of the Northwestern Queen Elizabeth Islands. *Canad. J. Bot.* **39**, 909–942.

SCHAANING, H. L. T. (1933a). A contribution to the bird fauna of East-Greenland. *Norges Svalbard og Ishavsundersökelser. Skr. Svalbard of Ishavet* **49**, 25–39.

SCHOLANDER, P. F. (1934). Vascular plants from northern Svalbard. *Norges Svalbard og Ishavsundersökelser. Skr. Svalbard og Ishavet* **62**, 1–153.

SLADEN, W. J. (1960). The flora of a breeding area of pink-footed geese in central Iceland. *Proc. Linn. Soc. London* **171**, 30–52.

SÖRENSEN, T. (1933). The vascular plants of East Greenland from 71° to 73° 30′ N. Lat. *Medd. om Groenl.* **101**(3), 1–177.

SVERDRUP, H. (1957). The stress of the wind on the ice of the polar sea. *Norsk Polarinstitutt Skrifter* **111**, 1–11.

SWAN, L. W. (1961). The ecology of the High Himalayas. *Scientific American* **205**, 68–90.

TIKHOMIROV, B. A. (1951). On the role of the wind in the plant distribution in the Far North (in Russian). *Priroda 1951* 23–25.

TIKHOMIROV, B. A., SHAMURIN, V. F., and SHTEPA, V. S. (1960). Temperature of Arctic plants (in Russian). *Isvestiya Akademii Nauk SSSR, Ser. Biol.* **3**, 429–442.

WITHERBY, H. F., JOURDAIN, F. C. R., TICEHURST, N. F., and TUCKER, B. W. (1939). *The Handbook of British Birds.* H. F. and C. Witherby, London.

YOCOM, C. F. (1947). Observations on bird life in the Pacific Ocean off the North American shores. *Condor* **49**, 204–208.

ON THE HISTORY AND AGE OF SOME ARCTIC PLANT SPECIES

EMIL HADAČ

Department of Botany, Czechoslovakian Academy of Sciences, Průhonice, near Praha, Czechoslovakia

THE flora of the Arctic is very variable. We find there plant species which are broadly Circumpolar and others which are confined to some part of the Arctic territory. There are also species of American, Asiatic, or European origin mixed with the Circumpolar High Arctic element.

If we want to know how old the Arctic flora really is, we must first answer several questions: How long have conditions favoring the tundra vegetation existed in the Arctic? Was there any tundra vegetation during the Tertiary epoch, or was it formed during the Ice Ages? If they already existed in the Tertiary epoch, could they have survived all the glaciations? Is there really any indigenous Arctic flora, or are plants now living in the Arctic all immigrants from the mountains of the adjacent continents?

Many questions and no easy answers!

We have as far as I know no direct proof for a tundra vegetation earlier than the Quaternary period. On the other hand, we know that the Taiga formation (Piceetea) was already widely distributed in a large part of Siberia in the second half of the Miocene and in the Pliocene. If Taiga existed as far south as Baikal Lake, then there must have been conditions for a tundra vegetation north of this vegetation type, if not in lowlands, then at least in the Arctic mountains.

If Lindquist's (1947) identification of *Betula callosa* in the Icelandic Miocene is correct, we can expect true Arctic conditions not far to the north of the Arctic Circle during that time.

Now it is well known that in the Neogene the continents, at least in the Northern Hemisphere, were raised perhaps several hundreds of meters (cf., for example, Strachov, 1948). By this movement a land connection between America, Iceland, and Scandinavia could be and most probably was formed. Terrestrial sediments are found in this region originating mainly from the Eocene (Kjartansson, 1940; cf. also Dahl, 1958), and the submarine relief of the northern Atlantic shows us that there was a land connection not only between Greenland and Scandinavia, but also between Northeast Greenland and Spitsbergen (Fig. 1).

The influence of such a land connection upon the climate and vegetation must have been enormous, especially because in the Neogene the Arctic Sea was cut off from its broad connection with the warm southern part of the Ocean; in the Paleogene this connection was realized through Siberia (cf. Strachov, 1948). If there was any warm current like the Gulf Stream, it must

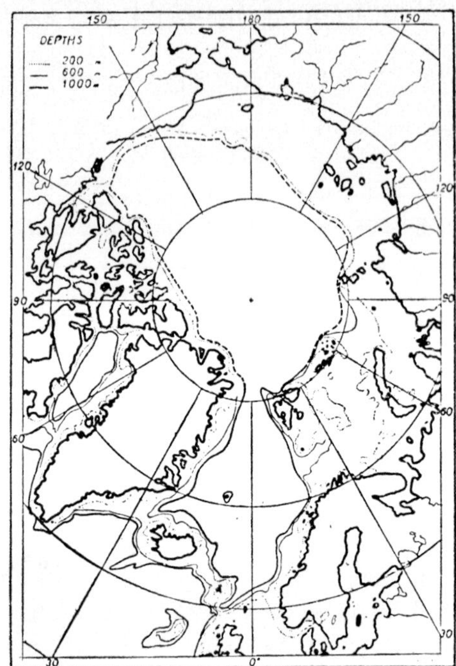

FIG. 1. The submarine relief of the Arctic basin and the northern Atlantic.

have stopped on a line from southern Greenland over Iceland to Scotland. Most of its heat was given off on this coast and a mild Atlantic climate must have resulted from this change. But how was it north of this land connection? When no warm waters could enter the Arctic Basin, a real High Arctic climate could be felt already in the central parts of the present Arctic. In the contact between the cold Arctic air and the mild, wet Atlantic winds, there was probably heavy precipitation and large glaciers could be formed in the contact zone, whereas in the Arctic itself a continental climate could have favored continental refugia.

This hypothesis is of course pure fantasy based on a few solid facts only; the paleogeographers and the paleoclimatologists will have the last words on these problems. But if we accept such suppositions as a working hypothesis we can arrange our biological data concerning the Arctic and Atlantic biota in a relatively satisfactory and logical way.

If the Arctic climate already existed in the Arctic in the Neogene during *ca.* 7,000,000–10,000,000 years, this period was certainly sufficient for the formation of the bulk of the Eoarctic flora from the Temperate or Sub-Arctic flora growing there in the Tertiary.

But previously to this, a very similar flora was formed in the high mountains of Eurasia and America. This flora was isolated for a long time and could develop well-characterized taxa of even higher ranks than species. At the end of the Tertiary new possibilities arose for such floras—the Arctic vegetation reached as far as some mountain ridges and the mountain flora of North America and northeastern Asia could migrate into the Arctic and vice versa–Arctic elements could penetrate into the interior of the continents or far to the south.

In the beginning the conditions were somewhat different in Europe itself. Although certainly the Alps, the Pyrenees, the Caucasus, etc., had their own mountain floras, they had no connection with the Arctic at first. Even during the first Ice Age the contact between the Arctic and the Alpine floras was probably minimal. The Arctic flora existed mainly north of the continental ice-shield. Now the migration of plants occurs differently if these have to penetrate into regions already occupied by other plants or if they have to colonize land laid bare by sea or ice regression. We must therefore suppose that the penetration of the Arctic element southwards was much slower, more difficult and less effective than the advance of the mountain flora northwards. The First Ice Age could therefore hardly bring any Arctic elements to central Europe and the central European mountain flora could scarcely give more than a small contribution to the Arctic flora because the ice shield did not reach so far south at that time (Fig. 2).

Only during the Mindel and Riss Glacials, and partly also during the Würm period, could a greater exchange of plant species take place between the central European mountains and the Arctic as well as between the Alpine and Siberian elements.

The exchange of the flora of the Arctic and of the mountains of America and Eurasia was only partial; we know well enough that only certain mountain species migrated to the north and that not all Arctic species migrated to the south although climatic conditions seemed favorable to both. We must take into consideration the ability of the mountain plants to live in the tundra communities; there are sharp differences in the life conditions of the steep mountain slopes and ridges and the mostly flat tundra. The capacity of seed transport was also of some importance. These two factors combined brought about a situation where certainly old oreophytic species of the European mountains, as, for example, *Carex firma* (forming extensive and very characteristic plant communities in the Alps, the Pyrenees, the Carpathians, and the Karavanken, and elsewhere) did not reach north of the Tatra Mountains, whereas *Salix herbacea* and other similar species migrated towards the north.

It seems that there must also have been other factors influencing this migration: e.g. the physiological qualities of the plants themselves. There are probably several stages in the development of every plant species. Young ones are plastic ecologically as well as morphologically. At this stage the species are able to migrate long distances if climatic and geographic factors allow it, and they easily form new taxa under the influence of different conditions.

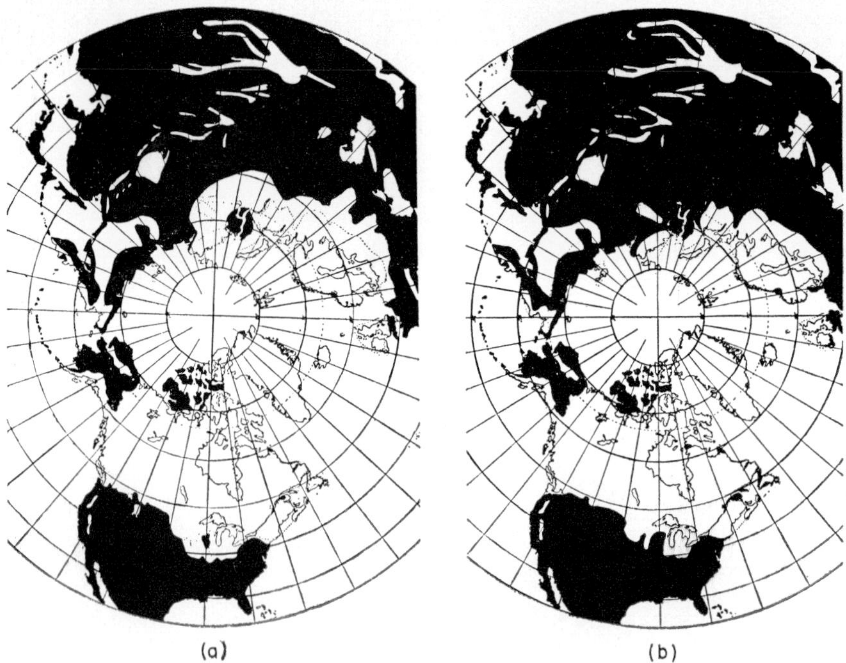

FIG. 2 (a). The extent of ice-shields during the Great glaciation. (Compiled after several authors.)

(b). The extent of ice-shields during the Last glaciation. (Compiled after several authors.)

"Mature species" have a stabilized morphology, but they are still plastic enough ecologically. Thus, if they get the opportunity to migrate, they may reach distant regions, but do not change in subsequent periods even if they are isolated for a long time. These are the species with disjunctive areas, which mostly are relics from former periods. "Old species" lose even their ecological plasticity, they cannot spread even over short distances, their energy seems to suffice only for holding their former area. If their life conditions change, they die out.

The question of the survival of the Arctic flora *in situ* is, I think, positively established by biological as well as by geological arguments. An example is Bear Island, which, though small and situated far to the north, was only partly glaciated. I have shown (Hadač, 1941, 1960) that practically all its rare flora, all its relics, grow in places never glaciated during the Last Ice Age.

Spitsbergen, Siberia, Alaska, eastern North America and Greenland have vast areas of never glaciated territories where, by adaptation and isolation during the Ice Age or Ages, new species could be formed, as, for example, *Coptidium spitsbergense*, *Pedicularis dasyantha*, *Puccinellia vilfoidea*, etc.

Meanwhile, during the Mindel and Riss Ice Ages, many Arctic elements penetrated southwards. I must say that I was very sceptical towards reports of Arctic plant species from far distant mountains in the south until I myself collected *Oxyria digyna* in the mountains of the Iraqi Kurdistan.

In discussions on the Arctic flora and its migrations several authors have emphasized that the migration followed step by step (i.e. not, or very seldom, as single plants but rather in whole plant communities) which is possible only over land connections. Dahl (1958) has shown (by statistical analysis of the Scandinavian Amphi-Atlantic element and its adaptation to, or incapability of, long-distance dispersal) that the occurrence of "western" elements in the Scandinavian flora is not due to long-distance dispersal. This is a negative proof. But we can test this problem also in another way.

Let us suppose, for example, that the flora of Spitsbergen was supplied by long-distance dispersal from the south, east, and west, and that its plant communities were formed by free combination of all these geographical elements according to their requirements. In such a case the different geographical elements of the flora should be represented in plant communities of Spitsbergen according to the law of probability, and not all grouped together.

The most common plant association of the Spitsbergen tundra in the Inner Fjord zone is *Tomentohypnetum involuti* (cf. Hadač, 1946, p. 155). The climax community seems to be *Cassiopetum tetragonae*. The most luxuriant community of this region is *Trisetetum spicati*. Let us now compare the percentage occurrence of different geographical groups (which will be discussed later on) in the associations mentioned with the average of the whole flora, i.e. with the "probable" occurrence: "probable" under the supposition that their species came to Spitsbergen independently by long-distance dispersal (Table 1).

More instructive may be the actual and "expected" numbers of species in geographical groups (Table 2).

We can see that the actual numbers of plant species in individual groups very seldom agree with the "supposed" numbers and that the differences in several cases (designated with*) exceed the standard deviation; the differences are thus statistically significant.

It is also evident that in most communities plants of the same origin remain together; they came to Spitsbergen not as single species but as members of the same plant community. This can be proved as well for Iceland and Greenland, as elsewhere.

I would like to bring in a striking example of this nature from a region far from the Arctic. In high mountains of the Iraqi Kurdistan, A.D.Q. Agnew and I found two well-defined plant communities side by side: a community of *Prangos ferulacea* and *Astragalus kurdicus* (sect. *Tragacantha*) and other more or less endemic species, which have survived there or in the neighborhood from the Tertiary. We also noted some other hygrophytic communities of an alliance which we call Primuleto-Blysmion compressi, with *Primula auriculata* and not few European or Eurasiatic elements like *Eleocharis quinqueflora, Carex panicea, C. distans, Juncus Gerardii, Juncus inflexus, Triglochin palustre, Deschampsia cæspitosa, Sagina saginoides, Cerastium cerastoides*, etc., practically without any local endemic element. This last community immigrated into this area very probably during the Second or Third Pluvial.

TABLE 1

THE OCCURRENCE (IN %) IN CERTAIN PLANT COMMUNITIES OF PLANTS BELONGING TO VARIOUS GEOGRAPHICAL GROUPS

Geographical groups	% in the whole flora	% in the *Tomento-hypnetum*	% in the *Cassiopetum tetragonae*	% in the *Trisetetum spicati*
1. Circumpola Oreo-Arctic	15.2	22.2	36	31.5
2. Circumpola Arctic–Sub-Arctic	25.0	18.5	20	31.5
3. Circumpola Arctic	13.2	29.6	32	21.0
4. Circumpola High Arctic	14.6	11.1	4	
5. Amphi-Atlantic–Arctic–Sub-Arctic	2.1	3.7	4	
6. Amphi-Atlantic–Arctic	4.2	3.7		5.2
7. European–Alpine–Atlantic	6.9	7.4		5.2
8. European–Asiatic	1.4			
9. Beringian	2.8			
10. East Siberian	5.5	3.7		5.2
11. Greenland–Spitsbergen	2.8			
12. Novaya Zemlya–Spitsbergen	3.5		4	
13. Spitsbergen endemics	2.1			
14. Recent immigrants	0.7			

But this holds true not only for plants: in the communities of the order Prangetalia live reptiles and insects of an Irano-Turanian type of distribution, whereas in the alliance Primuleto-Blysmion we meet frogs like *Rana ridibunda* and *Hyla arborea*—typically European or Eurasiatic—or "European" insects like *Tipula maxima, T. lunata, T. lateralis, Pales crocata*, and *P. pratensis* (J. Slípka, unpubl.). We can thus state that not only plant communities, but whole biocoenoses migrate step by step, even if their individual members could migrate over long distances.

Obviously, the history of the Arctic flora is very intricate. It is not easy to

TABLE 2

STATISTICAL COMPARISON BETWEEN ACTUAL AND EXPECTED NUMBERS IN CERTAIN PLANT COMMUNITIES OF PLANTS FROM VARIOUS GEOGRAPHICAL GROUPS.

(For identification of "geographical group", see Table 1.)

	Geographical groups												
	1	2	3	4	5	6	7	8	9	10	11	12	13
Tomentohypnetum													
Actual number	6*	5	8*	3	1	1	2			1			
Expected number	4.1	6.7	3.5	3.9	0.6	1.2	1.9	0.4	0.8	1.5	0.6	0.9	0.6
Standard deviation ±	1.87	2.23	1.76	1.83	1.7	1.0	1.3	0.6	0.8	1.2	0.8	0.9	0.7
Cassiopetum													
Actual number	9*	5	8*	1*		1						1	
Expected number	3.8	6.2	3.3	3.6	0.5	1.0	1.7	0.4	0.7	1.4	0.5	0.9	0.5
Standard deviation ±	1.8	2.17	1.69	1.77	0.7	1.0	1.3	0.6	0.8	1.1	0.8	0.9	0.5
Trisetetum													
Actual number	6*	6	4*	—*		1	1			1			
Expected number	2.8	4.7	2.5	2.7	0.4	0.8	1.3	0.2	0.5	1.0	0.4	0.7	0.4
Standard deviation ±	1.56	1.89	1.48	1.54	0.6	0.9	1.1	0.5	0.7	1.0	0.7	0.8	0.6

* Statistically significant difference.

define its different components, especially the old ones. Only detailed world monographs of whole genera, their cytotaxonomy and ecology combined with a solid paleogeographic knowledge will throw a clear light onto the origin of the Arctic species.

To get at least some information I have analysed here the flora of Spitsbergen by mapping the distribution of all its vascular plant species. I found several types of distribution, which can be applied also for other parts of the Arctic, but these cover only a part of the whole Arctic flora components. Since there are some serious changes from some of the categories which I published in 1960, I shall repeat here all the groups of the Spitsbergen flora (used in our considerations above) and try to explain their characteristic distribution (cf. Hadač, 1960).

1. THE CIRCUMPOLAR OREOPHYTIC–ARCTIC GROUP

(I prefer to use the term *oreophytic*, i.e. mountain type, rather than "alpine", to avoid confusion with plants growing in the Alps.) The species of this group occur in all the Arctic as well as in the mountains of Eurasia and America. Some of them reach even the mountains of the Southern Hemisphere.

They certainly belong to the "Eoarctic" component, but it is difficult to say where their place of origin is found. It could be in some of the mountain ranges of Asia or North America, but also some place in the Arctic itself. Anyway, they must have been relatively old, "mature" species already at the end of the Pliocene. During the Pleistocene they had good opportunities of spreading over all the Arctic as well as into very distant mountain ridges They have persisted in different refugia during the whole of the Pleistocene.

To this group belong, among others, *Equisetum variegatum*, *Cystopteris Dickieana*, *Woodsia glabella*, *Eriophorum Scheuchzeri*, *Carex rupestris*, *Kobresia caricina*, *Juncus triglumis*, *Oxyria digyna*, *Bistorta vivipara*, *Saxifraga oppositifolia* and several others. The last three species were found in Rissian deposits in Poland by Środoń (1954).

Some of the species which I previously grouped in this element, due to a more accurate taxonomic investigation now appear to belong elsewhere. Thus, *Empetrum hermaphroditum* Hagerup (or *E. Eamesii* Fern. & Wiegand ssp. *hermaphroditum* D. Löve) appears to have a distribution similar to that of *Arabis alpina*, *Salix herbacea*, or *Saxifraga aizoides* and belongs therefore rather to my European–Alpine–Atlantic group (cf. Vassiljev, 1961; D. Löve, 1960). Also *Lycopodium* (or *Huperzia*) *selago* seems to be a heterogeneous taxon deserving an accurate monograph.

2. THE CIRCUMPOLAR ARCTIC–SUB-ARCTIC GROUP

The origin of this group seems to be somewhere in the Arctic during or before the early Pleistocene; during the Ice Ages it attained a broad circumpolar Arctic–Sub-Arctic distribution. Part of it reached even some relatively adjacent mountain ridges in the nearest continents. There it has a pronounced relic character with species like *Ranunculus pygmaeus* and *Saxifraga nivalis*. The whole group is represented in Scandinavia and Iceland.

In Spitsbergen the following species belong to this group: *Phippsia algida*, *Festuca Richardsonii* ssp. *cryophila*, *Carex subspathacea*, *Carex saxatilis*, *Juncus biglumis*, *Koeniga islandica*, s.l., *Tofieldia pusilla*, *Stellaria humifusa*, *Ranunculus hyperboreus*, *Cardamine bellidifolia*, *Draba alpina*, *Saxifraga hirculus*, *Cassiope tetragona*, and others.

Some of them, like *Cassiope tetragona*, seem to be Preglacial.

3. THE CIRCUMPOLAR ARCTIC GROUP

This is another group of the Eoarctic species adjusted to Arctic conditions but not occurring in the Sub-Arctic regions. In Scandinavia it has a centric distribution, but it is more or less lacking in Iceland.

Its age may be Late Pliocene or Early Pleistocene. To this group belong, for example, *Equisetum scirpoides*, *Hierochloë alpina*, *Arctagrostis latifolia*, *Poa arctica*, *Carex misandra*, *Luzula nivalis*, *Melandrium apetalum*, *Braya purpurascens*, *Draba lactea*, *Pedicularis hirsuta*, and other species.

4. THE CIRCUMPOLAR HIGH ARCTIC GROUP

The Eoarctic species of this group are very old—probably from the Pliocene. *Dupontia Fisheri* and *Pleuropogon Sabinei* belong to the endemic genera in the Arctic. I think that the occurrence of *Pleuropogon* in Altai is due to migration from the Arctic. Whether *Pleuropogon* originated in Beringia (as assumed by Roshevizh, 1952) or in another part of the Arctic cannot be proved at present.

Some of the plants have their nearest relatives in the Eurasiatic or American mountains. Thus, for example, *Saxifraga setigera* has a related species in central Asia; *Eutrema Edwardsii* has one in Altai and Sayan mountains; *Festuca brachyphylla* one in the mountains of North America. They came very early to the Arctic and completed their circumpolar distribution during the Ice Ages.

Alopecurus alpinus must be an old species. It occurs in Scotland but not in Scandinavia; it has been found in the stomach of the Siberian mammoth (Tikhomirov and Kupriyanova, 1954). In Scandinavia, some of the species of this group have formed related species or subspecies probably during the Last Glaciation: *Arnica angustifolia* has a very closely related species in Scandinavia, *Arnica alpina*; *Melandrium furcatum* has a near relative, *M. angustiflorum*, in Scandinavia and western Siberia.

Besides the species mentioned we can include in this group, e.g. *Deschampsia brevifolia*, *Poa abbreviata*, *Puccinellia angustata*, *Draba subcapitata*, and several others.

5. THE ARCTIC–SUB-ARCTIC AMPHI-ATLANTIC GROUP

The "Amphi-Atlantic element" is very heterogeneous and should be divided into more homogeneous sub-groups. This group is at home in the Arctic and Sub-Arctic, but not in central Europe. It has crossed the Atlantic either via northeast Greenland–Spitsbergen, or via south Greenland–Iceland (or vice versa). In Spitsbergen only a few species belong to this group: *Harrimanella hypnoides* is probably Preglacial, *Deschampsia alpina* and *Draba rupestris* are probably of Early Pleistocene age.

6. THE ARCTIC AMPHI-ATLANTIC GROUP

Plant species of this group have their distribution in the Arctic on both sides of the Atlantic. It is probable that they migrated by a northern land connection, i.e. via Greenland–Spitsbergen–Novaya Zemlya or vice versa. This land connection is supposed by Sörensen (1945) to have existed as late as during the Mindel-Riss Interglacial. If this is right, the species of this group must be of Early Pleistocene age.

Here belong *Carex ursina*, extending from Taimyr to the American Arctic, *Carex nardina* growing from Alaska to Novaya Zemlya and Scandinavia; *Campanula uniflora* and *Papaver Dahlianum* ssp. *Dahlianum* have a similar distribution. *Minuartia Rossii* reaches from its Arctic American area to Spitsbergen but not farther.

In this group I have also included *Eriophorum triste*, but recent records seem to speak for its inclusion in an Arctic Circumpolar group (No. 3). On the other hand, *Cerastium Regelii* probably belongs here rather than to the third group.

7. THE EUROPEAN ALPINE–ATLANTIC GROUP

The origin of these species lies in European mountains, in the Alps, the Pyrenees, or the Carpathians perhaps as early as the Pliocene or even before. Anyway, in early Pleistocene they were well established, "mature" species. During the Ice Age they descended from the mountains, forming a part of the leading vegetation type of this time, the tundra. In the "Dryas flora" of the Riss deposits in, for example, Poland (cf. Środoń, 1954), were found *Arabis alpina*, *Betula nana*, *Salix herbacea*, *S. reticulata*, together with several species of the Circumpolar Oreo-Arctic group. Following the retreating ice-shield they came to Scandinavia, Iceland, Greenland, and Arctic America, to western Siberia, Novaya Zemlya, and Spitsbergen.

To this group in Spitsbergen belong: *Salix reticulata*, *S. herbacea*, *Betula nana*, *Beckwithia glacialis*, *Arabis alpina*, *Saxifraga aizoides*, *Potentilla Crantzii*, *Poa alpina vivipara*, and perhaps *Festuca vivipara*. *Empetrum hermaphroditum* seems also to belong to this interesting group as may be seen from the map in Vassil'ev's (1961) recent monograph.

8. THE EURASIATIC GROUP

This group is represented in Spitsbergen by two species only: *Potentilla multifida* and *Comastoma tenella*. Both have a very broad distribution, the first one growing in Himalaya, Altai, and northeast Scandinavia, the second one in the central Asiatic mountains, Siberia, Scandinavia, Iceland, reaching even Greenland. They are certainly of Preglacial age.

9. THE BERINGIAN GROUP

This group, formed in Late Pliocene or Early Pleistocene in Beringia and spreading since to east and west, is also poorly represented in the Spitsbergen flora. To it belong: *Arctophila fulva*, which attained Scandinavia only in Late Glacial time when the Bothnian Bay communicated with the Barents Sea: *Coptidium lapponicum*, *Rubus chamaemorus*, and *Chrysosplenium tetrandrum*.

Previously I included in this group also *Puccinellia phryganodes* in the sense of Sörensen (1953) in his recent monograph. But now I agree with Löve and Löve (1961b), who distinguish two species, *Puccinellia vilfoidea* and *P. phryganodes*.

The geographic distribution and cytology of taxa, belonging to this complex, can perhaps be explained in the following manner: the mother species of this complex already existed at the end of the Pliocene somewhere in the Beringian region. By geographic changes caused by glaciation and submergence the Asiatic and American populations were split and gave rise to *Puccinellia phryganodes* and *P. vilfoidea*, both *sensu lato*. During the Late Pleistocene both evolved two subspecies in isolated refugia: *P. phryganodes* formed one subspecies, now distributed in Greenland and northeastern America, and another in the Beringian area. In the large ice-free area of eastern Siberia *Puccinellia vilfoidea* formed the subspecies *sibirica*, occurring also in Scandinavia, whereas in Spitsbergen and Novaya Zemlya may be found ssp. *vilfoidea* itself. This last subspecies must have been developed after the land connection between Spitsbergen and Greenland was destroyed, i.e. probably after the Mindel–Riss Interglacial. It must have occurred after the time when the connection between the Novaya Zemlya-Spitsbergen complex was isolated from the mainland, but before the isolation of Spitsbergen from Novaya Zemlya was realized.

Puccinellia vilfoidea spreads mostly by vegetative means. The relatively short distance between Spitsbergen and Greenland seems to be insurpassable for it; even the channel between Novaya Zemlya and the mainland is a barrier to it. The occurrence of its ssp. *sibirica* in the Bothnian Bay indicates that it was already present on the Arctic coast of Scandinavia in the early Post-glacial, when the direct connection between the Bothnian Bay and the Barents Sea still existed.

10. THE EAST SIBERIAN GROUP

This group originated probably in the Early Pleistocene in the ice-free parts of eastern Siberia. *Salix polaris* is known from the "Dryas flora" of the Rissian Ice Age in Poland, and its arrival in Spitsbergen must have been after the Penultimate Interglacial, because it has not reached Greenland. This fits also for most of the other members of this group with the exception of *Polemonium boreale* and *Taraxacum arcticum*.

To this element belong: *Phippsia concinna*, *Luzula Wahlenbergii*, *Petasites frigidus*, *Parrya nudicaulis*, *Polemonium boreale*, and *Taraxacum arcticum*.

11. THE GREENLAND–SPITSBERGEN GROUP

This group is problematic. It may perhaps be included in the Arctic–Amphi-Atlantic group. *Ranunculus Wilanderi* and *Poa Hartzii* might be of Early Pleistocene age. *Festuca hyperborea* was described recently and therefore its place in this group is provisional. *Carex pseudolagopina* belongs to *C. amblyorhyncha* Krecz., which has a broader distribution and therefore must be removed from this group.

12. THE NOVAYA ZEMLYA–SPITSBERGEN GROUP

The center of origin of this group seems to be in a previous land-mass connecting Novaya Zemlya and Spitsbergen. Some of the species have reached Greenland and Scandinavia (*Carex parallela*, *Arenaria pseudofrigida*). *Taraxacum brachyceras* extends from Vaygach Island to Greenland, but *Pedicularis dasyantha* grows only in Arctic Siberia, Novaya Zemlya and Spitsbergen and forms thus a transition to the next group.

13. THE SPITSBERGEN GROUP OF ENDEMICS

This group originated probably in the Late Pleistocene and is therefore the youngest of the Spitsbergen flora. *Puccinellia vacillans* has several localities in Spitsbergen and one in Novaya Zemlya. *Coptidium spitsbergense*, comb. nova (based on *Ranunculus spitsbergensis* Hadač 1944 in *Norges Svalbard og Ishavsunders*. Skr. 87, p. 36) occurs in several distant places of Spitsbergen. Its distribution can be explained only by supposing that it already existed in the last Interglacial period. *Papaver Dahlianum* ssp. *Hadačianum* is hitherto known only from Spitsbergen.

14. RECENT IMMIGRANTS

The only recent natural immigrant seems to be *Cakile maritima* (or *C. edentula*?—there were no fruits!). There are plenty of other species introduced by man.

The analysis of the Spitsbergen flora shows that most of its species are Preglacial or from the early Pleistocene; only 2.8 per cent are "Neo-Arctic" species from the Late Pleistocene.

From all I have said above, it can be concluded that the Arctic flora is in a great part Preglacial and only a small portion of it can be dated to the Late Pleistocene. It was formed during the Neogene and Pleistocene partly from plant species occurring in the Arctic itself, partly from plants of American and Eurasiatic mountain ridges.

I am indebted to Miss Jaroslava Riedlová for help with the statistical problems, and to Dr. Lumír Klimeš for correcting my English. The nomenclature followed in this paper may be found in Hadač (1942, 1960) and Löve and Löve (1961b).

REFERENCES

DAHL, E. (1946). On different types of unglaciated areas during the Ice Ages and their significance to phytogeography. *New. Phytol.* **45**, 225–242.

DAHL, E. (1958). Amfiatlantiske planter. *Blyttia* **16**, 93–121.

HADAČ, E. (1941). Et bidrag til historien om Björnöyas flora. *Naturen* 1941 (5).

HADAČ, E. (1944). Die Gefässpflanzen des "Sassengebietes" Vest-Spitzbergen. *Norges Svalbard og Ishavsundersökelser, Skrifter No.* 87, 1–71.

HADAČ, E. (1948). On the history of the flora of Iceland. *Studia Botanica Czechoslovaka* **9**, 18–25.

HADAČ, E. (1960). The history of the flora of Spitsbergen and Bear Island and the age of some Arctic plant species. *Preslia* **32**, 225–253.

HORN, G. and ORVIN, A. K. (1928). Geology of Bear Island. *Norges Svalbard og Ishavsundersökelser, Skrifter No.* 15, 1–152.

KNABEN, GUNVOR (1959). *Papaver*-studier, med et forsvar for *P. radicatum* Rottb. som en islandsk–skandinavisk art. *Blyttia* **16**, 61–80.

KJARTANSSON, G. (1940). Um aldur tertíeru basaltspildnanna í nordanverdu Atlantshafi. *Náttúrufr.* **10**, 118–128.

KUPRIYANOVA, L. A. and TIKHOMIROV, B. A. (1954). Issledovanie pyltzy is rastitel'nych ostatkov beresovskovo mamonta. *DAN* 45 (6).

LINDQUIST, B. (1947). Two species of *Betula* from the Icelandic Miocene. *Svensk Bot. Tidskr.* **41**, 339–353.

LÖVE, Á. and LÖVE, D. (1959). Biosystematics of the black crowberries of America. *Canad. J. of Gen. et Cyt.* **1**, 34–38.

LÖVE, Á. and LÖVE, D. (1961a) Some nomenclatural changes in the European Flora. I. Species and supraspecific categories. *Bot. Notiser* **114**, 33–47.

LÖVE, Á. and LÖVE, D. (1961b). Chromosome numbers of Central and Northwest European plant species. *Opera Botanica* **5**, I–VIII, 1–581.

LÖVE, D. (1960). The red-fruited crowberries in North America. *Rhodora* **62**, 265–292.

MARKOV, K. K. (1951). *Paleogeografiya*. Moscow 1951.

ROSHEVIZH, R. Y. (1952). Analis arealov nekotorich kharakternich dlyaA rktiki slakov (eoarktikov). Areal I.

SÖRENSEN, TH. (1945). Summary of the botanical investigations in N.E. Greenland. *Medd. om Groenl.* **136** (3), 1–179.

SÖRENSEN, TH. (1953). A revision of the Greenland species of *Puccinellia* Parl. *Medd. om Groenl.* **136** (3), 1–179.

STRACHOV, N. M. (1948). *Osnovy Istoricheskoy Geologii* I–II. Moscow–Leningrad.

ŚRODOŃ, A. (1954). *Flory Plejstocenskie z Tarzymiechow nad Wieprzem*. Warsaw.

TIKHOMIROV, B. A. (1946). K filotzenogenesu nekotorich rastitelnych formatziy arkticheskoy Evrasii. *Bot. Zhurn.* **31** (6), 27–41.

TOLMACHEV, A. I. (1952). K istorii rasvitiya flor sovetskoy Arktiki. Areal I.

VASSIL'EV, V. N. (1961). Rod *Empetrum*. Akad. Nauk SSSR, Leningrad 1961.

PROBLEMS OF IMMIGRATION AND DISPERSAL OF THE SCANDINAVIAN FLORA

KNUT FÆGRI

Botanical Museum, University of Bergen, Bergen, Norway

IN discussing the characteristics of the Scandinavian flora, botanists have, since Blytt's days at least, been inclined to speak of and think in "flora elements".

The concept of a flora element presumes a high degree of generalization, which is not always unambiguous. If Scandinavian phytogeographers speak about the West-Arctic flora element, they think of a group of plants with a certain total geographical distribution outside of Scandinavia. If they speak of an oceanic element, distribution within Scandinavia is meant. A flora element may even be defined by temporal relations, or by ecological ones. Even if these ambiguities are under control the generalization as such is dangerous. A common distribution area does not in itself explain anything. On the contrary, it is a problem in itself, and what is generally done, is to consider the hypothetical explanation of the reason why a group of plants occur together as a fact to be used in the analysis of other problems as well. But in nature there is nothing like a flora element behaving as a collective unit. There are only individual plants (not plant species!) reacting each in an individual way. And the more or less fortuitous occurring together may be the result of widely differing histories and ecologic demands.

Like that of any area, the flora of Scandinavia comprises elements of different age. Leaving apart the endemic element—which is in our case insignificant—we may summarize the history of any plant by the following main points:

1. Origin and road of immigration.
2. Dispersal during immigration.
3. Conditions in Scandinavia at immigration.
4. History of the plant in Scandinavia after immigration.

In the current discussion these points have been taken into consideration in varying degree, as they are also of different importance for different plants.

The simplest group to explain is that of the most recent immigrants, the anthropochorous apophytes. The importance of this group of plants increases with increasing intensity of traffic, whereas increasing "cleanliness" and efficiency of modern transport counteracts the spread of such plants. Ouren has recently (1959) shown that a maximum of "transport efficiency" of accidental diaspores was reached during the latter part of the nineteenth century with gravel ballast. Many plants, which were then more or less regularly imported to Scandinavia and were considered at least transient members of the flora, are now rarely seen, or not seen at all except as old herbarium specimens, and might perhaps just as well be omitted from future handbooks of the flora. Similarly, the recent habit of many mills to grind or grit also the sorted-out weed seeds before selling them for fodder deprives the avid collector of many interesting (but insignificant) finds.

Nevertheless, there are still many sources of introduction left even today: packing material, wool rejects, etc. Most of the plants introduced this way either (1) are already represented in our flora, or (2) cannot establish themselves; but sometimes an immigrant secures a foothold. *Bunias orientalis* or *Matricaria matricarioides* may be quoted among the classical examples, the immigration of which dates back, respectively 200 and 100 years (Holmboe, 1900). And from today *Epilobium adenocaulon* may be mentioned, which evidently has spread very rapidly since World War II, although it had been found in Scandinavia before that time.

With anthropochorous dispersal being overwhelmingly important in our days, one is likely to overlook the contemporaneous "natural" long-distance dispersal. It is very difficult to decide if man has had nothing to do with the case—most of the cases in which man's activity can be ruled out, are undateable. The case of *Coleanthus subtilis* is one of those that can probably be comparatively well dated (Lid, 1948). Unfortunately, the plant failed to establish itself. Another most probably recent and non-anthropogeneous (Holmboe, 1930) case is that of *Elisma natans* (*Luronium natans*). The plants that introduce themselves by natural means are generally more successful immigrants than the anthropogeneous ones, within which group the percentage of failures is very great. Unsuccessful immigrants of the former group are usually not observed, but there is no reason to believe that they do not occur, cf. the *Mucuna* seeds found on our shores. It is of importance that the two cases mentioned above presume modern, spontaneous, long-distance dispersal of the magnitude of at least some 300–400 and 1000 km. Other instances of spontaneous, long-distance diaspore transport readily come to mind. Although one cannot exclude the possibility that disjunct finds may represent relict occurrences, many of them also must represent long-distance dispersal, not only where the dispersal mode is more or less evident (sea transport, waders, ducks, etc.), but also in plants with a less obvious dispersal ecology.

One may discuss how far back the "modern" era of dispersal should stretch. The great discoveries of the fifteenth and sixteenth centuries seem to furnish a good delimitation. Before that time whatever transport there was, was confined to the relatively small area of the Medieval World. The increasing intensity of traffic could not bring anything new to Scandinavia that had not had a chance of immigration hundreds of years before.

The importance of the opening up of new routes is vividly realized by any European botanist visiting the U.S.A. for the first time. Along all the roads, in all waste places in the northeast, the ruderal flora is completely "European" in appearance, and a botanist could not tell from the flora on which side of the ocean he was. The few non-European plants are such ones that also occur in similar places in Europe: *Erigeron canadense*, *Oenothera biennis*, etc.

Obviously, the reason for the dominance of European weeds is the fact that these, coming from an area of more intensive agricultural practice and human activity as a whole, had been more rigidly selected and adapted to ruderal conditions. European agricultural practice and settlement density created conditions under which the local flora could not compete—except for a few species, which, on the contrary, managed to establish themselves in Europe as well. This example is important because it shows the significance of ecological changes taking place within the area concomitant with or at least more or less contemporaneous with the introduction of alien plants. Due to the changes, new ecologic niches are created which may open up room for immigrants. What has happened in North America during the last few hundred years is important as a picture of what must have happened when Neolithic man first came to northwestern Europe with his husbandry and agriculture.

Whereas ecologic conditions in America have changed radically during the "modern" period, due to the introduction of European agriculture, those in Europe have not changed similarly during the same period. The changes in agricultural methods have altered the aspects of the weed flora, but not fundamentally. We may therefore, in the discussion of this group, neglect point 4. Coming now to the next group we shall see how the historical development is of much greater importance.

The "middle" period is introduced by two overlapping events, the advent of agriculture and the deterioration of climate. In some places the first, in other places the latter, is the older of the two. In southern coastal districts agriculture arrived during the Post-Glacial Hypsithermal period; in central and northern districts it came (much) later. The effects of agriculture thus intergrade with those of a major climatic change.

Before the introduction of agriculture, vegetation must have proliforated itself to an extent inconceivable today. The picture drawn by Iversen (1949) is based upon the flat Danish landscape; in Norway it must have been more varied, but, even so, there is no doubt that the forested pre-agricultural landscape was a relatively monotonous one. Within the conifer region we still have relatively untouched areas which in their floristic composition are even more monotonous than the oceanic heaths in their terrible poverty. Even the smallest clearing around a dairy chalet in the forest looks like an oasis in these green deserts. Just as our ruderal and weed flora had been subjected to a very strong selection before being spread to America, so our pre-agricultural flora had been subject to a very strong forest selection; only those biotypes able to survive under the conditions of dense forest could persist unless they found refugium in an "atypical" habitat. Such habitats were found above the (dense) forest limit in the mountains or in places covered by some non-climax vegetation. That would mean bogs, beaches (of the sea, lakes or rivers), screes, or fissures, cracks, or shelves in steep rocks. This again means that species with ecologically special requirements (chamaephytes, halo- or hydrophytes, etc.) would have a certain chance of survival, and so would plants that could grow in the upper, open mountain forests. On the other hand, the ordinary open-ground species, above all those of the meadows, would have a very difficult time, although we should not underrate the effect of grazing by the spontaneous (deer) fauna. To what extent spontaneous forest fires or catastrophic gales (Sernander, 1936) influenced the picture, remains conjectural.

What happened when land was originally cleared for agricultural purposes is a phenomenon whose nature cannot only be inferred but also confirmed, on the whole, by information from pollen analyses. The effects may be summarized in the following statements:

1. Certain plants were directly used for different purposes and their number reduced by selective utilization.
2. Certain plants occur in soil which was preferred for agriculture, for which reason they were more or less completely exterminated together with the corresponding vegetation types.
3. On the soil thus vacated there were possibilities for the establishment of new vegetation types composed of (a) archaeophytes—many of them previously suppressed or restricted by and in the climax vegetation, (b) cultivated plants, and (c) immigrant weeds and ruderals.

The difficulty here consists in distinguishing between Groups 3 (a) and (c). To cite an example, pollen evidence shows unmistakenly that *Plantago lanceolata* expanded enormously with the introduction of agriculture, but are the very few *P. lanceolata* grains observed before the land-clearing phase due to long-distance dispersal and/or contamination, or do they mean that some few *P. lanceolata* specimens existed even before agricultural land was cleared? And what about the many subspecific taxa within this species? A similar question may be raised for *P. major*, but whereas it is easy to imagine a possible refugium for this species on beaches (the beach-form may be secondary!), it is more difficult to visualize where *P. lanceolata* could have taken refuge, except on those shelves in rock walls where I am afraid we shall feel obliged to put up a major part of our flora if we do not accept the possibilities of its anthropogeneous origin. Where else can we place a plant like *Digitalis purpurea*?

It is very difficult to give any estimate of the number of species in these three groups. We know of very few plants belonging to Category 1 being utilized to such an extent as to be exterminated locally (*Archangelica officinalis*, *Gentiana purpurea*) or very much reduced in number (*Ulmus scabra*). We must assume that under Category 2 we have completely lost important plant communities of easily arable soil and that vegetation types known today are a one-sided selection of those that would have existed in the absence of agriculture. How many species are involved in the third principle will forever remain conjectural, but I should personally be inclined to assign to this group (3c) a rather high percentage of our flora—some 20 per cent perhaps.

The development of climate and vegetation since the advent of agriculture must be taken into account. For those parts of the country where land occupation took place during the Iron Age, the remaining spontaneous vegetation types are probably not too different from those existing before the land was cleared. For the old agricultural regions we may presume that changes due to climate—in addition to those due to agriculture—have completely altered the face of the land, and that nothing remains of what was the original vegetation. When discussing these problems, we should keep in mind that much good soil, i.e. soil that is considered good today, was unsuitable for farming with the primitive tools of the pre-Iron Age man.

Wendelbo (1957) has suggested a very interesting recent replacement of species, viz. the disappearance of *Centaurea pseudophrygia* and its gradual replacement by *C. nigra*. The former is a species of open deciduous forests, such as are now gradually disappearing with the abandonment of grazing in forested areas. *C. nigra*, however, grows in meadows, on roadsides, etc., and is better adapted to conditions of modern agricultural practices. Interbreeding and introgressive hybridization may contribute to speeding up the replacement. One must assume that similar processes took place on a grand scale during the more radical transformation of the landscape concomitant with the primary introduction of agriculture.

During the very long time between the disappearance of the Pleistocene ice and the advent of agriculture, vegetation could develop under the influence of two major factors: the changing climate, and the immigration of species. The latter was again a function of the changing climate, but also of two other factors: the location of glacial refugia, and the speed and possibilities of dispersal. There is no doubt that in the discussion of the immigration of the Scandinavian flora, these conditions have not been adequately treated.

It has become increasingly clear that the sequence of forest types met with in pollen-analytical investigations in Scandinavia cannot be interpreted in such a one-sided climatological manner as has been the case. Registered regional reversals must have a background in climatic shifts: thus the vegetational changes indicating the onset of the Younger Dryas and the Sub-Atlantic periods are generally due to climatic deterioration. But we have no guarantee that the immigration of, for example, *Corylus* came just at the moment when the "Corylus climate" first established itself. The sequence (*Populus–*)*Betula–Pinus*/*Corylus*–broadleaf forest is very reminiscent of what one would expect from an ordinary succession under relatively uniform climatic conditions. We possess at least one positive indication that differentials of immigration speed are of importance: the gradual delay of *Pinus* in relation to *Corylus* along a line from Denmark to western Norway. One might conceive of climate first running through a *Pinus*-non-*Corylus* type in Denmark and through a *Corylus*-non-*Pinus* type in west Norway, but the assumption is not very probable. Different rates of dispersal give a better explanation. It should be noted that, of the two, *Pinus* diaspores are better adapted for long-distance dispersal, but *Corylus* nevertheless advances faster.

Given the disadvantageous climate of the Younger Dryas period, we must conceive of a comparatively rapid amelioration most probably bringing climate up to at least present-day level in a rather short time. The omnipresence of a (sub-)pioneer *Betula* phase at the beginning of the Post-Arctic forest period indicates that the present laws of plant succession were valid then also.

The succession of forest types in northern Europe on the whole matches the one to be expected under a static climate (which does, of course, not prove anything). But there are some remarkable exceptions, the main one being the history of *Alnus*. There is hardly any doubt that the species generally registered in the lowlands is *A. glutinosa*. Its appearance has been seen in connection with the old conception of a change from a drier to a more humid climate at the Boreal–Atlantic transition, and it is difficult to suggest a better alternative explanation. There has been a tendency on the part of Quaternary geologists to operate with precipitation and temperature as if they were independent entities instead of being tied together in the same circulation system. However, it must be admitted that till today meteorologists have not been able to give much help in explaining the changes inferred from geologic–biologic evidence, and even less the astonishing parallelism in alternations between humid and dry periods according to the Blytt–Sernander concept in the cyclonic belts of north Europe, and of the Sahara desert as shown by recent finds (Mériel, 1962).

The occurrence during the Hypsithermal of exigent species which are today much rarer (*Cladium*) in or even absent (*Trapa*) from Scandinavia undoubtedly indicates that climate deteriorated, and so does the general recession of vegetation boundaries both from the mountains and from the north. It is very doubtful if new competition can completely exterminate a species within its proper climatic area, but it is obvious that every new immigrant that reaches domination must do so at the expense of the plants previously extant. The changes from, for example, *Quercetum mixtum* to *Picea* in Scandinavian pollen diagrams at the last zone transition (Sub-Boreal–Sub-Atlantic) first and foremost indicates that the newcomer has conquered its area at the expense of the broadleaf forests. That might have happened even under a uniform climate. On the other hand, the broadleaf forest also disappears where no *Picea* comes in, and one may also ask why the spruce has started its immigration at all. But conditions are by no means as simple as they are frequently described. In other cases, e.g. that of *Cladium*, the disappearance may be due to a change of environment. Again, one may raise the question whether menotrophication came as a result of a climatic change. The appearance of similar changes during the climatic decline at the end of the Last Interglacial is indicative.

The Post-Arctic climatic amelioration has a double aspect: the positive, viz. the immigration and settling of new plants and communities, and also the negative, viz. the crowding out of earlier types. The Late-Glacial climate is still enigmatic, and again we may have been deluded by overlooking ecological problems. The open, fresh soil left by the Pleistocene glaciers had a selective influence on the germination of the few diaspores that initially landed on it. To be able to establish themselves, the species have to be such plants that today also occur on open, humus-free soil, a soil type that is primarily found in the semi-deserts. It maybe that we have been too much inclined to interpret the finding of steppe plants (and animals) as witnesses of a steppe climate instead of a steppe soil. Even from a very early period pollen grains have been found of plants which are decidedly not Arctic in their requirements.

This has certain implications for our understanding of living conditions during the Late-Glacial, but even more so for our understanding of the disappearance of the Late-Glacial biota. Did animals and plants vanish because of a change from a steppe climate to a more humid type, or did they do so because the soil evolved towards a more humic type without change of climatic humidity? Or both? Or because of the onset of competition? The role played by mycorhiza should not be left out, but mycorhizal plants do appear rather early, at least in humid regions.

The absence of competition is another important factor not to be discounted. Where "Late-Glacial plants", e.g. *Ephedra*, can maintain themselves well into the Atlantic (at least) in Norway (Hafsten, 1953), this is certainly due not only to the fact that small crags and shelves in steep rock faces were not shaded by forest trees, but also to the fact that in such habitats competition never became very severe. Just as such localities have been proposed as possible stations for *Digitalis* and other species of the same ecology, they most probably have also furnished havens for the Late-Glacial flora long after it had been crowded out in soil progressing towards a climax condition.

We know that the Late-Glacial flora of southern Scandinavia contained a number of Alpine plants, i.e. plants that are today chiefly found in the Alpine zone of our mountains. *Dryas octopetala*, *Salix herbacea*, *Saxifraga oppositifolia*, and many others have been identified among pollen and macro-fossils. The fate of this flora has for a very long time been controversial. That these plants were crowded out from the flat lands in Denmark and a large part of south Sweden is generally accepted. But one should not forget the persistence of Glacial–Alpine elements in the flora both of the steep mountains in south Sweden (Omberg, Hesselman, 1935; Kinnekulle, Albertson, 1940) and the flat, thin, poor limestone soils of Oeland (Sterner, 1938). On the whole, however, very little is left, and the problem has been raised whether the peri-glacial Ice Age flora had any chance to reach the Scandinavian mountains this way. The absence of fossils of Arctic plants between south Sweden and Jämtland has been mentioned although the argument is perhaps not too convincing. Its value depends on how much has been done in order to find such fossils. There is no doubt that the climate was sufficiently congenial for a forest vegetation to follow very close to the ice edge. But dimensions are different in biology and geology: "very close" and "very fast" in a geologic sense may still leave plenty of place and time for Arctic plants to colonize. And besides, the bee-line route from Scania to the central Scandinavian mountains was not the only possible route: if Arctic plants were able to reach the outer part of the Oslo district (outside the Ra end-moraine line), they would also have very good possibilities of spreading towards the mountains this way. It should not be forgotten that Alpines still grow at low altitudes in the Oslo region (*Dryas*, *Carex rupestris* in Solbjergfjell, Lid, 1958; Arctic species in Krokkleiva, etc.). Without insisting that these plants *must* be true relics from the Late-Glacial (or rather pre-Boreal, as the areas were ice-covered until then), we may safely state that no other explanation of their presence is more convincing.

Before proceeding with the Arctic–Alpine species I should like to draw attention to the so-called xerothermic element of the flora of southeastern Scandinavia. In Oeland it grows intermingled with Arctic–Alpine plants, and the problem is how great a part of this element immigrated during the Late-Glacial, and how great a part during the presumed xerothermic later period. A plant like *Coronilla emerus* might well be a Late-Glacial relic, occurring today in Oeland and at one station on the Norwegian southeast coast.

Returning now to the Arctic–Alpine plants of south Norway, my main thesis would be that unless immigration via the Oslo area can be definitely ruled out, there is nothing in dispersal to prevent the mountain flora of south Norway from having been recruited from the flora surviving at the southern edge of the ice. Which, of course, is no proof that it has been furnished that way.

Whatever are the concepts about ice limits farther north, there can be no doubt that Norway south of 61° N. Lat. was completely ice-covered, cf. the date 13000 B.P. for a chionophilous ice-edge community at Jaeren or 12500 B.P. for a sub-moraine deposit at Blomvaag (Nydal, 1960) at the extreme edge of the land towards the sea. The ice edge must have gone far out in the sea. Nevertheless, the Jaeren deposit exhibits a typical Arctic–Alpine flora which must have immigrated across very great distances. True, the number of species known from this flora is low, and they are well equipped for dispersal. Nevertheless, their early appearance at Jaeren—isolated by ice and sea—can hardly be explained unless iceberg transport from Denmark or some other place is resorted to. Even today icefloes transport great quantities of Danish rocks to the Oslo area. There is nothing inconceivable in iceberg (or -floe) transport of diaspores as well as of the flint and amber (Holmboe, 1912; Johansen, 1957) found in west Norway.

Whereas the possibility of immigration from Denmark has been recognized for a long time, other possibilities have opened up later. The role played by the North Sea continent is certainly very difficult to evaluate, but in Britain more and more remains of an Arctic Ice Age flora are coming to light.

The recent finds in the British Isles of such exclusively Arctic species as *Koenigia*, *Artemisia norvegica*, *Diapensia lapponica*, and others throw a new and unexpected light on the problems of survival of our mountain flora. Mention should also be made of the *Scapiflora Papaver* seeds found by Conolly (1958) although the possibility cannot be ruled out that they were not identical with the Scandinavian *Scapiflora*.

If Pleistocene Britain has been a refugium of our mountain flora it is no wonder that we find no traces left of it there: in the humid climate of the British Isles the ensuing humus cover must have been almost fatal for the Post-Glacial survival of these plants as were the salt waters covering the North Sea continent. It is remarkable that anything is left at all.

The restriction of the Scandinavian mountain flora to the two well-known centers represents a challenge. So does the apparent isolation of the West Arctic species. A solution to the problem has been offered by biologists: the hypothesis of Ice Age survival within Scandinavia. Incidentally, if survival is accepted for the Last Quaternary Glaciation, it is very difficult to get away from the same argument for earlier ones.

The idea of Pleistocene survival, so brilliantly presented and defended by Nordhagen (1933) has met with very strong, almost passionate resistance from geologists. Each argument has been met with a counter-argument, and for many years now little new has been presented: the protagonists of the two opinions have mostly been riding their rather age-worn hobby-horses.

It is easy to see that some of the consequences drawn from the Ice Age refugium hypothesis are incongruous, like Lindroth's (1949, p. 775) series of refugia in places where we know positively that there cannot have been any, or Lindquist's (1948) idea of the survival of *Picea abies* (cf. Fægri, 1950). However, it does not disprove a theory that erroneous conclusions have been drawn from it.

It should also be said that geologists have been completely negative in their argumentation: the two main problems of centricity and West-Arctic distribution exist, and they demand an explanation.

On the other hand, it must also be admitted that biologists should take up the problems for some fresh thinking. Is centricity anything more than one might expect from actual ecologic conditions? Nobody has tried to give an objective answer to this, but it is a fact that very few, if any, other areas in Scandinavia offer the same combination of favorable bed-rock, climate, and topography. If this is enough to explain the distribution without recourse to other factors, centricity loses much of its argumentative value.

Some of the "rare" mountain plants possess good means of dispersal; others seem to be in a rather unfavorable situation. The example of the Post-glacial immigration of *Pinus* and *Corylus* shows that our evaluation of dispersal potentialities does not always give the right result and should be an admonition of some prudence. But it must be admitted that a species like *Stellaria crassipes* certainly represents some problems, although an auxiliary hypothesis of a Late Quaternary development towards reproductive sterility is not in principle more—or less—improbable than the hypothesis of survival. With its present degree of sterility it is even difficult to think how the species could migrate from coastal refugia to its present stations.

Another species that has presented some difficulties is *Carex scirpoidea*, known in Europe from two stations at Solvaagtind only. The rest of its area is American, and the species is the most extreme West-Arctic of all. *Carex scirpoidea* is dioecious, and any attempt at explanation involving long-distance dispersal would have to account for simultaneous dispersal of a "male" and a "female" seed, which would seem rather unlikely. In itself that may be used as an argument for rarity of the species in Europe. However, a monoecious form, f. *isogyna* Dyring, has been described from Solvaagtind. This suggests another solution of that particular problem: the Solvaagtind occurrence may derive from accidental long-distance dispersal of a seed with a "monoecious" tendency. Similarly, monoecious plants are found in at least Greenland.

Conditions in north Scandinavia are more complicated than in the south. In the eastern part there is a separate flora element with *Crepis multicaulis* and *Oxytropis deflexa* as its most famous representatives. The nearest stations are far east in Asia, and none are known to occur in the intermediate mountains, especially not in the Urals. I would consider it very possible that these species have survived the last glaciation in or near Scandinavia, but can see no reason compelling us to reject the hypothesis that they survived at the edge of the glaciated area in the U.S.S.R. The absence of these species there now is easily explained by reference to their ecologic demands and the Post-Glacial Hypsithermal period forests that would have crowded out these and many other species from their former stations. As survival during a glaciation and re-immigration must entail great losses, the absence of these species in the Urals is not remarkable, although the Ice Age should have made itself less felt in those eastern areas.

Attempts have been made to elucidate the problem of Pleistocene survival by cytogenetic investigations. Unfortunately, the results are far from being unambiguous. Favarger has recently (1960) pointed out that polyploidy may indicate both youth and great age in a taxon, and moreover these terms are relative only, and cannot be adequately translated into geologic or absolute chronology. As long as we know nothing about the speed of evolution, cytogenetic data cannot contribute very much, nor can the presence or absence of endemic taxa. We should not forget that terms like "old" and "young" refer to a very local time-scale only. In biology each taxon has its own time-scale, and we have no possibility for translating these into terms of each other. To use a word like "young" derived from a biologic time-scale in a geologic argument is not admissible.

The current situation is extremely unsatisfactory. The present-day distribution pattern of the Scandinavian mountain flora has been referred to ecologic and to historical reasons: Ice Age survival has been referred to marginal areas in the east, south and west of the ice sheet, and, in addition, to the coastal refugia as well as to nunataks. None of the ideas has been properly proved, none of them definitely disproved. Biologists have a problem and an attempt at an explanation. Geologists refuse to accept the explanation and cannot offer any solution to the problem. And no new argument has been presented in this tug-of-war, only new versions of the old ones.

REFERENCES

ALBERTSON, N. (1940). *Scorpidium turgescens* (Th. Jens.) Moenkem. En senglacial relikt i nordisk alvar-vegetation. *Acta Phytogeogr. Suecica* **13**, 7–26.

CONOLLY, A. (1958). The occurrence of seeds of *Papaver* sect. *Scapiflora* in a Scottish late glacial site. *Veröff. Geobot. Inst. Rübel Zürich* **34**, 27–29.

FAVARGER, C. (1961). Sur l'emploi des nombres des chromosomes en géographie botanique historiques. *Ber. Geobot. Inst. E.T.H. Stiftung Rübel* **32**, 119–146 (1960).

FÆGRI, K. (1950). Studies on the Pleistocene of western Norway. IV. On the immigration of *Picea Abies* (L.) Karst. *Univ. Bergen Årbok 1949, Naturv. rekke* **1**, 1–52.

HAFSTEN, U. (1953). Nyopdagede pionerplanter i Norge etter istiden. *Naturen* **77**, 501–505.

HESSELMAN, B. (1938). Ombergs kärlväxtflora. *Svensk Bot. Tidskr.* **32**, 1–88.

HOLMBOE, J. (1900). Nogle ugræsplanters indvandring i Norge. *Nytt. Mag. Naturv.* **38**, 129–262.

HOLMBOE, J. (1912). Naturlig forekommende rav paa Karmøen. *Naturen* **36**, 381–383.

HOLMBOE, J. (1930). Spredte bidrag til Norges flora I. *Nytt Mag. Naturv.* **68**, 119–151.

IVERSEN, J. (1949). The influence of prehistoric man on vegetation. *Danmarks Geol. Unders. IV Række* **3** (6), 1–25.

JOHANSEN, E. (1957). Norsk og svensk boplasflint—er den hentet i Danmark-Skåne eller i norske strande? *Medd. Dansk. Geol. For.* **13**, 257–258.

LID, J. (1948). Eingong veks *Coleanthus subtilis* i Noreg. *Blyttia* **6**, 33–36.

LID, J. (1958). Two glacial relics of *Dryas octopetala* and *Carex rupestris* in the forests of southeastern Norway. *Nytt. Mag. Bot.* **6**, 5–9.

LINDQUIST, B. (1948). The main varieties of *Picea abies* (L.) Karst. in Europe. *Acta Hort. Bergiani* **14**, 249–342.

LINDROTH, C. H. (1949). Die fennoscandischen Carabidae. *Göteborgs Kgl. Vetensk. Vitterh. Samh. Handl.* **6 B** 4 (3).

MÉRIEL, Y. (1962). Les oscillations des climats de la zone aride dans le dernier million d'années. *La Nature* 1962, 67–74.

NORDHAGEN, R. (1933). De senkvartære klimavekslinger og deres betydning for kulturforskningen. *Inst. Sammenl. Kulturforsk. A.2. Oslo.*

NYDAL, R. (1960). Trondheim natural radiocarbon measurements II. *Amer. J. Sc. Radioc. Suppl.* **2**, 82–96.

OUREN, T. (1959). Om skipsfartens betydning for Norges flora. *Blyttia* **17**, 97–118.

SERNANDER, R. (1936). Granskär och Fiby urskog. *Acta Phytogeogr. Suec.* **8**, 1–232.

STERNER, R. (1938). Flora der Insel Öland. *Acta Phytogeogr. Suec.* **9**, 1–170.

WENDELBO, P. (1957). Arter og hybrider av *Centaurea* underslekt *Jacea* i Norge. *Univ. Bergen Årbok 1957, Naturv. rekke* **5**, 1–29.

After this paper was set, the following publication has come to my knowledge: TOLMAČEV, A. I. and O. REBRISTAFYA. O geografičeskom rasprostranenii *Crepis multisaulis* Ledeb. i o zabytom vide *Crepis gmelini* (L.) Tausch. *Bot. mater. gerb. bot. inst. B. L. Komarova Ak. N. SSSR* **21,** 402–415, which shows that the subspecies of *C. multicaulis* previously found in Norway has actually been found at the former border of the Ice Age ice sheet in Siberia.

SURVIVAL OF LICHENS DURING THE GLACIAL AGE IN THE NORTH ATLANTIC BASIN

ZDENĚK ČERNOHORSKÝ
Botanical Institute, Charles University, Praha, Czechoslovakia

THERE have been several students who have contributed to our knowledge of the lichen flora of the North Atlantic basin. The greatest merits in this respect go to the Scandinavian authors. Apart from monographs written on some genera, collective publications of the last 30 years are especially important for our consideration (e.g. Dahl, 1950; Dahl, Lynge and Scholander, 1937; Lynge, 1928, 1934, 1937, 1938, 1940a; Lynge and Scholander, 1932). As these publications contain historical chapters as well, they reveal names of men who, in the past, devoted their study to the exploration of the lichen flora of the North Atlantic basin.

Owing to these explorers we have nowadays quite a sound knowledge concerning macrolichens and their distribution in the said space. This is especially true of the conspicuous species, collected even by non-lichenologists. As far as microlichens are concerned, their systematic study has only begun (e.g. Lynge, 1940b). Furthermore, macrolichens in different regions are treated variously. Apart from this, we are lacking in paleontological records and this is the reason why I can contribute but partly to the solution of our general problem.

The knowledge of macrolichens led some authors to compare the lichen flora of various parts of the North Atlantic basin. We must mention especially the Norwegian lichenologist Lynge (1934, 1938, 1940a), who compared macrolichen floras, e.g. in Iceland, northeast Greenland, Svalbard, and Novaya Zemlya. He states that these islands have many species in common and that their floras are like that of Scandinavia. He mentions also that the most striking of these floras is that of Novaya Zemlya, due to the presence there of several eastern species not found farther to the west. The microlichen species, e.g. of the genus *Rhizocarpon*, indicate even greater differences.

The aforementioned similarity and the widening knowledge about distribution of the macrolichen species aroused among lichenologists a question concerning the history of these North Atlantic species. It was again Lynge who constantly approached this problem, and he had tried to summarize it before his death (Lynge, 1938, 1939a). He ascertained that in Svalbard (Spitsbergen and North East Land) grows a relatively considerable amount of conspicuous macrolichen species, known either from the northern coasts of these islands or concentrated there in a remarkable manner. It is to be stressed that the climate of the northern coast of Svalbard is highly arctic. One of the most interesting cases is the genus *Dactylina*, represented there by three species: *Dactylina arctica* (Richards.) Nyl., *D. madreporiformis* (Wulf.) Tuck., and *D. ramulosa* (Hook.) Tuck. From the maps (Lynge, 1933) we perceive that they have an enormous distribution in the world, but that this distribution is not continuous. They are unknown from large areas within their limits, e.g. there is a wide gap between the occurrence of *Dactylina madreporiformis* in Svalbard and in the high mountains of central Europe. Lynge (1938) concludes that they are very old relict plants which no doubt formerly had a wider distribution. Later, their area was reduced, resulting in these great gaps, although we have no fossil records to support this hypothesis. On the other hand, the comparison with some higher plants, known as fossils from previous geological periods, shows that this conclusion is reasonable.

From other north coast lichens Lynge (1938) indicates some conspicuous species of the genera *Parmelia* and *Cladonia*. To explain their existence on the north coast of Spitsbergen and North East Land he undertakes an analysis of their distribution in Norway. This analysis shows that only *Parmelia intestiniformis* (Vill.) Ach. is High Alpine. Most of the species are Sub-Alpine, with the weight of their distribution in the more continental Norwegian forest zone. Judging from their distribution in Svalbard and in Norway it can be assumed that they have great amplitude in their demands upon life and that time is the main factor in explaining their presence on the north coast of Spitsbergen and North East Land. As far as the existence of these species in Svalbard is concerned, Lynge draws the following conclusion: " . . . their area, or part of it, should have been ice-free refugia during the last glaciation, perhaps all through the time subsequent to the Tertiary Age, and that these lichens should be relics which have persisted, at least, from the Last Interglacial down to the present time".

Some of the indicated north coast lichens of Svalbard grow in central Europe as well, e.g. *Parmelia centrifuga* (L.) Ach. It is very rare, having its southern distribution limit here. *Parmelia centrifuga* is to be found on summits and ridges of mountains (Harz; a broad area of Riesengebirge, mostly at an altitude of 1000–1500 m; Böhmerwald at 820–850 m; the Alps at 1900–2000 m). As a rule it is sterile and does not reproduce here. In case it does reproduce, it is by means of thallus fragments. *Parmelia centrifuga* is fertile only in Harz and in Böhmerwald. No doubt it reproduces in Böhmerwald but its distribution there is limited. In central Europe its localities are scattered around the 50th parallel; they indicate a possible, more or less close relation to the border of the greatest glaciation. As the last glaciation was relatively small, *Parmelia centrifuga* hardly penetrated into central Europe from the north during the last Glacial Age only. The dispersal of our species over longer distances is limited. Apart from that, there were, after previous heavier glaciations, between Scandinavia and the Riesengebirge probably few suitable habitats for saxicolous species, so it could be assumed that its immigration into Czechoslovakia had already occurred during Mindel time (Černohorský, 1961).

Obviously *Parmelia centrifuga* is a very old type which has great ecological amplitude. In spite of the fact that the climatic conditions during the Glacial Ages in arctic and central Europe (especially below the firn line) were substantially different, I suppose that the inability of this species to occupy new localities, particularly on the northern and southern limits of its area, confirms Lynge's conclusion.

Later Dahl (1946, 1950), a close collaborator of the late Professor Lynge, tried to solve the survival question of the North Atlantic lichens during the Glacial Ages. His method was based on a much broader scale, which he further extended in his later works (Dahl, 1954, 1955, 1958).

In his first paper Dahl (1946) sketches the history of the Arctic–Alpine flora in Scandinavia from the Last Interglacial. During the Last Glacial Age the central part of Scandinavia was covered by ice, but unglaciated refugia existed in limited spots on the western and northern coasts. Some of the species survived the Last Glacial Age there, and after the retreat of the ice they migrated up into the mountains. Later, in the mountains, they met with other species which had penetrated to this region following the retreating ice from the south and east. The present Arctic–Alpine flora in Scandinavia is therefore a mixture of these two elements. Further, he describes the history even more precisely. He collects proofs to show the unglaciated refugia in the Northern Hemisphere during the Last Glacial Age. Then he distinguishes these refugia into two types: (a) the coastal mountain type (with high mountains near the border of deep oceans) that is further divided into two subtypes: (aa) the Scandinavian subtype—firn line never descends to sea level, Atlantic climate, rich vegetation of vascular plants, mosses and lichens; (ab) the Antarctic subtype—firn line descends to the level of the sea during the severest period, Antarctic climate, few or no vascular plants, few mosses, rich vegetation of lichens, especially microlichens; (b) the tundra type (with a continental climate, firn line never descends to sea level, rich vegetation of vascular plants, mosses and lichens). Refugia of the first type (Scandinavian subtype) are found in western and northwestern Scandinavia, probably in Scotland, Iceland, southern Greenland, and possibly Labrador; refugia of the second type in Siberia, possibly in the Kola peninsula, in Novaya Zemlya, northern Norway, Bear Island, Spitsbergen, northern Greenland, and Arctic Canada. The following Arctic–Alpine lichens are characteristic for the coastal mountain refugia (Scandinavian subtype): *Thyrea radiata* (Smft.) Zahlbr., *Agyrophora rigida* (Du Rietz) Llano, *Umbilicaria havaasii* Llano, and *Alectoria nitidula* (Th. Fr.) Vain. Dahl regards these macrolichen species as typical for the tundra refugia: *Dactylina arctica* (Richards.) Nyl., *D. ramulosa* (Hook.) Tuck., *D. madreporiformis* (Wulf.) Tuck., *Parmelia subobscura* Vain., *Omphalodiscus krascheninnikovii* (Sav.) Schol., and *Cetraria chrysantha* Tuck. Before he draws a conclusion, he shows also that some southern species could survive the Last Glacial Age on unglaciated coastal mountain refugia, and the more so the more Atlantic the climate was, for example on the west coast of Scandinavia and especially in the British Isles.

But Dahl does not enumerate any lichens of this latter type. No doubt, as an example there can be mentioned some of the southern species from southwest Greenland (Dahl, 1950, p. 157–158) and probably even some of the north coast lichens from Svalbard. *Placopsis gelida* (L.) Nyl., which forms a transition between macrolichens and microlichens, could probably also be named. This is a species of a more or less pronounced Atlantic (oceanic) nature, the distribution of which was mapped by Lamb (1947). Because it was previously mentioned even from Czechoslovakia, I carefully noted its occurrence in the southwestern part of Iceland in 1948. I collected it there in several low altitude localities, but also on the nunatak of the glacier Thórisjökull, 1060 m (with the firn line above the foot of the nunatak). Therefore we may conclude that it could have survived the Last Glacial Age even in the unglaciated refugia in Iceland.

Lamb (1947) writes that only the coastal mountain refugia would have been available for it during the Pleistocene age. He supposes that its present extention to Spitsbergen, Bear Island, northernmost Norway, and Novaya Zemlya in the east, and to the Boothia Peninsula of Arctic Canada in the west, must therefore be the result of migration in the Late Glacial and Postglacial times. This statement may be supported by the fact that soredia of *Placopsis gelida* are usually present. In this connection I would like to mention the said specimens from the nunatak Thórisjökull, which, compared with those from the lower localities of southwestern Iceland, have the whole thallus sorediate. It seems that this phenomenon is a reaction of the plant to external factors. Also Lynge (1939b) states that *Placopsis gelida* is sorediate in the eastern Spitsbergen islands. For our consideration this phenomenon is of great importance since *Placopsis gelida* is often sterile and without apothecia in the Arctic. Besides, reproduction by spores is relatively complicated, more so than we used to imagine not long ago (cf. Ahmadjian, 1960), and therefore not always effective in the Arctic.

On the other hand, the antiquity of this species must be stressed. This age derives from the fact that it is spread not only in the Northern Hemisphere, but also in the southern one, with a great gap between its distribution in the north Pacific and in the Southern Hemisphere. It is not unlikely, therefore, that it could have survived the Last Glacial period even in more northern localities than Lamb (*loc. cit.*) supposes.

Soredia otherwise are found only in a few Arctic macrolichens, and if seen, they are often poorly developed and corticated. The dispersal by means of these diaspores may not always be effective: the circumpolar sorediate lichens are usually common, but all the non-circumpolar sorediate species are rare in the Arctic (Lynge, 1934). Because the formation of apothecia (and spores) in many Arctic macrolichens is also limited, they can reproduce only by means of thallus fragments. These latter of course do not permit dispersal over long distances.

Now I return to the conclusion in Dahl's paper (1946). In it, Dahl solves the problem of the southwest Greenland macrolichen flora and its relation to the Scandinavian one, which it approaches in identity. In his later paper (Dahl, 1950) he goes into the same problem, using a rich material. Here he compares the macrolichen flora of southwest Greenland and the macrolichen species in the floras of Scandinavia and central Europe. He states that 24 species are found in southwest Greenland and in Scandinavia, but not in the mountains of central Europe. Analogically there are in Scandinavia 36 species of Alpine lichens which have not been discovered in the mountains of central Europe. The Scandinavian and the central European mountains possess 15 common Alpine macrolichen species. Only 11 Alpine species found in the central European mountains occur neither in Scandinavia nor in southwest Greenland. Consequently the relation between the macrolichen flora of southwest Greenland and the Alpine macrolichen flora of Scandinavian is closer than the relation between the Alpine macrolichen flora of Scandinavia and that of the central European mountains. Dahl explains the cause of this phenomenon: he supposes, that "(1) the lichen floras of Southwest Greenland and of Scandinavia date from a period when the correspondence in the whole flora between Europe and east America was closer than today. (2) The conditions, under which the lichens in Scandinavia and southwest Greenland had to live during the Last Ice Age, were almost the same in the two districts, but different from those in other areas like Novaya Zemlya or the Alps" (refugia of the coastal mountain type, the Scandinavian subtype).

Dahl (*loc. cit.*) came to the first point of his explanation by comparing vascular plants known in Europe only as fossils from Interglacial layers, but still growing today in America. From this he concludes that the flora of Europe during the Last Interglacial probably had a more American character. If this was really the case, then the Arctic–Alpine flora could either survive even the largest glaciation on some refugia in northwest Europe (when several of them in the Northern Hemisphere probably were of the Antarctic type), or else a closer connection existed between northwest Europe and northeast America during the Last Interglacial.

Later Dahl (1955) returns again to the question of unglaciated refugia in Scandinavia. He devotes his attention exclusively to vascular plants and underlines here the presence of West Arctic species which otherwise are lacking in Europe and west Asia. Further, he points to the endemism in the

Scandinavian flora and to the bicentric distribution of some rare plants in the Scandinavian mountains. Two facts are of the utmost importance: "Fossil records indicate that conditions in South and Central Sweden were not favorable for immigration from the south of much of this flora during the deglaciation period. Other fossil records indicate that Arctic–Alpine plants grew in the mountains immediately after deglaciation." By these facts, he gives additional evidence for the survival of the present Arctic–Alpine flora during the Last Glacial Age in refugia along the Scandinavian coast and adjacent mountains.

Among the Scandinavian lichens are also found West Arctic species, e.g. the previously mentioned *Agyrophora rigida* (Du Rietz) Llano and *Umbilicaria havaasii* Llano (Llano, 1950), and endemic types, e.g. *Rhizocarpon superficiale* (Schaer.) Vain. ssp. *splendidum* (Malme) Runemark (Runemark, 1956), as well as representatives of the bicentric distribution, e.g. *Philophoron robustum* (Th. Fr.) Nyl. (Dahl, 1950).

We have not mentioned, as yet, the epiphytic lichens. Degelius (1957) is applying himself to the question of epiphytic lichens and their survival during the Glacial Ages in Iceland. He points especially to *Parmelia aspera* Mass. Its habitats are situated near presumed refugia of vascular relict plants during the Last Glaciation. At the same time this obligately epiphytic species has a dominant place in the epiphytic vegetation of birch stands in Iceland (but not in Scandinavia). It is known from Scandinavia, where it shows a wide ecologic amplitude, and from North America, but not from Greenland. From these facts, as well as from others, Degelius presumes that it is a very old type, of Interglacial or perhaps Preglacial age. Supporting this view is also the fact that remnants of a birch closely related to recent forms growing in Iceland have been found in Tertiary layers, and remains of a birch in an old Interglacial layer have also been collected there. *Dermatina major* (Nyl.) Lettau may be of the same age, too. Other epiphytic lichens of Iceland are probably younger, some of them being introduced by man in recent times (e.g. *Xanthoria lobulata* (Flk.) B. de Lesd.).

In the above outline I have restricted myself to the probability of lichen survival in refugia in the North Atlantic basin during the Last Glacial Age. I did this mainly for the reason that we have no paleontological records of lichens from earlier geological periods. In spite of this fact, it is evident from this outline that the lichen flora in the described space includes various elements which of course are of a different age there. Various authors evaluate differently the age of the same type, when even the same author rates the age of a given type very vaguely. It can be said, in spite of this, that the oldest are the Arctic–Alpine species with immense, but not continuous distribution (i.e. showing great gaps) in the world. These species have persisted there probably since the Tertiary age. What a pity that we do not know better the distribution of Arctic–Alpine microlichens which undoubtedly survived even the Greatest Glaciation! Among them are some especially old types, as for example, *Rhizocarpon inarense* (Vain.) Vain. (mapped by Runemark, 1956). The species with a broad ecological amplitude (or with different ecotypes, unknown to us?) or with new resistent mutations probably also have survived the Greatest Glaciation. In any case, the glaciation caused a limitation of convenient habitats and a strong natural selection, which resulted in decreasing the number of species. On the other hand, it of course did not prevent new taxa from arising. The number of species increased again during the Interglacial ages. In the relatively short Postglacial age a small number of species have penetrated into the North Atlantic zone. Evidently the species have immigrated during the different periods and mainly over land.

In this connection I would like to finish with the conclusion of one of Dahl's last papers (1958):

> "... there is little to indicate that species unable to grow above 800 m in South Norway migrated across the Atlantic as more hardy species probably did.
>
> These observations suggest a climate on the hypothetical land bridge similar to that found in the birch belt in South Norway. Such climate probably did not occur in the region concerned until the Pliocene period and it is concluded that the land bridge existed in the Pliocene.
>
> Independent geological evidence suggests that a basalt plateau was formed stretching from Scotland to East Greenland in the early Tertiary period and existed as a land area until it was broken up in the Pliocene or perhaps as late as the Pleistocene age."

REFERENCES

AHMADJIAN, V. (1960). The Lichen association. *The Bryologist* **63**, 250–254.

ČERNOHORSKÝ, Z. (1961). Die Flechte *Parmelia centrifuga* (L.) Ach. im Böhmerwald. *Preslia* **33**, 359–364.

DAHL, E. (1946). On different types of unglaciated areas during the Ice Ages and their significance to phytogeography. *New Phytologist* **45**, 225–242.

DAHL, E. (1950). Studies in the macrolichen flora of South West Greenland. *Medd. om Groenl.* **150** (2), 1–176.

DAHL, E. (1954) Weathered gneisses at the island of Runde, Sunnmøre, Western Norway, and their geological interpretation. *Nytt Mag. Bot.* **3**, 5–23.

DAHL, E. (1955). Biogeographic and geologic indications of unglaciated areas in Scandinavia during the Glacial Age. *Bull. Geol. Soc. Amer.* **66**, 1499–1519.

DAHL, E. (1958). Amfiatlantiske planter. Problems of Amphiatlantic plant distribution. *Blyttia* **16**, 93–121.

DAHL, E., LYNGE B. and SCHOLANDER, P. F. (1937). Lichens from Southeast Greenland. *Skr Svalbard og Ishavet*, No. 70, 1–76.

DEGELIUS, G. (1957). The epiphytic lichen flora of the birch stands in Iceland. *Acta Horti Gotoburg.* **22** (1), 1–51.

LAMB, I. M. (1947). A monograph of the lichen genus *Placopsis* Nyl. *Lilloa* **13**, 151–288.

LLANO, G. A. (1950). *A Monograph of the Lichen Family Umbilicariaceae in the Western Hemisphere.* Washington.

LYNGE, B. (1928). Lichens from Novaya Zemlya. *Rep. Sci. Res. Norweg. Exped. Novaya Zemlya 1921, Oslo*, No. 43, 1–229.

LYNGE, B. (1933). On *Dufourea* and *Dactylina.* Three Arctic lichens. *Skr. Svalbard og Ishavet, Oslo*, No. 59, 1–62.

LYNGE, B. (1934). General results of recent Norwegian research work on Arctic lichens. *Rhodora* **36**, 133–171.

LYNGE, B. (1937). Lichens from West Greenland collected chiefly by TH. M. FRIES. *Medd. om Groenl.* **118** (8), 1–193.

LYNGE, B. (1938). Lichens from the west and north coast of Spitsbergen and the North East Land. I. Macrolichens. *Skr. Norske Vid.-Akad. Oslo, cl. math.-naturv.* 1938 (6), 1–136.

LYNGE, B. (1939a). On the survival of plants in the Arctic. *Norsk Geogr. Tidsskr.* **7**, 489–497.

LYNGE, B. (1939b). A small contribution to the lichen flora of the eastern Svalbard Islands. *Norges Svalbard Ishavs Unders. Medd.* No. 44, 1.

LYNGE, B. (1940a). Lichens from Iceland. I. Macrolichens. *Skr. Norske Vid.-Akad. Oslo, cl.math.-naturv.* 1940 (7), 1–56.

LYNGE, B. (1940b). Lichens from North East Greenland collected on the Norwegian scientific expeditions in 1929 and 1930. II. Microlichens. *Skr. Svalbard og Ishavet, Oslo,* No. 81, 1–143.

LYNGE, B. and SCHOLANDER, P. F. (1932). Lichens from North East Greenland collected on the Norwegian scientific expeditions in 1929 and 1930. I. Macrolichens. *Skr. Svalbard og Ishavet, Oslo,* No. 41, 1–116.

RUNEMARK, H. (1956). Studies in *Rhizocarpon. Opera Bot., Lund,* 2(1/2), 1–152, 1–150.

RECENT DISCOVERIES IN THE SOUTH NORWEGIAN FLORA AND THEIR SIGNIFICANCE FOR THE UNDERSTANDING OF THE HISTORY OF THE SCANDINAVIAN MOUNTAIN FLORA DURING AND AFTER THE LAST GLACIATION

ROLF NORDHAGEN

Botanical Museum, University of Oslo, Oslo, Norway

THE mountain flora of Scandinavia, and particularly that of Norway, contains types of plant distribution which by no means can be explained according to the theory that the Scandinavian Peninsula was completely buried under the ice during the Last Glaciation. This idea has received the epithet of *tabula rasa* theory because according to it all life existing in this part of Europe during the Last Interglacial was completely eradicated during the Last Ice Age. After this calamity all the present flora and fauna of Scandinavia had to immigrate anew, preferably from south, east and northeast.

One of the first Scandinavian botanists to oppose the *tabula rasa* theory was the Norwegian Axel Blytt (1881, 1882). Judging from his papers in the 1880's he evidently realized that a number of hardy species in the Norwegian flora had survived the Last Glaciation inside Norway. In 1882 he wrote: "Es ist möglich, jawohl sogar warscheinlich dass jene grönländischen Elemente in unserer Flora Reste aus den interglazialen Zeiten sind" (It is possible, yes, even probable that this Greenlandic element in our flora is a remnant from the Interglacial times). Other statements by Blytt in his papers from the 1880's are, however, on the whole rather haltering.

However, in a later paper Blytt (1893) contested the idea put forward by the Swedish botanist F. W. C. Areschoug (1869) that the so-called "Arctic flora" n Scandinavia should have a north Siberian origin. Regarding the Norwegian mountain flora, Blytt states that it has rather a Greenlandic or Greenlandic–American origin. Here he points his finger to something of utmost importance, to still actual problems of a historical–phytogeographical nature that Nordic natural science will never be able to by-pass.

Whereas most of the present plant species on the Scandinavian Peninsula are to be found in Europe—though in many cases in distinctly disjunct areas—

the Scandinavian and particularly the Norwegian mountain flora contains a group of species with its main center in Greenland and North America. In Norway and Sweden there are a number of these very rare and exclusive species such as the little yellow-flowered *Draba crassifolia*. A still more striking example is offered by *Carex scirpoidea* (Fig. 1). This species was

FIG. 1. The only European localities of *Carex scirpoidea* (asterisk); *Oxytropis deflexa* (circle with cross), and *Crepis multicaulis* (square) in north Norway.

discovered in 1854 on the Solvågtind Mt. (66° 55′ N. Lat.) in Nordland Fylke. During the past 100 years, numerous Norwegian and Swedish botanists have searched in vain for *Carex scirpoidea* in other localities. The nearest occurrences of this species in relation to its Norwegian locality are found in western Greenland. As a third and a fourth example in this connection, I want to mention the mountain species *Pedicularis flammea* and *Arenaria humifusa*. Both occur at present in northern Norway and northern Sweden, but are rare. The nearest localities for *Pedicularis flammea* are in Iceland and Greenland; *Arenaria humifusa* has a single locality on Spitsbergen but is not very rare in west Greenland and occurs frequently over extensive areas in northern North America. It has never been found in east Greenland, a fact which is of considerable interest (cf. Nordhagen, 1935, 1954).

In order to explain the occurrence of the Greenlandic–American element in the mountain flora of Norway (and of Scandinavia), Blytt postulated a land-bridge during the Quaternary time joining Greenland with western Norway via Iceland and the Faeroes. This land-bridge should have been glaciated only in part, and never throughout simultaneously, thus permitting dispersal of plants in both directions. At present it is submerged but is often referred to as the "Iceland–Faeroe ridge".

In other respects, admittedly, Blytt was "skating on thin ice". He was wrong at least in part in his uncritical characterization of the Scandinavian mountain flora as emanating from Greenland and North America and not from northern Siberia. If we include the Sub-Arctic flora from the northernmost counties of Norway—a flora which is found also in the mountains—we will find just as remarkable examples of disjunct distribution as those mentioned above. One is represented by *Oxytropis deflexa* (Fig. 1), discovered in 1879 on a low mountain at Masi in west Finnmark. Norwegian, Swedish, Finnish, and Russian botanists have failed ever since to locate this species in any other place in Europe. Its nearest localities occur in Altai and along the River Olenek in northeastern Siberia (cf. Hultén, 1950). Another species from northern Norway worth mentioning because of its highly disjunct area is *Crepis multicaulis* (Fig. 1). It was discovered as early as in 1851 in a single locality on the south side of the Varanger Peninsula in east Finnmark. For more than 100 years botanists from northern Europe have looked in vain for it in other areas. Altai, Mongolia, and northeastern Siberia provide the nearest localities (cf. Nordhagen 1935).

I also want to draw the attention here to *Scirpus pumilus* (syn. *S. alpinus*, *S. emergens*) (Fig. 2) with its highly paradoxical distribution area. In northern Europe it was originally known only from the Eocambrian dolomite outcrop at Porsanger Fjord in Finnmark where it was discovered in 1864. It grows here both at sea level and on a low mountain with a rich flora (it was found by the XIIIth International phyto-geographical excursion close to the top of the dolomite mountain depicted on page 8 in the paper by Gjærevoll, 1961). In 1939 this species was found in the low-alpine region of a mountain at Nordreisa in Troms Fylke and during the summer of 1961 in two localities on a small island in the Kvænangen Fjord, about 40 km north of Nordreisa.

The islands in the Kvænangen Fjord are all low and consist of schists with impressive layers of limestone, probably of Cambro-Silurian age. *Scirpus pumilus* is easily recognized, but it has never been seen outside of the counties Finnmark and Troms, thus never in the mountains of southern Norway,

FIG. 2. The north European distribution of *Scirpus pumilus*, only in north Norway. The nearest localities are in the Carpathians and the Alps.

where there are calciferous mica schist and limestone in many places. The nearest *Scirpus pumila* localities outside of Troms and Finnmark are found in the Alps and in the Carpathians.

No phytogeographer can possibly accept the *tabula rasa* theory in view of the examples from Scandinavia which I have enumerated above: on one hand *Draba crassifolia*, *Carex scirpoidea*, *Pedicularis flammea*, and *Arenaria humifusa*, so-called "West Arctic" species (from a Scandinavian point of view), and on the other *Oxytropis deflexa*, *Crepis multicaulis*, and *Scirpus pumilus*.

It is worth mentioning here what is written in a paper by the Swedish botanist Rutger Sernander (1896): ". . . that in the Norwegian mountains have been preserved a not negligible number of remnants from the Interglacial flora of Scandinavia, especially in Dovre, Nordland and Finnmark, which were not over-run by the second Inland Ice. From this time we have especially the American–Greenlandic element in the Scandinavian flora" (translated from Swedish). In the same treatise Sernander goes as far as to state: ". . . into our South-Swedish mountain regions in Jämtland and Härjedalen the most important elements have arrived from that western flora which was not destroyed by the second glaciation, and not, as has been suggested, from the glacial flora which dispersed from the south, following the rim of the regressing Inland Ice up through Norway and Sweden" (translated from Swedish).

The Norwegian geologist and prehistorian, Andreas M. Hansen tried (1904 a, b) to solve all the problems pertaining to the Norwegian mountain flora (above I have touched upon only a few of them) by launching a theory according to which there existed along the Norwegian Atlantic coast a broad, ice-free margin on which a large number of plant species could have "overwintered" the Last Glacial Age. In 1905 a thesis was published by the Norwegian botanist N. Wille in which he pointed out that Hansen's theory contains much exaggeration but holds nevertheless also a kernel of truth. Wille's thesis does not give much new information but he demonstrates by the aid of statistics that the number of "rare Arctic plants" in southern Norway decreases from the area of Dovre-Vågå-Lom southwards to the Valdres and Aurland Mountains and still more so towards the Hardangervidda. This gradation from north to south, in Wille's opinion, corresponds badly with the view that the south Norwegian mountain flora should have immigrated from the south after the Last Glacial.

Unfortunately, neither Blytt, Sernander, Hansen nor Wille tackled these difficult phytogeographical problems by a cartographic presentation of the distribution of the species concerned inside Scandinavia.

The theory of glacial survival must of course also be considered from the point of view of Quaternary geology. Hansen (1904) did so and believed he could trace a more or less continuous line of moraines in the fjord-districts of Norway. He supposed that this line marked the outer border of the last large ice-shield along the Norwegian Atlantic coast (Fig. 3). More recent investigations (Undås, 1942; Holtedahl, 1953) have shown, however, that this line, the so-called Ra-line (corresponding to the Finnish Salpaussälkä-line) marks a certain stage during the deglaciation of Norway and not the outer boundary of the last ice-shield. Nevertheless, there exist fragments of end-moraines in the west- and north-Norwegian coastal areas which are older than the Ra-stage. As a matter of fact, the older stages in the deglaciation of western and northern Norway have not been definitely established yet.

In a later paper, Wille (1915) drew attention to the conditions—even from a Norwegian point of view—of the literally brutal relief which characterizes certain parts of western Norway (especially the coast of Möre) and all the

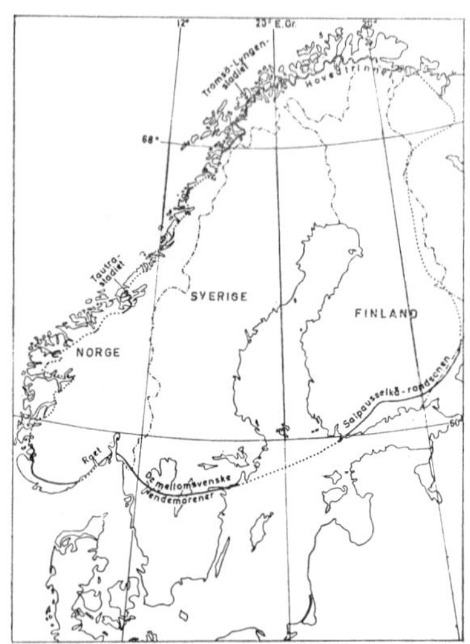

FIG. 3. Map of the Salpausselkä–Ra stage of end-moraines in Fennoscandia (after Martninussen, 1961).

coast of northern Norway (from the northernmost part of Nordland County northeast towards west Finnmark). He could not imagine that this coast had ever been totally covered by ice during the Last Ice Age and proposed that there had been *refugia* with plant life. (cf. Figs. 9 and 10).

Already in 1912 the late Norwegian geologist Th. Vogt had published a paper about the outermost (southern) islands of Lofoten, Værö and Röst, which he claimed to have been ice-free during the Last Glacial period.

It was, however, the Swedish botanist Th. C. E. Fries, who in his doctoral thesis from 1913 succeeded in pulling down the "survival theory" from its lofty heaven of speculations to *terra firma*. Inspired by Vogt's (1912) work, Fries made dot-maps of the present distribution of the mountain plants on the Scandinavian Peninsula. He adhered also enthusiastically to the theory of survival. Fries divided the Scandinavian mountain flora into four groups:

(a) *The ubiquist group*, or plants covering all of the Norwegian–Swedish mountain chain.

(b) *The bicentric group*, or plants concentrated—though without absolute congruence—in two distant "islands" in the mountain chain (Fig. 4). This condition is especially evident in Norway, where we find a concentration of interesting species partly in the area north of Jotunheimen over Mt. Dovre to Trollheimen and the Sunndal Mts., partly from Saltdal in Nordland County to west Finnmark (Fig. 5).

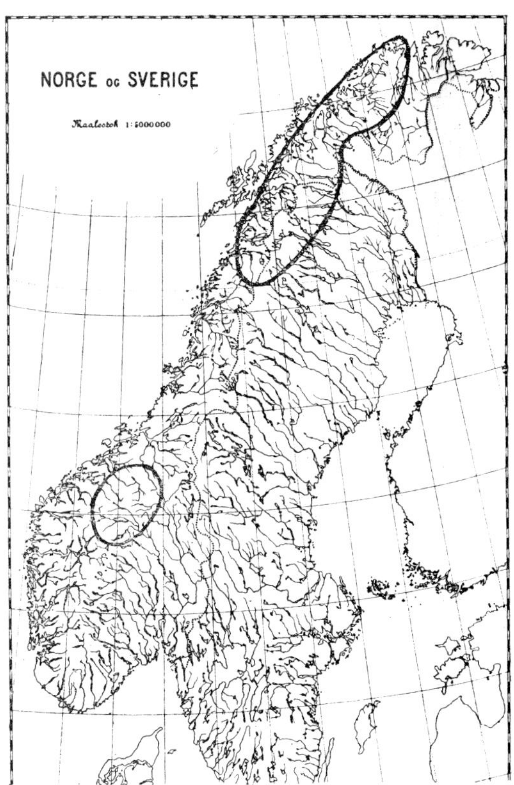

FIG. 4. Map of the two "island"-like areas in the Scandinavian Mts. which have an unusually rich mountain flora (after Nordhagen, 1936).

(c) *The northern unicentric group*, or plants confined to the northern "island", where it occurs together with a number of "bicentric" species (Fig. 5).

(d) *The southern unicentric group*, or plants connected exclusively to the "island" area in the southern Norwegian mountains (Fig. 5).

I was myself for a long while very sceptical towards the "survival" theory, which is evident in my thesis for the doctorate from 1921. But after an extensive journey in 1930 through Norway from the Valdres Mts. in the south all the way to the Varanger Peninsula in the northeast in order especially to study in nature the populations of *Papaver* sect. *Scapiflora* which appear in Scandinavia, I became a convert to this theory (Nordhagen, 1931, 1936).

The sequence of *Papaver* taxa (in part with $2n = 70$ chromosomes, and in part with $2n = 56$) (Fig. 6) occurring in Scandinavia from north to south, of which the northernmost populations on the Varanger Peninsula and the southernmost ones in the mountains of Valdres and Sogn have white latex, whereas all the others have yellow latex, is so remarkable from a phytogeographical point of view that it cannot possibly be explained as a result of Late Glacial immigration with a consecutive species formation. Here the "*tabula rasa*" theory literally crumbles. However, as I still do not consider the problem of *Papaver* taxonomy and nomenclature finally settled, I do not want to elaborate on it here.

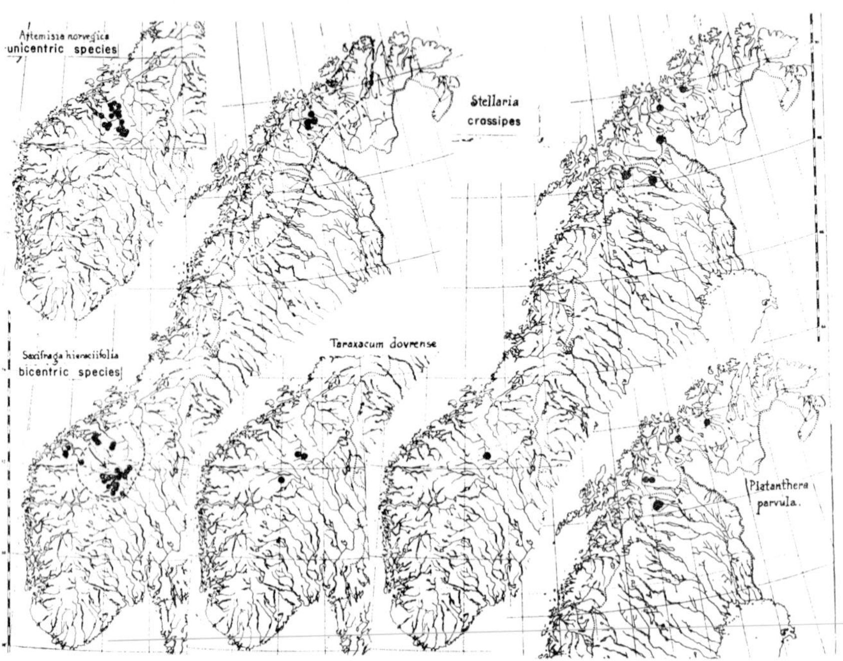

FIG. 5. Examples of uni-and bicentric distribution of mountain plants in Norway and Scandinavia (after Nordhagen, 1936).

Fries (1921) made it clear that the Scandinavian mountain flora possesses an endemic taxon, *Euphrasia lapponica*, belonging to the *salisburgensis* group (Fig. 7). It is a bicentric species, absent between South Tröndelag and the Polar Circle. Hugo Dahlstedt, the late, famous Swedish specialist on *Hieracium* and *Taraxacum*, demonstrated in 1928 that *Taraxacum Reichenbachii* Huter ssp. *dovrense* Dt. ought to be regarded as a species of its own, *T. dovrense* Dt. It is found exclusively in the south Norwegian mountains from Opdal in the north to Lom in the south. It is closely related to the extremely rare *T. Reichenbachii*, a taxon of the Tirolian Alps east of the Brenner Pass

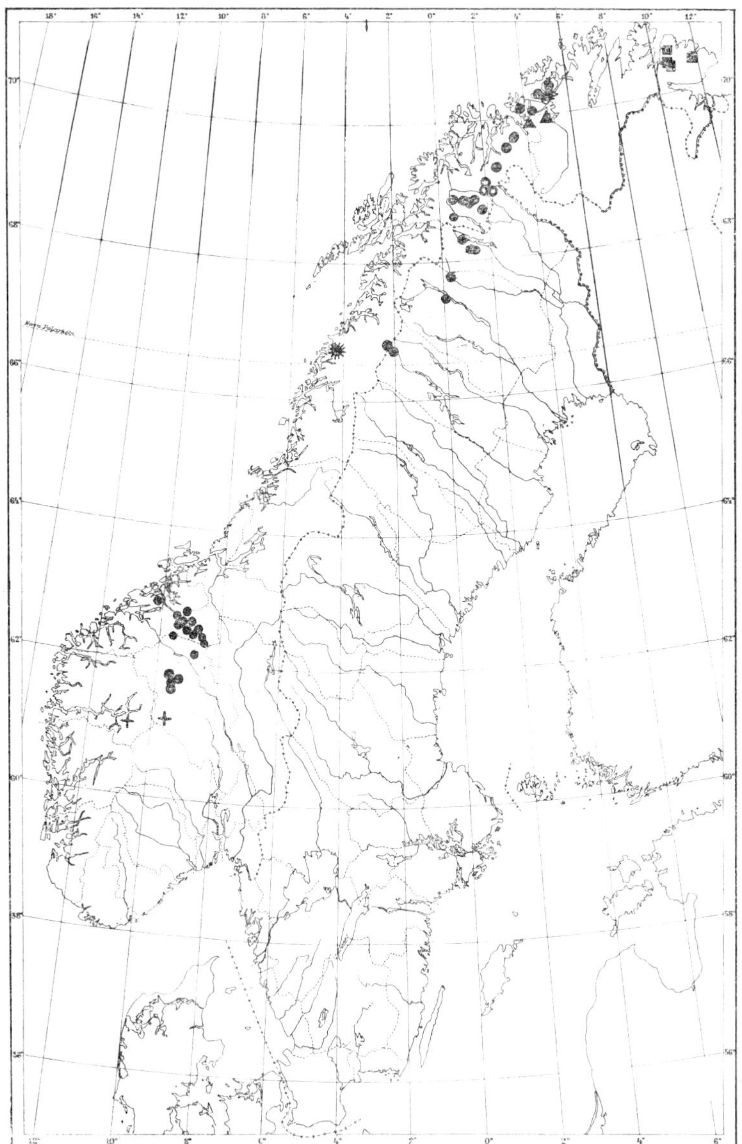

Fig. 6. Map of the occurrences of *Papaver* sect. *Scapiflora* in Scandinavia: *P. dahlianum* Nordh. (squares); *P. relictum* (Lundstr.) Nordh. (crosses); *P. lapponicum* (Tolm.) Nordh. (triangles); *P. laestadianum* Nordh. (circles). Other signs mark the occurrences of taxa belonging to *P. radicatum* Rottb. sensu Nordhagen.

(cf. Dahlstedt, 1908). Besides this, several endemic species of *Taraxacum* sect. *Ceratophora* are found both in Norway and in the rest of Scandinavia.

FIG. 7. Map of the distribution of *Euphrasia lapponica* in south Norway. For the total distribution in Fennoscandia, see Hultén, 1950.

One of them, *T. aleurophorum* Hagl. (syn. *T. aleurodes* Hagl., *T. cornutum* Dt. var. *pruinstum* Dt.) is of special interest because a closely related species, the single representative of the *Ceratophora* group south of Scandinavia, is found in Engadin, Switzerland (cf. Dahlstedt, 1906).

The "survival"—or "refugium"—theory has lately been subjected to a rather rough criticism from several Norwegian and Swedish Quaternary geologists. They clamor distinct proofs for the existence of ice-free areas along the Norwegian coast as well as for nunataks farther inland. Other geologists do not totally deny the "refugium theory" but prefer to remain passive. I will here stick to the plants and their distribution, and especially to the distribution of the *bicentric* mountain species. Norwegian and Swedish botanists have cooperated conscientiously during the last generation, I dare say even to their utmost, in order to investigate in full the geographical distribution of the bicentric species. The result is that the bicentricity is a fact for a number of species. On the whole, it is possible to state that the botanical indicia in favor of the survival theory have increased, and many previously unknown conditions have been brought into light (cf. Elfstrand, 1927; Ekman, 1927; Nordhagen, 1930, 1936, 1940, 1952, 1954, and others).

In order to explain the bicentricity some authors have resorted to the Post-glacial Hypsithermal period. It caused a strong displacement northwards and upwards of the *Pinus silvestris* forests, and the authors in question maintain that the presently bicentric mountain species had a continuous distribution in the Norwegian–Swedish mountains before this warm time. The cause of the present bicentricity should be that precisely the area from north Tröndelag to Saltdal in Nordland County consists of mountains reaching a lower altitude than those to the south and the north of it, and thus largely were covered in the Hypsithermal by *Pinus silvestris* forest which due to its shading effect obliterated the light requiring bicentric species from this area. Such an explanation is, however, unacceptable. A great many of the bicentric species are today found right inside the upper reaches of the *Pinus silvestris* belt. *Saxifraga hieraciifolia* offers a good example. It was found already in the 1870's at an altitude as low as *ca.* 600 m above sea level at Lake Olstappen in the eastern part of Jotunheimen. One of the botany students at the University of Oslo, Sverre Lökken, has recently discovered it at only 450 m altitude in a river gorge at Garmo, inside the *Pinus*-belt, in the northern part of Jotunheimen. The finds from Olstappen and Garmo are very important. It is evident that Norway had also during the Hypsithermal a very broken relief with eroding rivers, gorges and lakes. Thus, if in recent times a plant like *Saxifraga hieraciifolia* can occur not only above the timberline, but also here and there at a lower altitude, down to 450 m, inside the *Pinus* region, a displacement upwards during the Hypsithermal of the *Pinus silvestris* forests cannot possibly be used to explain the bicentricity of this species. Below I will discuss the relationship between the bicentric *Rhododendron lapponicum* and the *Pinus* forests.

The survival theory postulates first and foremost that there were ice-free refugia along the coast of Möre in southern Norway (Undås, 1941), and from Saltdal and Lofoten to west Finnmark in northern Norway (Holtedahl, 1929;

Undås, 1938; Nordhagen, 1936; Marthinussen, 1961). Further it postulates that during the deglaciation of Norway the "over-wintering" species dispersed eastwards and inland, taking hold in the nearest mountainous regions at the same time as they lost foothold in the coastal areas, among others because other flora elements immigrated and occupied the coast as the climate underwent changes in Post-glacial time.

Since 1940 the plan for my scientific work has been to investigate especially the *coastal mountains* of southern Norway in order to find "traces" left by the bicentric mountain plants there. These species at present have their center far inland from the coastal districts where they must have survived the Last Glacial period if the survival theory holds true. To use a poetic expression from Macpherson (alias "Ossian"), I have been hunting for "fragments of ancient poetry" ever since 1940.

Already in 1941 a young geologist, Anders Heltzen, rendered me unexpected help. While investigating the massif of Lauparen between Romsdalsfjord and Storfjord in south Möre about 45 km east of the city of Ålesund, Heltzen discovered *Saxifraga hieraciifolia* at an altitude of 1200–1300 m above sea level in weathered gneissic soil on one of the peaks. The summer of 1944 I made an excursion to the said peak, and after a frightening steep ascent I rediscovered the locality (Heltzen and Nordhagen, 1944). *Saxifraga hieraciifolia* occurs very sparingly here together with among others *Pedicularls Oederi* which also has its western limit in Norway on this very peak. In the Sub-alpine region at the foot of the Lauparen Massif there are a number of typical coastal species, such as, for example, *Digitalis purpurea*, *Dryopteris Oreopteris*, and slightly farther to the north, *Luzula maxima*. In 1946, *Saxifraga hieraciifolia* was discovered also on a mountain northeast of Lauparen not far from the Romsdalsfjord itself.

Up to 1930 *Saxifraga hieraciifolia* had been regarded as something of a prime example of Axel Blytt's idea that at present time the "arctic flora" of South Norway is confined to those areas which lie in the rain shadow of the western mountains in south Norway. The species was considered a typical inland plant, avoiding the mild, humid climate along the west coast. But already in 1930 I was sceptical towards this dogma since I had discoveree the species in Eikisdalen, a valley east of the Romsdalsfjord (Nordhagen, 1930). Thus, during the years 1940–44 I saw this dogma foiled, and my dream to find the "fragments of ancient poetry" in the coastal mountains had become true.

On the whole, the survival theory cannot get a better support than the geographical distribution in southern Norway of *Saxifraga hieraciifolia*: it is now found to exist sporadically all the way to the coast of Möre. The remarkable distribution pattern of this species can definitely not be explained in accordance with any *tabula rasa* theory. As *S. hieraciifolia* at present occurs as a rarity in the Carpathians, the Steyermark and Auvergne, it was easy to propose that it could have immigrated to Norway from the south as late as during the deglaciation. But then, its distribution pattern should have been entirely different. Since the species is totally lacking south of the Jotunheimen Massif (in spite of the fact that there are innumerable suitable habitats for it, for example, on the Hardangervidda, the mountains in Valdres and Sogn, all botanically very well investigated areas), but appears far out in the coastal mountains of Möre, it is virtually impossible to accept the hypothesis that it should have immigrated from the south during the deglaciation.

Another important example is given us in the distribution of *Euphrasia lapponica.* Until 1947 this bicentric species had in southern Norway been found only inland, from Hardangervidda in the south to the Opdal Mts. in the north. But in the summer of 1948, I discovered *E. lapponica* growing on some relatively low mountains far out north of the Romsdalsfjord close to the sea but above the birch region. Besides the ordinary form with a white corolla I found a new race of the species with a deeply blue–violet corolla (*Euphrasia lapponica* Th. Fr. fil. var. *purpureocoerulea* Nordh.; cf. Nordhagen, 1952).

The last example of bicentric species to be mentioned in this paper is *Rhododendron lapponicum*, a dwarf shrub and the only European representative of the genus *Rhododendron* indigenous to northern Europe. In Scandinavia it has a typically bicentric area. A previous report of its occurrence on Bear Island has proved erroneous. The nearest localities of the species outside of Scandinavia is Greenland to the west and Lake Baikal and River Lena to the east.

The south Norwegian area of this species was very hard to interpret until 1957. Already during the last century it had been located in several places in the northernmost part of Jotunheimen, above the timberline, in the cantons Vågå and Lom and early in this century somewhat farther west in Skjåk but as a real rarity. To Axel Blytt, *Rhododendron lapponicum* functioned as a cornerstone in his scholarly construction concerning the continental character of the "Arctic flora" element in Norway since it seemed to be confined to areas situated in the rain shadow of the western mountains with their glaciers.

During the summer of 1957 I started, perhaps by instinct, to investigate the northernmost canton Lesja, in the valley of Gudbrandsdalen. It borders to Romsdalen. Perhaps it was the above-mentioned discoveries of *Saxifraga hieraciifolia* (Fig. 8) which stirred in my subconscious. Once more fate was kind to me. In Lesja a lady told me that in 1945 an English salmon fisherman, Mr. Jack, had divulged to her the precise locality of *Rhododendron lapponicum* southwest of Lesjaverk. I was accompanied on this occasion by Curator R. Berg, and thanks to our combined efforts we succeeded in relocating Mr. Jack's locality, and even found a new one near by.

Berg and I returned later to the mountains of western Lesja in the summer of 1960. In the meantime a dentist from the town of Molde had written to Professor O. Gjærevoll about a plant which he believed to be *Rhododendron lapponicum* and which he had found farthest to the west in Lesja on the Rånåkollen Mt. But the dentist had not taken a voucher specimen, neither

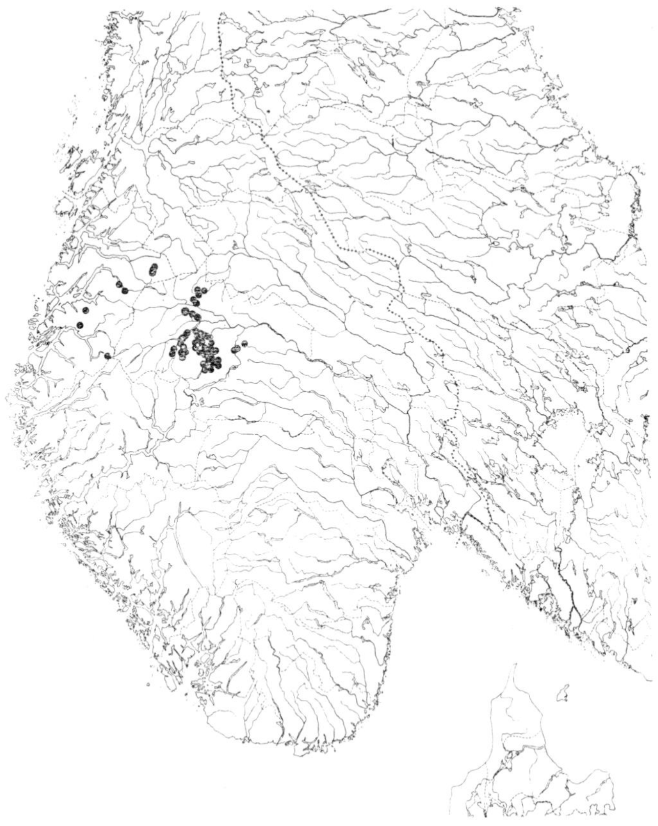

FIG. 8. The distribution in south Norway of *Saxifraga hieraciifolia*. For its occurrence in north Norway, see Hultén, 1950.

had he told from what side he had ascended Rånåskollen. Towards west–northwest this mountain precipitates almost vertically down to the River Rauma (after which Romsdalen, the valley of Rauma, is named) After a furtive ascent of the mountain from southeast, I decided to risk climbing its west–northwest face, and first Berg and later I myself succeeded in locating some very sparse occurrences of *Rhododendron lapponicum* at a little more than 1000 m altitude.

The most interesting facts concerning the occurrences of the individuals here were first and foremost their depauperated appearance and then the habitat, an ericaceous heath rich in lichens on the very rim of a rock ledge with no trace of accompanying calciphilous plant species. Rånåkollen is strongly humified above the timberline and has a very trivial vegetation; all we found were a few specimens of *Carex rupestris* along some rills and in a few rocky cracks a little of *Saxifraga oppositifolia*.

The occurrence of *Rhododendron lapponicum* on Rånåkollen must be interpreted as a typically relict habitat—the plant literally "hangs on by its fingernails" to the very rim of an acid humus surface. Since in Vågå and Lom as well as in northern Scandinavia this species is confined to calcareous

FIG. 9. Trolltindene in Romsdalen, seen from Storgravbotn. Norwegian botanists interpret these geological formations as "nunataks"; Norwegian geologists prefer another explanation.

rock, it is impossible to interpret its occurrence in western Lesja as a result of recent, or even Sub-Atlantic, dispersal westwards from an inland locality farther east. Personally, I am convinced that some energetic field botanist may succeed in finding more *Rhododendron lapponicum* (Fig. 11) still farther out towards the coast, especially if he decides to use a "fine toothed comb" on the mountains between western Lesja and Tafjord in south Möre. In the 1890's a comparatively rich mountain flora was discovered there in several localities. As *Rhododendron lapponicum* flowers early and is easily overlooked in its depauperate form during July and August, the species could possibly have been missed on the said mountains by collectors.

The results of my investigations in western Lesja are, thus, the following: from one or more refugia along the coast of Romsdal—Möre, *Rhododendron lapponicum* has dispersed inland during the deglaciation and arrived in an area where the rock substrate fully suited its ecological requirements, i.e. the area of Vågå–Lom–Skjåk.

Precisely in this district the relationship between *Rhododendron lapponicum* and *Pinus silvestris* is very instructive. Already in the last century *R. lapponicum* was discovered in pine forests, situated at a relatively high altitude in Lom. Recently the above-mentioned young Norwegian botanist Sverre Lökken found a mass-occurrence of this species at 650 m above sea level in an open, mixed *Pinus silvestris–Betula tortuosa* forest at Jullan in Lom. On this locality *R. lapponicum* descends even as far as to 500 m above sea level, but there it is, of course, very sparcely represented.

FIG. 10. Kvandalstind with "Thor's Hammer", Romsdalen, Norway. This formation is considered a nunatak by Norwegian botanists.

At last a few words about *Pedicularis Oederi* in Scandinavia (Fig. 12). Its present chief area in the Norwegian mountains reaches from Jotunheimen in the south to the southernmost part of the Tröndelag in the north with a western limit in the districts south of Romsdalsfjord and on north Möre. (cf. Fig. 12). Towards east this species follows the Dovre Ridge and its continuation northeastwards to the borderline to Sweden. In our neighborland Sweden it occurs in several localities in the provinces of Härjedalen and Jämtland. Here it gradually peters out, but the species has been discovered in a few, isolated

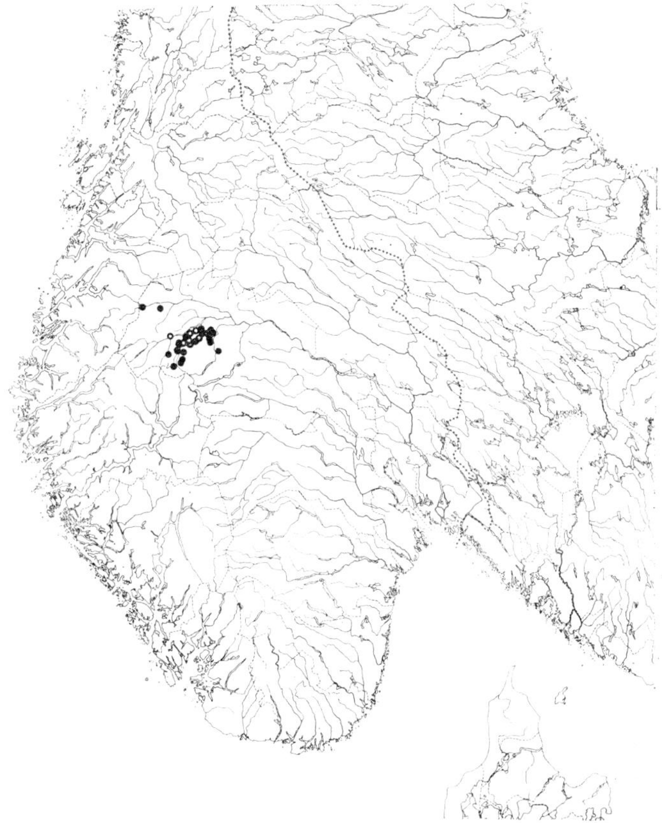

FIG. 11. The distribution in south Norway of *Rhododendron lapponicum*. For its occurrence in north Scandinavia, see Hultén, 1950. (cf. also Addendum).

localities as far north as to *ca.* 65° N. Lat. It is, however, its southernmost limit, in northernmost Hardangervidda, Norway, that attracts most interest.

Among Scandinavian field botanists it is a well-known fact that *Pedicularis Oederi* is favored by a calcareous substrate. Hardangervidda is an enormous massif which for a long time especially east of Sörfjord in Hardanger and north of the remarkable Mt. Hårteigen has been considered a botanist's "paradise", with a rock substrate rich in lime and schists. Here occur *Dryas octopetala*, *Arenaria norvegica*, *Euphrasia lapponica*, and many other "demanding" plant species. But precisely here, in this "paradise", *Pedicularis*

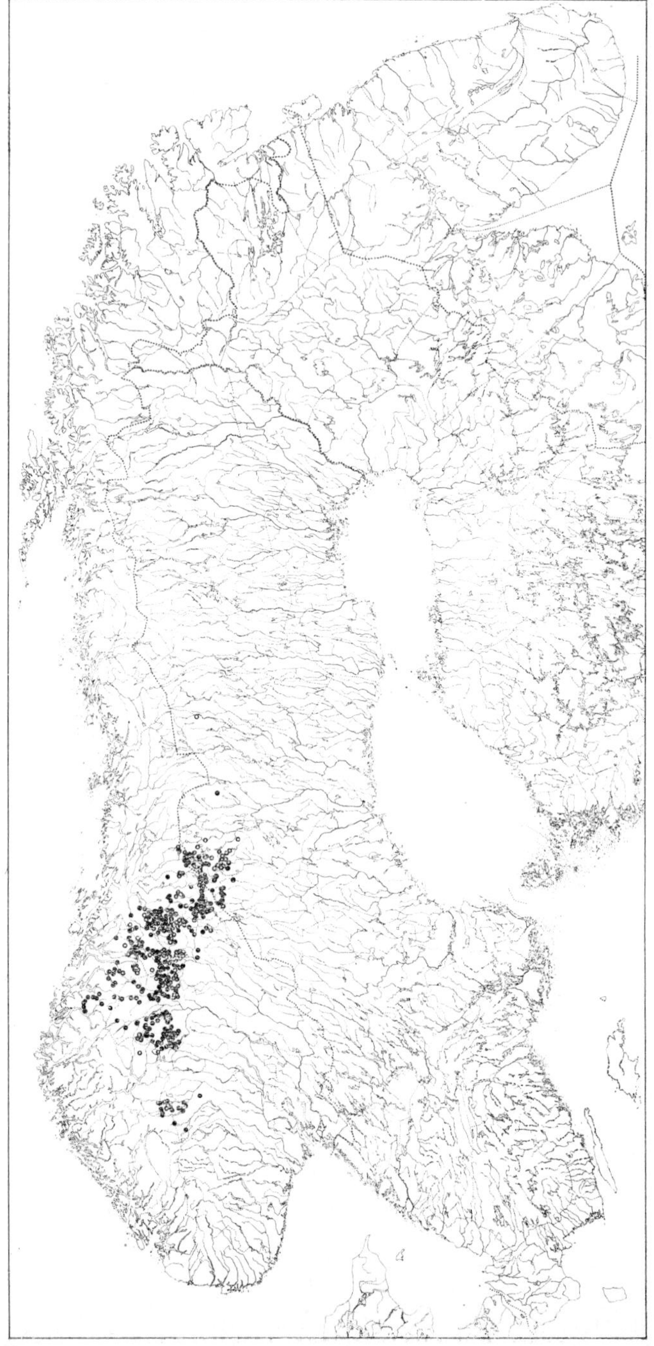

FIG. 12. Map of the distribution in Scandinavia of *Pedicularis Oederi*. Compiled 1961 by F. Wischmann from herbarium material and the diaries of R. Nordhagen.

Oederi is totally lacking. The same is true for all the Hardangervidda which has been thoroughly investigated by Curator Johannes Lid.

If *Pedicularis Oederi*, which does occur in the Alps, had dispersed to Norway from the south during the deglaciation, the species ought to have gained a foothold just in the petrographically so favorable area which is mentiond above. But instead it is really conspicuous by its absence there. The southern limit of this species shows with all desirable clarity that it has reached the northernmost part of Hardangervidda *from the north*, not from the south.

In a paper written already in 1930, I drew attention to this fact. *Pedicularis Oederi* must have survived the Last Glaciation on the Möre coast and from there spread towards east, northeast and south during the deglaciation. Investigations by other Norwegian botanists as well as by myself have also demonstrated that in those parts of Norway where the species has its main center it possesses biotypes which are able to grow on rock poor in lime, and also biotypes which can descend into low regions, as far down as to 400 m above sea level. The species has been observed both in south Tröndelag and in north Möre in hillside bogs in the *Pinus silvestris* region. During its dispersal southwards in Norway, the number of biotypes inside this species seems to have diminished strongly because at its southern limit the plant is confined exclusively to more or less calcareous habitats above the upper limit of the birch forest.

The peculiar geographical distribution in Norway of *Pedicularis Oederi* seems to be, really, the strongest botanical argument that we have in favor of the survival theory.

REFERENCES

ARESCHOUG, F. W. C. (1869). Om den europeiska vegetationens ursprung. *Skand. Naturforsk. Möde Forhandl.* **10**, 54–80.

BLYTT, A. (1881). Theorien om vexlende kontinentale og insulære klimater anvendt på Norges stigning. *Forhandl. Vidensk. Selsk. Christiania* 1881, No. 4.

BLYTT, A. (1882). Die Theorie der wechselnden kontinentalen und insularen Klimate. *Englers Bot. Jahrb.* **2**, 1–50, 177–184.

BLYTT, A. (1893). Zur Geschichte der nordeuropäischen, besonders der norwegischen Flora. *Englers Bot. Jahrb.* **17**, Beibl. No. 41.

DAHLSTEDT, H. (1906). Arktiska och alpina arter inom formgruppen *Taraxacum ceratophorum* Led. *Arkiv f. Bot.* **5** (9), 1–44.

DAHLSTEDT, H. (1908). *Taraxacum Reichenbachii* Huter subsp. *dovrense*. *Arkiv f. Bot.* **7** (1), 1–11.

DAHLSTEDT, H. (1928). De svenska arterna av släktet *Taraxacum*. III. *Dissimilia*, IV. *Palustria*, V. *Ceratophora*, VI. *Arctica*, VII. *Glabra*. *Kgl. Sv. Vetensk. Akad. Handl.* **6** (3), 1–66.

ELFSTRAND, M. (1927). Var hava fanerogama växter överlevat istiden i Skandinavien? *Sv. Bot. Tidskr.* **21**, 269–284.

EKMAN, E. (1927). Three new bicentric plants in the south of Norway. *Nyt. Mag. f. Naturv.* **66**, 93–95.

FRIES, TH. C. E. (1913). *Botanische Untersuchungen im nördlichsten Schweden.* Akad. Abhandl. Uppsala and Stockholm.

FRIES, TH. C. E. (1921). Die skandinavischen Formen der *Euphrasia salisburgensis*. *Arkiv f. Bot.* **17** (6), 1–17.

GJÆREVOLL, O. (1961). *XIII. International Phytogeographi al Excursion to Finnmark and Troms 26.7–5.8 1961.* Trondheim.

HANSEN, A. M. (1904a). Hvorledes har Norge faat sit plantedekke? *Naturen* **28**, 143–156, 168–179.

HANSEN, A M. (1904b). *Landnåm i Norge.* Kristiania.

HELTZEN, A. M. and NORDHAGEN, R. (1944). En vestlig utpost av *Saxifraga hieraciifolia. Naturen* 1944.

HOLTEDAHL, O. (1929). Some remarkable features of the Sub-marine relief on the north coast of the Varanger Peninsula, Northern Norway. *Norske Vidensk. Akad. Avhandl. I. Mat.-naturv. klasse* 1929, No. 12, 1–14.

HOLTEDAHL, O. (1953). Norges Geologi II. *Norges Geol. Unders. No.* 164.

HULTÉN, E. (1950). *Atlas över växternas utbredning i Norden.* Stockholm.

MARTHINUSSEN, M. (1961). Brerandstadier og avsmeltningsforhold i Repparfjord—Stabbursdal-området, Finnmark. Et deglaciasjonsprofil fra fjord til vidde. *Norges Geol. Unders. Årbok* 1960, No. 213.

NORDHAGEN, R. (1921). Kalktufstudier i Gudbrandsdalen. *Norske Vidensk. Selsk. Skrifter I. Mat.-naturv. klasse* 1921 (9), 1–155.

NORDHAGEN, R. (1930). En botanisk ekskursjon i Eikisdalen. *Bergens Mus. Årbrok 1930. Naturv. rekke* **8**.

NORDHAGEN, R. (1931). Studien über die skandinavischen Rassen des *Papaver radicatum* Rottb., sowie einige mit denselben verwechselte neue Arten. *Bergens Mus. Årbok 1931, Naturv. rekke* **2**, 1–50.

NORDHAGEN, R. (1935). Om *Arenaria humifusa* Wg. og dens betydning for utforskningen av Skandinavias eldste floraelement. *Bergens Mus. Å bok 1935, Naturv. rekke* **1**, 1–185.

NORDHAGEN, R. (1936). Skandinavias fjellflora og dens relasjon til den siste istid. *Nord. (19. ska d.) naturforskarmötet i Helsingfors* 1936, 93–124.

NORDHAGEN, R. (1940). Staurene ved Ofjordnæringen på Söröya. Et eldgammelt strandnivå i Vest-Finnmark. *Norsk Geogr. Tidsskrift* **8** (4), 124–155.

NORDHAGEN, R. (1952). Bidrag til Norges flora II. Om nyere funn av *Euphrasia lapponica* Th. Fr. fil. i Norge. *Blyttia* **10**, 29–50.

NORDHAGEN, R. (1954). Some new observations concerning the geographic distribution and the ecology of *Arenaria humifusa* Wg. in Norway as compared with *Arenaria norvegica* Gunn. *Bot. Tidsskr.* **51**, 248–262.

SERNANDER, R. (1896). Några ord med anledning av Gunnar Andersson: Svenska Växtvärldens Historia. *Bot. Notiser* 1896.

UNDÅS, I. (1938). Kvartärstudier i Vest-Finnmark og Vesterålen. *Norsk Geol. Tidsskr.* **18** (2), 81–217.

UNDÅS, I. (1942). On the Late-Quaternary history of Möre and Tröndelag. *Kgl. Norske Vidensk. Selsk. Skrifter* 1942 (2), 1–92.

VOGT, TH. (1912). Landskapsformene i det ytterste av Lofoten. *Norsk Geogr. Selsk. Årbok* 1911–1912.

WILLE, N. (1905). Om invandringen af det arktiske floraelement til Norge. *Nyt Mag. f. Naturv.* **43** (4).

WILLE, N. (1915). The flora of Norway and its immigration. *St. Louis, Missouri, Bot. Gard. Annals* 1915 (2), 59–108.

ADDENDUM

In August 1962, Nordhagen and S erre Lökken succeeded in finding *Rhododendron lapponicum* on still another mountain in western Lesja (Kværhushö, southwest of Rånåkollen; cf. p. 255 and Fig. 11).

SURVIVAL OF PLANTS ON NUNATAKS IN NORWAY DURING THE PLEISTOCENE GLACIATION

O. GJÆREVOLL

Royal Norwegian Society of Sciences, Trondheim, Norway

DURING the 80 years that have passed since Axel Blytt (1876) set up his theory about an Interglacial element in the mountain flora of Scandinavia, a very comprehensive record of supporting biological arguments has been acquired. From the point of view of a botanist, the distribution of numerous species cannot be satisfactorily explained without assuming their survival during at least the Last Glaciation on refugia along the west coast of southern as well as of northern Norway. I will not here resume the arguments, nor the discussion, that are still going on between biologists and disbelieving geologists. I take it for granted that a great part of our alpine vegetation is of an Interglacial age.

The question of where the plants might have survived has been subject to much discussion. The main view has been that the plants persisted on refugia close to the coast, partly outside the present coast line on the continental shelf not submerged during the Ice Age. The shelf is narrowest outside Möre in southern Norway and Troms–Finnmark in northern Norway. From Greenland and other Arctic areas we know that the alpine plants are descending toward sea level.

At the same time it is evident—to judge from the present situation in Greenland—that if coastal refugia have existed in areas adjacent to high mountains in the neighborhood, these mountains must have protruded from the ice-shield as nunataks. Would it have been possible for alpine plants to persist in the nunatak areas?

In his epoch-making paper "Essay on the immigration of the Norwegian flora during alternating rainy and dry periods", Blytt (1876) pointed out a group which he called "Arctic plants" occurring in northern as well as in southern Norway, *particularly in the continental mountains.*

From the work of Th. C. E. Fries (1913), "Botanische Untersuchungen in nördlichsten Schweden", the theory of survival got its cartographical foundation. He showed that many important species in the Scandinavian alpine flora have a centric distribution (Fig. 1). About 25 species display a *bicentric* distribution occupying one area in southern Norway and one in northern Scandinavia. The *unicentric* ones are found only in one of these areas, about

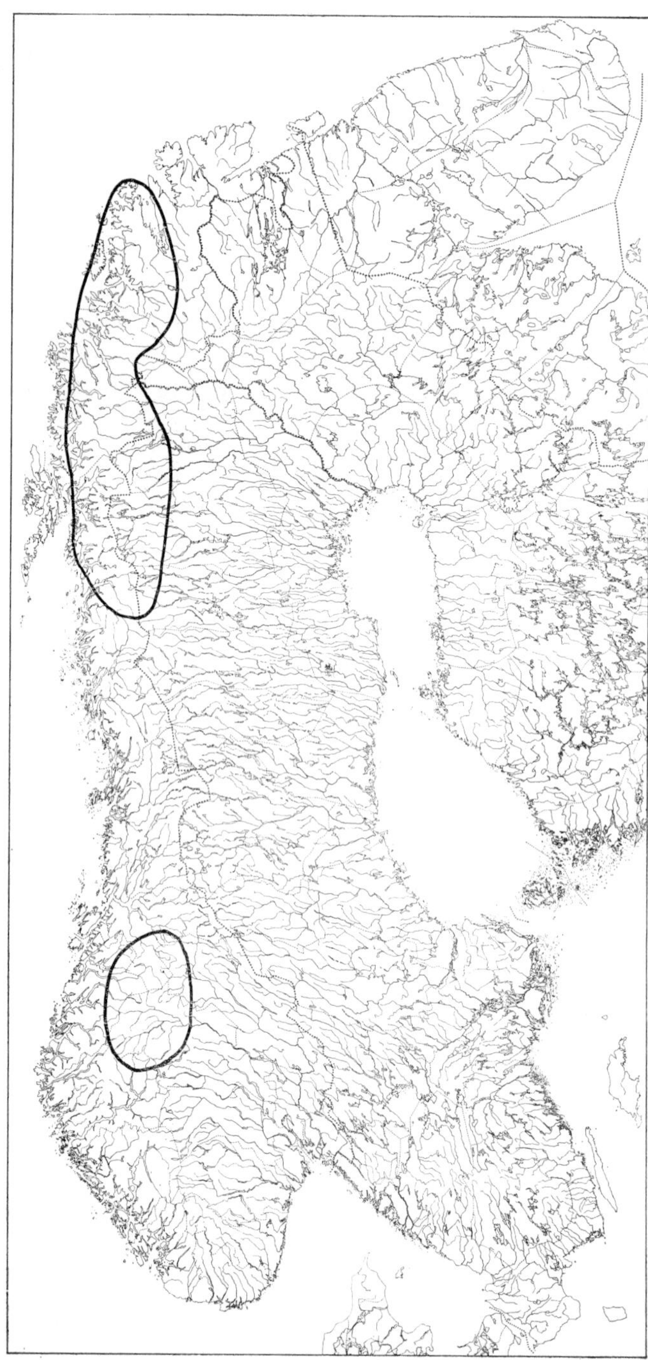

FIG. 1. Map showing the two Scandinavian areas harboring an alpine flora very rich in species.

10 (species and subspecies) in the southern one and about 30 in the northern one. In numerous papers (Nordhagen, 1931, 1935; Nannfeldt, 1940) strong evidence is given for the probability that this centricity must have a historical explanation. Briefly recapitulated, this explanation is to the effect that there must have been two areas where the glaciation has not been total: one area of ice-free refugia in the district of Möre, another from about the Polar Circle to western Finnmark. Owing to the reduced ability and possibility of dispersal of some of the species a centric distribution has been formed. By far the greater part of the problematic species of the Scandinavian alpine flora is found in these two areas.

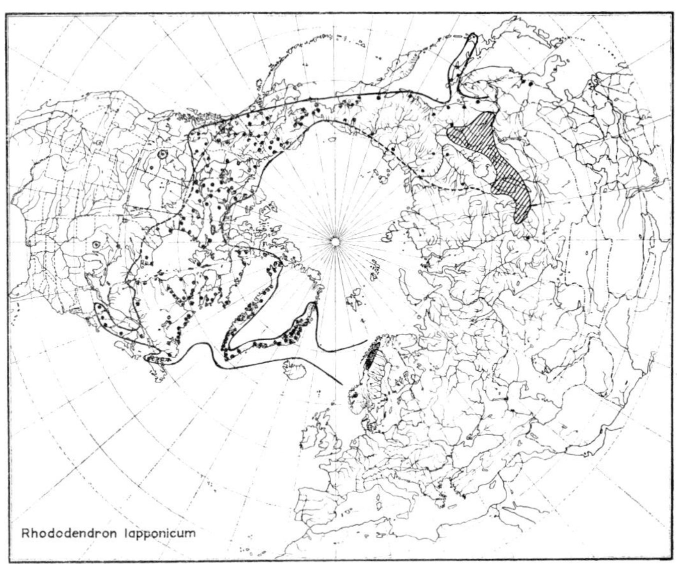

FIG. 2. The total distribution of *Rhododendron lapponicum* (incl. *R. parvifolium*) (after Hultén, 1958).

Blytt also indicated an American–Greenlandic element in the Scandinavian flora. Today the species belonging to this element in Scandinavia are called West Arctic. They total about 30 taxa most of which belong to the centric groups. Nearly all of them are found in the northern area, but only one-third in the southern one.

Rhododendron lapponicum in Europe is only known from Scandinavia where it occurs—often predominating—within a large area in the north, and a small one in the south, thus it belongs to the bicentric species (Fig. 2).

Pedicularis flammea is, in the same manner, very distinctly a West Arctic species, but it is restricted to the northern area (Fig. 3).

There are also some eastern species displaying the same distribution.

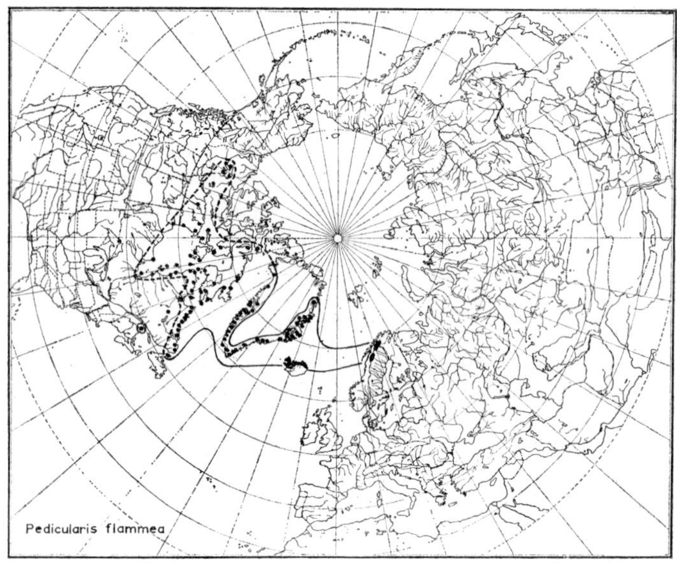

FIG. 3. The total distribution of *Pedicularis flammea* (after Hultén, 1958).

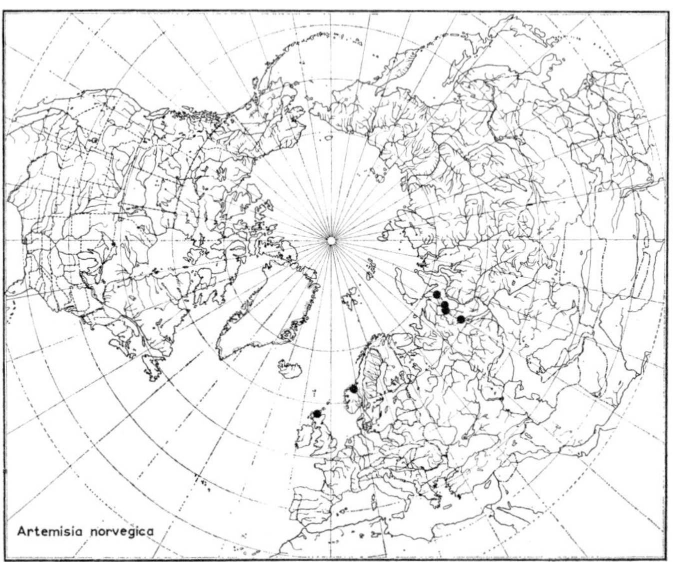

FIG. 4. The total distribution of *Artemisia norvegica* (after Hultén, 1954).

Artemisia norvegica is one of them (Fig. 4). It is known from the Urals, southern Norway, and a single locality in Scotland. This species is closely related to *Artemisia arctica* of eastern Siberia and North America. *Platanthera oligantha* occurs in the northern area only. As seen from the map the nearest locality is found in the Yeniseysk area (Fig. 5).

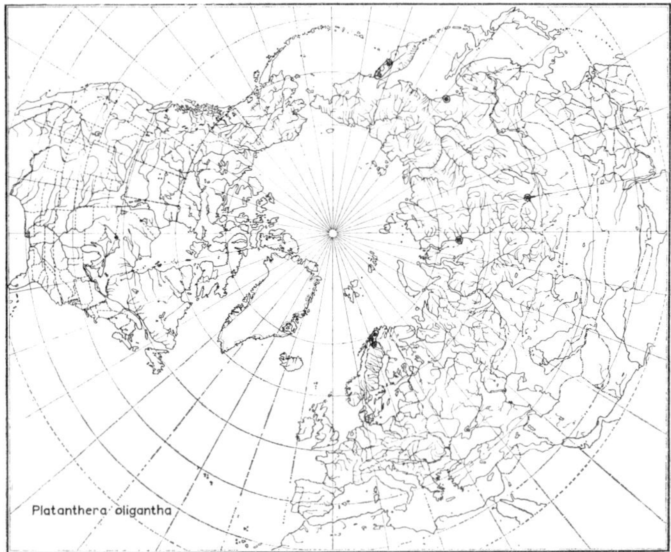

FIG. 5. The total distribution of *Platanthera oligantha* (after Hultén, 1958).

It should furthermore be mentioned that an Arctic element is represented in the southern area by *Phippsia concinna* without a single locality in northern Scandinavia. On the other hand there are representatives in the northern area of a European (or Eurasian) alpine element lacking localities in the southern area. *Scirpus pumilus* (Fig. 6) and *Antennaria carpatica* have this distribution.

The Scandinavian Alpine flora is poor in endemic taxa, and this has been taken as an argument against the theory of survival. Detailed taxonomic investigations have brought to light more endemics than previously assumed. In this connection we should notice that practically all the endemics belong to the centric groups. Nannfeldt (1940) has shown that within the polymorphic *Poa arctica* complex there are several endemic races, some of them southern unicentric, others northern unicentric.

The alpine poppies belonging to the *Papaver radicatum* complex have on the whole a bicentric distribution. From the investigations by Nordhagen (1931) it is elucidated that this complex is chiefly represented by southern and northern unicentric endemics. I will return later to the problem of the southern

Norwegian *Papaver*-populations as seen in the light of recent cytological investigations (Fig. 7).

This concentration of rare species in two widely separated areas cannot be accidental. As we have seen, the species belong to entirely different geographical elements, partly they are West Arctic, partly Arctic–Alpine, partly Asiatic, partly endemic.

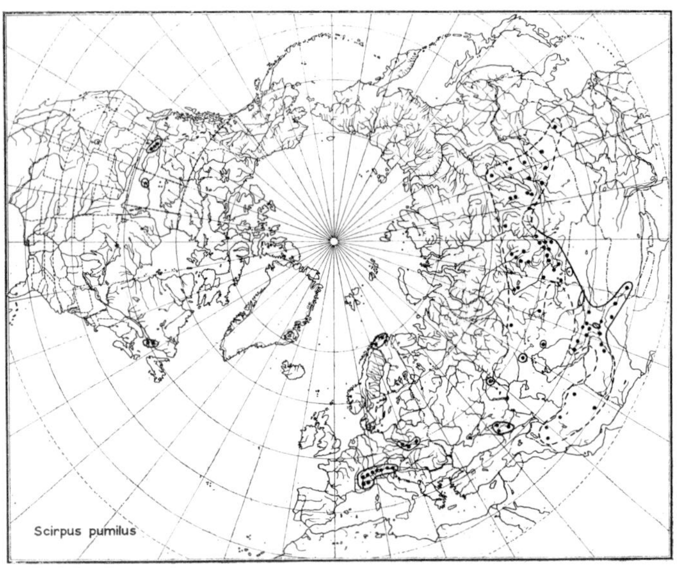

FIG. 6. The total distribution of *Scirpus pumilus* (after Hultén, 1958).

With regard to the poppies, Nordhagen (1931) has drawn the conclusion that their peculiar distribution cannot be explained by Post-glacial migration, but more likely is the result of survival in separate refugia along the west coast of Norway. The present distribution of the poppies indicates that there must have been several refugia. This leads to still another question: is it possible from the present-day distribution of the species to delimit the refugia more exactly? We know that plants are able to disperse—in some cases very rapidly— but we also know, for instance from the Alps, that relic species may be so depauperated that their ability to disperse is strongly reduced.

In 1935, Nordhagen gave a very striking example indicating a refugium in the district of Nordland. I want to recall this example, supplemented by some recent observations. The map (Fig. 8) shows the concentration of a number of rare species east of the Salten Fjord in the area of the Swedish–Norwegian boundary.

1. A short distance south of this area there is a peculiar *Papaver* locality, a local endemic, *Papaver radicatum* ssp. *subglobosum*.

2. The West Arctic species *Arenaria humifusa* is known from several localities in the Sarek Mts. on the Swedish side of the border and, so far, from a single, isolated locality farther south. It is a northern unicentric species. According to Polunin (1943) the nearest locality is on Spitsbergen, and beyond that no closer than east Greenland.

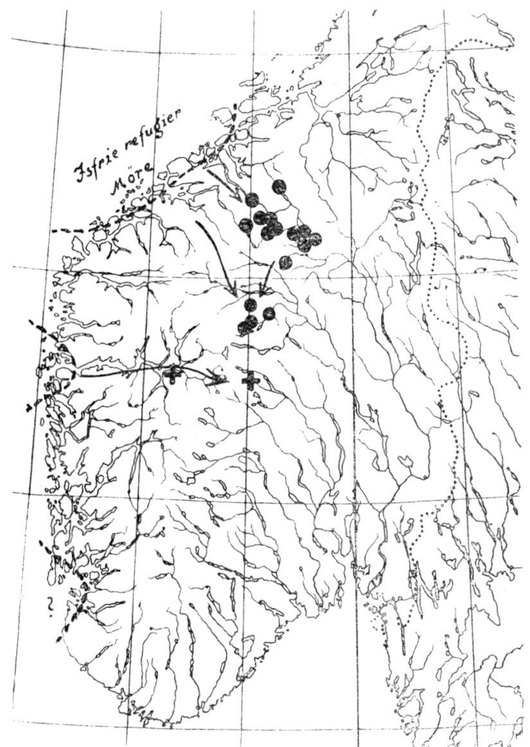

Fig. 7. The distribution in southern Norway of *Papaver radicatum* ssp. *ovatilobum* (dots) and *P. relictum* (crosses) (after Nordhagen 1936).

3. Another West Arctic and northern unicentric species, *Draba crassifolia*, is also found in several localities in the same areas on both sides of the boundary.

4. At Lake Balvatnet is found *Saxifraga aizoon*. In Norway it is found furthermore in a restricted area in the southernmost mountains (Ryfylke). Nordhagen (1936) has shown that the southern population is identical with the central European *S. aizoon*, whereas the population at Lake Balvatnet is so different that it must be given the rank of a subspecies; thus it is endemic to this area. The occurrence and the taxonomical difference can only be explained by the theory of survival.

5. In 1942 the Swedish botanist Sten Selander discovered in the Sarek Mts.,

another West Arctic species, *Potentilla hyparctica*, new to Scandinavia. In Eurasia this species was previously known from Kanin, Vaygach, Novaya Zemlya and Spitsbergen.

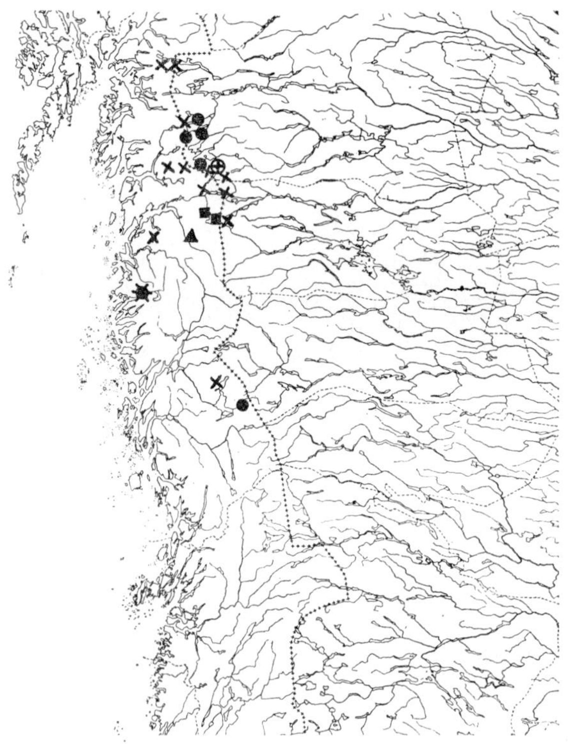

FIG. 8. Important botanical indications of refugia in the district of Nordland, Norway. *Arenaria humifusa* (dots); *Papaver radicatum* ssp. *subglobosum* (asterisks); *Carex scirpoidea* (triangles); *Saxifraga aizoon* ssp. *laestadii* (squares); *Draba crassifolia* (crosses); and *Potentilla hyparctica* (circles with cross) (partly after Nordhagen, 1935).

6. Another interesting West Arctic species is the dioecious *Carex scirpoidea*, known from a single mountain in Saltdal, the only locality in Europe. It is widely distributed in Greenland and North America (Fig. 9). According to my own experience in Alaska it is a species with a very wide ecological amplitude. In the Norwegian locality Mt. Solvågtind, it grows in abundance, but within a very narrow ecological limit. It has not been able to disperse to the neighboring mountains where the conditions seem to be very suitable. It gives the impression of a depauperated relic, and I am inclined to believe that *C. scirpoidea* inhabits just the very area where it survived the glaciation, i.e. on the south-facing slope of the nunatak Mt. Solvågtind. According to the geologist Gunnar Holmsen, Mt. Solvågtind is supposed to have been a nunatak.

This strange concentration of rare species cannot be explained as casual. The geologist O. T. Grönlie (1927) has published numerous observations from northern Norway showing that there must have been quite extensive ice-free areas. He is of the opinion, among others, that ice-free areas have existed as far east as the boundary between Norway and Sweden, exactly in this area where the concentration of important species is found.

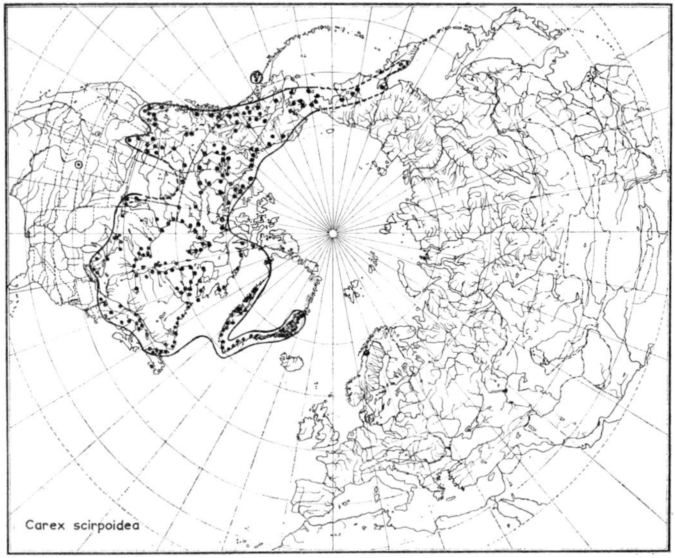

FIG. 9. The total distribution of *Carex scirpoidea* (after Hultén, 1958).

Let us return to southern Norway. As already mentioned, Blytt (1876) pointed out that his Arctic element was encountered exclusively within continental mountains consisting of calcareous rocks and schist. Our knowledge of the distribution of the plants has increased gradually so that we now have a very detailed picture of it. A sensational observation might still be made, of course, but most likely the present picture of distribution will be but slightly altered.

If we look at the distribution of the bicentric and the southern unicentric species, we see that they are restricted to the interior mountains, thus confirming the theory of Blytt (1876). He maintained, indeed, that they were continental, and undoubtedly he had in mind the mountains of Dovre and Jotunheimen. Since then it has been proved that the mountains south of Sunndalen and the Trollheimen Mts. should be included in the "species-rich area". Particularly the mountains of Trollheimen are strongly influenced by oceanic weather conditions (high precipitation).

Let us again look at *Artemisia norvegica* and its Norwegian distribution which is very concentrated, comprising the mountains of Dovre, Sunndalen, and Trollheimen (Fig. 10). Within this area, it is a very common species. This picture of distribution has not changed in the time of botanical explorations. One might infer that its delimitation is a geological one. *Artemisia norvegica* is undoubtedly most common on easily disintegrating schist, but is not merely restricted to that kind of soil. It is also commonly encountered on mineral soil, poor in lime. At the eastern and southern borders of this area there are schisty rocks everywhere, and accordingly a geological obstruction

FIG. 10. The distribution of *Artemisia norvegica* in Norway.

cannot be the delimiting agent. Though the geological situation is different at the western border, there are, according to my own experience, plenty of suitable localities. Nor may the altitudinal conditions, bearing in mind the Post-glacial Hypsithermal period, hamper the dispersal of the species.

If we consider the centric species one by one, we will find the same distribution. Among the West Arctic, bicentric species *Campanula uniflora* is found in the area of Jotunheimen—Trollheimen, and so are also *Sagina caespitosa*,

Carex arctogena, and *C. parallela*. The circumpolar, bicentric species *Minuartia rubella*, *Luzula arctica*, *Carex misandra*, and *Ranunculus nivalis* all have a similar distribution (Figs. 11–15).

Furthermore, the same type of distribution is met with for some endemic species. Thus *Taraxacum dovrense* occurs in the area of Jotunheimen–Trollheimen (Fig. 16). Ecologically, if differs from all other alpine *Taraxaca* by

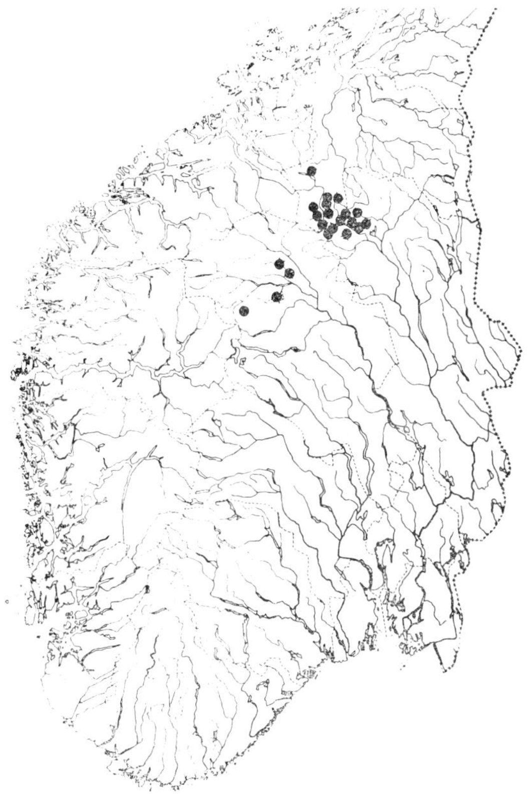

FIG. 11. The distribution of *Sagina caespitosa* in southern Norway.

growing in exposed localities, frequently together with *Campanula uniflora*. It belongs to the *arctica*-group, being its only representative in Scandinavia. Its closest relative (*T. reichenbachii*) occurs in the Alps, and Dahlstedt, who described the species, expressed the opinion as early as 1928 that these two species originally were identical, occupying a common area before the Ice Age.

Draba dovrensis has a similar, but somewhat wider distribution. *Stellaria crassipes* belongs to the bicentric element, and in the southern area it is represented by an endemic race, var. *dovrense* Hult. So far it is known from three localities only (Fig. 17). Normally, it seems to reproduce vegetatively.

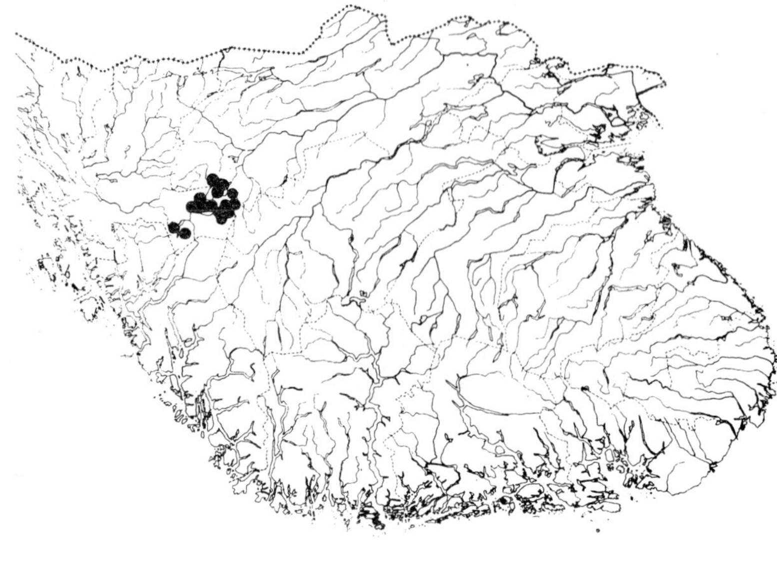

FIG. 13. The distribution of *Luzula arctica* in southern Norway.

FIG. 12. The distribution of *Minuartia rubella* in southern Norway.

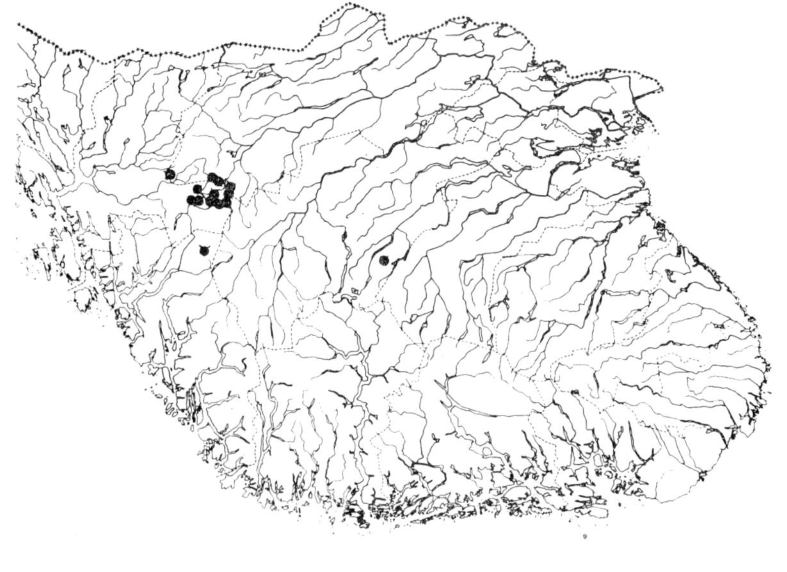

Fig. 15. The distribution of *Ranunculus nivalis* in southern Norway.

Fig. 14. The distribution of *Carex misandra* in southern Norway.

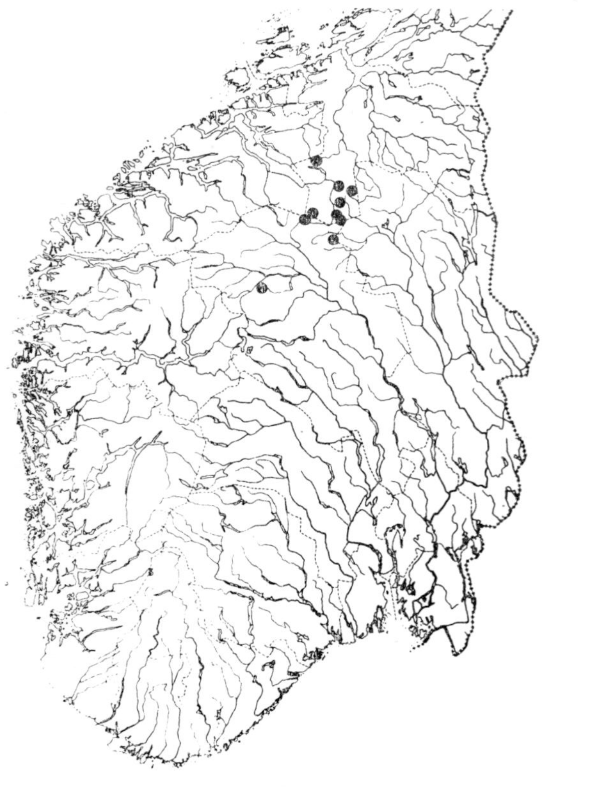

FIG. 16. The total distribution of *Taraxacum dovrense*.

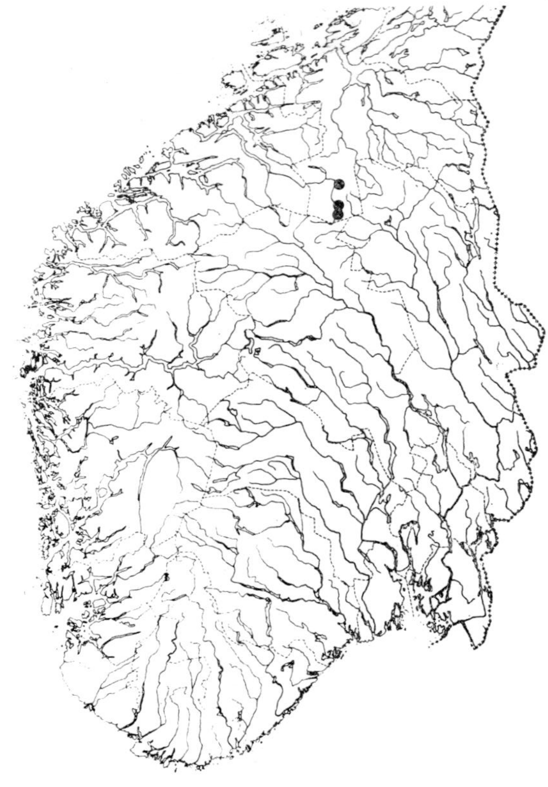

FIG. 17. The distribution of *Stellaria crassipes* var. *dovrense*.

Regarding Nannfeldt's (1940) map of the different *Poa arctica* races, we find that ssp. *depauperata* occurs in the region from Jotunheimen to Trollheimen, and outside this area it is known only from northwestern Iceland. In southern Norway, ssp. *elongata* is endemic, showing a somewhat wider distribution than the former (Fig. 18).

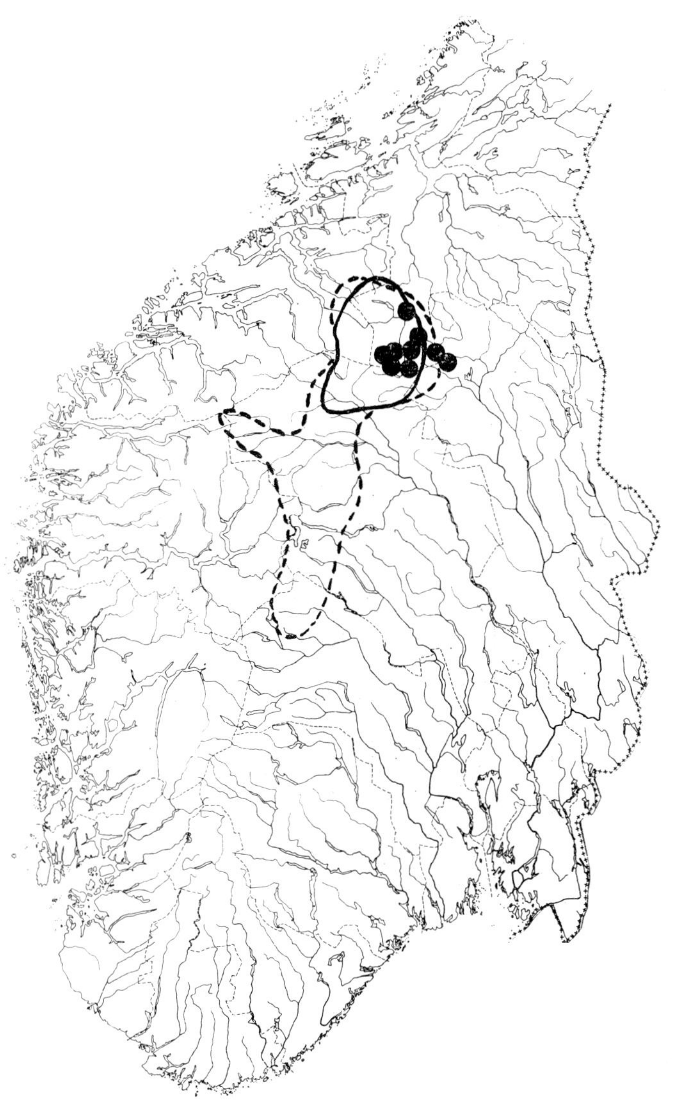

Fig. 18. The distribution in southern Norway of the different races of *Poa arctica* (after Nannfeldt, 1940). Area of ssp. *depauperata* (solid line); area of ssp. *elongata* (broken line); localities of *Poa stricta* (dots).

Nannfeldt (*loc. cit.*) also includes the endemic, viviparous *Poa stricta* in the same complex. This race has an abundant and very concentrated occurrence in the Dovre Mts. (Fig. 18).

I have tried to show that the greater part of the problematic plant species of the south Scandinavian alpine flora is confined to the mountains some distance from the coast. Many of the plants are fairly evenly distributed within this southern area, but there are also striking irregularities. *Rhododendron lapponicum* and *Braya linearis* are known only from the northern part of Jotunheimen, *Stellaria crassipes* and *Carex bicolor* only from Dovre. *Poa stricta* has a small area in Trollheimen, but its main distribution is in Dovre, and it is not found at all in Jotunheimen. *Ranunculus nivalis, Carex arctogena*, and *Draba nivalis* do not occur in Trollheimen.

Saxifraga hieraciifolia with a single coastal locality in the Romsdal Mts. has its main distribution in Sunndalen, Jotunheimen, and the southern part of Dovre. It is not known from the rich areas of central Dovre and Trollheimen.

How is it then possible to explain this peculiar distribution and the disjunctions within the southern area?

It has been assumed commonly that the species must have survived in the coastal districts of Möre. When the ice began to retreat, the plants followed the retreating ice to the mountains of Sunndalen, Trollheimen, Dovre, and Jotunheimen where they are met with today. The humid, oceanic climate is unfavorable to alpine species, due for instance to peat formation. Therefore, these species have suffered competition and disappeared.

I myself have not been content with the assumption of only a coastal survival area. It is not possible to explain the total absence in the coastal mountains of all the species mentioned by referring to peat formation and soil conditions. It is a fact that there are high mountains close to the coast where neither peat formationn or climate may represent any danger to these species. I have had the opportunity to make some investigations in the Romsdal Mts., and there are plenty of suitable localities, e.g. for *Artemisia norvegica*.

There are also coastal mountains consisting of calcareous rocks and schist, where the calciphilous *Dryas octopetala* grows abundantly. This is usually the best indicator of "rich areas". In this connection Mt. Talstadhesten in outer Romsdal is very interesting. It is a limestone area and harbours a flora comparatively rich in species, but none of those mentioned above are present even though the geological conditions ought to be suitable. Large areas are not at all subject to critical humus production. Most likely this mountain has been a nunatak, and, according to Nordhagen (1952), *Euphrasia lapponica* is represented here by a variety known only from this locality and the mountains of Hardangervidda. Furthermore, according to Porsild (1958) the *Dryas* growing very abundantly here is not *D. octopetala* s.str., but *D. Babingtoniana*, otherwise known only from the British Isles.

I should like also to call attention to the fact that a snow-bed species like

Phippsia algida is not found in the outer mountains either. Through my investigations of the snow-bed vegetation of the Scandinavian mountains I have observed that the extension of some communities varies from the continental mountains to the coastal ones. The sociological structure, however, is strikingly identical. This means that the deciding factors are the duration of the snow cover and the soil conditions. In view of this, the absence of *Phippsia algida* is remarkable.

From Greenland we know that under certain conditions even nunataks may harbor a comparatively rich flora. From this fact the following question appears self-evident: Did inland nunataks also exist in Norway during the Ice Age?

Dr. N. A. Sörensen treated this possibility in a paper published in 1949. There is some disagreement regarding the position of the rim of the ice sheet during the maximum of the glaciations. Thorough investigations have been performed by the geologist Undås (1938, 1942). Taking into account his opinion of the ice border and further on the known normal gradient of a large ice-mass, a number of mountains in the district of Möre must evidently have been nunataks. Furthermore, there is good reason to believe that some of these nunataks offered the plants very tolerable living conditions. Experiences from Greenland have revealed that a "suitable" nunatak must consist of loose rocks and moreover there must be south-facing slopes strongly exposed to the heat of the sun.

I want to draw attention to a certain area in the Trollheimen where I (at the start together with Dr. N. A. Sörensen) have had the opportunity to perform some investigations. The area in question is Gjevilvasskammene Mts. on the north side of Lake Gjevilvatnet (Fig. 19). From the altitude at this lake of 663 m, the mountains ascend with steep south-facing slopes and precipices to an elevation of 1640 m. The effect of this exposure is a growth period about one month longer than is normal for this area.

The mountains are built up by loose schists, mainly mica schist. West of the Gjevilvasskammene Mts. the elevation of the lowest passes to the nearest fjords varies from 800 to 950 m. With an ice border as proposed by Undås (*loc. cit.*) and a normal gradient of the ice, the height of the ice front and the rise of the land cannot have permitted an ice level in the Gjevilvasskammene Mts. higher than about 1350 m. This agrees very well with the observations made by the geologist A. Grönlie (1950) indicating an ice level of 1300–1350 m for this area. Other geologists are of a different opinion, maintaining that ice covered all the mountains in the Trollheimen area.

Some peculiar soil layers constitute a special phenomenon to be found situated on the tops and highest ridges of these mountains. Apparently these layers are now subject to heavy wind erosion (cf. Figs. 20, 21). Several geologists have examined the layers, and it has now been sufficiently demonstrated that they consist of soil disintegrated *in situ*. By means of X-ray

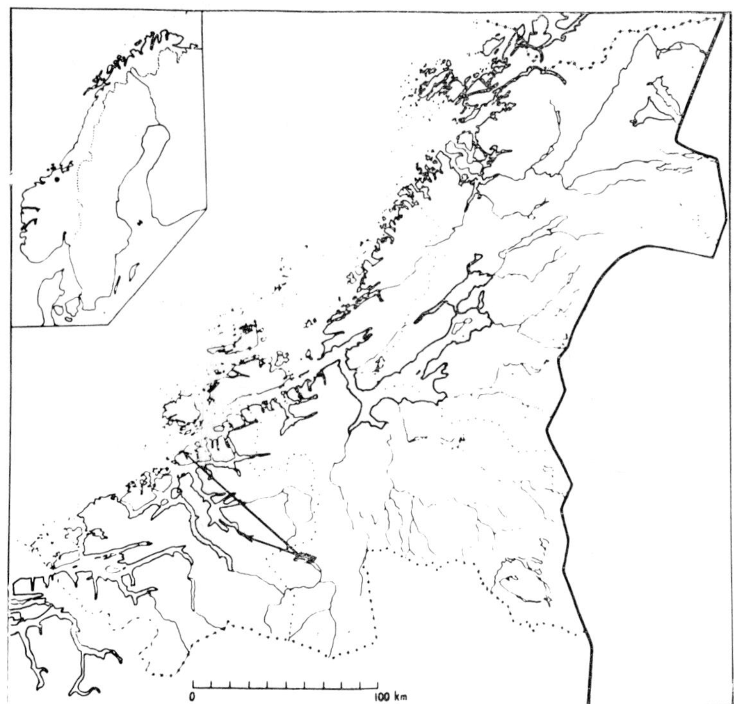

FIG. 19. The position of the Gjevilvasskammene Mts. in southern Norway.

FIG. 20. From Gjevilvasskammene Mts. The soil layer is situated on the flat top of the mountain.

examinations Dahl (1961) has proved that the soil contains the minerals vermiculite and hydrobiotite formed by an advanced disintegration of biotite. Dahl is of the opinion that the degree of disintegration is much higher than that hitherto known for the biotite in the lowland of southern and central Scandinavia. As this disintegrated soil rests in such a strongly exposed position it does not seem likely that it could have been able to resist the erosion of a thick ice sheet. Accordingly, the soil layers also indicate nunataks in this area.

FIG. 21. Photo of the soil layer on the highest peak of the Gjevilvasskammene Mts. at 1640 m altitude.

Botanical investigations have revealed a very rich and interesting flora. *Artemisia norvegica* is extremely common. Among the bicentric species should be mentioned *Luzula arctica*, *Nigritella nigra*, *Carex parallela*, *C. misandra*, *Sagina caespitosa*, *Papaver radicatum*, *Draba fladnizensis*, *D. lactea*, *Minuartia rubella*, *Potentilla nivea*, and *Euphrasia lapponica*. Besides *Artemisia norvegica* there are several southern unicentric species such as *Taraxacum dovrense*, *Poa arctica* ssp. *elongata* and ssp. *depauperata*, and *Pedicularis oederi*. Another important species is *Arenaria norvegica* which has played an important part in the survival theory because of its strange distribution. Outside of Norway, it is known from northern Scotland, the Orkney Islands and Iceland. The same distribution, with the addition of southern Greenland and Labrador, is typical of *Poa flexuosa* which occurs also in the Gjevilvasskammene Mts.

Thus, there is again a remarkable concentration of species which have played a great part in the survival theory. It is necessary to be very careful when drawing parallels with the present situation in Greenland, but it is by no means an impossible hypothesis to postulate an inland nunatak refugium in the Gjevilvasskammene Mts. The steep south-facing slopes might have offered sufficiently favorable living conditions for a hardy flora. If this theory be correct, it gives us a much more likely explanation of the distribution and migration of many species than does a theory confining the plants to a coastal survival area only.

It should be added that the geologist H. Reusch proposed as early as 1884 that mountain areas in the central and western parts of southern Norway must have protruded from the ice sheet as nunataks. Recently Dahl (1961) has drawn attention to the "felsenmeers" (= mountain top detritus) of the mountain tops. He is of the opinion that on the basis of the degree of disintegration, the lower "felsenmeer" border corresponds to the surface of the inland ice. If this hypothesis proves correct, many and large nunatak areas have existed in southern Norway during the Ice Age.

Concerning the possibilities of higher plants persisting in a nunatak area, several geologists have expressed doubt that the climatic conditions would permit any kind of plant life. Observations from Greenland nunataks confirm that higher plants are able to persist there. Furthermore we know of a fairly rich flora from the tundra district of Peary Land. Holmen (1957) reported 96 phanerogams from this area. According to Koch (1928), the mean annual temperature is 20°C below zero. For about 100 days the temperature hovers around −40°C. The precipitation is mainly in the form of snow, and amounts to less than 100 mm. In this connection it is important to state that the summer temperature rises only to some few degrees above freezing (0°C); in July it has an average of *ca.* 6°C.

In North America it is now generally accepted that plants as well as animals found a refugium in the Canadian Arctic Archipelago. It would be very unlikely that more severe conditions existed on coastal mountain refugia in Norway than in the tundra refugia of Arctic Canada.

I have mentioned some of the detailed taxonomical investigations performed by Nordhagen (1931, 1935, 1952) and Nannfeldt (1940) and their great significance for the survival theory. In this connection I also want to recapitulate the recent cytological studies of *Papaver radicatum* performed by Dr. Gunvor Knaben (1959). During a number of years she crossed poppies in order to investigate variation within the *Papaver radicatum* complex. The evolution within many genera most certainly corresponds to structural chromosomal alterations. If the parent plants have the same chromosome number but a different chromosome structure the result of the cross gives an irregular meiosis.

Dr. Knaben crossed poppies from a number of localities in southern Norway and she reached the following conclusion: in southern Norway there are six different races of *Papaver radicatum*. They all have a different chromosome structure and at the same time they are also phenotypically distinct. As seen from Fig. 22, their areas as well are separated:

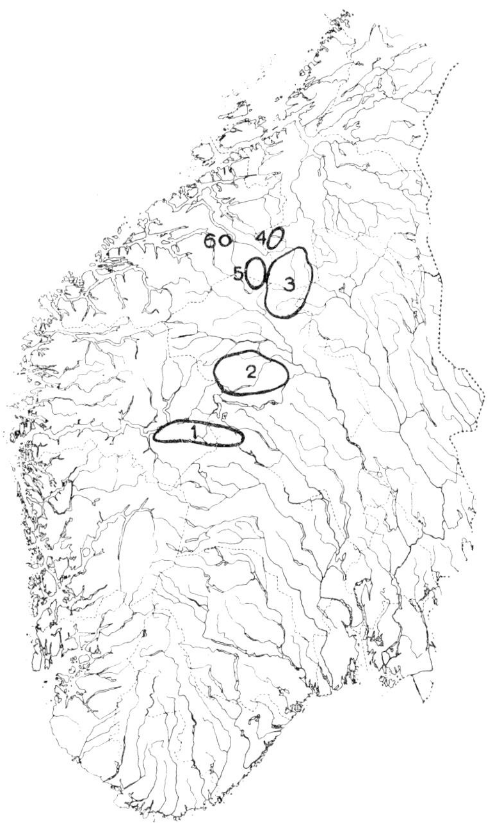

FIG. 22. The distribution in Norway southern of the different races of *Papaver radicatum*, based on the recent investigations by G. Knaben. Explanations in the text.

Papaver radicatum ssp.
- (1) *relictum*, Valdres-Sogn
- (2) *intermedium*, Jotunheimen
- (3) *ovatilobum*, Central Dovre
- (4) *gjaerevollii*, Trollheimen
- (5) *groevudalense*, Sunndal Mts.
- (6) *oeksendalense*, Öksendalen

Within the different races, the populations display slight alterations in their chromosome structure, but Dr. Knaben is of the opinion that this is due to recent changes. Furthermore, she has shown that the differences in chromosomal structure between the various south Norwegian races equal the differences between races of southern Norway, northern Norway, and the Faeroes as well as Iceland. Consequently, the south Norwegian races must have been separated during a period of about the same duration as that which divided the different races in the area surrounding the North Atlantic Ocean, i.e. they must have been separated for a period much longer than that of the Post-glacial time.

The studies performed by Dr. Knaben as well as her conclusion strongly support the hypothesis of nunatak survival. The distribution of the different races cannot be explained by referring them to coastal survival areas with a subsequent group migration to their present localities.

REFERENCES

ARWIDSSON, T. (1943). Studien über die Gefässpflanzen in den Hochgebirgen der Pite Lappmark. *Acta Phytogeogr. Suec.* **17**, 1–274.

BLYTT, A. (1876). *Essay on the Immigration of the Norwegian Flora during Alternating Rainy and Dry Periods.* Christiania.

DAHL, E. (1946). On different types of unglaciated areas during the Ice Ages and their significance to plant geography. *New Phytol.* **45**, 225–242.

DAHL, E. (1954). Weathered gneisses at the island of Runde, Sunnmöre, western Norway, and their geological interpretation. *Nytt Mag. for Bot.* **3**, 5–23.

DAHL, E. (1961). Refugieproblemet og de kvartœrgeologiske metodene. *Svensk Naturvetenskap* **14**, 81–96.

DAHLSTEDT, H. (1928). De svenska arterna av släktet *Taraxacum. Kgl. Sv. Vetensk. Akad. Handl.* Ser. 3, Bd 6 (3), 1–66.

FRIES, TH. C. E. (1913). *Botanische Untersuchungen in nördlichsten Schweden.* Akad. Abhandl. Uppsala & Stockholm.

GRÖNLIE, A. (1950). På kvartaergeologisk ekskursjon i Trollheimen. *Trondhjems Turistforenings Årbok 1950*

GRÖNLIE, O. T. (1927). The Folden Fiord. Quaternary Geology. *Tromsö Museums Skr.* I (II), 1–73.

HOLMEN, K. (1957). The vascular plants of Peary Land, North Greenland. *Medd. om Grönl.* **124** (9), 1–149.

HULTÉN, E. (1954). *Artemisia norvegica* Fr. and its allies. *Nytt Mag. for Bot.* **3**, 63–82.

HULTÉN, E. (1958). The Amphi-Atlantic plants and their phytogeographical connections. *Kgl. Sv. Vetensk. Handl. Ser.* 4, **7** (1), 1–340.

KNABEN, G. (1959). On the evolution of the *radicatum*-group of the *Scapiflora* Papavers as studied in 70 and 56 chromosome species. Part A. *Opera Botanica* **2** (3), 1–74.

KOCH, L. (1928). Contribution to the glaciology of North Greenland. *Medd. om Grönl.* **65**, 181–464.

NANNFELDT, J. A. (1940). On the polymorphy of *Poa arctica* R.Br. with special reference to its Scandinavian forms. *Symb. Bot. Upsaliensis IV* (4), 1–86.

NORDHAGEN, R. (1931). Studien über die skandinavischen Rassen des *Papaver radicatum* Rottb. sowie einige mit denselben verwechselte neue Arten. *Bergens Mus. Åbok 1931, Naturv. rekke* **2**, 1–50.

NORDHAGEN, R. (1935). Om *Arenaria humifusa* Wg. og dens betydning for utforskningen av Skandinaviens eldste floraelement. *Bergens Mus. Årbok 1935, Naturv. rekke* **1**, 1–185.

NORDHAGEN, R. (1936). Skandinavias fjellflora og dens relasjoner til den siste istid. *Nord. (19. Skand.) Naturforskarm. i Helsingfors 1936*, 93–124.

NORDHAGEN, R. (1952). Bidrag til Norges flora. II. Om nyere fund av *Euphrasia lapponica* Th. Fr. fil. i Norge. *Blyttia* **10**, 29–50.

POLUNIN, N. (1943). Geographical distribution of *Arenaria humifusa* Wahlenb., new to the flora of Spitsbergen. *Nature* **152**, 451–452.

PORSILD, A. E. (1958). *Dryas Babingtoniana*, nom. nov. An overlooked species of the British Isles and Western Norway. *Dept. Northern Affairs and Nat. Resourc. Bull.* **160**, 133–145.

REUSCH, H. (1887). Tstiden i det vestenfieldski Norge. *Nyt Mag for Naturv.***28**, 161–170.

SELANDER, S. (1942). *Potentilla emarginata* Pursh i Sverige. *Bot. Notiser* **1942**, 69–74.

SÖRENSEN, N. A. (1949). Gjevilvasskammene—nunatakker i Trollheimens midte? *Naturen* **3**.

UNDÅS, I. (1938). Kvartærstudier i Vestfinmark og Vesterålen. *Norsk Geol. Tidsskr.* **18**, 81–217.

UNDÅS, I. (1942). On the Late Quaternary history of Möre and Tröndelag. *Kgl. Norske Vidensk.-Selsk. Skr.* 1942 (2), 1–92.

PHYTOGEOGRAPHY OF GREENLAND IN THE LIGHT OF RECENT INVESTIGATIONS

TYGE W. BÖCHER

Institute of Plant Anatomy and Cytology, University of Copenhagen, Copenhagen, Denmark

GREENLAND is undoubtedly the most important working field for Danish botanists. Its phytogeography has always been of international importance. Although our present knowledge is comparatively large, new problems seem continuously to arise. The phytogeographical work going on is partly floristic, partly ecological or palynological (Böcher, 1954, 1963; Böcher and Lægaard, 1962; Fredskild, 1961; Holmen, 1957; Iversen, 1953; Schwarzenbach, 1961; Sörensen, 1953). Parallel to the field investigations, the species that are the bases of all phytogeographical discussion are examined separately by means of experimental cultivation and cytological studies. The survey given below of the phytogeography of Greenland deals primarily with the floristic problems; a few particularly important questions about the vegetation will also be touched.

In Greenland there are now known about 500 native vascular plant species of which about 50 per cent are circumpolar; about 114 species have their main area west of Greenland and 82 east of Greenland, whereas 35 (mostly apomicts) are endemic. Southwest Greenland is richest in species, having 335 native taxa, but even in northernmost Greenland the flora comprises 101 species (for further details see Böcher, Holmen and Jakobsen, 1957, 1959; Holmen, 1957).

It has been possible to divide Greenland into a number of natural floristic provinces and districts which are shown in Fig. 1. Their boundaries are placed along the area-limits of 282 species whose distribution has been mapped (see Böcher, 1938, 1963). The most important floristic boundary is undoubtedly that cutting off the provinces SW.–S.–SE. from the rest. This boundary has been studied since 1932, and as it seems to have more than local importance, it will be dealt with in some detail.

One of the main results of the early studies in middle east Greenland (Böcher, 1933, 1938) was a demonstration of a distinct floristic boundary on the Blosseville Coast about 68° 30′–69° N. Lat. This delimitation is caused by the disappearance northwards of a flora connected with oceanic climatic conditions and a similar diminution of true Arctic species in a southerly direction. Mapping of the species involved showed that in west Greenland they behaved similarly, but at the same time it became clear that full understanding of the nature of the boundary in east Greenland and a corresponding one in west Greenland could not be obtained until the inland

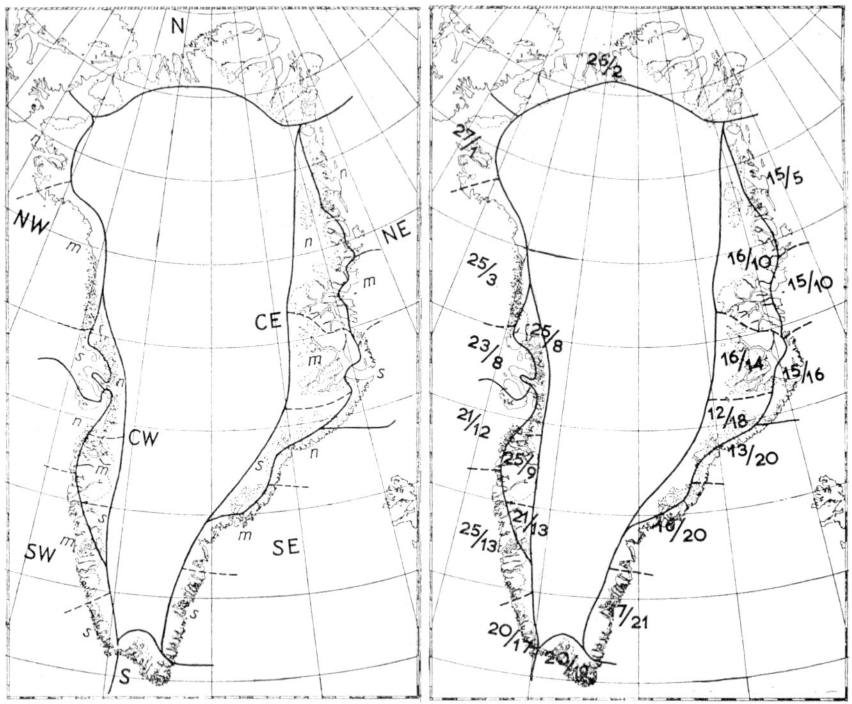

FIG. 1. On the left: floristic provinces and districts of Greenland. On the right: frequencies of western and eastern species indicated as per cent of the total native flora of each district. The first figure indicates western, the second figure eastern species. (From Böcher, Holmen and Jakobsen 1959.)

areas of middle west Greenland had been explored adequately and until the world ranges of the species were better known. Now both requirements are fulfilled. The interior of west Greenland has been studied during several expeditions and the world ranges of the Greenland plants are now well illustrated, thanks to the works of Hultén (1950, 1958), Porsild (1955, 1957) Raup (1947), Tolmachev (1960) and others.

Unglaciated middle west Greenland, which is broad enough to include areas of continental and maritime climatic types, is particularly well suited to phytogeographical studies. In fact, the detailed treatment of its flora gives us one key to a main phytogeographical division of the North Atlantic area.

Climatic curves for precipitation and annual temperature range bend from the interior of southwest Greenland towards the northwest and sooner or later reach the coast. Those expressing a high degree of oceanity veer away from the land in south Greenland where a species like *Juncus squarrosus* is present. Curves for a lesser degree of oceanity leave Greenland in middle west Greenland, but the northernmost ones cut off south Disko or penetrate into Disko Bay, reaching the mainland at Jacobshavn and Sargag.

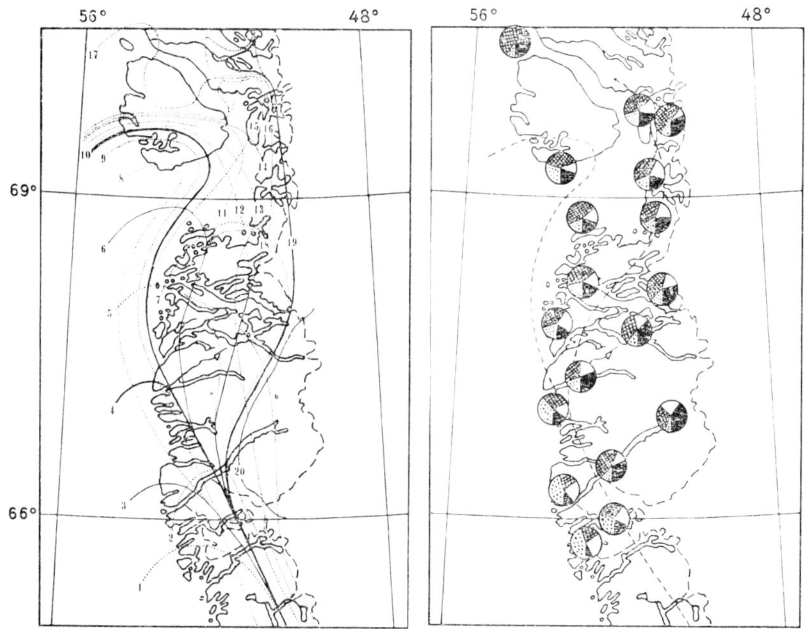

FIG. 2. On the left: eastern limits in middle west Greenland for southern species requiring humidity. On the right: percentage occurrence of Continental species (black), Oceanic-sylvicolous species (dotted), and arctic species (cross-hatched). Lines connecting 25 per cent Oceanic-sylvicolous and 25 per cent Continental species. (From Böcher, 1963.)

It has been shown that the majority of southern species follow the oceanity curves. This means that most such taxa in Greenland have high humidity, much snow, and perhaps high winter temperature as their main requirements. They are not primarily dependent on high summer temperatures. This fact may be of great importance in the discussion of their survival in Greenland during the Last Glaciation. Fig. 2 on the left shows the position of the eastern limits of such species in middle west Greenland. Line No. 4 indicates the limit for many species, e.g. *Thymus drucei*, *Alchemilla alpina*, *A. filicaulis*, *Hieracium hyparcticum*, *H.* sect. *foliolosa*, whereas No. 10 delimits another large group, e.g. *Polystichum lonchitis*, *Leuchorchis albida*, *Phleum commutatum*, and *Stellaria calycantha*.

A number of low-arctic snowbed-species, as well as species from the snow-protected heath vegetation are able to reach farther north, and they turn eastwards through the inland area at Nordre Strömfjord–Arfersiorfikjord to the Disko Bay mainland (Lines 11–19 in Fig. 2). They are absent from the extremely continental interior at the head of Söndre Strömfjord or, if present here, are montane and rare because they are restricted to certain rare types of habitat. In this group we have *Phyllodoce coerulea, Harrimanella hypnoides, Sibbaldia procumbens, Salix herbacea*; among dry soil species *Juncus trifidus* joins this group, and a species like *Luzula spicata* shows a marked decrease in frequency in the continental pocket at the head of Söndre Strömfjord (Böcher, 1963).

The world ranges of the species which follow the curves in Fig. 2 (left) are either North Atlantic montane species or sylvicolous boreal species. No true Arctic species behaves in this way. There is, however, one type of Arctic distribution which shows some relation to the southern oceanic type. Some few true Arctic species, near their southern limits in middle west Greenland, are found only in the coastal mountains. Being dependent on low temperatures and some humidity they are exclusively montane in the south though only in the coastal mountains where there is enough snow. This applies to *Potentilla hyparctica, Erigeron eriocephalus*, and *Melandrium apetalum* ssp. *arcticum*. Finally, some medium Arctic species are distributed in a similar way, being confined to the mountains surrounding the driest inland areas. As examples may be mentioned *Ranunculus nivalis, Antennaria intermedia, A. glabrata, Draba crassifolia*, and *Erigeron humilis*.

A distributional pattern opposite to that of the southern, humidity requiring plants is found in a number of Arctic–Continental species, some southern species which are dependent on high summer temperature, and some which require certain edaphic conditions connected with a dry climate. A map showing the western limits of these species is shown on the left in Fig. 3. On the right in the same figure is given the distribution of the most important member of the Arctic–Continental species, *Carex supina* ssp. *spaniocarpa*. There is a concentration of species at the head of Söndre Strömfjord. This is mainly the result of the edaphic conditions here. The climate causes the formation of ultrabasic soils on dry slopes with soil-water evaporation from the surface or along salt lakes formed in bowl-shaped depressions or valleys with no outflow to the sea. The most important species here may be *Braya novae-angliae, B. linearis, Primula stricta, Gentiana detonsa* var. *groenlandica, Ranunculus pedatifidus* (not the Arctic subspecies). Among species extending their ranges to the larger part of the cross-hatched area in Fig. 2 (left) there are, for example, *Draba lanceolata, Pedicularis labradorica, Antennaria affinis, Carex boecheriana*, and related forms (see Böcher, 1963; Böcher and Lægaard, 1962).

The southern Boreal plants which in the north are confined to this inland area (particularly the pocket at the head of Söndre Strömfjord) include not only many helo- and hydrophytes, e.g. *Potamogeton gramineus, Scirpus pauciflorus, Juncus alpinus, J. ranarius,* but also a species like *Arctostaphylos uva-ursi* (American variety). These southern species are with few exceptions absent from east Greenland but occur—again with few exceptions—in the interior of south Greenland.

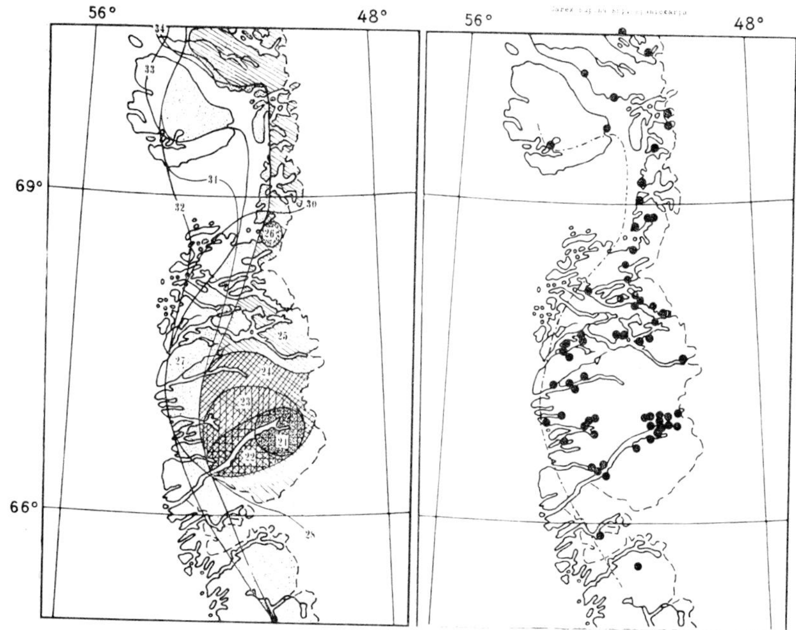

FIG. 3. On the left: western limits for a number of Continental species in middle west Greenland. On the right: one of the most important members of this group: *Carex supina* ssp. *spaniocarpa*. (From Böcher, 1963.)

In middle east Greenland almost the same species as shown in Fig. 1 (on the left) are found northwards up to the boundary on the Blosseville Coast or in the northern part of the Angmagssalik district. Many of the Arctic species occur north of these limits and inland at Kangerdlugssuaq (68° 10′–68° 30′) or inland at Angmagssalik (Böcher, 1938).

Calculations of the percentage occurrence of distributional types in a number of local floras in middle west Greenland are summarized in Fig. 2 (on the right). The most important groups of distributional types, viz. the Arctic, the Continental, and the Oceanic-sylvicolous, are shown. Only north of line 10 in Fig. 2 (on the left) and not south of Disko Bay are there floras with a majority of Arctic species. Middle west Greenland constitutes a transitional zone between a flora which is Arctic (Low-medium Arctic) and a flora which greatly approaches a Boreal one. The lack of forest in southwest

Greenland is perhaps more a result of climatic oceanity which prevents tree growth but does not present any obstacles for such forest floor species as *Coptis trifolia*, *Pyrola minor*, *Orthilia secunda* ssp. *obtusata*, *Linnaea borealis* ssp. *americana*, or a Boreal muskeg species such as *Ledum groenlandicum*.

The two lines in Fig. 2 (on the right) connect points (local floras) with more than 25 per cent Oceanic-sylvicolous species (western line) and more than 25 per cent Continental species (eastern lines). South of Holsteinsborg these two curves overlap but they diverge northwards in the inland archipelago of Nordre Strömfjord where the mountains are lower and the oceanic air masses sometimes are able to penetrate into the inland areas (Böcher and Lœgaard, 1962).

The old question about the occurrence of American and Eurasiatic flora elements in Greenland was recently considered (Böcher, Holmen and Jacobsen, 1959; Lindroth, 1960; Böcher, 1963). How to classify eastern and western species is always a matter of opinion because some of them are Amphi-Atlantic but with almost equally large areas on both sides. In such cases, however, an increased variability on one of the sides may give additional valuable criteria. But, although some of the species tabulated as eastern or western were removed, the material is sufficient to show that European plants play a subordinate role in all parts of Greenland except southeast and middle east Greenland where western and eastern species are present in almost equal numbers, although not with the same frequency. The eastern species are obviously more abundant (Böcher, 1938), a fact which has a connection to their climatic requirements. Most of the eastern plants are clearly montane North Atlantic (sometimes also North Pacific) and absent from the driest tundra areas of northernmost Asia and Canada. Ecologically they demand snow in great quantities and high humidity. Such conditions are found in the Alps, Norway, Scotland, the Faeroes, Iceland, and the southern part of Greenland (except for certain inland areas). These species have been able to migrate from Europe to North America via the Atlantic islands which are washed or influenced by the Gulf Stream and therefore have a suitable climate. On the other hand, the majority of American species require a continental climate. They occur in north Greenland and southwards, mainly inland. The American species came mostly from Arctic–Continental areas and hence many of them were unable to penetrate to south Greenland with its maritime climate. Some of them (11 per cent) were High Arctic and were able to reach east Greenland through the north Greenland barrens.

This different behavior of western and eastern species in Greenland is evidenced through the calculations summarized in Table 1. Most important is the fact that U-distributions (W.–S.–E.) are most frequent among the European species and ∩-distributions (W.–N.–E.) among the American species.

There are, of course, deviations. Thus, *Braya linearis*, *Draba sibirica*, and *Potentilla stipularis* exemplify eastern species which have reached continental

TABLE 1. GREENLAND DISTRIBUTION OF WESTERN AND EASTERN SPECIES
Data from Böcher, Holmen, and Jakobsen (1959)

	Area type within Greenland:											
	W	W + S	W + N	S	E	E + S	E + N	U[1]	∩[1]	C[1]	()[1]	O[1]
Per cent of Western species (114)	22	15	4	4	1	0	2	24	11	2	14	3
Per cent of Eastern species (82): Including *Taraxacum*	5	4	0	12	20	5	2	44	0	0	9	0
Per cent of Eastern species (82): Excluding *Taraxacum*	3	4	0	6	15	6	3	53	0	0	10	0

[1] U: Distribution W.–S.–E.; ∩: Distribution W.–N.–E.; C: With a gap in East Greenland; ( ): W. and E., not N. and S.; O: Circum Greenlandic distribution.

areas in Greenland, whereas western species such as *Hierochloë orthantha*, *Carex stylaris*, *C. deflexa*, and *Veronica wormskjoldii* reach areas of the maritime type in Greenland.

There has been much discussion about the time of these migrations (Iversen, 1953; Böcher, 1956). For the solution of the questions it is evidently of importance to realize that very many species of both elements, as well as the Circumpolar species in Greenland, have reached areas which are explained ecologically. Furthermore, as already mentioned, many southern species do not require high summer temperatures.

The majority of true Arctic species occurs also on nunataks (Schwarzenbach, 1961) and may be very old members of the Greenland flora which arrived during Interglacial times or even during the Late Tertiary and survived in unglaciated areas.

Nothing, however, would in my opinion prevent an early (Interglacial) migration of the montane North Atlantic species to Greenland and westwards. They have had long periods during which they became established in west Greenland (e.g. *Angelica archangelica*) and reached eastern America (e.g. *Saxifraga stellaris*). Some of them even seem to have suffered extinction in certain areas of Greenland. Thus, north of south Greenland a species like *Ranunculus acris* is now very rare and is found only in natural vegetation at places where hardly any Norsemen have lived (Kangerdluarsuk ungatdleq, stations at Angmagssalik), and where the topography indicates that during the Last Ice Age only local glaciation has taken place.

It is probable that a large number of south-facing slopes, during a very long period of time and also during the last glaciation, have served as bases for migration. We know such coastal areas today (e.g. the Blosseville Coast) which are composed of half-nunataks separated by big glaciers reaching the sea, and we find in such places many southern species of the montane North

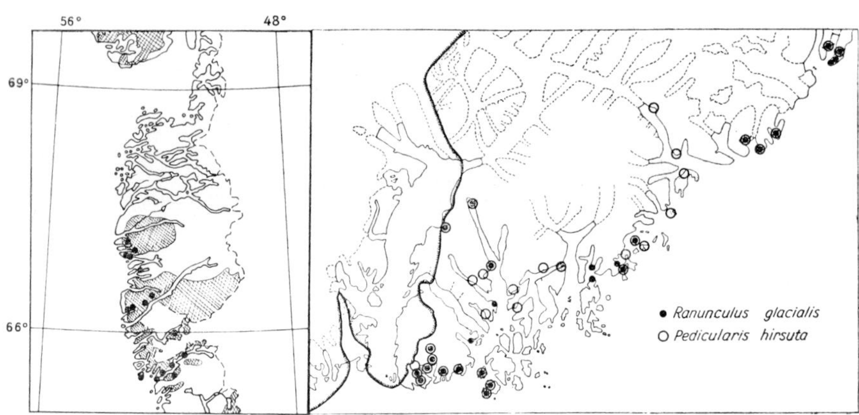

Fig. 4. On the left: areas in middle West Greenland with mountains more than 900 m high and the distribution of *Anemone richardsoni* (dots). Only the areas occupied by this species have sharp peaks or ridges. On the right: eastern limit of smoothed mountain form and the southernmost stations in east Greenland for *Ranunculus glacialis* and *Pedicularis hirsuta*. (From Böcher, 1956, 1963.)

Atlantic type. But half-nunataks which had suitable localities during the Last Glaciation are probably found only where high mountains reach the sea. There are large areas of this kind in east Greenland, including the Cape Farwell area in the south. In southwest Greenland one small coastal high mountain area is found at Arsuk and a large one between the two Isortoq fjords (66° 30′–67° 30′), the latter only interrupted by a rather small area south of Holsteinsborg. *Anemone richardsonii* is confined to the coastal part of the latter area in which the mountains are formed by local glaciers only (Fig. 4), and a species like *Athyrium alpestre* is restricted to the southeast coast (including Cape Farwell) and the Arsuk area. These coincidences of plant occurrences and alpine topography suggest survival but cannot be regarded as a definite evidence for it (see Böcher, 1951, 1956, 1963, and Fig. 4).

As a whole, Greenland has mostly been considered to have an Arctic flora. This is a result of the definition of the Arctic range as the area north of the timber-line. But, in the North Atlantic the timber-line depends also on oceanity and the species which in other areas have limits at the timber-line do not behave in this manner in the Atlantic area. From a plant geographical point of view the timber-line is more a physiognomical division than a floristic

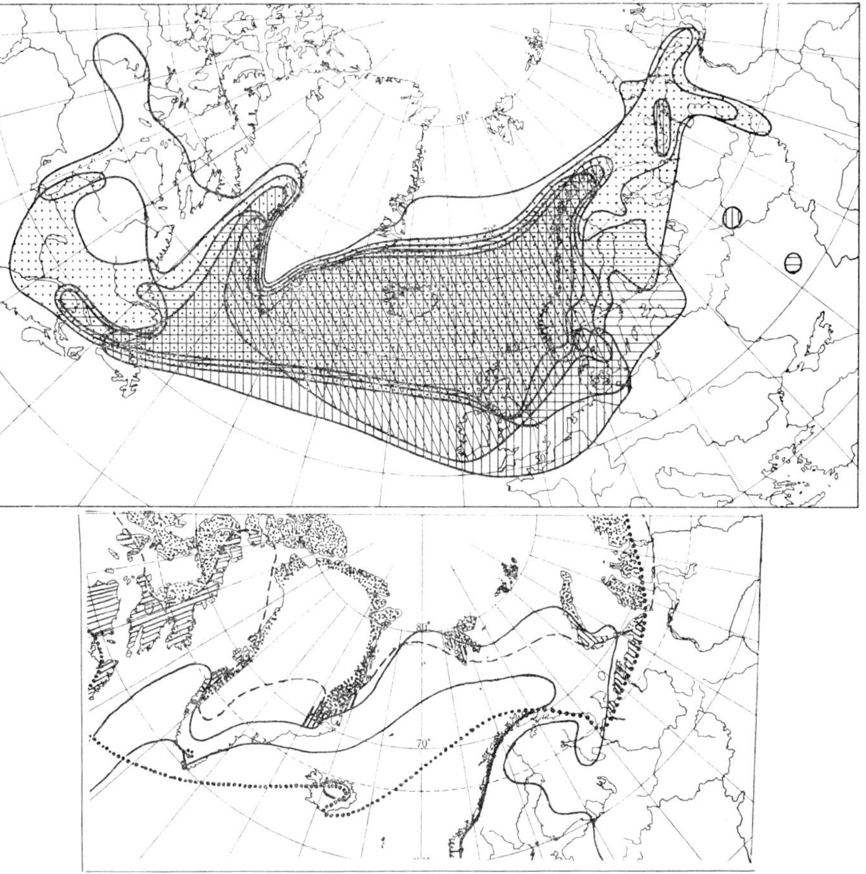

FIG. 5. Above: North Atlantic areas of a number of species forming the floristic boundary in Greenland (*Sibbaldia procumbens* (without hatching), *Phleum commutatum* (dotted area), *Leucorchis albida* (vertical hatching), *Alchemilla filicaulis* (horizontal hatching), and *A. alpina* (oblique hatching)). Below: North Atlantic area showing the annual isohyet 250 mm (broken line), and lines for mean annual temperature range of 15°C (southernmost full line) and 25°C (northernmost full line). Dotted line indicates the 10°C. July isotherm. Continental Arctic area indicated by hatching and dotting. (From Böcher, 1954.)

boundary. In this situation the boundary previously mentioned, between a flora which is mainly montane (connected with humid mountains south of the true Arctic areas) and a true Arctic flora (connected with the dry Arctic areas), seems to be much more significant. The northern limit of sylvicolous Boreal plants such as *Coptis*, *Pyrola minor*, *Platanthera hyperborea*, *Deschampsia flexuosa*, *Chamaenerion angustifolium*, *Cornus suecica*, and some of the montane Sub-Arctic or Low Arctic species, e.g. *Alchemilla alpina*, *Angelica*, *Gnaphalium norvegicum*, etc., gives a much more interesting boundary line.

It divides the North Atlantic area into a true Arctic (High Arctic) part, including Baffin Island, Ellesmere Island, northern Greenland, Spitsbergen, Franz Josephs Land, and northern Novaya Zemlya, and a southern Sub-Low-Arctic-Montane part ranging from southern Labrador to the southern part of Greenland, Iceland, the Faeroes, the Scottish Highlands, and the Scandinavian Mountains. Connected with the true Arctic part are those continental areas warm enough for Boreal or Temperate plants which do not require oceanic humidity at their northern limits. Typical examples of such regions are found in the inland of middle west Greenland, inland at Scoresbysound, and undoubtedly in Canada and northern Russia. In northernmost Scandinavia many places will approach this transitional type between Arctic and Boreal Continental floristic régimes (see Fig. 5).

Many plant communities are distributed on one of two sides of this main boundary line. In a previous paper (Böcher, 1954) an attempt was made to divide the southwest Greenland vegetation into two complexes, an Oceanic and a Continental. Ecologically and floristically the communities of these complexes are clearly closely related and merge into one another. A natural group of the Oceanic complex is formed by snow-bed vegetation, herb fields, snow-protected heaths of the *Phyllodoce* type, and willow copses with hygrophilous herb vegetation. A similar Continental complex consists of dry rock vegetation, steppe communities, dry heath vegetation, and willow copses with xerophytes. In spite of the interest, however, connected with the study of such complexes it is felt that the old dividing system using life-forms as primary criteria should not be abandoned. In a recent paper (Böcher, 1963) an attempt has been made to classify the middle Greenland vegetation using life-forms in the main division and distributional types in the first subdivision while dominance and floristic composition are used only in the definitions of the smallest entities, e.g. the plant sociations.

REFERENCES

Böcher, T. W. (1933). Phytogeographical studies of the Greenland flora. *Medd. om Grönl.* **104** (3), 1–56.

Böcher, T. W. (1938). Biological distributional types in the flora of Greenland. *Medd. om Grönl.* **106** (2), 1–339.

Böcher, T. W. (1951). Distributions of plants in the circumpolar area in relation to ecological and historical factors. *J. Ecology* **39**, 376–395.

Böcher, T. W. (1954). Oceanic and continental vegetational complexes in Southwest Greenland. *Medd. om Grönl.* **148** (1), 1–336.

Böcher, T. W. (1956). Area-limits and isolations of plants in relation to physiography of the southern parts of Greenland. *Medd. om Grönl.* **124** (8), 1–40.

Böcher, T. W. (1963). Phytogeography of Middle West Greenland. *Medd. om Grönl.* **148** (3) (in press).

Böcher, T. W., Holmen, Kj., and Jakobsen, K. (1957). *Grönlands Flora.* Copenhagen.

Böcher, T. W., Holmen, Kj., and Jakobsen, K. (1959). A synoptical study of the Greenland Flora. *Medd. om Grönl.* **163** (1), 1–32.

Böcher, T. W. and Lægaard, S. (1962). Botanical studies along the Arfersiorfik Fjord, West Greenland. *Bot. Tidskr.* **58**, 168–190.

Fredskild B. (1961). Floristic and ecological studies near Jakobshavn, West Greenland. *Medd. om Groenl.* **163** (4), 1–82.

Holmen, Kj. (1957). The vascular plants of Peary Land, North Greenland. *Medd. om Groenl.* **124** (9), 1–149.

Hultén, E. (1950). *Atlas över växternas utbredning i Norden. Fanerogamer och ormbunksväxter* (Atlas of the distribution of vascular plants in N.W. Europe). Stockholm.

Hultén, E. (1958). The Amphi-Atlantic plants and their geographical connections. *Kgl. Sv. Vetensk. Akad. H ndl.* 4, *Ser.* **7** (1), 1–340.

Iversen, J. (1953). Origin of the flora of Western Greenland in the light of pollen analysis. *Oikos* **4**, 85–103.

Lindroth, C. (1960). Is Davis Strait—between Greenland and Baffin Island—a floristic barrier? *Bot. Notiser* **113**, 129–140.

Porsild, A. E. (1955). The vascular plants of the western Canadian Arctic Archipelago. *Nat. Mus. Canad. Bull.* **135**, 1–226.

Porsild, A. E. (1957). Illustrated flora of the Canadian Arctic Archipelago. *Nat. Mus. Canad. Bull.* **146**, 1–209.

Raup, H. M. (1947). The botany of southwestern Mackenzie. *Sargentia* **6**, 1–275.

Schwarzenbach, F. H. (1961). Botanische Beobachtungen in der Nunatakkerzone Ostgrönlands zwischen 74° and 75° N. Br. *Medd. om Grönl.* **163** (5), 1–172.

Sörensen, Th. (1953). A revision of the Greenland species of *Puccinellia* Parl. *Medd. om Groenl.* **136** (3), 1–179.

Tolmachev, A. I. (1960). *Flora Arctica USSR. I.* Acad. Sci. SSSR. Inst. Bot. Komarova. Moskwa–Leningrad.

THE ELEMENTS AND AFFINITIES OF THE ICELANDIC FLORA

EYTHÓR EINARSSON
Museum of Natural History, Reykjavík, Iceland

THE scientific investigation of the Icelandic flora started a little more than two centuries ago with the observations by Eggert Ólafsson and Bjarni Pálsson during their journeys through Iceland in the years 1752–57. In their travelogue (Ólafsson and Pálsson, 1772) considerable information is given on floristics and about 130 species of vascular plants are mentioned.

The first scientific treatise on the Icelandic flora, however, was written by the Dane O. Fr. Müller and published in 1770. It was based entirely on the investigations and collections made in Iceland by J. G. König in 1764–65, and in it 337 species of vascular plants are mentioned. The first Icelandic Excursion Flora was written by Oddur Hjaltalín and published in 1830. This flora was based only partly on Hjaltalín's own investigations, but mostly on a Danish manual by J. W. Hornemann (1821), which also contained descriptions of all Icelandic spermatophytes known at that itme. In his flora, Hjaltalín records 337 species of vascular plants from Iceland. In 1871, C. C. Babington published *A Revision of the Flora of Iceland*, based on his own investigations of the Icelandic flora and all previously published plant lists from Iceland, together with information extracted from the herbaria of Icelandic plants preserved in Copenhagen by Joh. Lange. In his paper, Babington states that the Icelandic flora is essentially European; only 62 species are found which do not grow in the British Isles, nearly all the species inhabit Scandinavia and not more than 3 species are decidedly Arctic. Babington finally records 467 species of vascular plants as found in Iceland.

During the years 1870–85, Chr. Grönlund published some papers on the Icelandic flora, the most important one being his *Islands Flora* (Grönlund, 1881), where 357 species of Icelandic vascular plants are described. In a later paper Grönlund (1884) adds nine species to this number and states that the number of Icelandic vascular plants given by Babington (1871) and some other authors of previous Icelandic plant lists is much too high. In this same paper, Grönlund (*loc. cit.*) compares the flora of Iceland to that of Greenland, Scandinavia and the Faeroes. His conclusions are practically the same as those of Babington, i.e. that the Icelandic flora is mostly north European and all the vascular plants with the exception of five species are found in

Scandinavia. More than half of the Icelandic species are also found in Greenland, and in the Faeroes the situation is about the same. Because many of the north European species are found throughout the Arctic, a considerable part of the Icelandic species are also found in Siberia, Spitsbergen, and northern North America. The only endemic species of vascular plants in Iceland, according to Grönlund, is *Carex lyngbyei*, and in addition there are three varieties of more widely distributed species.

Strömfelt (1884) mentions 371 species of vascular plants from Iceland. Like Babington and Grönlund, he considered that only five of the Icelandic species, or 1.5 per cent are not found in Scandinavia, while 35.7 per cent of the species are not found in Greenland, among them some of the most common Icelandic lowland plants; 39.5 per cent of the Icelandic species are not found in the Faeroes, and that the character of the Icelandic flora, thus, is almost entirely Scandinavian.

In his statistical treatise on "The flora of Greenland, Iceland and the Faeroes", Warming (1888) mentions 417 species of vascular plants from Iceland and says that the Icelandic flora is a typical European one. He divides the flora of these countries into 20 groups. He counts more than one-third of the Icelandic plants, or 151 species in his Group 3, Temperate-zone species; 70 belong to Group 2, Boreal-zone species; 64 to Group 1, Circumpolar species; and 48 belong to his group 4, European–American species. Three Icelandic species have a western distribution (not found in Europe), whereas 74 have an eastern distribution (not found in America).

During the last decade of the nineteenth century, the Icelandic flora was carefully investigated, mostly by Helgi Jónsson and Stefán Stefánsson, and many papers were published on the subject. Helgi Jónsson (1896) records 435 species of vascular plants from Iceland, but in a later paper (Jónsson 1905) he sets the number at 360. In his first paper on the Icelandic flora, Stefán Stefánsson (1890) reports 423 species of vascular plants known there. His *Flóra Íslands* (Flora of Iceland, 1901), a valuable manual firmly based on his own investigations of the flora, however, contains only 359 species of vascular plants, 10 of which belong to the genera *Taraxacum* and *Hieracium*.

Thus, Jónsson and Stefánsson are even more sceptical than Grönlund regarding some of the species mentioned in the old plant lists and especially in Babington's paper, but never found again—and perhaps not found at all—in Iceland.

In 1924, the second edition of Stefánsson's *Flóra Íslands* appeared, containing 363 species of vascular plants, five "species" of *Taraxacum* and 43 "species" of *Hieracium* excluded. Some few species, new to the Icelandic flora, had been added; some of the excluded species from the old plant lists had been rediscovered and some of the accidentally introduced species had been naturalized since 1901.

Mölholm-Hansen (1930) divided the Icelandic vascular plants (375 species, excluding most species of *Taraxacum* and *Hieracium*) into two main groups, A and E. Group A comprises Arctic and Subarctic species, having their main distribution near or north of the forest limit; they are common in Greenland, Spitsbergen, and on the Scandinavian mountains, but absent or occurring sporadically in more southerly countries. To this group belong 151 species or *ca.* 40 per cent of the Icelandic vascular plants. Group E comprises species of common occurrence in central Europe, which have their main distribution south of the forest limit. This group consists of 224 species, or *ca.* 60 per cent of the vascular plants of Iceland, about half of which are also found in Greenland. According to Mölholm-Hansen, there is also some difference in the distribution of the groups in various parts of Iceland. In north Iceland 60.3 per cent of the species belonging to Group A are common but only 38.8 per cent of the species belonging to Group E. In southwest Iceland, on the contrary, 53.6 per cent of the A species and 41.5 per cent of the E species are common.

Ostenfeld and Gröntved (1934) mention about 390 species of vascular plants from Iceland, *Taraxacum* and *Hieracium* excluded. In 1942, Gröntved published a treatise on the Icelandic flora, in which every species of vascular plants ever recorded from Iceland is mentioned, i.e. about 660 species. The author considered critically which of these really belong to the Icelandic flora. His conclusions are that about 400 species, *Taraxacum* and *Hieracium* excluded, should be considered as Icelandic. During the last 20 years, however, some of the species from the old plant lists, which were excluded by Gröntved, have been rediscovered in Iceland.

Áskell Löve (1945) records 425 species of vascular plants from Iceland, *Taraxacum* and *Hieracium* excluded, and finally in the third edition of Stefánsson's manual, Steindór Steindórsson (1948) mentions 429 Icelandic vascular plants, indigenous and naturalized, introduced species, with *Taraxacum* and *Hieracium* excluded. Besides, both Stefánsson (1901, 1924), Ostenfeld and Gröntved (1934), Gröntved (1942), Löve (1945), Steindórsson (1948) and other authors record a considerable number of accidentally introduced, but not naturalized species from Iceland.

In a paper on the age and immigration of the Icelandic flora, Steindórsson (1954) is of the opinion that between 430 and 440 species of vascular plants, *Taraxacum* and *Hieracium* excluded, are native in Iceland. No sexually reproducing species can be considered as endemic, but some endemic varieties and subspecies of wider distributed species are found in Iceland. According to Steindórsson (1954), about 21 per cent (*ca.* 90 species) of the 430–440 species have been introduced to Iceland by man during the last 1100 years and are now more or less naturalized in the country. Steindórsson points out, as do all the previous authors, that the main part of the Icelandic vascular plants is European, mostly Scandinavian species. Only six of the species, i.e. 1.4 per cent of the flora, are western and not found in Europe, whereas 106 species or almost 25 per cent are eastern and not found in America. He states further that 74 Icelandic species, or 17 per cent of the flora, are not found in the British Isles, whereas 184 species, or *ca.* 42 per cent are not found in Greenland.

Löve and Löve (1956) set the total number of spermatophyte species in Iceland at 540, of which 387 are regarded as being definitely indigenous, the rest alien. They divide the indigenous species into five groups, or elements: To the Circumpolar element, comprising all species with a Circumpolar area of distribution and some species with an almost Circumpolar area of distribution but with a gap in their distribution in the Pacific region, belong 148 Icelandic spermatophytes. The majority of these Circumpolar plants do not show any variation from the representatives of these species in other countries. Some of them, however, show a closer relationship to the same species in Scandinavia than elsewhere, whereas others are more closely related to the populations in the British Isles. Still others are represented in Iceland by the same races as in Greenland and differ somewhat from the European ones.

The second element is the bis-Atlantic, comprising species met with on both sides of the Atlantic, but not reaching very far inland in continental Eurasia or North America. It includes 113 Icelandic species. Some of these are found mainly west of Iceland, while others have their main area east of Iceland. The third element is the eastern one, comprising those species which have a European or Eurasiatic distribution; some of them however, are also found in western North America. There are 95 Icelandic spermatophytes in this element. Some of them show strong affinities to Scandinavian specimens of these species, but still others bear more likeness to British specimens.

The fourth element is the western one, comprising species with their main distributional area west of Iceland. The authors, Löve and Löve (1956) point out, that the majority of the 14 species which they classify as western, are probably not very old in Iceland, and some of them probably are the most recent, prehistoric invaders of the flora. Some of these 14 taxa are varieties or subspecies of wider distributed species. Finally, regarding the 17 taxa belonging to the endemic element, they are also for the most part races of species known from other regions, Circumpolar or European as, for example, *Papaver*, or belonging to genera reproducing by apomixis or autogamy, as *Alchemilla* and *Euphrasia.* The only exception is *Alchemilla faeroeënsis*, an endemic species growing in eastern Iceland and the Faeroes.

The great majority of the Icelandic "species" belonging to *Hieracium* are endemic (Óskarsson, 1955), but for the most part they show a close relationship to Scandinavian, Faeroese, or British "species".

According to my own opinion, the Icelandic vascular plant species number *ca.* 440, including naturalized, introduced species, but 116 "species" of *Taraxacum* and *ca.* 180 "species" of *Hieracium* excluded.

About 10 of these 440 species are somewhat doubtful; they have only been found once in a single locality each and never again. During the last years, however, some few of the species mentioned from Iceland in the plant lists from the nineteenth century, but excluded from the Icelandic flora by all later authors, have been rediscovered in Iceland. Besides that, about 140 accidentally introduced species have been recorded from Iceland, and most likely some of them will later become naturalized. About 290 of these 440 species, or *ca.* 66 per cent, are found also in Greenland; some of them are without doubt introduced in Greenland and they may be so in Iceland, too. Most of the Icelandic species, not found in Greenland, are European or Eurasiatic Boreal taxa.

About 250 of the Icelandic plants, *ca.* 57 per cent are found also in the Faeroes. The majority of the Icelandic plants, *ca.* 85 per cent, grow in the British Isles as well, whereas the remaining 15 per cent comprise mostly Arctic species and some species with a western distribution. Not less than 426 of the Icelandic species of vascular plants, or *ca.* 97 per cent, are found also in Scandinavia, a few of them, however, being represented in Iceland by other races or subspecies than in Scandinavia. Ten species, or 2.3 per cent of the vascular plants of Iceland, are western species, which are not found on the European continent nor in the British Isles. When the genera *Taraxacum* and *Hieracium* are excluded, the endemic element of the Icelandic vascular flora is very small, and is entirely composed of "species" of other genera reproducing by apomixis, like *Alchemilla*, some varieties and subspecies of taxa with a much wider distribution area, as well as some *Euphrasia* species.

In his work on the Amphi-Atlantic plants, Hultén (1958) enumerates 278 species. Of these, 146 belong to the Icelandic flora. Earlier, Hultén (1950) had divided all the vascular plants of northwest Europe into 48 distribution groups. It is possible to fit into these groups all the 426 Icelandic species also occurring in Scandinavia. Using Hultén's classification, the Icelandic flora can be divided as follows: 118 species, *ca.* 27 per cent of the Icelandic vascular plants, belong to the Boreal–circumpolar plants (Hultén's Groups 16, 17, 29, 30, 31, 32, and 33); 90 species, *ca.* 20 per cent, belong to the European-Eurasiatic plants (Groups 12, 13, 14, 15, 25, 26, 27, 28), which are found in the Boreal region of Eurasia; 71 species, *ca.* 16 per cent, belong to the Arctic–alpine–circumpolar plants (Groups 6, 7, 8, 9), while 14 species, or *ca.* 3 per cent, belong to the Arctic–circumpolar plants (Groups 1 and 2). The Amphi-Atlantic plants (Groups 10 and 11), comprise 32 species, or *ca.* 7 per cent of the vascular plants of Iceland. European coastal, Atlantic, and Sub-Atlantic plants (Groups 18, 19, 20) comprise 19 species, 4.3 per cent; and Circumpolar coastal and Sub-oceanic plants (Groups 21 and 22) comprise 10 species, or 2.3 per cent of the Icelandic vascular flora. Group 41, including plants with two or more widely separated areas of distribution, comprises 13 species, or *ca.* 3 per cent of the flora. Group 46, including species strongly dispersed by man, comprises 29 species in Iceland, or 6.6 per cent; and Group 48, including taxa with insufficiently known areas of distribution, comprises 12 species, or 2.7 per cent of the Icelandic vascular plants. Finally, as mentioned above, the 10 western species make up 2.3 per cent of the flora.

As seen by this classification, more than half of the Icelandic vascular plants are species with a Boreal distribution, whereas Arctic–Alpine species comprise only *ca.* 33 per cent of the flora. Most of the Arctic ones have a Low-Arctic distribution, but High Arctic species are practically absent from Iceland. Those with an Eastern distribution are more than nine times as numerous as the Western species in Iceland. Many of the Icelandic vascular plants have an Oceanic or Sub-oceanic distribution, whereas typical Continental species are practically absent from Iceland.

REFERENCES

BABINGTON, C. C. (1871). A revision of the flora of Iceland. *J. Linn. Soc. Botany* **11**, 1–68.

GRÖNLUND, C. (1881). *Islands Flora.* Kjöbenhavn.

GRÖNLUND, C. (1884). Karakteristik af Plantevæksten paa Island, sammenlignet med Floraen i flere andre Lande. *Naturhist. For. Festskr. 1884*, 1–39.

GRÖNTVED, J. (1942). The Pteridophyta and Spermatophyta of Iceland. *Botany of Iceland* **4**, 1–427.

HJALTALÍN, O. J. (1830). *Íslenzk grasafraedi.* Kaupmannahöfn.

HORNEMANN, I. W. (1821). *Forsög til en dansk oekonomisk Plantelære. Forste Deel.* Tredie, forögede Oplag. Kjöbenhavn.

HULTÉN, E. (1950). *Atlas över växternas utbredning i Norden.* Stockholm.

HULTÉN, E. (1958). The Amphi-Atlantic plants and their phytogeographical connections. *Kgl. Svenska Vetensk. Akad. Handl.* **4**, No. 7 (1), 1–340.

JÓNSSON, H. (1896). Bidrag til Öst-Islands flora. *Bot. Tidsskr.* **20**, 327–357.

JÓNSSON, H. (1905). Vegetationen i Syd-Island. *Bot. Tidsskr.* **27**, 1–82.

LÖVE, Á. (1945). *Íslenzkar jurtir.* Kaupmannahöfn.

LÖVE, Á. and LÖVE D. (1956). Cytotaxonomical conspectus of the Icelandic flora. *Acta Horti Gotoburg.* **20**, 65–291.

MÜLLER, O. F. (1770). Enumeratio stirpium in Islandia sponte crescentium. *Nova Acta Acad. Nat. Curios.* IV, 203–216.

MÖLHOLM-HANSEN, H. (1930). Studies on the vegetation of Iceland. *Botany of Iceland* **3**, 1–186.

ÓLAFSSON, E. og PÁLSSON, B. (1772). *Reise igiennem Island, etc.* Soröe.

ÓSKARSSON, I. (1955). Um undafífla. *Náttúrufr.* **25**, 72–86.

OSTENFELD, C. H. and GRÖNTVED, J. (1934). *The Flora of Iceland and the Faeroes.* Copenhagen.

STEFÁNSSON, S. (1890). Fra Islands Vækstrige I. Nogle "nye" og sjældne Karplanter samlede i Aarene 1888–89. *Vidensk. Medd. Naturhist. Foren. i Kjöbenhavn 1890*, 1–16.

STEFÁNSSON, S. (1901). *Flóra Íslands.* Kaupmannahöfn.

STEFÁNSSON, S. (1924). *Flóra Íslands*, 2. útgáfa, aukin. Kaupmannahöfn.

STEINDÓRSSON, S. (1948). Stefánsson, S.: *Flóra Íslands*, 3. útgáfa, aukin. Akureyri.

STEINDÓRSSON, S. (1954). Um aldur og innflutning íslenzku flórunnar. *Ársrit Ræktunarfél. Nordurlands* **51**, 3–23, 53–72, 101–115.

STRÖMFELT, H. F. G. (1884). Islands kärlväxter, betraktade från växtgeografisk och floristisk synpunkt. *Öfvers. Kgl. Vetensk. Akad. Förh. 1884* (8), 79–124.

WARMING, E. (1888). Tabellarisk Oversigt over Grönlands, Islands og Færöernes Flora i 1887. *Vidensk. Medd. Naturhist. Foren. i Kjöbenhavn 1887*, 236–292.

ICE AGE REFUGIA IN ICELAND AS INDICATED BY THE PRESENT DISTRIBUTION OF PLANT SPECIES

Steindór Steindórsson

Akureyri College, Akureyri, Iceland

One of the most striking features of the flora of Iceland is its paucity of species. According to *Flóra Íslands* (Flora of Iceland; Stefánsson, 1948), only about 430 species of Pteridophyta and Phanerogams can be considered as native to the whole country. Without doubt some species have been added since that time, but the entire number does not noticeably exceed 440. To this number we can add the genera *Hieracium* and *Taraxacum*, but about 190 species of *Hieracium* have been recorded from Iceland and a rather uncertain number of *Taraxacum*, since some specialists put the number at 20, others at somewhat more than 100. From the distribution of these genera, one could undoubtedly find certain features concerning the problem which is dealt with in the present paper, but I have omitted these genera here especially because we know so little about their real distribution (cf. Steindórsson, 1962).

The total number of species, 440, however does not tell the whole story. After a closer investigation we find that a considerable number of these have been introduced by man since the first settlement of the country nearly eleven hundred years ago. In another paper I have produced some arguments to show that about 100 species have been brought into the country by human agency. Although this number after a closer study may prove too high, it is certain that up to 20 per cent of the flora of Iceland (*Hieracium* and *Taraxacum* excepted) is anthropochorous.

Although our knowledge of the origin of the flora of Iceland and its relationship to the floras of our neighboring countries is far from complete, it is obvious that it is more closely related to the flora of Scandinavia than to any other country. A considerable component of the flora is Circumpolar, or at least is found on both sides of the North Atlantic Ocean, and the American element is probably greater than hitherto generally considered. The cytological investigations of Áskell Löve point in that direction. It is certain that the flora of Iceland does not differ remarkably from that of other countries around the North Atlantic Ocean in other respects than its poverty of species.

Then there is the question whether a considerable element of it is comprised of survivors which have overwintered at least the Last Glaciation or perhaps the whole Ice Age in more or less isolated refugia. If we consider the overwintering a reality, it remains for us to find evidence as to the existence of such refugia and where they are situated.

As we know, the prevailing opinion in the last century was that both Scandinavia and Iceland were fully glaciated during the Ice Age, and consequently that all biota must have ceased to exist there. According to this opinion, the so-called *tabula rasa* theory, all biota of these countries must have immigrated since the end of the Ice Age, or at the same time as the glaciers melted away.

During the last fifty to sixty years various scientists have expressed their doubts about the correctness of the *tabula rasa* theory, not only in Scandinavia but also in Iceland. Arguments have been put forth that there is great likelihood that some biota have lived there at least during the last glaciated period of the Ice Age.

Before discussing the possibilities of such refugia I will mention briefly the likelihood of natural immigration of plants to Iceland. We can imagine three ways by which plants might have immigrated to Iceland, i.e. by ocean currents, by air, and by help of migrating birds.

Regarding immigration by the aid of ocean currents, a large-scale migration seems very improbable except in the case of some beach plants which are more or less halophilous. The great distances from other countries make it improbable that seeds might have kept their germinating power to any extent. On the other hand, the beach of the country is very inhospitable, offering unfavorable conditions for the seeds to take root. Furthermore, if a great number of plants were brought to the country by the ocean currents, the Gulf Stream on one side and the Polar Stream on the other, one might expect a greater American element and especially a larger Arctic–Asian element than is actually found in the flora of Iceland.

There is a greater possibility that seeds have been carried by birds. I think a considerable influx of plants by the help of birds is quite unlikely because of the paucity of species with edible fruits. For example, of the many *Rubus* species growing in the neighboring countries only a single one, *R. saxatilis*, occurs in Iceland. As far as we know, the migration of birds to and from Iceland goes by way of the British Isles. If migratory birds were really an active factor in the introduction of plants to Iceland, a greater affinity to the flora of the British Isles would at least be very probable.

Last to be considered is immigration by air currents, which in various respects is more probable as we know that small particles can be carried for long distances in the air. But if the greater part of the flora has been brought to the country in this way, there should certainly be signs of it, e.g. in the occurrence of an unusually great number of plants with seeds specifically adapted to wind dispersal.

Furthermore, it is probable that species endowed with such great capacity for dispersal would spread over the entire country in a relatively short time, wherever conditions were favorable for their growth. But the fact remains that only a little more than half of the Icelandic higher plants occur all over the country. Even so, there are often considerable gaps in their distribution, although no natural obstacles to their continuous distribution be found.

Then the question is posed: how did the plants originally reach Iceland? There we must hold to the theory that a land-bridge connected Iceland to the neighboring countries during the Tertiary period, or that at least there may have been a lesser distance between Iceland and other countries both before and during the Ice Age itself than there is now. This might have facilitated the migration of biota, both before the Ice Age and in the Interglacial periods.

Assuming that biota have survived the Ice Age in Iceland, we must obtain answers to two questions. First, are there geological possibilities for the existence of ice-free regions in the country during the Ice Age? Second, has the existence of vegetation in the Interglacial periods been proved?

The first question has been answered by Thorarinsson (1937), who pointed out at least four districts in the country, which in all probability have only been partially glaciated during the Last Glaciation.

The answer to the second question is also in the affirmative, as fossil plants from Interglacial formations are found at several places in the

Although the evidence of some ice-free areas in the country during the Ice Age can be proved, we cannot state with certainty that plants have survived in such places when the greater part of the country was covered by glaciers, and the climate was entirely of an Arctic character. But inferences may be drawn from the conditions prevailing at the present time in Arctic countries such as Greenland, where a fair number of species are found on nunataks which are completely surrounded by the inland glacier, and the climate cannot differ very much from that of the Ice Age.

In this connection it may be pointed out that near the glaciers in the central plateau of Iceland are found patches with luxuriant vegetation on the south sides of hills and slopes.

The first hints about survival of biota in refugia in Iceland were expressed by scientists some thirty years ago (Lindroth, 1931; Gelting, 1934). I myself took up the question for closer investigation in the years 1936–40. I especially tried to find out whether the distribution of species in any way indicated the possibility of overwintering in probable refugia. I published the first remarks on this problem in a small paper in 1937, and in a somewhat more exact form in a second paper in 1949. In the latter I pointed out five districts in the country which I considered as probable refugia. This view was based on the strange mode of distribution of almost 100 species of plants which seemed to be concentrated in these districts and their immediate vicinity. Further investigations have confirmed my early statements on this subject.

The first striking feature in the distribution of a great many Icelandic plants is the evident discontinuity, i.e. many of the plants seem to be accumulated in cer:ain dist icts with large gaps in their distribution where no natural obstacles can be observed to explain this discontinuity.

Searching for the causes of this phenomenon one is led sooner or later to the opinion that these species might be remnants of an older flora, one which has been isolated in these areas. The only time such an isolation could have taken place is during the Ice Age.

TABLE 1

THE DISTRIBUTION IN ICELAND OF WEST ARCTIC AND NORTH ATLANTIC GROUPS

	The Breidifjördur district	The Vestfirdir district	The Eyjafjördur district	The Austfirdir district	The Mýrdalur district	The Hvalfjördur district	Nunataks
Campanula uniflora			×××				×
Carex macloviana			×××				×
Carex nardina			×××	(××)			
Cerastium arcticum			××	×××		×	×
Erigeron unalaschkensis			×××	(×)			
Pedicularis flammea	×××	(××)	×××	×			×
Sagina caespitosa			××				×
Stellaria calycantha		××					×
Alchemilla faeroeënsis			×	×××			×
Poa laxa ssp. *flexuosa*			××	××			××
Saxifraga Aizoon				×××			×
Carex bicolor		×	××	×			××
Carex rufina *Draba norvegica* *Epilobium lactiflorum* *Euphrasia frigida* *Festuca vivipara* *Arenaria norvegica*	Distributed over the whole country without any distinct center						

A fairly thorough study of the distribution of Icelandic plants made it obvious that there are six districts which can be considered as centers of distribution and occurrence of the various species; apart from them, a few smaller areas were found in different parts of the country where the same species occur. Comparing these plant centers with these districts, which Thorarinsson (1937) has pointed out as possibly ice-free during the Ice Age, on the basis of their landscape forms, it appears that they correspond surprisingly well. The smaller areas are all situated at such places where there have been possibilities for ice-free nunataks during the glaciation. These plant centers are as follows: (1) *The Breidifjördur district*, (2) *The Vestfirdir district*, (3) *The Eyjafjördur district*, (4) *The Austfirdir district*, (5) *The Myrdalur district*, (6) *The Hvalfjördur district* (Fig. 1 and Table 1).

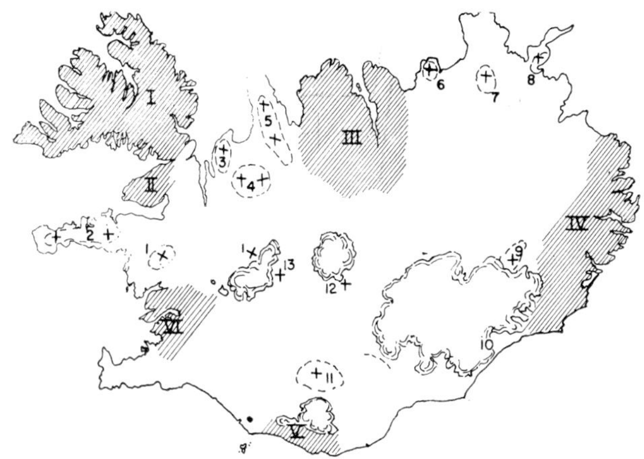

FIG. 1. Sketch map showing possible refugia areas (I–VI) and single nunataks (1–13): I, the Vestfirdir district; II, the Breidifjördur district; III, the Eyjafjördur district; IV, the Austfirdir district; V, the Mýrdalur district; VI, the Hvalfjördur district.

When looking for possible survivors of the Ice Age, attention will first be drawn to those species which have been established with certainty as survivors in other northern countries. Of these, the plant group which has been characterized as "West Arctic" species in Scandinavia, is the most remarkable.

There is hardly any disagreement among Scandinavian plant-geographers about the West Arctic plant group being a survivor of the Ice Age in Scandinavia, and that its plants have migrated from America to Europe at least before the Last Glaciation. On the whole, 27 species have been classified with various degree of certainty as West Arctic, and at the same time considered as overwinterers in Scandinavia. Thirteen of these species are definitely found in Iceland, and perhaps 2 more. In Scandinavia all the West Arctic species are mountain plants. The same applies to the majority of the West Arctic plants found in Iceland, as 8 of them have their main distribution above 300 m, and some of them are found growing up to 1000 m above sea-level.

These 13 West Arctic species in Iceland are: *Campanula uniflora*, *Carex macloviana*, *Carex nardina*, *Carex rufina*, *Cerastium Edmondstonii* (*C. arcticum*), *Draba rupestris* (*D. norvegica*), *Epilobium lactiflorum*, *Erigeron unalaschkensis*, *Euphrasia frigida*, *Festuca vivipara*, *Pedicularis flammea*, *Sagina caespitosa*, and *Stellaria calycantha*.

When we observe the distribution of these 13 species, various peculiarities will appear. Five of them, *Carex rufina*, *Draba rupestris*, *Epilobium lactiflorum*, *Euphrasia frigida*, and *Festuca vivipara*, are common throughout the whole country, so we cannot point out any center for their occurrence; but *E. lactiflorum* shows faint tendencies to centricity in three different districts.

FIG. 2. *Campanula uniflora.*

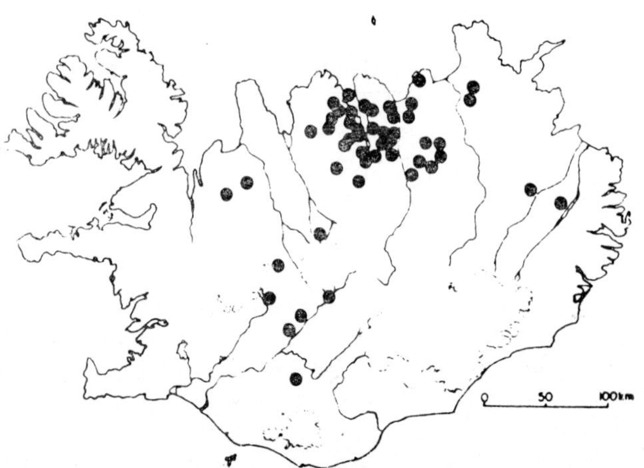

FIG. 3. *Carex Macloviana.*

Five others of these species have a distinct center in the Eyjafjördur district, i.e. *Campanula uniflora*, *Carex macloviana*, *Carex nardina*, *Erigeron unalaschkensis*, and *Sagina caespitosa* (Figs. 2–5).

The localities outside the district where these species are found can either be explained with a view to direct distribution from the center or as being situated on some nunataks. The latter is especially the case with *Sagina caespitosa* and *Carex macloviana.*

FIG. 4. *Carex nardina.*

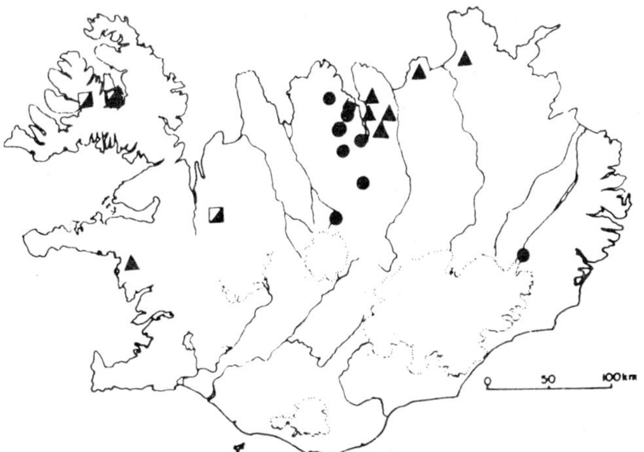

FIG. 5. *Erigeron unalaschkensis* (dots), *Sagina caespitosa* (triangles), and *Stellaria calycantha* (squares).

Cerastium Edmondstonii has two centers, the Eyjafjördur and the Austfirdir districts; *Pedicularis flammea* seems to be tricentric, and *Stellaria calycantha* (Fig. 5) seems to have a center in the Vestfirdir district. Two of these species, *Sagina caespitosa* and *Stellaria calycantha*, are among the rarest of plants in Iceland.

Closely connected to the West Arctic group are five species which have been characterized as North Atlantic, i.e. *Alchemilla faeroeënsis, Arenaria norvegica,*

Poa laxa ssp. *flexuosa*, *Saxifraga Aizoon*, and *Carex bicolor*. The distribution of these species in Iceland is very particular and all these species are considered as survivors of the Ice Age.

Fig. 6. *Alchemilla faeroeënsis*.

Fig. 7. *Poa laxa* ssp. *flexuosa*.

Alchemilla faeroeënsis (Fig. 6) is limited to the Austfirdir district and its closest vicinity. *Poa laxa* ssp. *flexuosa* (Fig. 7) seems to have two main centers, in the Eyjafjördur district and in the southern part of the Austfirdir district; it is also found in mountains both in the Breidifjördur and Vestfirdir districts. Outside these centers hardly any other Icelandic plant seems so closely connected to nunatak areas.

Saxifraga Aizoon (Fig. 8) has its main center in the Austfirdir district; it is found in the Eyjafjördur district and in mountains at Vatnsdalur in Húnavatnssysla; a second center seems to be in the Hvalfjördur district or more likely in the nunatak area in the mountain range of Snæfellsnes.

Arenaria norvegica and *Carex bicolor* do not have a distinct centricity. But several points indicate a center of *C. bicolor* in the Eyjafjördur district, and its distribution is connected to nunatak areas, especially in the highlands north of the glacier Vatnajökull.

FIG. 8. *Saxifraga Aizoon.*

When we summarize what has been mentioned about the distribution of these 18 species the result will be as follows: eleven species have a distinct centric distribution, and 2 more show tendencies of the same kind. Only 6 species display no centricity at all. The distribution of the centric species is mostly limited to four districts, and where the plants are found outside these districts, distinct nunataks characterize the landscape.

Seeing that the majority of the species in this group, which with certainty is considered as overwintering in Scandinavia, is almost exclusively found in limited areas in Iceland, one may ask whether the peculiar distribution of these species is a mere accident. If that were the case, it would certainly be a strange accident. It would be more natural to seek the cause of this peculiar distribution in the conclusion that these species have actually survived the Ice Age in refugia in the districts mentioned above, and that they have not been able to disperse more widely through the country in Post-glacial times.

Furthermore, the West Arctic plants are not the only ones in Iceland which have such a peculiar distribution; about 80 other species have been found to have a very similar distribution, chiefly within the same districts and nunatak areas. If these facts are taken into consideration, the accidental spread of the species in the districts mentioned above is still more improbable.

It would take too long to present a detailed description of the distribution of all the centric species, but an example should be given:

Papaver radicatum (Fig. 9) is one of the species, which is considered as a survivor in Scandinavia. No other Icelandic plant seems to be so closely connected to the probable refugia and nunataks as *P. radicatum*. Although the Icelandic material of *P. radicatum* has been divided into some subspecies and varieties, it will be treated here as a single species only.

FIG. 9. *Papaver radicatum.*

The chief center of the species is the Vestfirdir and Breidifjördur districts together with their closest vicinities. Over the whole of the Vestfirdir district, *P. radicatum* is very common in the lowlands. On the other hand, the species is not found at higher altitudes on the slopes and mountains of that district. Outside the Vestfirdir district the species grows almost exclusively in the mountains, with the exception of the peninsula Vatnsnes where its habitats are similar to those of the Vestfirdir district.

In the Vestfirdir and Breidifjördur districts the distribution of *P. radicatum* is almost continuous, but outside this center its spread is broken and the species is found only in isolated mountains and mountain ranges, as far as we know, both in north and west Iceland. In the Austfirdir district, on the other hand, the distribution is more continuous, although there seems to be a gap in the central part of the district. Hardly any other Icelandic species shows such distinct affinity to the possible refugium areas, since it is more or less common in all the refugia except one, and outside of them it grows only in such mountain ranges where there possibly have been ice-free peaks during the glaciation of the Ice Age. In other localities in the country *P. radicatum* is not found.

As mentioned before, there are six districts in the country where species with centric distribution are concentrated. Outside these districts no such tendencies are found, except for some anthropochorous plants, which have obviously been introduced a comparatively short time ago. Below I will give a short survey of the districts in question and the species with a central distribution occurring in each of them.

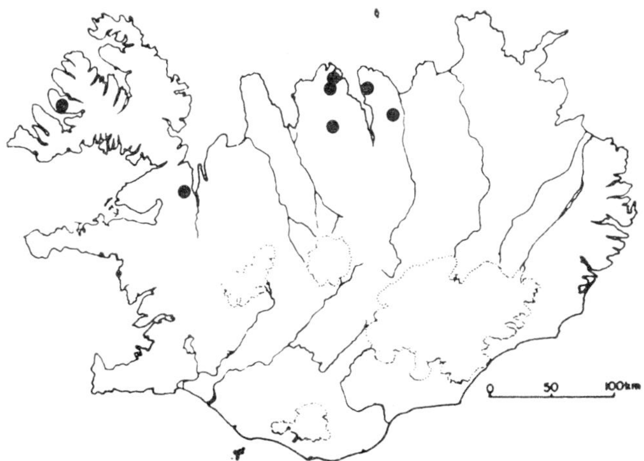

FIG. 10. *Botrychium boreale.*

1. *The Eyjafjördur district* is situated between the fjords Skagafjördur towards the west and Skjálfandiflói and the valley Bárdardalur towards the east.

As mentioned before, 8 species of the West Arctic and North Atlantic groups have distinct centers in the district, either only there or in some other centers as well, i.e. being bi- or tricentric. Besides these, 33 species have a fairly similar distribution, i.e. they have their central area in the Eyjafjördur district, although most of them are also found in other possible refugia.

I have divided these species into two groups, alpine plants and lowland plants, according to whether their main distribution is above or below the 200 m line above sea level.

The alpine group contains 18 species. Only 3 of them can be characterized as unicentric in the Eyjafjördur district, i.e. *Carex glacialis, Diapensia lapponica,* and *Saxifraga foliolosa,* but all of them occur in isolated localities at nunatak areas outside the district. *C. glacialis* has a fairly wide distribution east of the Eyjafjördur district, in almost continuous connection with it.

Six species of the group are distinctly bicentric, *Antennaria alpina, Botrychium boreale* (Fig. 10), and *Luzula sudetica* have their centers in the Eyjafjördur and Vestfirdir districts, but *Antennaria* may also have a center north of Vatnajökull. *Draba alpina*, *Erigeron eriocephalus*, and *Phyllodoce coerulea* (Fig. 11) are bicentric in the Eyjafjördur and Austfirdir districts.

Five species are tri-centric in the Eyjafjördur, Austfirdir and Vestfirdir districts: *Botrychium lanceolatum*, *Draba nivalis*, *Erigeron uniflorus*, *Phippsia algida*, and *Ranunculus glacialis*, but all of them except *Botrychium* also occur in nunatak areas. *Ranunculus glacialis* does not have such a distinct centric distribution as most of the centric species.

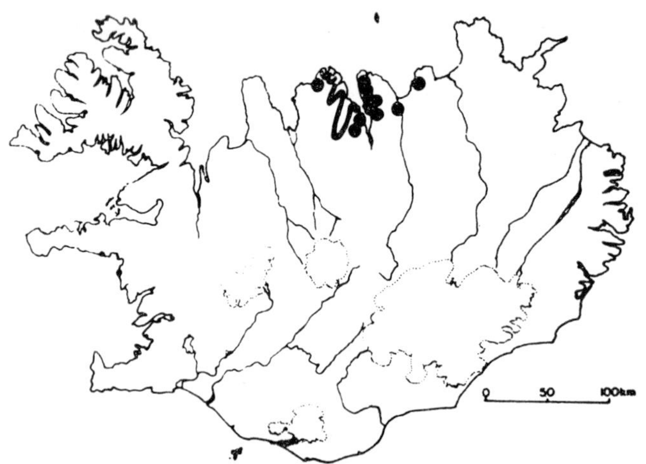

FIG. 11. *Phyllodoce coerulea.*

Finally, there are 4 polycentric species: *Cardamine bellidifolia*, *Minuartia biflora*, *Saxifraga cernua* and *Ranunculus pygmaeus*. The first 2 occur in all the possible refugia except Mýrdalur and Hvalfjördur, but the last 2 are missing in Mýrdalur and Breidifjördur. All of them occur in nunatak areas.

All the species of this group are considered either genuine or at least probable survivors in Scandinavia, and some of them in North America and Greenland as well.

The lowland group contains 15 species. Three are unicentric, i.e. *Agropyron trachycaulum* (*Roegneria borealis* var. *islandica*), *Carex flava* (Fig. 12), and *Crepis paludosa* (Fig. 13). Four species are bicentric: *Agropyron* (*Roegneria*) *caninum*, *Carex livida* (Fig. 12), *Primula stricta* (Fig. 14), and *Viola epipsila* (Fig. 15) have a second center in the Austfirdir district, but *Carex livida* seems to have a third center in the nunatak area of the Snæfellsnes. *Potentilla Egedii* occurs also in the Hvalfjördur district. None of these species except *Carex livida* occurs in nunatak areas.

Carex brunnescens and *Carex subspathacea* are tricentric; *Carex rupestris*, *Gentiana detonsa*, *Oxycoccus microcarpus*, *Pyrola rotundifolia*, and *Pyrola secunda* are polycentric. The only species of this group that are found in the Mýrdalur district are *P. secunda* and *Oxycoccus*.

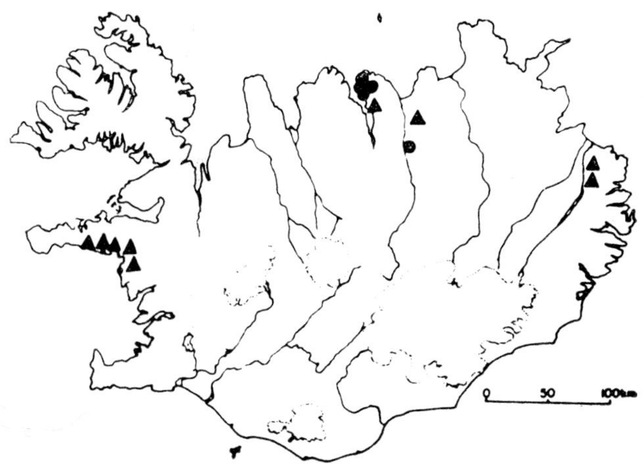

FIG. 12. *Carex flava* (dots), *Carex livida* (triangles).

FIG. 13. *Crepis paludosa*.

Since the latest edition of Flóra Íslands appeared (Stefánsson 1948), 3 species new to the flora of Iceland have been established in the Eyjafjördur district, i.e. *Asplenium septentrionale*, *Primula egaliksensis* (Fig. 14), formerly classified as a variety of *P. stricta*, and *Roegneria doniana* var. *Stefanssonii*, formerly classified as *Agropyron trachycaulum*. At least the last 2 are probable overwinterers.

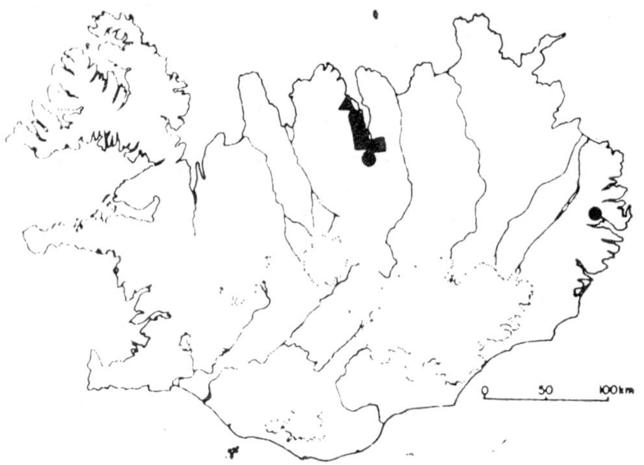

FIG. 14. *Primula stricta* (dots and squares), *Primula egaliksensis* (triangle).

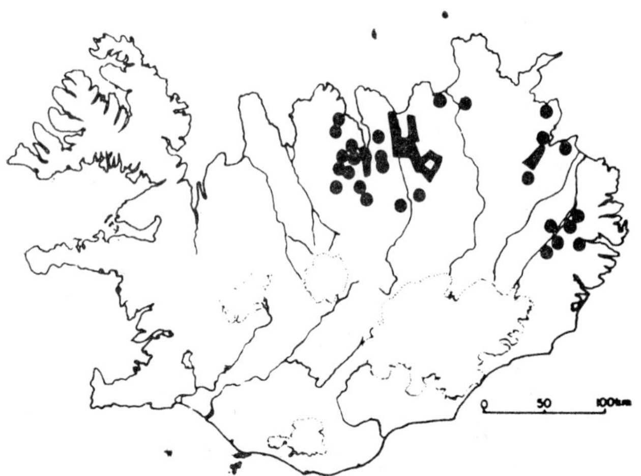

FIG. 15. *Viola epipsila.*

2. *The Vestfirdir district* is the Vestfirdir Peninsula, and in close connection with it are the mountains at the head of the fjord Breidifjördur, which I have called the Breidifjördur district.

Of the West Arctic group, *Stellaria calycantha* is the only species which has its chief distribution in the Vestfirdir, and of the centric species of the group only *Pedicularis flammea* occurs there.

Besides these plants 22 species are found to have their chief distribution in the Vestfirdir district. In contrast to the Eyjafjördur district all the centric species are lowland plants.

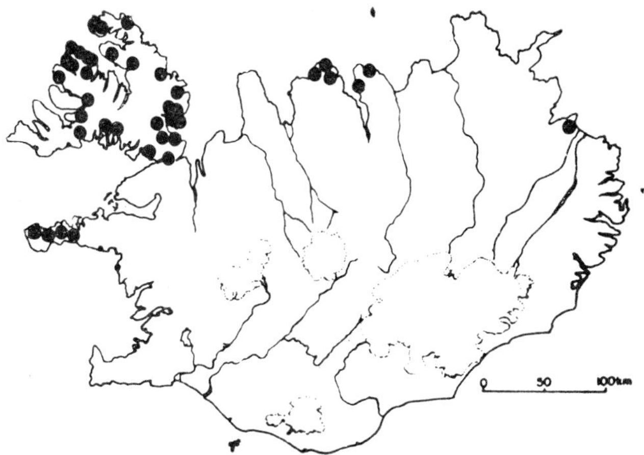

FIG. 16. *Cornus suecica.*

FIG. 17. *Juncus castaneus* (dots), *Juncus squarrosus* (triangles).

Carex adelostoma and *Cryptogramma crispa* are unicentric. *Cornus suecica* (Fig. 16), *Juncus castaneus* (Fig. 17), *Juncus squarrosus* (Fig. 17), *Equisetum silvaticum*, and *Melampyrum silvaticum* are bicentric. The second center of these species is the Austfirdir district, except in the case of *Cornus* which has its second center in the Eyjafjördur district, but is also found in a nunatak area closely connected with the Austfirdir district. All the other species are polycentric.

Admittedly, only half of the centric species of the Vestfirdir district are considered as overwinterers in other countries. But the similarity between their distribution and that of other centric species can hardly be explained if overwintering were not the case.

As an example of such species I will take *Melampyrum silvaticum* (Fig. 18). Its main center is in the Vestfirdir district where the localities are concentrated in three separate groups in the fjords: Thorskafjördur, Ísafjördur, and Steingrímsfjördur-Bjarnarfjördur. Although the distance between

FIG. 18. *Melampyrum silvaticum.*

these areas is not very great, it is not likely that the plants have been distributed from the same center. It is more probable that they have survived in small refugia and have not spread beyond their immediate vicinity, which has also been the case with many of the species that have their centers in the refugial districts. It is difficult to believe in Post-glacial migration of this species into these remote places where the climate is rather rough and cold, as long as the plant has not yet established itself in the forests in other parts of the country. Outside Vestfirdir the species occurs at only one locality, Fáskrúdsfjördur in the Austfirdir district. As already mentioned, the distribution of *M. silvaticum* indicates distinctly that the species is an overwinterer. And if that is so, and this is a species rather sensitive to cold and also a forest plant which has been able to survive in refugia throughout the last Glacial period, the possibilities are undeniably great for the survival of a great part of the Icelandic flora in such refugia.

3. *The Austfirdir district* comprises the true Austfirdir and the mountain range behind the fjords from the Héradsflói in the north and southwards to Hornafjördur. In close connection to the main district is the Austur-Skaftafellssýsla as a whole.

The great majority of the West Atlantic group is found here, and *Cerastium Edmondstonii* has its chief center here. All the North Atlantic plants occur here too, and two of them, *Alchemilla faeroensis* and *Saxifraga Aizoon*, have their main centers here. Plant-geographically speaking, there is an obvious relationship between the Austfirdir and the Eyjafjördur districts. None of the central species is a real alpine plant.

In this district, 6 species are monocentric, i.e. *Asplenium viride, Lycopodium clavatum, Oxalis acetosella, Saxifraga aizoides* (Fig. 19), *Saxifraga cotyledon*, and *Vaccinium vitis-idaea*, and none of them is found outside the district

FIG. 19. *Saxifraga aizoides*.

except *Vaccinium vitis idaea* which occurs in the nunatak area in north-eastern Iceland, where *Roegneria doniana* var. *Stefanssonii* is also found. Last year, *Asplenium trichomanes* was found in the Öræfi district, and it may possibly also be an overwinterer.

Four species are bicentric: *Ranunculus auricomus, Trientalis europaea, Carex pulicaris*, and *Populus tremula*, and finally there are 2 tricentric, or perhaps rather polycentric, species: *Campanula rotundifolia* and *Carex pilulifera*.

4. *The Mýrdalur and Hvalfjördur districts* have few distinctly centric species, and none of them will be dealt with specifically here. On the whole, the Mýrdalur district may be considered a dubious refugium area.

There still remain 15 species which either occur in these 2 last mentioned districts or are found in all the six possible refugial districts, but not outside of them except in nunatak areas.

In the foregoing, six districts have been pointed out as probable refugia for biota during the Ice Age. In them some 100 species occur, the modern distribution of which is almost exclusively limited to inside the districts mentioned, or outside of them only in such places where the landscape indicates nunataks during the glaciation.

Postglacial immigration of these plants does not seem probable, as in that case they might have taken root just as easily in other parts of the country which they do not. The same would hold true for all other sections of Iceland. If we put it the other way around, i.e. that ice-free areas existed at least during the last glaciation, the concentration of centric species in special limited areas is quite natural. As far as our present knowledge reaches, no more probable explanation of that phenomenon can be put forth, especially since a great majority of the centric species in Iceland are exactly the same as established survivors of the Ice Age in other northern countries.

REFERENCES

GELTING, P. (1934). Studies on the vascular plants of east Greenland between Franz Josephs Fjord and Dove bay. *Medd. om Grönl.* **101** (2), 1–340.

LINDROTH, C. H. (1931). Die Insektenfauna Islands und ihre Probleme. *Zool. Bidrag fr. Uppsala* **13**, 105–599.

LÖVE, Á. and LÖVE, D. (1956). Cytotaxonomical conspectus of the Icelandic Flora. *Acta Horti Gotoburg.* **20**, 65–291.

NORDHAGEN, R. (1935). Om *Arenaria humifusa* og dens betydning for utforskningen av Skandinavias eldste floraelement. *Berg. Mus. Årbock 1935, Naturv. rekke* **1**, 1–183.

STEFÁNSSON, S. (1948). *Flóra Íslands*, 3. útg. (Steindór Steindórsson ed.) Akureyri.

STEINDÓRSSON, S. (1937). Jurtagródurinn og jökultíminn. *Náttúrufr.* **7**, 93–100.

STEINDÓRSSON, S. (1949). Flórunýjungar 1948. *Náttúrufr.* **19**, 110–121.

STEINDÓRSSON, S. (1962). On the age and immigration of the Icelandic flora. *Soc. Scient. Isl.* **35**, 1–157.

THÓRARINSSON, S. (1937). Vatnajökull. Scientific results of the Swedish–Icelandic investigations 1936–1937, Chapter II. The main geological and topographical features of Iceland. *Geogr. Ann. 1937*, 161–175.

SOME COMMENTS ON THE "ICE-FREE REFUGIA" OF NORTHWESTERN SCANDINAVIA

GUNNAR HOPPE

Department of Geography, University of Stockholm, Stockholm, Sweden

PECULIARITIES in the distribution of plants and animals in northwestern Scandinavia and the occurrence of endemic species in that region have induced many biologists to postulate the existence of ice-free areas during the last (Würm) glaciation. Two main refugia have been localized tentatively, one consisting of coastal areas in northern Norway, including the Lofoten and Vesterålen Islands, the other situated in western Norway and composed of the Stad-Sunmöre area and the districts at the mouths of Sognefjord and Stavangerfjord. The "unglaciated" areas are said to be of two kinds: small nunataks rising above the inland ice and larger foreland areas situated above as well as below the present shoreline.

In order to prove the existence of refugia, other arguments than biological ones have been used. Areas characterized by glacial cirques, such as the Lofoten Islands, have obviously been sculptured by glaciers, but the preservation of these landforms is interpreted as evidence that there was no continuous inland ice overriding them; if so it should have smoothed out the cirque topography. Pinnacle-like mountain peaks have been regarded as former nunataks. Mountain-top detritus ("Felsenmeer") and the deep weathering of rocks, both supposed to require a very long time to develop, have been considered as other indications of non-glaciation. Furthermore, the continental slope is said to be the definite limit of an inland ice with its fringe of ice shelves; as this slope is not very far from the present shoreline—outside of Vesterålen only about 10 km—and the inland ice surface probably did not slope steeply, conditions suitable for the existence of nunataks should have been present. Finally, the absence of erratics and glacial striae supported the idea of unglaciated areas.

However, among other groups of scientists, especially geologists and physical geographers, there was strong opposition to the refugium theory. Some of the arguments for this hypothesis, for instance certain deep-weathered profiles, were rejected. Observations of glacial striae and erratics made in "refugium areas" were said to disprove the hypothesis in those areas.

The positions for and against the refugium hypothesis were taken up several decades ago, and the main arguments were presented at the same time.

The discussion, however, has continued and to a certain extent has also been affected by the progress in different scientific fields connected with the actual problem, by the development of new techniques, by parallels with other areas, etc. The present paper should be regarded primarily as an attempt to apply experience from other fields and areas to the refugium problem.

SOME EVIDENCE FROM ANTARCTICA

During the last 15 years a large number of expeditions visited Antarctica and have added immensely to our knowledge of that continent. Many of the results are pertinent to the problem under consideration, and reference should be made to some of them. Naturally this discussion will not solve anything, but it may give some ideas as to the nature of the inland ice of northern Europe, and of what is possible and what is impossible. I might first mention that the size of the ice sheet of northern Europe is open to debate, but it ought to have been between 35 and 50 per cent as large as that in Antarctica.

Seismic, gravity and altimetry measurements have given much information about the thickness of the Antarctic ice sheet. In East Antarctica a value of more than 3000 m was found in a vast area around the U.S.S.R. bases Vostok I and Komsomol'skaya (Shumskiy, 1959). The bedrock topography is totally hidden; the thickness of the ice, however, may be as little as 1000 m in places. For the smaller region of West Antarctica a mean ice thickness of 1500 to 2000 m has been suggested. The greatest thickness, 4270 m, was measured in a place where the bedrock surface lies 2500 m below present sea level. This depth is in a 400 km wide sub-ice channel, which probably bisects West Antarctica. Even if the ice should melt and the rock surface rebound to isostatic equilibrium, the deepest part of the channel would still be as much as 1500 m below present sea level. It has been suggested that the West Antarctic ice sheet originated as two separate ice sheets in two separate mountainous areas. As these sheets expanded they converged over the intervening open water; they were probably joined at first by a floating ice shelf, which then grew thick enough to fill the trough completely and produce the present single ice sheet which is aground (Bentley and Ostenso, 1961, p. 895). The minimum time required to build up such a thickness has been computed by Wexler (1961) on the basis of a series of assumptions. Thereby one alternative gives about 20,000 years, another about 40,000 years. Quite recently new calculations of the mean thickness of the Antarctic and other ice sheets have been undertaken (cf. Donn, Farrand and Ewing, 1962). The values obtained for Antarctica vary between 2000 m and 2500 m. On the basis of such data and the statement by Nye (1959) that the thickness of an ice sheet at equilibrium is essentially a function of the areal dimensions of the sheet rather than the accumulation, Donn, Farrand and Ewing have calculated a mean thickness of 1700 to 1800 m for the Scandinavian ice sheet during the Würm maximum.

The lowering of sea level at the same time is computed as being between 105 and 123 m.

Another result of the measurements in Antarctica is an increased knowledge of the subglacial relief. In several places the ice sheet covers alpine landscapes with valleys of the fjord type as well as well-defined peaks (Fig. 1). Such observations demonstrate the impossibility of recognizing a real "nunatak topography". Furthermore Robin (1958, p. 130) found in the "mountain ice sheet area" of Queen Maud Land that "in the case of larger features, such as the valleys at 180, 310 and 410 km (Fig. 1) from Maudheim, the rock relief controls the direction of ice flow, so that the greatest velocities of movement will be along the line of such valleys. The erosion resulting from the flow of the glacier will therefore tend to accentuate the underlying relief."

The slope of the ice surface varies considerably. For instance, a number of outlet glaciers leading to the Ross Ice Shelf have slopes between 1:90 and 1:25 (Kosack, 1955, p. 86), whereas Robin (1958, p. 109) has listed inclinations between 0 and 1:16. For a part of the "mountain ice sheet area" Robin's thorough investigation has confirmed Nye's general hypothesis that the thinnest ice cover is indicated by the steepest surface slope.

In many cases ice shelves exist over considerable depths of water. In front of the Ross Ice Shelf systematic soundings have demonstrated that depths of 500 to 700 m are normal (according to U.S. Navy Hydr. Office, 6636, 1957), while the Filchner Ice Shelf seems to extend over depths of more than 1000 m (Thiel and Ostenso, 1961, p. 828). The considerable depths under the inland ice—referred to above—emphasize that sea depths greater than those of a normal shelf do not form a definite limit for expanding ice sheets. "Whether or not the ice would extend further out to sea would depend largely on the heat supply and circulation of the sea water" (Robin 1958, p. 132).

According to Bauer (1955) 0.6×10^6 km^2, or about 4 per cent of the Antarctic continent is ice-free. Nunataks are common features, especially in the marginal zones. At the edge of the continent ice-free lowlands appear, forming re-entrants in the ice sheet. Such so-called "oases" are known from almost all parts of the coastal region of Antarctica. The largest one, Bunger's "oasis" (Fig. 2), has been described in several Russian reports (for instance: Avsyuk, Markov and Shumskiy, 1956a, 1956b). It has an area of about 600 km^2 and is surrounded by ice, which consists in part, however, of shelf ice and old pack ice. Roches moutonnées, striae, erratics, and till demonstrate that the "oasis" once was glaciated, but it seems to have been ice-free for at least 4500 years (*loc. cit.* p. 15; cf. Rozycki, 1961); it now seems to be quite stable. The deglaciation of this "oasis" as well as of others (cf. Bull, McKelvey and Webb, 1962) is believed to be the result of starvation, caused by a decrease in the surface level of the ice sheet in connection with an increasing influence of rock thresholds. A quite unique climate is formed in the "oasis". Precipitation is rather heavy, probably 600–700 mm a year, only in the solid state. In

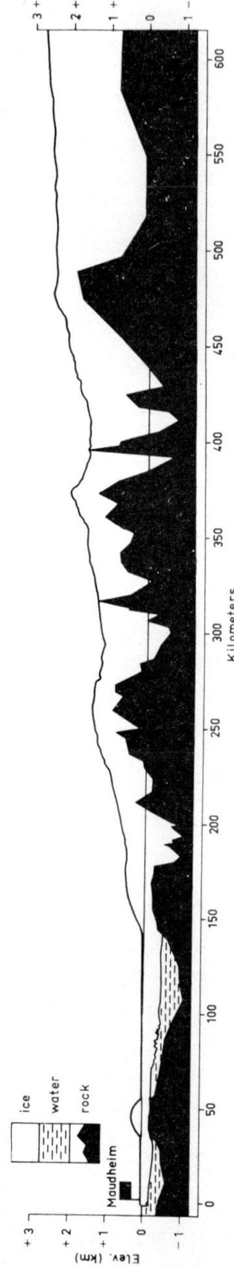

FIG. 1. Seismic profile, Queen Maud Land, Antarctica (after Robin, 1958)

spite of this high value the snow cover, which is very unevenly distributed, quickly disappears during the short warm season, when temperatures of 25 to 30°C were measured on rock surfaces. Evaporation is more important than melting because of the dryness of the air. A normal value for the relative

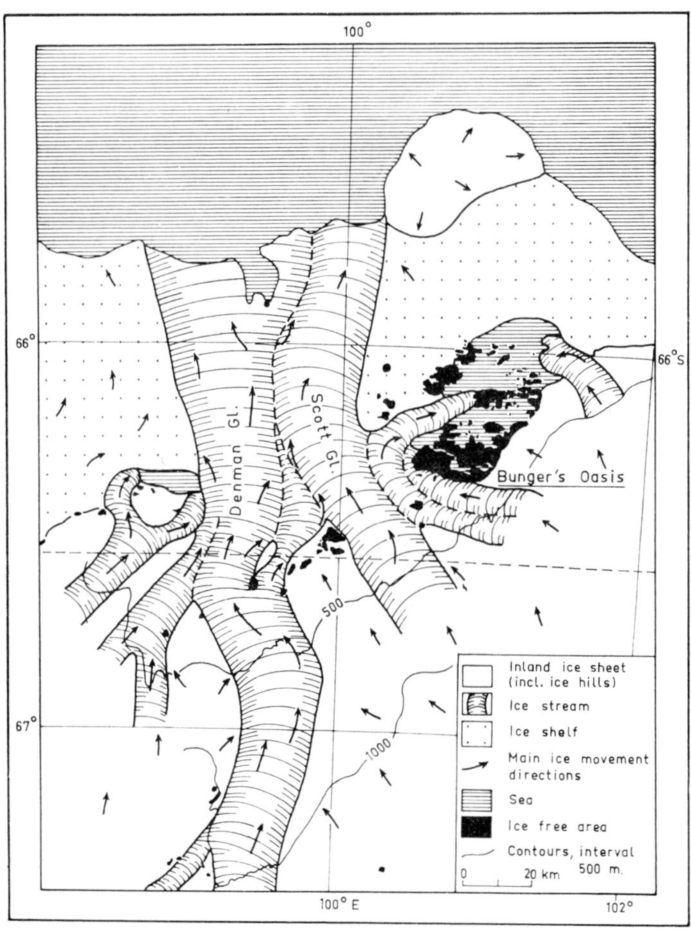

FIG. 2. Bunger's Oasis, East Antarctica (after Dolgushin, 1958).

humidity seems to be only 25 per cent. The flora of Bunger's "oasis" is very meagre (Gollerbach and Syrojeckowskij, 1958), and probably the extreme dryness of the climate is one of the main reasons for this. However, lichens and algae are found everywhere, and mosses appear in wetter places. The dark colours of the plants are very characteristic, making possible a strong absorption of solar radiation.

MAIN FEATURES OF THE WÜRM GLACIATION IN NORTHERN EUROPE

The Würm glaciation seems to have begun about 70,000 years ago. As a result of investigations of several *Globigerina*-ooze cores from the Caribbean Sea and the Atlantic Ocean, a temperature minimum of the early Würm (Wisconsin) was dated at about 60,000 years ago, while the temperature maximum of the last interglacial occurred 95,000 years ago (Rosholt, 1961).

The Scandinavian ice sheet began as a glacierization in the highest parts of the mountain chain, the Scandes. Cirque and valley glaciers first coalesced to form transection glaciers in the mountains and piedmont glaciers in the forelands; further enlargement led to the development of glacier caps. Finally the ice caps from different mountainous areas coalesced into a continuously expanding inland ice sheet. This development was followed by continuing movements of the ice divides; in northern Scandinavia, for instance, an ice divide was situated for a long, though undetermined, time far to the east of the Scandes.

Penck's classical scheme considered the Würm to represent a single climatic cycle (1922). This idea has been supported more recently by Büdel (1960), Graul (1952), Weidenbach (1953) and Fink (1961), among others. (The discussion about the Late Pleistocene climate of Europe has been summarized in an excellent way by Wright (1961).) A different scheme of subdivision of the Würm was developed by Soergel (1919), based on loess stratigraphy; it presumes a bi- or tripartition. Interstadials have been suggested, one more marked 44,000 to 28,000 years ago ("Göttweig") and another representing a minor warm oscillation 25,000 years ago ("Paudorf") by Gross (1958), Woldstedt (1958), and others; however, "the recognition of a major early Würm interstadial should be considered tentative" (Wright, 1961, p. 965). Recently the idea of an interstadial has received support from a series of C^{14} datings on a marine clay between beds of gravel and sand in the neighbourhood of Gothenburg, southwestern Sweden, i.e. well within the area covered by the last Scandinavian ice sheet. The result of the datings is 26,000 to 30,000 years (Brotzen, 1961). Radiocarbon datings of shells, which occur on raised beaches at 44–47 m but which are believed to originate in the underlying till in Nordaustlandet, Spitsbergen, have given an age of 35,000 to 40,000 years. Since risks for contamination exist, however, this must be regarded as a minimum value. "Thus the ice-free period was in all probability pre-40,000 years ago" (Blake, 1961) and it cannot yet be placed in the Pleistocene timetable. It is obvious that the duration and possible division of the Würm period must have had a great influence on the extension and thickness of the ice sheet in northern Europe.

Numerous scientists have tried to evaluate the climatological situation in Europe during the Würm "Pleni-Glacial" on the basis of the depression of the snow-line and the distribution of plants, animals, and frost features (Büdel,

1951; Gross, 1958; Klein, 1953; Klute, 1951; Manley, 1951; Mortensen, 1952; Penck, 1938; Poser, 1948; Woldstedt, 1958; etc.). For central Europe a reduction of 10 to 13°C in the mean annual temperature is commonly accepted; for western Europe a somewhat smaller temperature decrease is thought to have occurred. From a biological viewpoint, however, information about the *summer* temperature ought to be of even greater interest. The arctic tree line which approximately coincides with the July 10°C isotherm, seems to have run south of the Pyrenees in western Europe (Büdel, 1951; Frenzel and Troll, 1952); for the coldest part of the Würm, Gross (1958) has calculated a temperature of about 5°C in middle Germany. i.e. about 14°C lower than now. Naturally such temperature calculations are very rough; but at least they justify the hypothesis that the temperature must have been very low on the northwestern side of the Scandinavian ice sheet, much too low to make forest vegetation possible on ice-free areas, if such existed.

The meteorological situation also has been treated in connection with the climatological considerations. One such discussion may be mentioned, owing to the importance of the problems involved and the special competence of the author. On the basis of his meteorological studies in Antarctica, Liljequist (1956) deals with the effect of the growing Scandinavian ice sheet. According to him an accentuated temperature contrast between snow- and ice-covered areas and bare ground should have developed. As the ice sheet grew this frontal zone—and the cyclonic tracks corresponding to this zone—moved southward. During the maximum of the glacial epoch the main cyclonic tracks thus ought to have come from west–northwest or west, passing middle Europe on their way to the eastern part of the Mediterranean region and southern Russia (Fig. 3). This atmospheric circulation ought also to have influenced the sea-currents according to Liljequist. South of the main cyclonic tracks westerly and southwesterly winds dominated, whereas to the north, easterly winds prevailed. This should have caused the warm North Atlantic Drift to bend toward the Bay of Biscay and Spain, while a cold current probably went to the west between Iceland and the British Isles.

The regressive stage of the Würm glaciation at first was characterized by lability, by fluctuations in the climatic trend. The Younger Dryas was a rather cold period, when the ice border according to general opinion made long stillstands at the Salpausselkä (Finland)—Middle Swedish moraines—Raerne (Norway). During that time the July temperature in Denmark went down again to about 10°C (Iversen, 1954); in the Netherlands cryoturbation in the earlier deposited Alleröd layers has been demonstrated to have occurred and the existence of permafrost during Younger Dryas seems thereby to have been proved (van der Hammen and Maarleveld, 1952). The last ice remnants, still active glaciers, receded to the highest mountain regions, such as the Sarek area in northern Sweden (Hoppe, 1960), and disappeared 7000 to 8000 years ago.

THE POSTULATED REFUGIUM AREAS

For the following discussion it seems convenient to deal with three different cases: (1) nunataks, (2) foreland refugia in western Norway, and (3) foreland refugia in northern Norway.

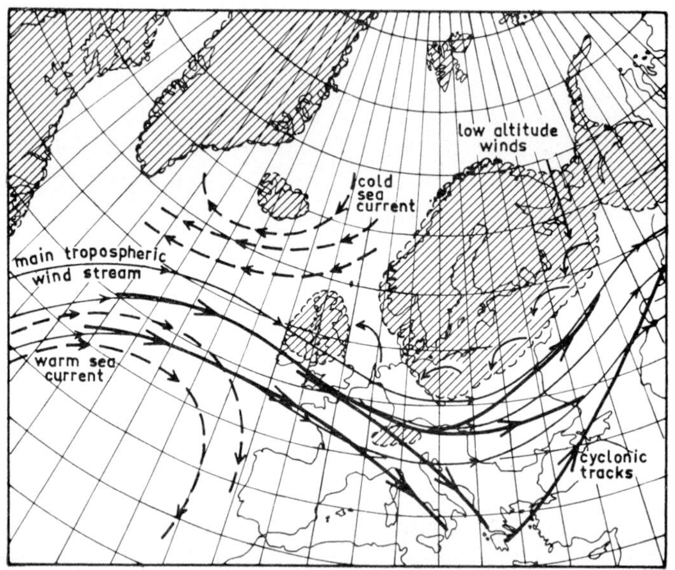

FIG. 3. Probable circulation pattern in atmosphere and sea during the last glaciation, acc. to Liljequist (1956).

1. *Nunatak refugia.* It must be admitted that the chance that nunataks rose above the Scandinavian ice sheet is rather great. This conclusion is based on the topography of the Scandes in their western part, where the ice sheet probably was not very thick, and on the occurrence of nunataks near the coasts of Greenland and Antarctica.

On the other hand we do not have yet, as far as I can see, any means by which we are able to identify former nunataks. So-called "nunatak topography" can be preserved or even created under an ice-sheet surface (cf. above). Nor does a topography characterized by well-developed glacial cirques guarantee any ice-free areas between them, resp. lack of inland ice glaciation. In Sweden, on the eastern side of the mountain chain, for instance, there are many well developed cirques, as low in altitude as 800 to 1000 m in areas that unquestionably have been covered by the last inland ice sheet.

Dahl (1955 and 1961) has argued that the occurrence of mountain top detritus ("Felsenmeer") should be a proof of a nunatak. He also gives a map of the northwestern part of southern Norway (Dahl, 1961, p. 89), demonstrating that the lower limit of such detritus—a limit not necessarily representing the ice surface of Würm time but rather that of the maximum Pleistocene glaciation (*loc. cit.*, p. 92)—is only hundreds of meters above present sea level in the coastal areas, whereas it reaches values of 1700 to 1900 m in the southwestern part of the investigated region. This hypothesis of Dahl's does not agree with the distribution pattern of mountain top detritus in Sweden. For instance, in the southern part of the Scandes at about the same latitude and at altitudes between 900 to 1200 m, many of the peaks have well developed boulder fields of autochtonous character. From the province of Dalarna, Lundqvist (1951, p. 81, etc.) mentions Slugufjället, Nipfjället, Städjan, Drevfjället, Fulufjället and Getsjöhöa. An early reference to these boulder fields on mountain tops was made by Samuelsson (1914). Glacial and glaciofluvial features of different kinds demonstrate also that the peaks must have been covered by the last inland ice sheet at a very late stage.

From more northern parts of the Swedish mountains, Rapp and Rudberg (1960) have assembled some data on the lower limit of the boulder field zone: southern Jämtland, 1500–1600 m, Västerbotten, 1100–1200 m, the amphibolite mountains at Abisko, 1000–1200 m. These figures refer to areas where covering by the ice sheet is indisputable. In addition, in Finnish Lapland low-lying mountain top detritus has been observed, for instance, on Levitunturi (about 20 km. north of Kittilä) 531 m above sea level (V. Okko, pers. comm. 1961).

The formation of mountain top detritus certainly is a complicated process with many variables, such as the properties of the bedrock, its condition before glacierization, the velocity and eroding capacity of the ice sheet in different situations, the conditions of deglaciation, postglacial climate, etc. I think that something similar can be said about the more fine-grained weathering material, including the clay minerals from mountain tops which have also been used by Dahl as a proof of nunatak situations. Here as elsewhere, however, Dahl stimulated the debate in an effective way.

Initially it was stated that nunataks very probably existed during Würm time. Finally it should be added that plants and animals, if any survived, must have lived under extremely harsh conditions.

2. *Foreland refugia in western Norway.* The presence of glacial striae and erratics in many places in areas postulated as foreland refugia has been taken as evidence of glacierization by the opponents of this concept. The proponents of the refugium hypothesis reply, however, that such evidence may remain from a previous glacial stage, but this is energetically denied by the opponents.

The successive destruction of striated surfaces can be followed everywhere in Sweden and plotted against a quite detailed time scale. In many areas it is absolutely impossible to find any striae on bedrock surfaces which have been exposed only a few thousand years (e.g. since the emergence of the land above the surface of the sea); this seems to be especially true in coarse-grained rocks. In other areas, however, quite well preserved striae appear, even after 10,000 years. Striae may also be preserved for long periods of time on outcrops of quite soft rocks, particularly where these rocks are fine-grained and the surfaces are well polished by the ice. Such observations, however, do not change my opinion that glacial striae on exposed rock surfaces cannot have survived since the Riss Glaciation (possibly with extremely rare exceptions). However, the discussion would be easier if the weathering of rock surfaces—including the destruction of striae—could be illustrated by quantitative data.

Andersen (1954, 1960) has investigated the end moraines of southwestern Norway. Outside the Ra moraines, 10,300 to 10,800 years old, are three sets of end moraines. These are partly below sea level, and they have been tentatively dated as being 12,500 to 14,000 years old by Andersen. His very cautiously expressed conclusion is that the front of the inland ice sheet during earlier stages of the Last Glaciation was far outside the present coastline. This conclusion fits well with the idea expressed at different times (Hoppe 1959) that the Scandinavian and British ice sheets were connected during Würm time, as well as during earlier glaciations. Recently Valentin (1957) has advocated this connection on the basis of studies of the morphology of eastern England and the bottom topography of the North Sea (Fig. 4). This interpretation is also supported by the pattern of glacial striae in the Shetland Islands, presented more than 80 years ago by Peach and Horne (1879) which clearly demonstrates an ice sheet moving westward, whose front retreated to the east (Fig. 5). If the two ice sheets coalesced, it is most unlikely that ice-free foreland refugia existed in western Norway; therefore the Shetland Islands may play a decisive role in the refugium discussion, and thorough investigations there must be considered very desirable.

3. *Foreland refugia in northern Norway.* Thanks to studies of end moraines and strandlines in combination with C^{14} datings the glacial history of northern Norway has become established on a firmer basis during the last few years. Marthinussen (1960, 1961), Andersen and Feyling-Hanssen (both quoted by Holtedahl, 1960), and Bergström (pers. comm.) have definitely demonstrated the position and age of a well-developed "Ra-line" of end moraines as well as the existence of older end moraines outside. The conclusion of Marthinussen (1960, p. 421) concerning Finnmark, based in part also on the degree of weathering and the occurrence of glacial striae and erratics, is that "there can be no doubt but that the ice sheet of the last glacial period at its maximum has covered all the present land". According to the investigations by Bergström, the Lofoten and Vesterålen Islands have glacial erratics of continental origin (conclusion by T. Vogt, according to Bergström, pers. comm.) on the higher peaks, showing clearly that these islands must have been covered by an

inland ice sheet at least once. Referring to the fact that the erratics are often lying in very unstable positions, Bergström suggests (1959, p. 122) that they were transported and deposited during Würm time. The proximity of the continental slope does not justify any definite conclusion about nunataks. A number of C^{14} datings have been made of samples from this area with the intention of throwing light on this particular problem but in no case a higher age than 9000 years has been obtained.

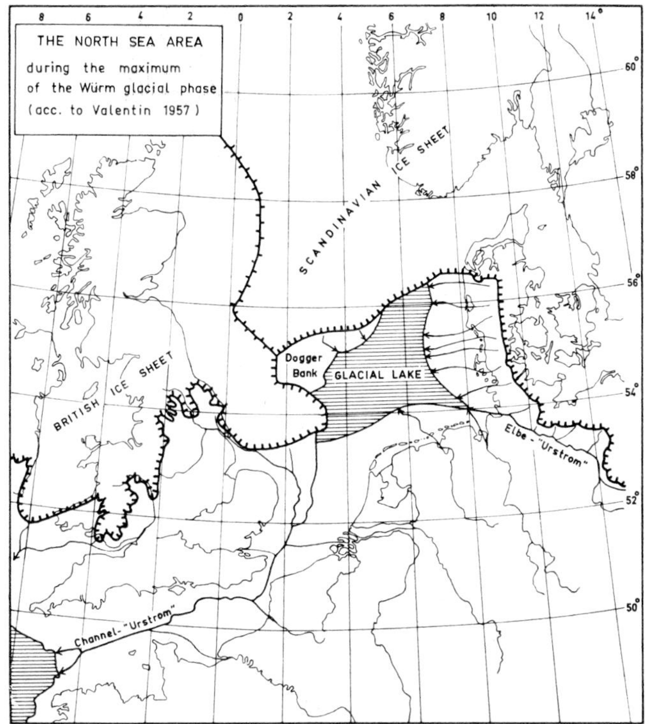

FIG. 4. The North Sea area during the maximum of the Würm glaciation, acc. to Valentin (1957).

At this time we do not know the position of the ice-front north of Scandinavia during the Würm maximum. The Barents Sea is quite shallow, with depths seldom exceeding 400 m and over vast areas much less. An ice sheet could easily have covered this region. It has been proposed in recent papers (Büdel, 1960; Corbel, 1960), that the Scandinavian and Spitsbergen ice sheets joined during Würm time. However, only very weak arguments favoring this hypothesis have been presented as yet. In 1934, Krasnov found boulders at the Shapkina River in northermost Russia which Likharev and Yakovlev suggested were erratics from Spitsbergen or Bear Island on the

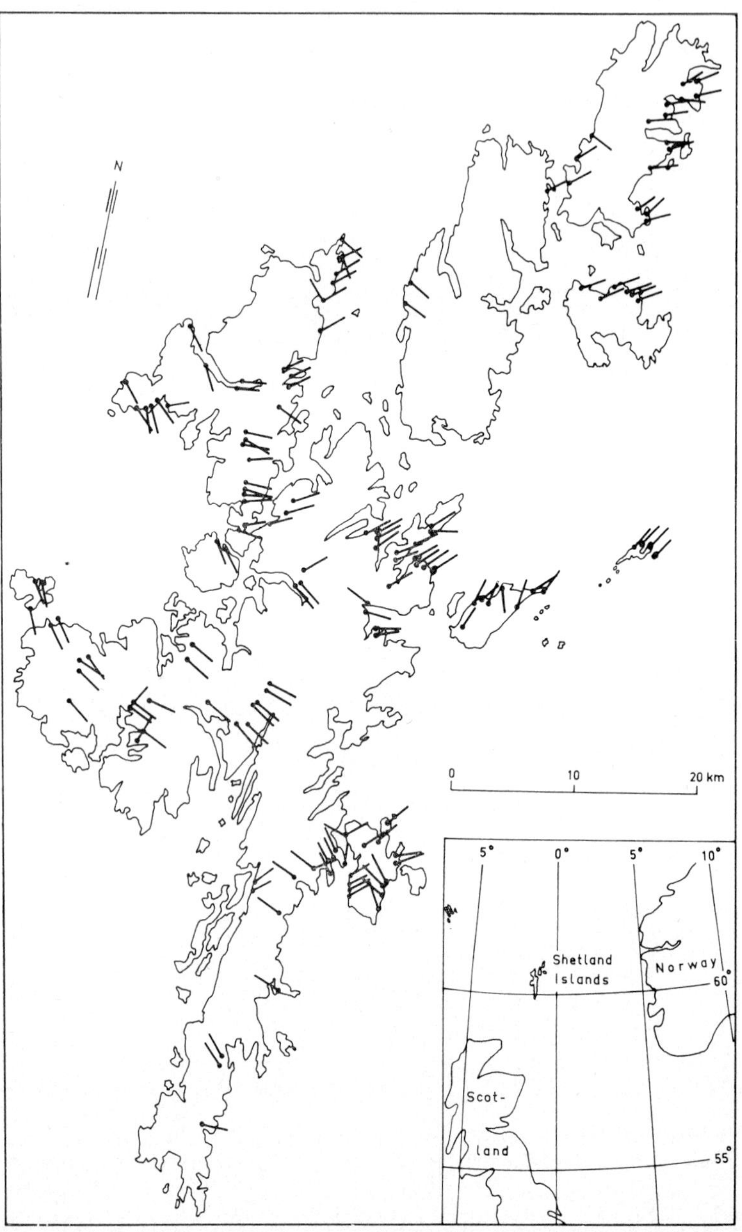

FIG. 5. Glacial striae on the Shetland Islands, acc. to Peach and Horne (1879).

basis of paleontological correlation. They lay in "the middle moraine". (The author is indebted to Dr. L. Serebryanny, Moscow, for the information.)

As long as we are unable to distinguish definitely between real till and glacial marine sediments in samples from the sea bottom, the possibility of solving this problem is relatively small.

CONCLUSIONS

Until now there is no geological or geomorphological proof of any refugium areas in Scandinavia during the Würm glaciation; on the contrary strong arguments can be raised against the existence of each such "refugium". The presence of nunataks, however, cannot be excluded but parts of them must have had a more or less permanent snow cover, and the microclimate must have been very harsh.

One of the strongest arguments for the refugium hypothesis is the existence of plants and animals with a so-called bicentric distribution. There may, however, be other ways of explaining such distributions. Attention may be called to the fact that the supposed refugium areas probably were deglaciated earlier than the rest of northern and western Scandinavia, and thus both flora and fauna have had a longer time to become established.

REFERENCES

ANDERSEN, B. G. (1954). Randmorener i Sørvest-Norge. *Norsk Geogr. Tidsskrift*, **14**, 273–342.

ANDERSEN, B. G. (1960). Sørlandet i sen- og postglacial tid. *Norges Geol. Unders*, **210**, 1–142.

AVSYUK, G. A., MARKOV, K. K. and SHUMSKIY, P. A. (1956a). Kholodnaya pustynya v Antarktide. *Izvestiya Akademii Nauk SSSR, Seriya Geograficheskaya, Moscow*, 1956, **4**, 16–25. (Also translated: "Cold wasteland in the Antarctic continent", The Israel program for scientific translations; "Geographic and oceanographic observations in the Antarctic").

AVSYUK, G. A., MARKOV, K. K. and SHUMSKIY, P. A. (1956b). Geograficheskiye nablyudeniya v antarkticheskom "oazise". *Izvestiya Vsesoyuznogo Geograficheskogo Obshchestva (Moscow)*, **88** (4), 316–350. (Also translated: "Geographical observations in an Antarctic "oasis", The Israel program for scientific translations: "Geographic and oceanographic observations in the Antarctic").

BAUER, A. (1955). Über die in der heutigen Vergletscherung der Erde als Eis gebundene Wassermasse. *Eiszeitalter und Gegenwart* **6**, 60–70.

BENTLEY, C. R. and OSTENSO, N. A. (1961). Glacial and subglacial topography of West Antarctica. *J. Glaciology* **3**, 29. 822–910.

BERGSTRÖM, E. (1959). Utgjorde Lofoten och Vesterålen ett refugium under sista istiden? *Svensk Naturvetenskap*, 1959, 116–22.

BLAKE, W. JR., (1961). Radiocarbon dating of raised beaches in Nordaustlandet, Spitsbergen. *Geology of the Arctic*, 133–45.

BROTZEN, F. (1961). An interstadial (radiocarbon dated) and the substages of the last glaciation in Sweden. *Geol. för. förh.* **83**, 144–50.

BULL, C., MCKELVEY, B. C. and WEBB, P. N. (1962). Quaternary glaciations in southern Victoria Land, Antarctica. *J. Glaciology* **4**, 31, 63–78.

BÜDEL, J. (1951). Die Klimazonen des Eiszeitalters. *Eiszeitalter und Gegenwart*, **1**, 16–21.

BÜDEL, J. (1960). Die Gliederung der Würmkaltzeit. *Würzburger Geogr. Arbeiten*, **8**, 1–45.

CORBEL, J. (1960). Le soulèvement des terres autour de la mer de Barentz. *Revue de Geogr. de Lyon* **35**, 253–74

DAHL, E. (1955). Biogeographic and geologic indications of unglaciatedare as in Scandinavia during the glacial ages. *Bull. Geol. Soc. Amer.* **66**, 1499–1519.

DAHL, E. (1961). Refugieproblemet og de kvartærgeologiske metodene. *Svensk Naturvetenskap*, 1961. 81–96.

DOLGUSHIN, L. D. (1958). Glyaciologicheskie nablyudeniya v Antarktide. (Glaciological observations in Antarctica). *Izvestiya Akademii Nauk SSSR, Seriya Geograficheskaya, Moskow*, 1958, 6, 16–25.

DONN, W. L., FARRAND, W. R. and EWING, M. (1962). Pleistocene ice volumes and sea-level lowering. *J. Geology*, **70**, 206–214.

FINK, J. (1961). Die Gliederung der Würmeiszeit in Österrich im Lichte der Terrassen- und Loessforschungen. *Abstracts of papers, INQUA, VIth Congress*, 152–153.

FRENZEL, B. and TROLL, C. (1952). Die Vegetationszonen des nördlichen Eurasiens während der letzten Eiszeit. *Eiszeitalter und Gegenwart*, **2**, 159–167.

GOLLERBACH, M. M. and SYROJECKOWSKIJ, E. E. (1958). Biogeograficeskie issledovanija v Antarktide 1957 g. (Biogeographical observations in Antarctica, 1957). *Izvestiya Akademii Nauk SSSR, Seriya Geograficheskaya, Moscow*, 1958, 6, 59–68.

GRAUL, H. (1952). Bemerkungen zur Würmstratigraphie im Alpenvorland. *Geol. Bavarica* **14**, 124–131.

GROSS, H. (1958). Die bisherigen Ergebnisse von C^{14} -Messungen und paläontologischen Untersuchungen für die Gliederung und Chronologie des Jungpleistozäns in Mitteleuropa und den Nachbargebieten. *Eiszeitalter und Gegenwart*, **9**, 155–187.

VAN DER HAMMEN, T. and MAARLEVELD, G. C. (1952). Genesis and dating of the periglacial deposits at the eastern fringe of the Veluwe. *Geologie en Mijnbouw*, Nw serie, 2, **14**e Jaargang, 47–54.

HOLTEDAHL, O. (1960). Geology of Norway. *Norges geol. Unders.* **208**, 1–540.

HOPPE, G. (1959). Några kritiska kommentarer till diskussionen om isfria refugier. *Svensk Naturvetenskap*, 1959, 123–134.

HOPPE, G. (1960). Glacial morphology and inland ice recession in northern Sweden. *Geogr. Annaler* **41**, 193–212.

IVERSEN, J. (1954). The late-glacial flora of Denmark and its relation to climate and soil. *Danmarks geol. Unders.*, II Række, **80**, 87–119.

KLEIN, A. (1953). Die Niederschläge in Europa im Maximum der letzten Eiszeit. *Petermanns Geogr. Mitt.* **97**, 98–104.

KLUTE, F. (1951). Das Klima Europas während das Maximums der Weichsel-Würm Eiszeit und die Änderungen bis zur Jetztzeit. *Erdkunde*, **5**, 273–283.

KOSACK, H.-P. (1955). *Die Antarktis*. Heidelburg, 310 p.

LILJEQUIST, G. H. (1956). Meterorologiska synpunkter på istidsproblemet. *Ymer* **76**, 59–74.

LUNDQVIST, G. (1951). Beskrivning till jordartskarta över Kopparbergs län. *Sveriges Geol. Unders.*, Ser. Ca, **21**, 1–213.

MANLEY, G. (1951). The range of variation of the British climate. *Geogr. J.* **117**.

MARTHINUSSEN, M. (1960). Coast and fjord area of Finnmark. In O. Holtedahl: Geology of Norway. *Norges Geol. Unders.* **208**, 416–431.

MARTHINUSSEN, M. (1961). Brerandstadier og avsmeltningsforhold i Repparfjord-Stabbursdal-området, Finnmark. *Norges Geol. Unders.* **213**, 118–169

MORTENSEN, H. (1952). Heutiger Firnrückgang und Eiszeitklima. *Erdkunde* **6**, 145–160

NYE, J. F. (1959). The motion of ice sheets and glaciers. *J. Glaciology* **3**, 26. 493–507

PEACH, B. N. and HORNE, J. (1879). The glaciation of the Shetland Isles. *Quartern. J. Geol. Soc. London* **35**, 778–811.

PENCK, A. (1922). Ablagerungen und Schichtstörungen der letzten Interglazialzeit in den nördlichen Alpen. *Preuss. Akad. Wiss., Phys.-Math. Kl., Sitzungsber*, 214–251.

PENCK, A. (1938). Das Klima der Eiszeit. *Verhandl. d. III. Internat. Quartär-Konferenz, Wien, 1936*, 1, 83–97

POSER, H. (1948). Boden- und Klimaverhältnisse in Mittel- und West- Europa während der Würmeiszeit. *Erdkunde* **2**, 53–68.

RAPP, A. and RUDBERG, S. (1960). Recent periglacial phenomena in Sweden. *Biuletyn Peryglacjalny* **8**, 143–154,

ROBIN, G. DE Q. (1958). Seismic shooting and related investigations. *Norwegian-British-Swedish Antarctic Expedition, 1949–52. Scientific Results*, vol. V, 1–134

ROSHOLT, J. H. (1961). Pleistocene chronology by the Pa^{231}/Th^{230} method—*Abstracts of papers, INQUA, VIth congress*, 180.

ROZYCKI, S. Z. (1961). Changements pleistocènes de l'extension de l'inlandis en Antarctide oriental d'après l'étude des anciennes plages élevées de l'Oasis Bunger, Queen Mary Land.—*Biuletyn Peryglacjalny* **10**, 257–283.

SAMUELSSON, G. (1914). Om Dalafjällen. *Ymer* **34**, 331–345.

SHUMSKIY, P. A. (1959). Is Antarctica a continent or an archipelago? *J. Glaciology* **3**, 26, 455–457.

SOERGEL, W. (1919). *Lösse, Eiszeiten, und paläolithische Kulturen*, Jena, 177 p.

THIEL, E. and OSTENSO, N. A. (1961). The contact of the Ross Ice Shelf with the continental ice sheet, Antarctica. *J. Glaciology* **3**, 29, 823–832

VALENTIN, H. (1957). Glazialmorphologische Untersuchungen in Ostengland. *Ablandl. d. Geogr. Inst. d. freien Univ. Berlin*, 1–86.

WEIDENBACH, F. (1953). Zeitliche Einordnung der jungpleistozänen Ablagerungen Mitteleuropas. *4th Int. Quat. Congr, Actes, Rome.*

WEXLER, H. (1961). Growth and thermal structure of the deep ice in Byrd Land, Antartica. *J. Glaciology* **3**, 30, 1075–1087.

WOLDSTEDT, P. (1958). Das Eiszeitalter.—*Grundlinien einer Geologie des Quartärs, 2: Europa, Vorderasien und Nordafrika im Eiszeitalter*, 1–438.

WRIGHT, H. E. JR. (1961). Late Pleistocene climate of Europe: a review. *Bull. Geol. Soc. Amer.* **72**, 933–982.

FIELD PROBLEMS IN DETERMINING THE MAXIMUM EXTENT OF PLEISTOCENE GLACIATION ALONG THE EASTERN CANADIAN SEABOARD—A GEOGRAPHER'S POINT OF VIEW*

J. D. IVES†

Geographical Branch, Department of Mines and Technical Surveys, Ottawa, Canada

THE main obstacles to evaluation of the maximum extent of glaciation in eastern Canada are simply a combination of vast area, difficulty of access and acute shortage of field investigators. These problems naturally pervade the entire discussion which follows and they cannot be overstressed: however, some of the gaps can be partially filled by reference to work in other sectors of the North Atlantic, particularly in Norway and Iceland. It should be apparent, moreover, that even these much smaller areas have not been studied in great detail and, as members of the symposium will undoubtedly agree, the interpretation of the available field evidence has divided us into two camps —the protagonists, and the antagonists of the nunatak hypothesis.

It is apparent from the literature that much controversy has arisen concerning the significance of certain glacial erratic blocks on high coastal summits. Bergström, Hoppe and others maintain that blocks on the Lofoten Island summits are glacial erratics (Bergström, 1959; Hoppe, 1959) and the tendency is to proceed from this point to the suggestion that all the Lofoten summits must therefore have been inundated at one and the same time, namely, during the final glaciation. Dahl, on the other hand, has enunciated a plea that evidence for the existence of true glacial erratics must include positive proof that the rock in question is foreign geologically to the basement upon which it rests—in other words, the possibility that the rock is an erosion residual must be definitely excluded (Dahl, 1961). Also, absence of proof of glaciation does not warrant the conclusion that glacier ice has not passed across a specific area, nor does positive proof of glaciation determine which particular glaciation was involved. One of the more difficult field problems is to determine the relative age of an erratic. Usually this is impossible and the deduction frequently resorted to is highly subjective. Neither is it

*Published with the permission of the Director, Geographical Branch, Dept. Mines and Technical Surveys, Ottawa.

† Senior Geographer, Geographical Branch, Ottawa Canada.

possible to ascertain whether or not the entire coastal zone was submerged by ice at one and the same time. An extension of this discussion can be found in the literature and it cannot be pursued any further in the present instance. An additional problem, probably largely confined to the High Arctic, is that certain types of inert ice cover could have existed in the past, no trace of which remains today. This is especially important in the areas designated as High Arctic refugia in the Queen Elizabeth Islands.

It is upon this basis of fundamental disagreement in interpretation of the available evidence, however, that a review will now be made of the physical conditions of the eastern Canadian seaboard. The available, and frequently conflicting, evidence from this region will then be presented and its significance discussed.

PHYSICAL CONDITIONS OF THE EASTERN CANADIAN SEABOARD

From Cape Breton Island the eastern Canadian seaboard stretches generally northwards for approximately 4500 km (Fig. 1). It may be divided into four great sectors: the Maritime-Newfoundland sector which has predominantly low coastal areas, excepting Long Range and the Shickshock Mountains; Labrador, with moderate to low coasts in the southern half and mountainous fjord coasts north of Nain; Baffin Island, with a fjord and high mountain coast along its entire 1600 km length; here coastal summits exceed 1500 m altitude and at least two groups of high rocky islands lie up to 30 miles off the coast; and finally the Devon–Ellesmere sector which extends for more than 1000 km in a general north–south direction and is somewhat similar in character to the Baffin Island sector.

One very important consideration is that the present climate of the eastern seaboard ranges from moist temperate in the south to High Arctic desert in the north, and this great range of climate presumably existed throughout the Pleistocene period. One reflection of this climatic range is that present-day glacierization increases in extent northwards from the Kaumajet Mountains so that from Pond Inlet to northern Ellesmere Island more than 70 per cent of the coastal zone is ice-covered. Another important consideration is the extent of the continental shelf: little can be said of the area north of Hudson Strait, but southwards the shelf is moderately to extremely broad ranging from 100 to 400 km. Finally, the character of the bedrock geology is vital, although in this respect also little systematic data is available. With a few small areas excepted, the coastal zone from the Gulf of St. Lawrence to northern Ellesmere Island is composed of Archaean rocks, principally a suite of acidic granitic gneisses, much of which are probably meta-sediments. Abrupt local variations occur within the gneissic group yet there is a general lack of distinctive rock types. Furthermore, distinctive rock types do not generally occur within several hundred kilometers of the east coast. Thus great difficulties arise when Dahl's (1961) criteria for the confirmation of true glacial

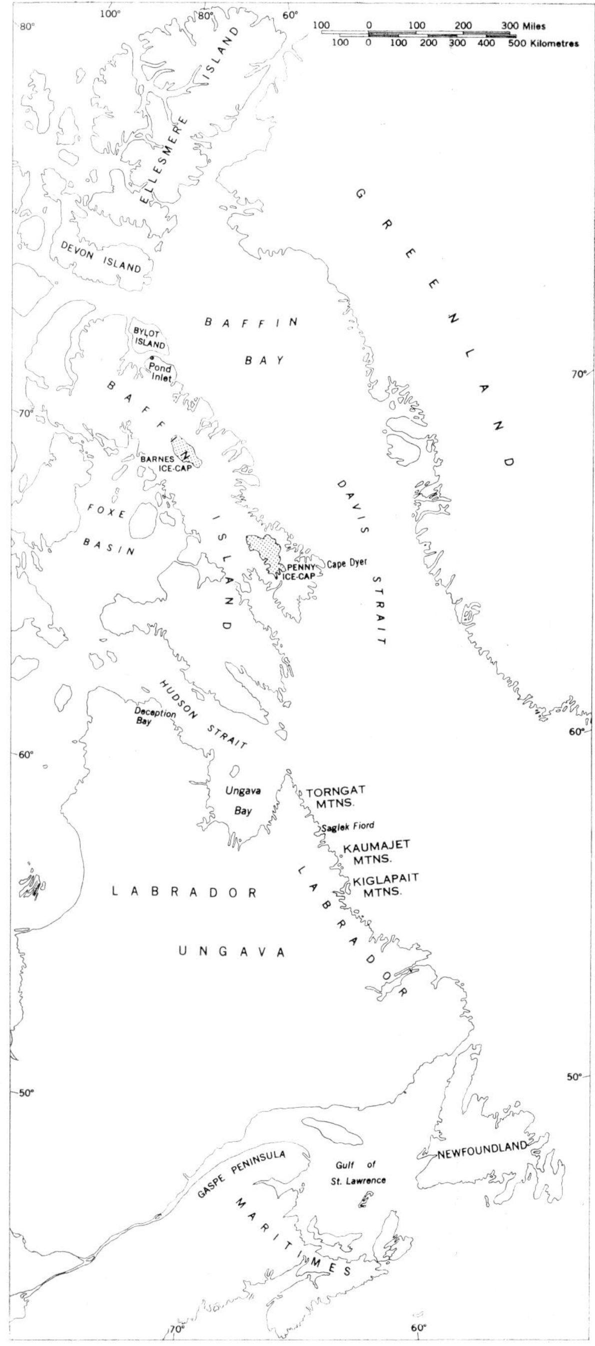

FIG. 1. General map showing the eastern seaboard of Canada and the major localities referred to in the text.

erratics are applied. The coarsely crystalline nature of the rock ensures rapid destruction of glacial polish and striations. Their meta-sedimentary character militates against the successful application of Dahl's X-ray analysis methods for determination of weathering products of the surface mantle. Hence it is difficult to establish the relative age of the mountain-top detritus. Thus the small areas of distinctive rock type become of critical importance. These include: the Kaumajet Mountains which are composed of basic lavas of probable Proterozoic age; part of the southern Torngat Mountains, embracing the slates and quartzites of the Ramah sedimentary series; the distinctive Tertiary lavas of Cape Dyer in southeastern Baffin Island and a small area of sandstones and shales on northeastern Bylot Island. A factor which emphasizes the importance of the first three of these areas is that the sedimentary and volcanic rocks occur at elevations in excess of 1200 m immediately overlooking the sea.

THE AVAILABLE EVIDENCE IN LABRADOR

Evidence implying extensive glaciation at high altitudes is so far restricted to the Shickshock Mountains and northern Labrador. Odell was the first to conclude that ice had passed over the highest summits of the Torngat and Kaumajet mountains (Odell, 1933), and the author has located several glacial erratics at altitudes in excess of 1200 m and two in excess of 1500 m (Ives, 1957 and 1958a). Dahl (pers. comm. 1958) maintains that these "erratics" are probably erosion residuals and the author would agree that they do not satisfy Dahl's criteria. The great contrast in degree of weathering and in relative abundance of glacial evidence above and below the general 750 m level has been noted by several workers (Daly, 1902; Coleman, 1921; Ives, 1958b; Løken, 1962a and 1962b) and has been interpreted as dependent upon the relative time available for sub-aerial weathering. Daly, Coleman and Løken (Løken, pers. comm. 1961) have all failed to find any indications of glacial inundation at the higher levels. Thus in view of Dahl's refusal to accept the validity of the Torngat "erratics," the available data from the Kaumajet Mountains is of critical importance. Following Odell's work, Wheeler (1958) found positive proof of total glacial submergence of these 1200 m coastal summits. He describes erratics of gray gneiss, amphibolite and pale garnet-biotite gneiss within 100 m of the summit of Mount Brave, the highest point, and these erratics lay on the local bedrock which comprises a basic volcanic series (Mugford Series) (Wheeler, *loc. cit.*). Tomlinson has since found numerous gneissic erratics on the Mugford volcanics at altitudes exceeding 1000 m (Figs. 2 and 3) and states that in places they are so numerous as to be used as stepping stones in walking over the contrasting dark ground mass of the volcanics (Tomlinson, 1958, 1962, and pers. comm. 1962). In this instance, Dahl's criteria appear to be fulfilled and his plea that the erratics could be weathered-out inclusions in the lavas (Dahl, pers. comm.

1959) is discounted due to their abundance, to the lack of metamorphic alteration rims and to the absence of such inclusions in the existing lavas (Wheeler, pers. comm. 1960). Finally, in the Nain–Kiglapait area farther south unequivocal erratics have been found within 20 m of the summit of

FIG. 2. Gneissic boulder resting on disintegrated bedrock of basic volcanics of the Mugford Series. The altitude is in excess of 1000 m. (*Photo by R. F. Tomlinson, July 1958. Kaumajet Mountains.*)

Man-O'War Peak which exceeds 1050 m and lies close to the outer coast. Here erratics of garnetiferous gneiss rest upon anorthosite bedrock (J. P. Johnson Jr., pers. comm. 1962). By extending this argument, it seems satisfactory to interpret the Torngat blocks as true glacial erratics.

The evidence implies only that at some time during the Pleistocene the high summits were inundated by ice from the west. The work of Flint,

Demarest and Washburn (1942) in the Shickshock Mountains is faced with the same problem of relative age of the erratics and Flint has commented that such fresh-looking erratics are no proof that the glacial inundation did not pre-date the Wisconsin stage (Flint, pers. comm. 1958). Similarly, it is not implied that all summits were necessarily inundated at the same time, so that

FIG. 3. A large block of granite gneiss resting upon Mugford Volcanics. The figure gives an indication of the scale. Altitude 650 m. (*Photo by R. F. Tomlinson, July 1958, Kaumajet Mountains.*)

the possibility of plant refugia remains. Furthermore, from the evidence presented below, it is argued, for northern Labrador at least, that the glaciation responsible for emplacement of the high-level erratics was certainly earlier than the Classical Wisconsin equivalent, and possibly much earlier.

Next it will be profitable to examine the evidence supporting the existence of ice-free areas during the Pleistocene; in particular the importance of the mountain-top detritus must be evaluated in the light of the available data. Both the author and Løken conclude that a distinctive lower limit to the mountain-top detritus can be recognized in the Torngat Mountains. This is described as a glacial trim line and can be seen to slope from west to east, and from south to north from a high point west of the head of Saglek Fjord. The slope is equated with that of the upper surface of the inland-ice and outlet glaciers during a recent glaciation, termed the Koroksoak Glaciation (Ives, 1958a). The northerly slope of the trim line traced roughly along the axis of the Torngat peninsula is from 830 m in the Saglek Fjord vicinity to 430 m south of Telliaosilk Fjord, 160 km farther north (roughly 2.5 m/km). Løken has calculated a minimum isostatic tilt of 1:1000 up towards the south-southwest (Løken, 1962b) so that the slope of the trim line should be reduced by at least this amount. Despite this, the loss of elevation towards the north is still significant and it is tempting to relate it to the juxtaposition of the mountains and the broad and deep Hudson Strait which must have acted as a major discharge channel for the inland-ice.

With the exception of the evidence already presented indications of glacial activity above the trim line in the zone of mountain-top detritus is entirely lacking (Figs. 4 and 5). Coleman, Daly and Løken all maintain that the trim

FIG. 4. An "old" weathering surface: mature mountain-top detritus at 1050 m west of Saglek Fjord in the Torngat Mountains. (*Photo by the author, August 1957.*)

line is the upper limit of glaciation within the area investigated by them, and X-ray analyses by Dahl of fines collected by Løken from within the mature detritus have led to the suggestion that their contained abundance of vermiculite, hydrobiotite and montmorillonite imply Tertiary, warm-climate weathering processes (Løken, pers. comm. 1962). Figure 6 provides a provisional picture of the distribution of mountain-top detritus. In Labrador the knowledge of its distribution is adequate for the formulation of a working hypothesis as the strong correlation between occurrence of mature detritus and altitude above present sea level is readily apparent. It is postulated, therefore, that the detrital trim line marks the upper limit of a glaciation at one particular stage, although it is not yet possible to determine which stage. It is recognized that this hypothesis is fraught with major difficulties and Hoppe and Rudberg (pers. comm. 1962) have both maintained that altitudinal variation in the lower limit of mature detritus in Sweden is related to rock type rather than vertical extent of glaciation and that mature detritus undoubtedly exists in areas proven to have been completely inundated during the last glaciation. The controversy of the mode and time sequence of development cannot be

FIG. 5. Mature mountain-top detritus above 1000 m in the Kaumajet Mountains. Note the small gneissic erratic in the foreground indicated by the arrow. (*Photo by R. F. Tomlinson, July 1958.*)

examined exhaustively within the limits of the present paper. Suffice it to say that in northern Labrador, where rock type is relatively uniform and almost universally Archaean, it is altitude, and therefore vertical extent of glaciation which is the important dominant, rather than rock type. It is urged, therefore, that until evidence is available to the contrary, the surfaces which carry mature detritus have been subjected to sub-aerial weathering for a far longer

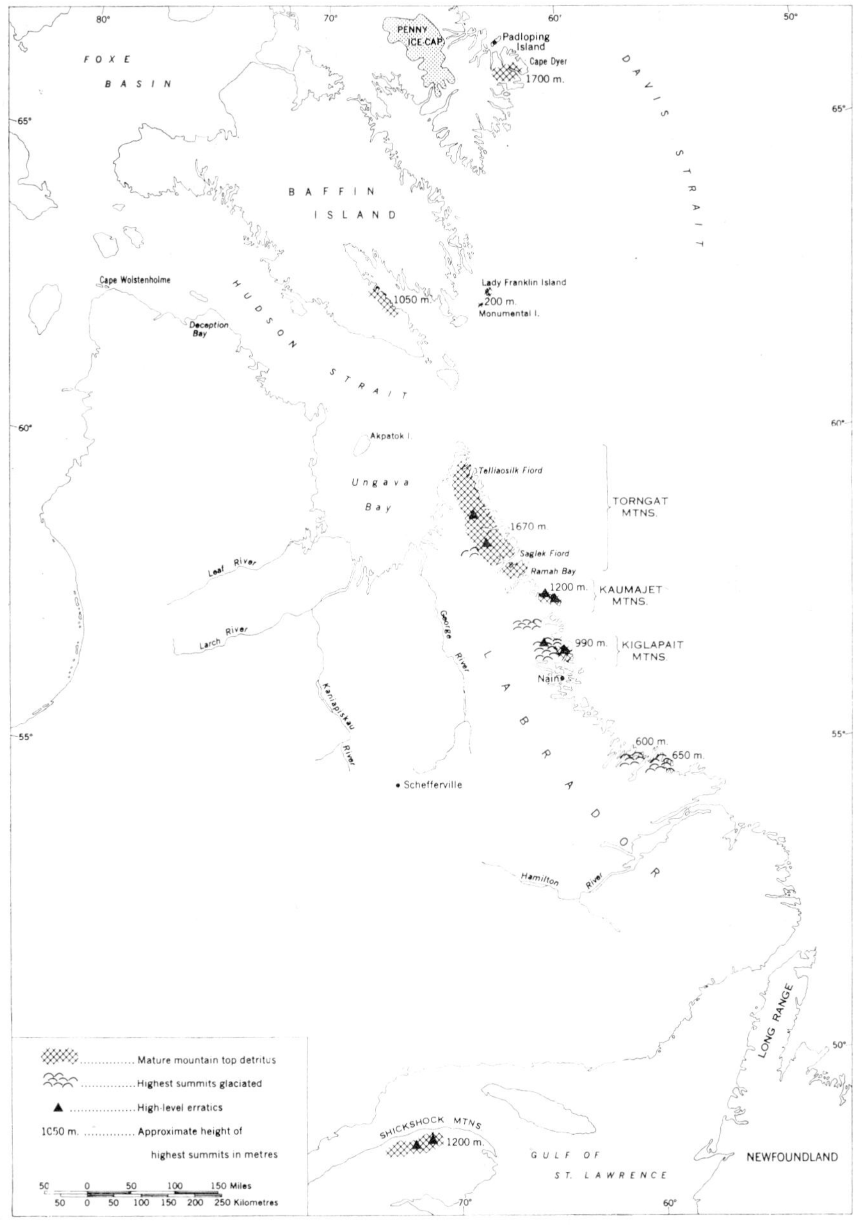

FIG. 6. Sketch map of the known distribution of mature mountain-top detritus in Labrador–Ungava and southern Baffin Island. Maximum altitudes of individual mountain groups are shown, together with the location of critical glacial erratics and glacially scoured summits.

period than those areas below the trim line, and that this period embraced the maximum of at least the Classical Wisconsin glacial equivalent.

For 100 to 125 m below the trim line, both Løken and Ives have described the occurrence of incipient mountain-top detritus (Ives, 1958b; Løken, 1962a). Andrews, furthermore, has described the same phenomenon in the Kiglapait-Nain area farther south (Andrews and Matthew, 1961). This may be equated with Dahl's incipient detritus in Norway (Dahl, 1961) and it is again argued that the time factor is vital to an understanding of its development. Its lower limit is marked by a striking series of lateral moraines and kame terraces, below which evidence of recent glacial activity is everywhere abundant. The present author originally interpreted the upper trim line as marking the maximum vertical extent of the last or Koroksoak Glaciation, and the lateral moraine system as representative of a recessional phase of the Last Glaciation (Ives, 1958a, 1960). Andrews followed Dahl by suggesting that the incipient detritus developed, in part at least, during the last glaciation and that the lateral moraine system marks the upper limit of that glaciation to which he gave the name "Saglek" (Andrews, 1961; Dahl, 1961). In this scheme the Koroksoak becomes the penultimate glaciation, and the Torngat Glaciation, during which the high level erratics are believed to have been emplaced, older still.

The Saglek lateral moraine system has been traced both in the field and on air photographs over a north–south distance of more than 400 km (Ives, 1960; Løken, 1962a; Tomlinson, pers. comm. 1961; Andrews and Matthew, 1961). Below them extensive end moraine systems occur and Løken has related individual end moraines to Late–Glacial sea level phases. He has also obtained a radiocarbon date of 9000 years B.P.* for a condition when some of the northern fjords already contained no tide-water glaciers, while farther south outlet glaciers still reached the Atlantic Ocean (Løken, 1962b). Andrews has studied several massive end moraine systems in the Kiglapait–Nain area which appear to overlie extensive deposits of varved clays up to 20 m thick. The implication is that subsequent to the Saglek lateral moraine phase, several major halt and readvance phases occurred. This evidence supports the contention that the Saglek moraines are appreciably older than 9000 years and may indeed represent the equivalent of the Classical Wisconsin maximum.

From the foregoing discussion it will be seen that an attempt is being made to tackle the problem of the relative age of the mature mountain-top detritus indirectly—namely, by considering the relative and absolute ages of the extensive lateral and end moraine systems, thereby obtaining a minimum age for the mature detritus. One further step in this reasoning process is

* Personal communication from Dr. W. S. Broecker, 1961. Marine molluscs were collected at 29 m above sea level by Dr. O. Løken and submitted to Dr. Broecker by the Geographical Branch. The Lamont Geological Observatory laboratory number of the sample is L-642.

necessary before turning to Baffin Island where conditions are similar to those of northeastern Labrador–Ungava. Matthews has collected marine molluscs up to an altitude of 120 m above present sea level in the Deception Bay vicinity, south Hudson Strait (Matthews, pers. comm. 1961). Deception Bay lies nearly 600 km from the open Atlantic Ocean and the local marine limit is approximately 150 m above sea level. Marine molluscs collected from the 86 m level by Matthews have yielded a radiocarbon age of 10,450 ±250 years. (Geographical Branch No. J.D.I.-61-S6; Isotopes Inc. No. I-488.) This implies that at the time of the Valders Readvance in the south, this sector of Hudson Strait was not only open to the Late-Glacial marine incursion, but that it had been inundated for a sufficient interval of time to allow a maximum of some 60 m of relative vertical isostatic recovery prior to 10,450 years ago. If this single date can be substantiated, the implications are most important. Assuming that the radiocarbon age of 18,000 years B.P. is accurate for the maximum of the Classical Wisconsin Glaciation in southern Canada and northeastern United States, it seems possible that contemporary conditions in Hudson Strait were characterized by partial, or total absence of glacier ice. This possibility has a most important bearing on the dating and significance of the Saglek moraine system. At least it can be said that the Saglek moraines are more than 10,500 years old and the implication is that large areas along the Labrador coast, northwards of Nain, remained ice-free at the Classical Wisconsin maximum. Thus it seems probable that the areas occupied by mature detritus, and possibly even that occupied by incipient detritus, were not ice-covered at the Classical Wisconsin maximum. This would corroborate conclusions drawn by Dahl in Norway (Dahl, 1961), and concurs with Andrews' interpretation of the significance of the Saglek and Koroksoak levels (Andrews, 1961). By comparing the enormous difference in glacial conditions between an ice stand at the Saglek moraines or the Koroksoak trim line, and one that overtopped the highest summits, as during the Torngat Glaciation, it seems probable that the Torngat Glaciation is pre-Sangamon in age. If this hypothesis can be substantiated it would provide for a considerable period of time for the development of mature mountain-top detritus.

Admittedly, the preceding hypothetical discussion leans too heavily upon two isolated radiocarbon dates and extensive subjective interpretation and extrapolation. The argument, therefore, is tentative and is intended as a suggestion for a future line of inquiry rather than as a positive conclusion.

CORRELATIONS WITH BAFFIN ISLAND

Little information is available for Baffin Island, but some significant statements can be made. According to that acute observor, Dr. A. P. Low, the glaciers of northern Baffin and Bylot islands were probably never much more extensive than they are today (Low, 1906, pp. 233–236). Falconer has substantiated this conclusion with the proviso that it must be strictly applied to the mountain glacierization of the east coast (Falconer, 1962) for it can be shown that the mountains were at least partially inundated by the outlet glaciers of an extensive inland-ice with its centre over western Baffin Island and Foxe Basin (Ives, 1962; Andrews and Ives, 1963). The development of this inland-ice was the predominant factor in the extent of the glacial inundation of the fjords and coastal mountains and in this instance the close parallel

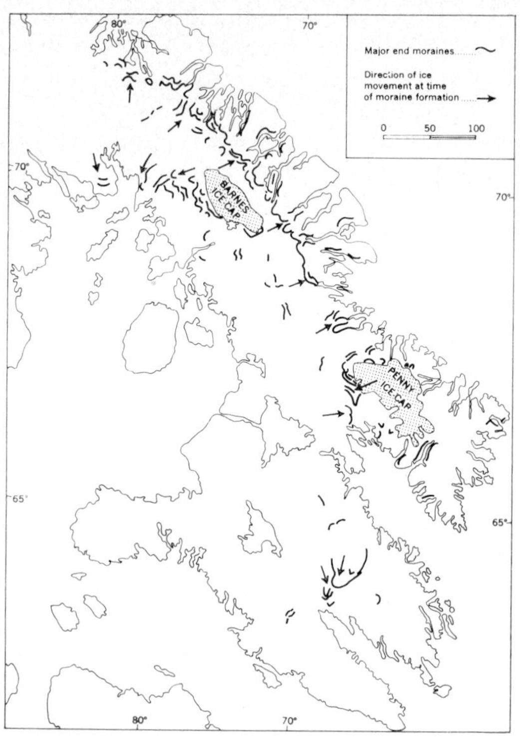

FIG. 7. Map of the end and lateral moraine systems of Baffin Island reduced from field and air photograph interpretation. The Cockburn Moraines are not differentiated but are represented by the almost continuous black lines running northwards from the western side of the Penny Ice Cap. (*Compilation by J. T. Andrews Geographical Branch.*)

with glacial conditions in Labrador–Ungava is stressed. Thus the Clyde lateral moraines, which mark the upper known limit of the outlet glaciers in the eastern Baffin fjords, are compared with the Saglek lateral moraines of Labrador–Ungava. Secondly, an extensive system of end moraines has been traced over a distance of 700 km. They lie inland from the heads of the fjords, but have many arcuate extensions (convex eastwards) implying that outlet glaciers descended to tide-water. These have been named the Cockburn end moraines and their extensive development and degree of continuity (Fig. 7) prompt the suggestion that they may have full stadial, or at least important sub-stadial significance. Whatever the true stratigraphic position of the Clyde and Cockburn moraines, it seems certain that, as in northern Labrador, extensive coastal tracts remained ice-free during the Classical Wisconsin equivalent, and possibly throughout the entire Wisconsin stage.

From the foregoing discussion the question arises as to whether or not potential ice-free areas can be correlated with the occurrence of mountain-top detritus. Few observations have been made in Baffin Island, although Gribbon

FIG. 8. The outer part of Sam Ford Fjord in the general vicinity of Clyde, Baffin Island. In the middle right prominant lateral glacial terraces can be seen which may be related to the Clyde lateral moraine system. In this instance their altitude is about 300 m above sea level. Above them mature detritus is abundant as can be seen in the foreground. (*Photo by G. Falconer, September 1961.*)

has described mature mountain-top detritus on summits above 700 m in the vicinity of Cape Dyer (Gribbon, 1960, and pers. comm. 1961). Similarly, Falconer has made summit landings by helicopter for the Geographical Branch in the Cape Dyer and Clyde vicinities, and has had occasion to examine mountain tops from the air on southern Bylot Island. In each case it seems likely that mature mountain-top detritus occurs (Fig. 8), although this has yet to be firmly substantiated (Falconer, pers. comm. 1961). Finally, lying off Hall Peninsula in southeastern Baffin Island are two groups of small islands, Lady Franklin and Monumental islands. They are situated about 45 km off the coast and rise precipitously to heights exceeding 200 m. Figure 9 is a photograph of the summit of Lady Franklin Island taken from a helicopter. Light snow limits the value of the photograph and no scale is available, although it can be seen that the cliffs fall sheer to the sea. The appearance of mountain-top detritus is striking, and the Hydrographic Service officer who had been requested to make observations for the Geographical Branch, on landing, was unable to detect any evidence of glaciation. Clearly these islands are an obvious place to look for evidence of nunataks at the Pleistocene maxima because of their altitude and position.

FIG. 9. The summit of Lady Franklin Island as seen from a helicopter. The cliff descends more than 200 m vertically to the sea (black in the photo). The surface is mantled with mature detritus. (*Photo by Canadian Hydrographic Service, September 1961*).

DISCUSSION

The presentation of the evidence has been restricted to Labrador–Ungava and Baffin Island with a few cursory remarks being devoted to the Shickshock Mountains. Nothing can be said about the Devon–Ellesmere islands sector.

A few major points emerge from the available evidence: first, it seems certain that most of the highest summits in northern Labrador, if not all of them, have been inundated at some time prior to the Last Glaciation, although no evidence is available for Baffin Island; secondly, either the detrital trim line, or the Saglek moraines, may be taken to mark the upper limit of the Last Glaciation in Labrador, which would indicate that large areas remained ice-free; finally, conditions may have been very similar in Baffin Island, and by extsion, along the entire eastern Canadian seaboard.

Much more work remains to be done before any of these contentions can be substantiated and, but for the problems of vast area and scarcity of workers, these contentions would never have been proposed until systematic research had been completed. However, controversial and hypothetical discussions are healthy aspects of research and a somewhat premature publication can be justified provided the facts are separated from the hypotheses and the limitations are adequately stressed. In this manner some directive for future study might be developed which would lead to the careful testing of the hypotheses in critical areas.

FIG. 10. Mature mountain-top detritus on gentle slopes above 700 m inland of Cape Dyer, southeast Baffin Island. (*Photo by G. Falconer, September 1961.*)

Little more can be said about the origins of the mountain-top detritus except that a relatively long time was required for its development. In this respect the author cannot go as far as Dr. Dahl in his conclusion that the existence of mature detritus indicates the preservation of ice-free areas throughout the Pleistocene. The mantle could be largely a relic of Tertiary weathering processes, but the erratics in the Torngat and Kaumajet Mountains indicate that if this is so, then it has been overridden by glacier ice sometime in the past. In certain circumstances thin ice patches may well have developed over mountain-top detritus and, because of limited ice movement, the detritus may have been preserved underneath without modification. This has undoubtedly occurred in Baffin Island, and a study of air photographs has revealed instances where mature detritus is today emerging from beneath such thin plateau ice caps and ice patches. However, the emplacement of erratics on the high summits in northern Labrador demands a vigorous movement of ice across them. It is inferred that the summits must have been covered by a minimum thickness of 300 m of ice before the ice sheet would have been able to drag erratics up from lower elevations to altitudes exceeding 1000 m (Ives, 1957).

Another difficulty arises in High Arctic areas where the temperature of the ice mass is below the pressure melting point. Under such conditions it appears that the ice caps and glaciers may be frozen to their beds; consequently the ice becomes a protective rather than an erosive agent. The former existence of a thin ice cover in north-central Baffin Island has been determined by the study of rock lichens. It has been concluded that up to 70 per cent of the interior upland was ice-covered as recently as 150 to 200 years ago, whereas the present-day coverage is less than 3 per cent (Ives, 1962). Once sufficient time has elapsed for rock lichen growth to reach maturity, no sign of the former ice cover will remain. In this instance there is strong evidence for glacierization during the Pleistocene, but the evidence for a recent, thin ice-cover provides an interesting example of the problem. Thus, if the question is transferred to the suggested Queen Elizabeth Island refugia, it must be borne in mind that the low islands, which today have so far yielded no proof of glacierization, could have been completely inundated in the distant past by the type of ice referred to in northern interior Baffin Island. With the elapse of 1000 to 2000 years (the time required for mature development of rock lichens according to Beschel, 1961) following the melting off of such an ice cover, no physical evidence for its former existence need remain. Recent botanical work in the northwest Queen Elizabeth Islands (Savile, 1961), although far from complete, points out an unusual scarcity of both species and individual plants which is hardly commensurate with the concept that some of these islands provided a major plant refugium throughout the Pleistocene.

CONCLUSIONS

1. Weight of evidence warrants the conclusion that large areas in northern Labrador and Baffin Island remained ice-free at the maximum of the Last Glaciation (Classical Wisconsin equivalent) and that the situation may have been similar along the northern sectors of the eastern seaboard and also in the Shickshock Mountains. This prompts the speculation that appreciable areas of the continental shelf may have been dry land and thus have provided ample habitats for the survival of a wide range of flora and fauna. Similarly sectors of the northern Labrador coast, at or below present sea level, where backed by high mountains, are likely to have remained ice-free.

2. The mountain-top detritus required a considerable period of time for mature development and this indicates that for a similar period areas occupied by mature detritus remained ice-free or covered by only thin, stagnant ice for part of that time. However, most, if not all of the high Labrador mountains were completely submerged some time during the Pleistocene.

3. Wide areas of the High Arctic may have been covered by cold, thin, stagnant ice, of which no trace remains today.

From these three points it is apparent that much more systematic research is needed. The following problems present themselves for urgent consideration:

Outline of Problems for Future Investigation

1. How does mountain-top detritus form? Detailed quantitative studies of its structure and internal temperature conditions are required under existing climatic conditions. Studies of the structure should establish whether or not individual boulder fields pass downwards into bedrock and are therefore the product of weathering *in situ*. Similarly, additional mineralogical studies and intensive work on areal and vertical distribution in areas of contrasting rock types are needed.

2. Further investigations are needed to establish the presence or absence of glacial erratics on high coastal summits. Thus the Kaumajet Mountains, southern Torngat, and Cape Dyer become critical areas. In the Cape Dyer area it is believed that the outer coastal mountains, which rise to elevations exceeding 1200 m, are composed of a Tertiary volcanic sequence. The Tertiary outcrop is not more than ten miles wide and farther inland the mountain country is composed of the regular Archaean gneisses. This should provide an ideal situation for such a study. In any future attempt to establish the occurrence of erratics at high altitudes, Dahl's criteria should be used (Dahl, 1961).

3. Perhaps the most fruitful line of approach would be a more extensive study of the history of glaciation in Labrador–Ungava and Baffin Island. In this, particular attention should be paid to the problem of dating the lateral and end moraine systems and to relating them to late and Post-glacial marine phases. Especially important is the need to follow up the hypothesis that Hudson Strait may have been largely ice-free during the Classical Wisconsin maximum.

All of these problems are being investigated as part of the northern research programme of the Geographical Branch, Department of Mines and Technical Surveys, Ottawa, Canada.

Acknowledgments—The author expresses his indebtedness to numerous colleagues who have either directly assisted in the field work or who have discussed many aspects of the problems of interpretation of the field data. Special thanks are due to Professor R. F. Flint, Dr. R. P. Goldthwait, Dr. E. Dahl, Drs. Áskell and Doris Löve, Professors G. Hoppe and S. Rudberg, for their many critical discussions and suggestions. In particular, the author was fortunate to accompany Dr. Dahl on an excursion through parts of central and western Norway in 1960 where the striking field evidence relating to the mountain-top detritus and the nature of its lower limit (detrital trim line) was so ably demonstrated. Finally, special thanks are due to Dr. J. Ross Mackay for critically reviewing the manuscript.

REFERENCES

ANDREWS, J. T. (1961). The glacial geomorphology of the northern Nain-Okak section of Labrador. Unpubl. M.Sc. thesis, McGill Univ., Montreal, 1961. 280 p.

ANDREWS, J. T. and IVES, J. D. (1963). Studies in the physical geography of north-central Baffin Island, N.W.T. *Geogr. Bull.* No. 19. In press. Geographical Branch, Ottawa.

ANDREWS, J. T. and MATTHEW, E. M. (1961). Geomorphological studies in northeastern Labrador–Ungava. *Geogr. Paper*, No. 29. 29 p. Geographical Branch, Ottawa.

BERGSTRÖM, E. (1959). Utgjorde Lofoten och Vesterålen ett refugium under sista istiden? *Svensk Naturv.* **12**, 116–122.

BESCHEL, R. E. (1961). Dating rock surfaces by lichen growth and its application to glaciology and physiography (lichenometry). In *Geology of the Arctic*, Univ. of Toronto Press, 1044–1062.

COLEMAN, A. P. (1921). Northeastern part of Labrador and New Quebec. *Geol. Surv. Canada*, Mem. 124. Ottawa.

DAHL, E. (1961). Refugieproblemet og de kvartærgeologiske metodene. *Svensk Naturv.* **14**, 81–96.

DALY, R. A. (1902). The geology of the northeast coast of Labrador. *Harv. Coll. Mus. Comp. Zoology Bull.* **38**, 205–270.

FALCONER, G. (1962). Glaciers of Northern Baffin and Bylot Islands. *Geog. Paper* No. 33. In press. Geographical Branch, Ottawa.

FLINT, R. F., DEMAREST, M. and WASHBURN, A. L. (1942). Glaciation of Shickshock Mountains, Gaspé Peninsula. *Geol. Soc. Amer. Bull.* **53**, 1211–1230.

GRIBBON, P. W. F. (1960). Flora and fauna at Bagnall Fiord, central Baffin Island. Unpubl. MMS., Royal Military College, Kingston, Ontario.

HOPPE, G. (1959). Några kritiska kommentarer till diskussionen om isfria refugier. *Svensk Naturv.* **12**, 123–134.

IVES, J. D. (1957). Glaciation of the Torngat Mountains, northern Labrador. *Arctic* **10**, 76–87.

IVES, J. D. (1958a) Glacial geomorphology of the Torngat Mountains, northern Labrador. *Geogr. Bull.* No. 12: 47–75. Geographical Branch, Ottawa.

IVES, J .D. (1958b) Mountain-top detritus and the extent of the last glaciation in northeastern Labrador–Ungava. *Can. Geogr.* **12**, 25–31.

IVES, J. D. (1960). The deglaciation of Labrador–Ungava—an outline. *Cahiers de Géogr. de Québec IV*, 323–343.

IVES, J. D. (1962). Indications of recent extensive glacierization in north-central Baffin Island, N.W.T. *J. Glaciology* **4** (32), 197–205.

LØKEN, O. (1962a). Deglaciation and postglacial emergence of northernmost Labrador. Unpubl. Ph.D. thesis. McGill Univ. 1962. Montreal.

LØKEN, O. (1962b). The late-glacial and postglacial emergence and the deglaciation of northernmost Labrador. *Geogr. Bull.* No. 17, 23–56.

LOW, A. P. (1906). *Cruise of the Neptune, 1903–1904: Report on the Dominion Government Expedition to Hudson Bay and the Arctic Islands.* Ottawa. 355 p.

ODELL, N. (1933). The mountains of Northern Labrador. *Geogr. J.* **82**, 193–211 and 315–326.

SAVILE, D. B. O. (1961). The botany of the northwestern Queen Elizabeth Islands. *Canad. J. Botany* **39**, 909–942.

TOMLINSON, R. F. (1958). Geomorphological investigations in the Kaumajet Mountains and Okak Bay (North River) region of Labrador. *Arctic* **11**, 254–256.

TOMLINSON, R. F. (1962). Pleistocene evidence related to glacial theory in northeastern Labrador. Unpubl. MMS, 1962.

WHEELER, E. P. 2nd (1958). Pleistocene glaciation in northern Labrador. *Geol. Soc. Amer. Bull.* **69**, 343–344.

POLLEN-ANALYTICAL STUDIES ON THE VEGETATION AND CLIMATE HISTORY OF ICELAND IN LATE AND POST-GLACIAL TIMES

THORLEIFUR EINARSSON

University Research Institute, Reykjavík, Iceland

THE pollen-analytical work in Late and Post-Glacial bog- and lake-deposits in Iceland has recently been started. Previous pollen analyses have been carried out by Thorarinsson (1944, 1955), Okko (1956), and Straka (1956). The present author started his studies in 1954 and has since examined 20 bog profiles from different localities in Iceland. The older investigations fit well into the present zonation scheme (Th. Einarsson, 1961).

This late start of such studies in Iceland is due mainly to the following facts. The Icelandic Flora counts only 440 species of vascular plants, when the genera *Hieracium* and *Taraxacum* are excluded. The only forest tree in Iceland is *Betula pubescens-tortuosa*. Therefore the pollen production is very low and there is a scarcity of pollen grains in the young bog and lake deposits (peat and diatomite mud).

The climate of Iceland is oceanic, i.e. humid with cool summers and relatively mild winters. The mean temperature in July is 9°–11°C, in January about 0°C in southern Iceland and –2 to –6°C in northern Iceland. The mean precipitation is as high as 2200 mm in southern Iceland (Vík Mýrdal) but only 465 mm in Akureyri, northern Iceland. The weather is very changeable due to the low-pressure tracks in the North Atlantic. The mild climate is a result of the strong influence exerted by the Gulf Stream.

Approximately 10 per cent of Iceland is covered with bogs which can be divided into two groups:

(1) The "Flói" bogs, i.e. topogenic bogs; and,
(2) The "Hallamýri" bogs, i.e. bogs on hill and mountain sides, which are fed mainly by precipitation and run-off water.

Most of the Icelandic pollen profiles are from bogs of the latter type.

The first two profiles show the typical trend in ordinary pollen diagrams from Iceland. In pollen diagram 1 from Moldhaugar, Eyjafjördur, northern Iceland (Fig. 1), three *Betula*-maxima can be seen:

A. The first *Betula*-maximum is probably of Late Glacial age, but in the absence of C^{14} datings this cannot be verified.

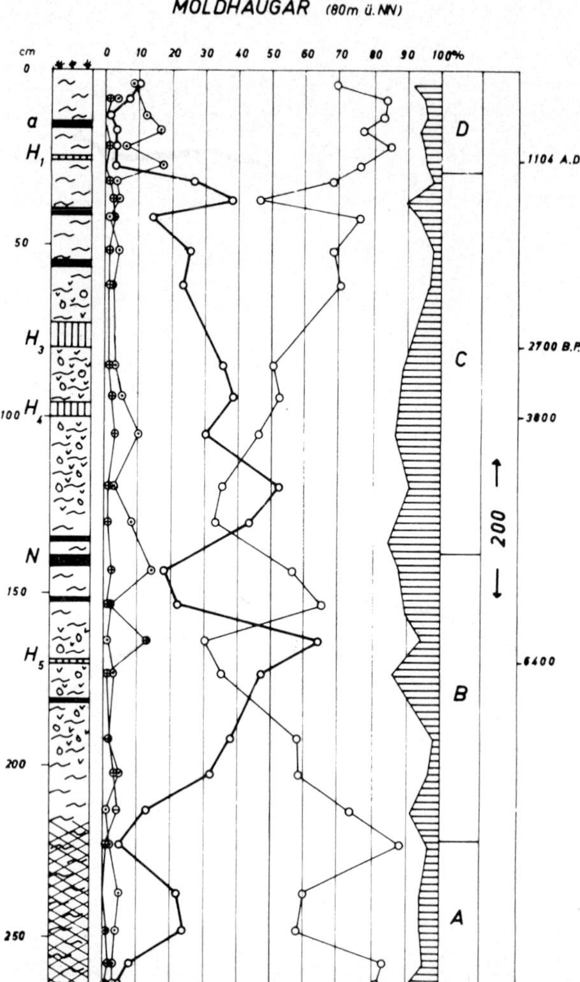

FIG. 1. Pollen diagram from a bog, 80 m above sea level, at Moldhaugar, Eyjafjördur, N. Iceland. Pollengraphs from left to right: *Salix*, Gramineae, *Betula*, Cyperaceae. Hatched area: herbs. (Cf. also Fig. 5.)

B. The first great *Betula*-maximum can be equated with the Boreal and the lower part of the Atlantic in continental Europe. In this zone falls the Hekla volcanic ash layer H_5 (6600 B.P.).* This *Betula*-maximum is followed by a *Betula*-minimum which corresponds to the wet Atlantic period of continental Europe. The birch forest that grew in the "Hallamýri" bogs was receding. In

*C^{14} values on Fig. 1 have not been corrected for Suess-effect. Corrected values appear in text.

this interval appears a great maximum of *Sphagnum*, a plant which today is not spore-producing in Iceland.

C. This *Betula*-minimum is thereafter followed by a second great *Betula*-maximum which corresponds to the Sub-Boreal and the lower part of the Sub-Atlantic periods. In this pollen zone, most probably in the interval 4000–2500 B.P., falls the Hypsithermal period in Iceland. At this time at least 50 per cent of Iceland was covered with birch forest as contrasted to 1 per cent in modern times. Within this pollen zone occur two rhyolithic tephra (volcanic ash) layers from Hekla, H_4 (4000 B.P.) and H_5 (2700 B.P.).

The numerous, partly C^{14}-dated, tephra layers in the Icelandic peat deposits greatly aid pollen analytical work. The tephra layers have been thoroughly studied by Thorarinsson (1944, 1954, 1958) and facilitate the geological work in Holocene deposits. They are also of great importance for the study of the volcanic history of Iceland in Post-Glacial times.

Another feature that can be seen from the tephra layers is that the pre-historic ones are straight and even in the bog profiles, in contrast to the historic ones which are uneven and lenticular. This deformation of the historic tephra layers is probably a result of the beginning of the cryoturbant "thúfur"-(hillock)-formation in Iceland in the last thousand years. The "thúfur"-formation could indicate a climatic deterioration in historic times or be the result of deforestation. In places where forest and/or shrub cover is lacking snow is blown away by wind. Absence of the insulating snow cover thus results in a much more effective frost action in deforested areas.

The *Betula*-curve thereafter decreases generally with some local deviations from 2500 B.P. to the time of settlement (ninth century A.D.) in accordance with the climatic deterioration at the beginning of the Sub-Atlantic period. At the beginning of pollen zone D, historic times, the *Betula*-curve decreases very rapidly and the Gramineae-curve rises, indicating the influence of man.

In pollen diagram 2 from Sogamýri, Reykjavík, southwestern Iceland (Fig. 2), the pollen zone A is *Betula*-free. This suggests that the *Betula* was growing for a much longer time in northern Iceland east of the Eyjafjördur mountains to the Austfjördur mountains. Perhaps it has survived there on ice-free areas in the mountains and/or on a dry coastal shelf during the last Glacial, as this interpretation of the pollen diagrams seems to indicate.

As has been mentioned in other lectures in this symposium, the Early Tertiary flora of Iceland was characterized mainly by deciduous-trees whereas the Late Tertiary was dominated by conifers (Pflug, 1959). With the setting in of the Pleistocene Glacials the heat-demanding trees were eliminated and only species of *Alnus*, *Betula*, and *Salix* survived the First Glacial. In the second to last Glacial *Alnus*, too, disappeared from the flora.

Kjartansson (1955, 1961) has shown, through studies on Glacial striae, that the ice-divide in late stages of the retreat of the ice-sheet in the Last Glacial was near the Torfajökull-area, i.e. more than 50 km south of the

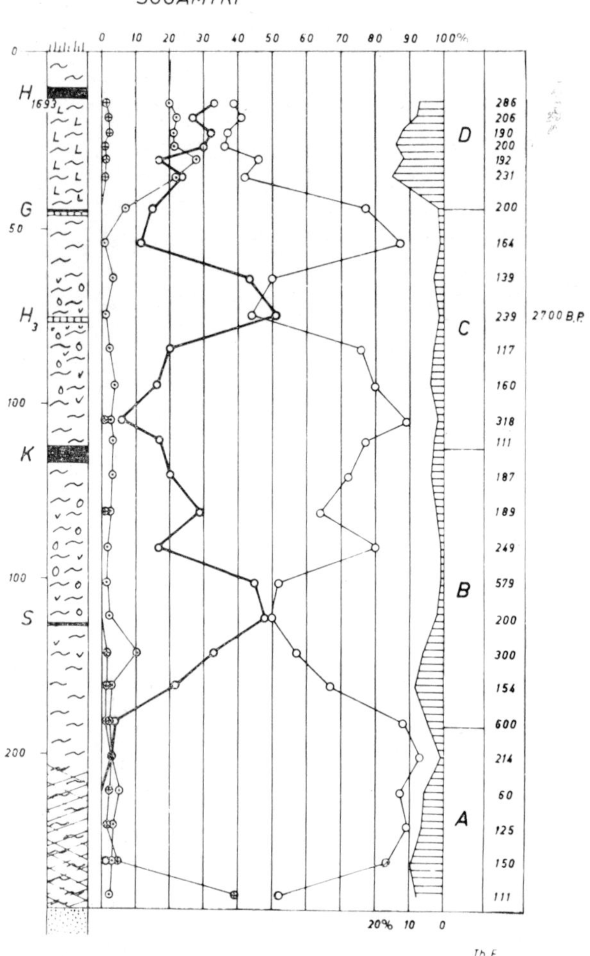

FIG. 2. Pollen diagram from Sogamýri, southwestern Iceland.

present water-divide. Therefore it seems probable that the ice-sheet in northern Iceland during the Last Glacial was much thinner than in southern Iceland. Perhaps there was only a great valley glaciation in northern Iceland, where mountains and mountain ridges protruded as nunataks through the ice, as indicated from geomorphological studies by Thorarinsson (1937) and Trausti Einarsson (1959) (Fig. 3).

On the northwestern peninsula there was another ice-center but on the outer mountain ridges there may have been ice-free areas. The sea level during

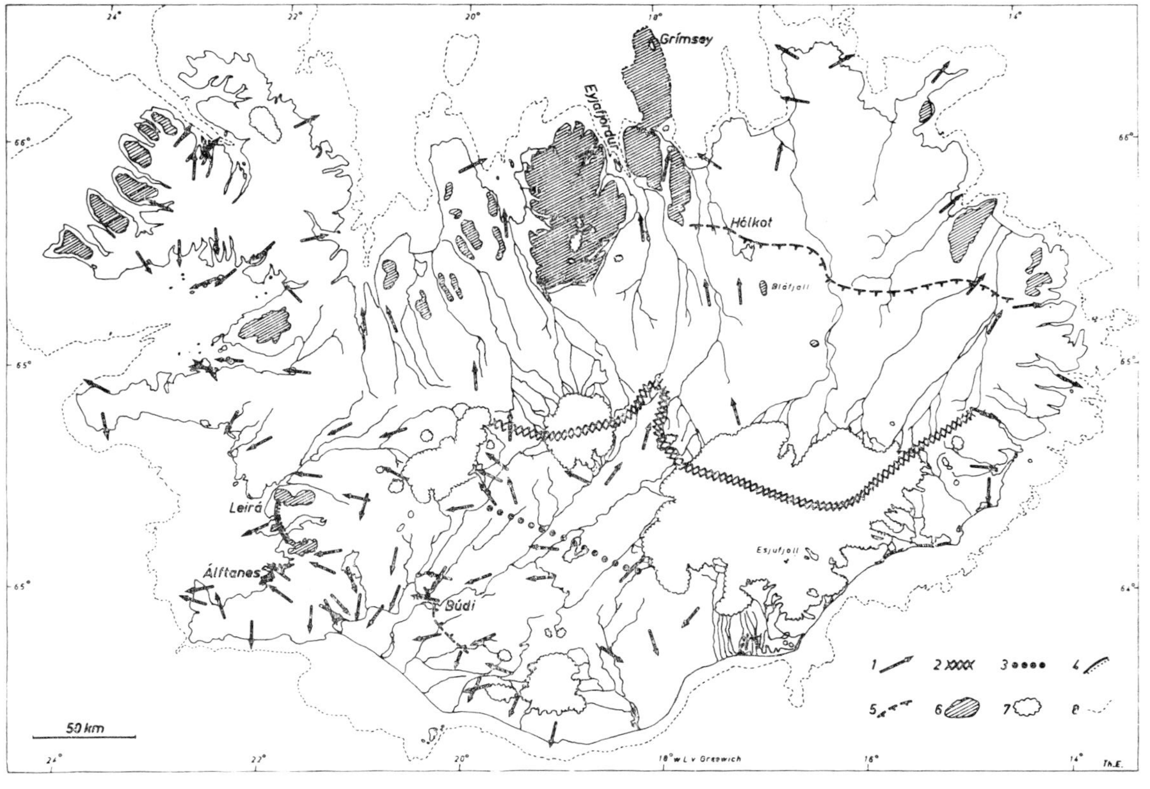

FIG. 3. Map showing the main features of the Glacial geology in Iceland. Explanation of symbols: (1) Glacial striae, (2) present water-divide, (3) Pleistocene ice-divide, (4) Álftanes stage end-moraines, (5) Búdi-Hólkot end-moraines, (6) probable ice-free areas from the Last Glacial, (7) present glaciers, (8) 100 m depth line outside the present coastline.

the high point of the Last Glacial was more than 100 m lower than today. Due to these facts there have probably been ice-free and dry areas also on the northern coastal shelf of Iceland.

The present interpretation of the pollen diagrams seems to support the opinion of botanists (Steindórsson, 1954; Löve and Löve, 1956) that a part of the Icelandic flora has survived on ice-free areas during the Last Glacial (see also Fig. 3).

The *Betula* immigrates rapidly into southern Iceland about 9000 B.P. as the Sogamýri diagram (Fig. 2) indicates. The diagram then shows the first *Betula*-maximum followed by the Atlantic *Betula*-minimum. The younger *Betula*-maximum is thereafter very distinct. The slight rise of the *Betula*-curve in pollen zone D (historic time) may be a result of re-bedded pollen grains that were blown into the bogs from the hills in the vicinity. The loess soils were eroded very rapidly in historic times and the dust, too, was re-bedded partly in the bogs.

Raised beaches are known in all parts of Iceland (Fig. 7). The evidence of higher sea-level are gravel terraces, old sea-cliffs and bedded marine clays with sub-fossil molluscs. The height of the marine limit differs from place to place in Iceland. In southern Iceland (Holt, Hreppar, Landssveit) the marine limit is *ca.* 110 m, at Reykjavík *ca.* 45 m, in Borgarfjördur 80–100 m, and in western, northern, eastern, and southeastern Iceland 40–50 m, i.e. the raised beaches are much lower at the coast than farther inland. The highest shoreline seems to be synchronous all over the island. The varying height of the raised beaches is a result of the different downwarping of Iceland caused by the ice-sheet during the last glaciation, and of the subsequent isostatic recovery.

The age of the highest shoreline is still not definitely known. The first investigators believed, that the marine limit was of Post-glacial age according to the heat-demanding molluscs in the raised marine deposits (all these sub-fossil molluscs exist today along the Icelandic coast), equating the Late Glacial Icelandic subfossil mollusc fauna with that of Scandinavia, without regard to the great eustatic changes of sea level and the different land–sea distribution in the Pleistocene. The Gulf Stream had much more influence on the Icelandic coast during the Glacials, and especially in Late Glacial times, than it did on the coasts of Scandinavia. According to Kjartansson (1958) the sea level had sunk approximately 10–15 m below its maximum height at the end of the Búdi stage. He concludes, that the Búdi stage may be comparable to the Salpausselkä-Raerne stage in Scandinavia, i.e. Younger Dryas. Pollen-analytical studies by the present author indicate that the highest shorelines are probably older, but in the absence of C^{14} datings this cannot be definitely stated yet.

The isostatic recovery was relatively rapid, as the sea level had reached the present level by 9000 B.P. The lagoon Seltjörn near Reykjavík was isolated at this time and normal peat formation started in the basin. Only the deepest

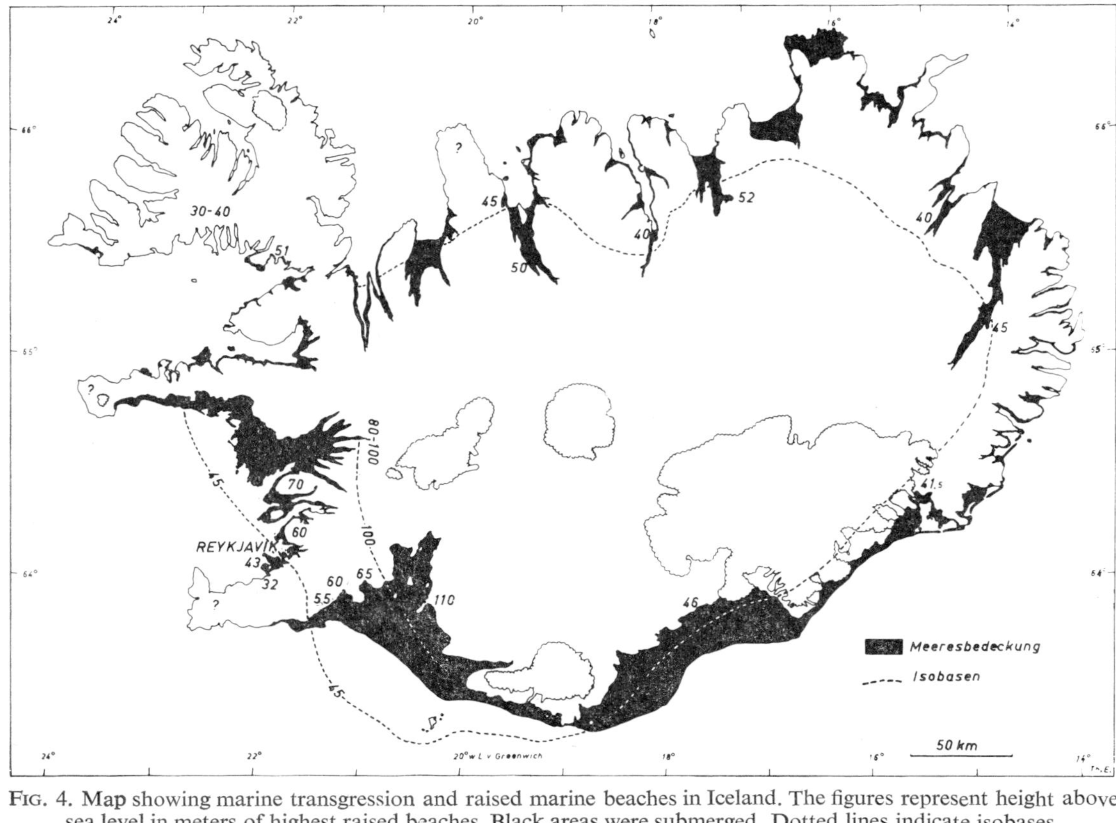

FIG. 4. Map showing marine transgression and raised marine beaches in Iceland. The figures represent height above sea level in meters of highest raised beaches. Black areas were submerged. Dotted lines indicate isobases.

part of the peat contains marine diatoms whereas the higher part has only freshwater diatoms (Jónsson, 1956, 1957). The isostatic recovery continued and kept pace with the eustatic sea level rise during the Boreal and Atlantic periods.

A pollen diagram from Seltjörn (Th. Einarsson, 1956, 1961) shows the first great *Betula*-maximum (pollen zone B), the following Atlantic *Betula*-minimum, and the first part of the second great *Betula*-maximum. The transgression submerged the Seltjörn bog and stopped the peat formation in Sub-Boreal time. Seltjörn is today a bay. The subsidence in this area is more than 4 m, and the transgression is still continuing. Submerged peat has been found in many localities in Iceland (Bárdarsson, 1923; Thorarinsson, 1956; Jónsson, 1957). Only at Hrútafjördur, northern Iceland, is there evidence of a transgression in Sub-Boreal time, the *Purpura* (*Nucella*) transgression, with a following regression (Bárdarsson, 1910; Thorarinsson, 1955). Trausti Einarsson (1961) has argued against the transgressive trend on the Icelandic coasts in the last few thousand years, and denies the submerged peat as proof for a subsidence.

As mentioned before, the birch forest declined from *ca.* 2500 B.P. to the onset of the settlement, the "landnám". In a short history of Iceland (Islendingabók), written about 1120, Ari the Wise Thorgilsson (1067–1148) says that Iceland was covered with woods between "coast and mountain", when the "landnám" began. Iceland was colonized mainly from Norway in the years A.D. 870–930. After the beginning of the "landnám", the birch forest was devastated very rapidly as can be seen from the detailed pollen diagram from Skálholt in southern Iceland (Fig. 5). Skálholt was probably settled early in the tenth century and in 1056 the farmstead became the residence of the Icelandic bishops and was until the end of the eighteenth century the cultural center of Iceland. In the pollen diagram from Skálholt (Fig. 5) the first column shows the sediment (*Carex*-moss-peat) with the tephra layers K-*ca.* 5500 B.P., H_4 —4000 B.P., H_3 —2700 B.P., and G, which according to the pollen studies was formed during an eruption in the Torfajökull area, southern Iceland, during the "landnám" period, i.e. A.D. 870–930. The rhyolithic tephra layer H_1 was formed in a Hekla eruption in the year A.D. 1104. This ash-fall destroyed the district Thjórsárdalur 30 km east of Skálholt. The two top-most basaltic tephra layers were deposited during the eruptions of Hekla in 1693 and of Katla in 1721 respectively.

Column A shows the proportion of inorganic-organic constituents of the peat. The inorganic constituents are much higher in historic times than before, because of the sedimentation of eolian dust from the soil erosion that began after the settlement (Bjarnason, 1952; Th. Einarsson, 1961; Thorarinsson, 1961). This soil deflation began early in historic times.

Column B shows the proportion of Cyperaceae pollen (shaded) to all other pollen grains. Column C shows the proportion of *Salix*, Gramineae, and

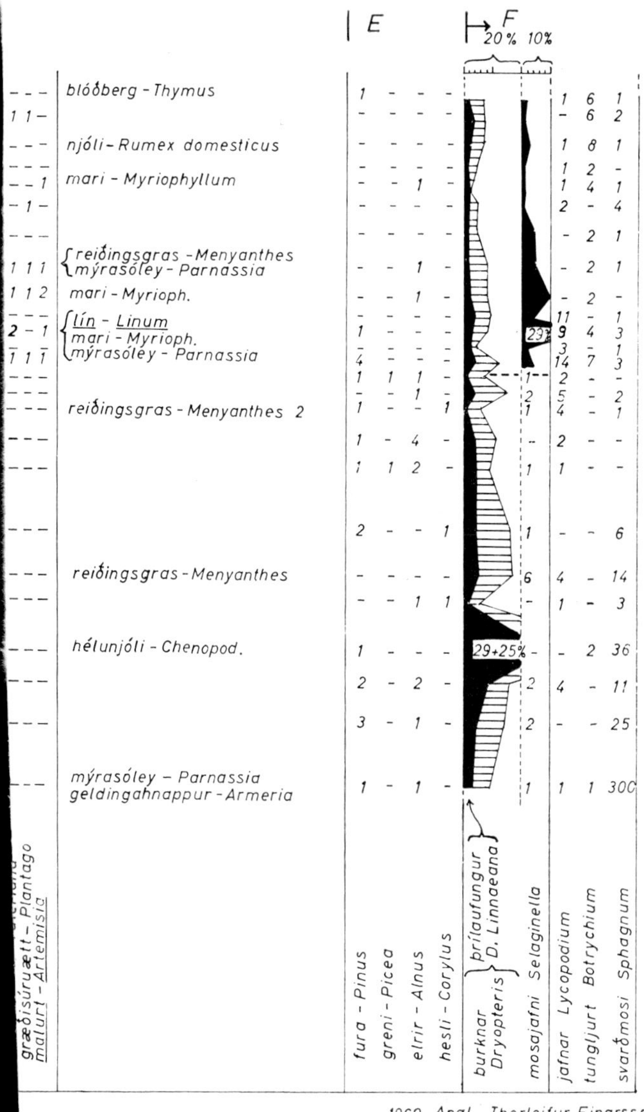

1960 Anal. Thorleifur Einarsson

Betula in contrast to the herb pollen (shaded) after the Cyperaceae pollen have been subtracted (ΣP–Cyp.). The diagram shows clearly the second great *Betula*-maximum, whose optimum lies between H_4 and H_3, i.e. 4000–2700 B.P. The *Betula* declines thereafter toward the "landnám" but the herbs increase (cf. Rosaceae). The *Salix*-curve goes as high as to 10–20 per cent in Skálholt, and the Gramineae make up 5–10 per cent. With the "landnám" the "wild" Gramineae increase very rapidly and are very characteristic of the influence of man in Iceland. A similar increase of "wild" grasses was found by Iversen (1934, 1953) in the vicinity of the Nordic ruins in western Greenland, and by Thorarinsson (1944) in Thjórsárdalur, southern Iceland.

Column D shows the differentiated herb curve, calculated on the total pollen minus Cyperaceae (ΣP–Cyp.). The number of "anthropophilous" plants increases. These are *Polygonum* (cf. *aviculare*), Caryophyllaceae (cf. *Stellaria media*, cf. *Cerastium caespitosum*), *Rumex*, Compositeae, Ranunculaceae, *Galium* (cf. *verum*), *Plantago* (cf. *maritima*) and new species like *Valeriana*, *Linum* (one grain from Skálholt), *Myrica Gale* and *Artemisia*. The last two plants do not grow wild in Iceland today, but have probably been raised in older times as medicinal plants, or been used for the brewing of ale.

Another interesting plant is *Hordeum*, cultivated in Iceland during the first centuries of historic times. After the fifteenth or sixteenth centuries *Hordeum* was not grown any more in Iceland, perhaps because the climate became worse or for some economical or other unknown reasons. At the end of the seventeenth century the Gramineae-curve shows a new rise at Skálholt and the small *Cerealia*-maximum perhaps indicates attempts to raise crops. Pollen of *Elymus arenarius* is a serious source of errors in studies of the *Cerealia*, since this species grows all over the country today, in coastal parts as well as in the highlands in loose eolian sand deposits. *Hordeum* and *Avena sativa* thrive in Iceland today again.

Plants which decreased after the beginning of the "landnám" besides *Betula* and *Salix*, are the Rosaceae (*Comarum* and *Filipendula*) and the Umbelliferae (*Archangelica officinalis*, *Angelica silvestris*). After the deflation had cleared the soils down to the barren-ground moraines, pollen of *Thalictrum* increases in many profiles.

Column E indicates a relatively small long-distance pollen transport of mainly *Pinus* and *Alnus* (*ca.* 1‰). There is apparently much more of long-distance transport in prehistoric times than later, perhaps because of the higher pollen production in Iceland after the "landnám" or because of the deforestation of the nearest countries: Iceland lies 1000 km from Norway and 800 km from Scotland.

Column F concerns the evidence of spores. Filicales are decreasing with the "landnám", but *Selaginella* (*selaginoides*) is increasing. The highest part of the Atlantic *Sphagnum*-maximum is clearly seen (300 = 60 per cent).

From the observations referred to above it is obvious that the same Late and Post-glacial climatical changes have taken place in Iceland as in continental Europe and that they are reflected in the vegetation pattern, though the number of indicative species is low. The dating of the changes, especially in Post-glacial and historical times, is greatly aided by the tephra layers. In historical times man's devastating influence on his surroundings is amply verified in the pollen diagrams. These show four pollen zones:

A. Late Glacial + Pre-Boreal. In northern Iceland there is a small *Betula*-maximum, whereas southern Iceland is *Betula*-free. This could perhaps support the theory that a part of the Icelandic flora has survived the Last Glacial in ice-free refugia in northern Iceland.

B. Boreal + Atlanticum. The first great *Betula*-maximum is followed by a *Betula*-minimum with a *Sphagnum*-maximum caused by the higher humidity in Atlantic times.

C. Sub-Boreal + lower part of Sub-Atlanticum. Second great *Betula*-maximum. After 2700 B.P. the climatic deterioration sets in.

D. Historic time, from A.D. 870. The influence of man is reflected; the *Betula*-forest decreases rapidly, and there is a sharp increase of the grasses as well as the appearance of cultural indicators.

REFERENCES

BÁRDARSON, G. B. (1910). Traces of changes of climate and level at Húnaflói, Northern Iceland. *Intern. Geol. Congr.*: 347–352. Stockholm.

BÁRDARSON, G. B. (1923). Old sea-deposits in Borgarfjördur and Hvalfjördur. *Soc. Sci. Island* **1**, 1–118.

BJARNASSON, O. (1952). Islenzki mórinn. *Fjölrit Rannsóknaráds* **3**, 1–100.

EINARSSON, TH. (1956). Frjógreining fjörumós úr Seltjörn. *Náttúrufr.* **26**, 194–198.

EINARSSON, TH. (1957). Tvö frjólinurit úr íslenzkum mýrum. *Ársrit Skógræktarf. Islands* 89–97.

EINARSSON, TH. (1961). Pollen-analytische Untersuchungen zur spät- und postglazialen Klimageschichte Islands. *Sonderveröff. Geol. Inst. Univ. Köln* **6**, 1–52.

EINARSSON, TR. (1959). Studies on the Pleistocene in Eyjafjördur. *Soc. Sci. Islands* **33**, 1–62. Reykjavik.

EINARSSON, TR. (1961). Das Meeresniveau an den Küsten Islands in post-glazialer Zeit. *N. Jahrb. Paläontolog.*, Mh., **9**, 443–473.

IVERSEN, J. (1934). Moorgeologische Untersuchungen auf Grönland. *Medd. Dansk. Geol. For.* **8**, 341–358.

IVERSEN, J. (1953). Origin of the flora of western Greenland in the light of pollen analysis. *Oikos* **4**, 85–103.

JÓNSSON, J. (1956). Kísilthörungar í Seltjarnarmónum. *Náttúrufr.* **26**, 199–205.

JÓNSSON, J. (1957). Notes on the change of sea-level in Iceland. *Geogr. Ann.* **39**, 143–212.

KJARTANSSON, G. (1943). *Árnesingasaga.* Reykjavík.

KJARTANSSON, G. (1955). Fródlegar jökulrákir. *Náttúrufr.* **25**, 154–171.

KJARTANSSON, G. (1958). Jardmyndanir í Holtum og nágrenni. *Univ. Res. Inst. Dept. of Agric. Rep. B.* **11**, 1–23.

KJARTANSSON, G. (1961). Um jardfrædi vesturhluta Árnessýslu. *Árb. Ferdaf. Íslands* 1961, 17–29.

Löve, Á, and Löve, D. (1956). Cytotaxonomical conspectus of the Icelandic flora. *Acta Horti Gotoburg.* **20**, 65–291.

Okko, V. (1956). Glacial drift in Iceland. *Acta Geogr. Fenn.* **15**, 1–133.

Pflug, H. D. (1959). Sporenbilder aus Island und ihre stratigraphische Bedeutung. *N. Jahrb. Geol. Paläontolog.*, Abh. 107, 141–172.

Steindórsson, S. (1954). Um aldur og innflutning islenzku flórunnar. *Arsrit Ræktunarfel. Nordurlands* **51**, 3–23, 53–72, 101–115.

Straka, H. (1956). Pollenanalytische Untersuchungen eines Moorprofiles aus Nord-Island. *N. Jahrb. Geol. Paläontolog.*, Mh. **6**, 262–272.

Thorarinsson, S. (1937). The main geological and geomorphological features of Iceland. *Geogr. Ann.* **19**, 161–171.

Thorarinsson, S. (1944). Tephrokronologiska studier på Island. *Geogr. Ann.* **26**, 1–217.

Thorarinsson, S. (1954). Tephra-fall of Hekla on March 29th 1947. *The eruption of Hekla 1947–1948*, II, **3**, 1–68.

Thorarinsson, S. (1955). Nákudungslögin vid Húnaflóa í ljósi nýrra aldursákvardana. *Náttúrufr.* **25**, 172–186.

Thorarinsson, S. (1956). Mórinn í Seltjörn. *Náttúrufr.* **26**, 179–193.

Thorarinsson, S. (1958). The Öræfajökull eruption of 1362. *Acta Nat. Island* II, **2**, 1–99.

Thorarinsson, S. (1958). Uppblástur á Íslandi í ljósi öskulagarannsókna. *Ársrit Skógræktarfél. Íslands* 1961, 17–54.

Thoroddsen, Th. (1906). Island. Grundriss der Geographie und Geologie. *Peterm. Mitt* Ergäns. Heft, 152–153, 1–358. Gotha.

PALYNOLOGY AND PLEISTOCENE ECOLOGY

G. ERDTMAN

Palynological Laboratory, Stockholm-Solna, Sweden

THE broad outline of Post-glacial plant development was emphasized by Andersson (1909) more than 50 years ago. His conclusions were based mainly on the occurrence of megascopic fossils in Scandinavian and Finnish peat deposits. It was, however, von Post (1918) who, in the second decade of the present century, introduced pollen statistics as a new botanical and geological research method, thereby inaugurating the present epoch of pan-global research into vegetational and climatical history. The main stages of the development, which can be condensed and vividly portrayed by following the story of "cryocrats", "protocrats", etc., have been elucidated by von Post (*loc. cit.*) and those who have followed in his footsteps (e.g. Firbas, 1949, 1952; Iversen, 1958).

Statocrats. Statocrats, as here defined (Greek *statos* = stationary, *kratos* = power), live in stable environments. In Quaternary climatic cycles—from an Ice Age to an Interglacial period to a new Ice Age and so forth—the first statocratic biota are *cryocrats* (Greek *kryos* = ice), i.e. elements that can live under the severe conditions of an Ice Age. They are gradually replaced by *protocratic* biota (Greek *protos* = first) which characterize the climatic amelioration (after the Ice Age). These, in turn, are succeeded by the mesocrats (Greek *mesos* = middle) of the Interglacial or Post-glacial Climatic Optimum. Eventually *telocrats* (Greek *telos* = end) close the circle, forming a connecting link between the mesocrats and the cryocrats of a new Ice Age (cf. Iversen, 1958).

Apocrats. Apocrats, as here defined (Greek *apo* = back, away), do not live in stable environments. Apocrats are opportunists, kinetophilous elements to which lack of competition generally means more than climatic and edaphic conditions. Thus granted freedom from competition, they can appear at practically any time, be it during an Ice Age or a Climatic Optimum. They invade virgin soil uncovered by a retreating glacier, the sudden drainage of an ice-dammed lake, etc. They likewise spread into areas emerging from the sea as the result of eustatic sinking of the Ocean level or isostatic upheaval of land. They also enter areas where a temporary freedom from competition accompanies the upsetting of the natural balance by axes, plows, bulldozers, etc., in fields and forests, along highways and railroads, in the outskirts of villages and towns, etc. Intermittent changes induced by volcanic activity or earthquakes, etc., and non-intermittent changes caused by erosion and deposition, etc., also favor certain apocrats. They may invade wide stretches of land and remain for a long time as the dominating element if the area in question—like the Alvar steppe on the Isle of Öland, Sweden—offers some kind of perpetual instability (in Öland the shallow soil is broken up each year by frost action). Usually, however, they are confined to narrow belts, as, for example, the Sea Buckthorn (*Hippophaë rhamnoides*) in the tension zone between sea and forest along the slowly emerging shores of the Gulf of Bothnia.

But conditions have changed. In this respect *Hippophaë* provides an instructive example. As the continental ice withdrew from Sweden, this species followed the receding ice-border not only along the coasts but practically all over the country. Fossil *Hippophaë* pollen grains were identified by Halden (1917), but it was von Post (1918) who emphasized the importance of these pollen grains as indicators of open, treeless areas. This, it seems, is the first important contribution to the theme "Palynology and Pleistocene Ecology".

Surface samples. The present often provides clues for unlocking the secrets of the past. However, attempts to draw historical conclusions from the actual distribution of biota have not always been successful. It is impossible, for instance, to draw any conclusions from the maps of the present-day distribution of *Artemisia* spp., *Centaurea cyanus*, chenopodiaceous plants, *Ephedra* sp., *Helianthemum* cf. *oelandicum*, etc., regarding the former occurrence of these species in the wake of the receding ice in northwestern Europe.

On the other hand, it is easy to study, practically all over the globe, the way in which the vegetation is reflected by the "pollen rain" of the present day. The amount and composition of the pollen rain can be ascertained by trapping pollen grains in different ways, including the collection of those that sink in lakes, etc. The composition of pollen rains, the effect of long-distance transport, etc., can also be studied by subjecting surface samples from living bogs (lichen thalli, moss tufts, and similar material) to pollen analysis.

In connection with the theory of pollen analysis, the effect of long-distance transport of pollen grains was first studied by Hesselman (1919). A comparison between the forests and the distribution of the different tree species in a certain area on one hand, and the pollen spectra in surface samples from the same area on the other was made a few years later (Erdtman, 1921). In 1943 a study of different types of pollen spectra was published, including "habitation spectra" particularly rich in pollen grains of "apocrats" (Erdtman, 1943).

Some apocrats produce pollen grains in great profusion, e.g. *Ambrosia, Artemisia, Urtica,* and certain chenopodiaceous species. In northern Sweden many surface samples contain at least a trace of *Artemisia* pollen although botanists roaming about in this part of the country may search for days without encountering a single specimen. If, however, the apocrats with regard to their pollen grains behave like *Trifolium pratense*, for instance, there will be only a slight chance, if any, of finding their pollen in surface samples.

From the study of surface samples—unfortunately much neglected hitherto—it is evident that pollen statistics affords a means of tracing the history of at least some apocrats and thus, at the same time, of the ecological conditions of which they are characteristic.

Fossil apocrat pollen grains. Hippophaë pollen has already been dealt with. Another interesting pollen type, at least in part apocratic, is *Artemisia*. These pollen grains were identified after having been referred to for many years as "*Salix* 2" by early pollen analysts, even though they realized that the pollen grains were not produced by species belonging to that genus.

Hippophaë and at least some of the Late Glacial *Artemisia* are examples of ananthropochorous apocrats whose appearance and dispersal have not been influenced by man. The history of anthropochorous apocrats as well as other plants, the distribution of which was disturbed by deforestation through clearing and cultivation, has been dealt with in great detail by Iversen in his important "landnam" paper (Iversen, 1941). Special attention should be paid to *Centaurea cyanus*, generally believed to be a typical anthropochorous element that attained its present distribution in Europe in connection with the cultivation of rye. After a report—in 1948—on findings of pollen grains of *Centaurea cyanus* in Late Glacial deposits, several stray finds of this characteristic pollen type have been made in various countries. Of particular interest is the report by Schmitz (1957) on pollen grains of *Centaurea cyanus* in a bog in northern Germany, from Late Glacial deposits right up to recent layers.

The finds were made not far from Kiel. In the neighborhood there is a place called Schwedeneck where the steep slopes of the Baltic end moraine are continuously being eroded and broken down by the sea. In the loose slopes grow the moss *Dicranella varia* and many other plants of a more or less decidedly apocratic habit. A narrow path borders the upper margin of the slope a foot or two from the declivity. Between this path and the slope is a characteristic assemblage of plants, including, i.a., *Artemisia* and *Centaurea*. There they are secure: nobody, neither man nor beast, walks along the edge of an abyss. Theoretically this assemblage could be a relict of Late Glacial vegetation that has maintained itself through all the vicissitudes of climate and vegetational change in Post-glacial times. Our scanty knowledge of the history of these plants seems to be due to the fact that their pollen grains cannot be expected to have been accumulated in appreciable numbers in bogs and other polliniferous deposits because such are rare in the vicinity.

A sort of parallel to the conditions at Schwedeneck is found at Mount Omberg in southern Sweden. Here it may be possible, as pointed out, e.g. by Hedberg (1949), that some plants now growing on or near the mountain are direct descendants from pioneers (partially at least of an apocratic habit) which, as described by Erdtman (1949) lived on a terrain that protruded as a small nunatak from the surrounding, rapidly shrinking continental ice. Among the pioneers were some plants now confined, in their capacity of more or less kinetophilous elements, to Öland, particularly on the Alvar steppe (*Helianthemum* cf. *oelandicum*, *Artemisia* cf. *rupestris*). Kinetophilous plants like these, disliking much competition, probably had a chance of surviving, e.g. in the sometimes almost vertical slopes of Mount Omberg facing Lake Vättern. No traces of them have been found there, however: a continuous existence as botanical "cat-burglars" over 10,000 years is not easily accomplished.

Detailed studies of the pollen or spore morphology also in "trivial" elements in the flora of Iceland and Scandinavia, etc., can lead to new, unexpected vistas. Thus, at the Palynological Laboratory in Solna, about 10,000 pollen slides of Scandinavian plants have been made and distributed to a number of scientific institutions in Sweden and Finland. Among these were also slides of *Rorippa silvestris*. One *Rorippa* slide, however, was returned with the comment that a mistake must have been made since pollen grains of the same type as those in the slide "do not occur in the Cruciferae". A check revealed that there was no mistake. Pollen grains from 40 different specimens of *Rorippa silvestris* from various parts of Europe were investigated. The grains in "statocratic" individuals were, it seemed, all normal, 3-colpate, whereas those in more or less sterile individuals of a somewhat "apocratic" habit (growing along roads, in grass swards in Stockholm and suburbs, etc.) were deviating. In certain examples the pollen grains were devoid of apertures or were provided with five to six colpi or colpoid apertures. In some specimens the outer part of the exine (the sexine) was reticulate, in others retipilate, i.e. provided with drumstick-shaped processes arranged in a reticuloid pattern. In some grains, finally, the sexine was considerably thinner than the inner part of the exine (the nexine). Other grains were, it seemed, destitute of nexine or almost so. A cytotaxonomic analysis of the *Rorippa silvestris*-complex is now being carried out at Uppsala (for further notes, illustrations, etc., cf. Erdtman, 1958).

I have deliberately dealt with *Rorippa silvestris* at some length, mainly for two reasons. The first is that this palynological investigation revealed something actually going on before taxonomists and cytotaxonomists had observed that there was anything "wrong" or peculiar with the Linnean species *Rorippa silvestris*. The second reason is strictly palynological: which factors are responsible for the variation of aperture patterns and the details of exine stratification? This is a question of great interest. Critical investigations into this theme would be much more worthwhile than uncritical speculations on the taxonomic and phylogenetic bearing of certain pollen grain characters now in vogue.

In speaking of the border-lines between palynology, cytology, and cytotaxonomy, a few words may be added concerning pollen grains in some species of *Sanguisorba* (cf. Erdtman and Nordborg, 1961). Here, from size and other morphological details, it seems possible to determine the chromosome race ($2n = 28$ or 56, etc.) to which the pollen grains belong. This is true both with regard to fresh grains and, in certain cases at least, with regard to fossil, e.g. Late Glacial, pollen grains. The example favors a view expressed by Stebbins (1959): "In view of the fact that the characteristics of pollen which distinguish modern species are becoming much better known while discoveries and analyses of fossil pollen are also greatly increasing in number, the combination of these two types of data for the purpose of tracing out the ancestry of polyploid complexes would seem to be a valuable new avenue of approach which deserves attention."

Apocrats and the history of the Icelandic biota. To me, mention of the nature of Iceland conjures up the vivid description in the book "Till Häcklefjäll" by the Swedish author and artist Albert Engström. Therefore I must restrain myself and point out only one or two things that may possibly be of interest to future palynological investigators concerned with ecological and phytogeographical conditions in Iceland.

The mixture of ice and fire, of volcanism and glaciation, contribute to make Iceland a rewarding place for the study of apocratic biota, "obligate" as well as "facultative". Furthermore, Iceland is only sparsely inhabited and one may thus expect a more distinct difference—or at least one more easily disentangled—between apocrats and statocrats than in densely populated, heavily trafficked areas.

"Tephrochronology" is a term introduced by Thórarinsson (1944). Not only volcanic ash (Greek *tefra* = ash) as indicated by this term, but also other products of volcanic activity have interfered with the natural vegetation. Which are, or were, the main phases of regeneration? Which apocrats correspond, ecologically, to, for example, the scattered, very characteristic *Eriogonum spp.* around Crater Lake, Oregon, or to the "pioneers" on the slopes of Mt. Etna and Mt. Vesuvius?

And, with regard to the immigration of plants on virgin soil laid bare at the retreat of glaciers, which plants in Iceland correspond to those invading similar soils in other parts of the world, in Alaska, at the end of the Rhône Glacier in Switzerland (cf. *Flora* **146**, p. 386, 1958), etc.?

The interrelationship between certain apocratic elements along the sea coast and common "weeds" as well as certain "continental" elements on high mountains, inland plateaus, etc., far from the coasts or other places where their nearest relatives occur, ought to be studied (cf. also Godwin, 1960). Ten to twenty years ago some of the leading taxonomists and phytogeographers apparently paid only scant attention to some of the apocratic news of that time (e.g. the occurrence of pollen grains of *Artemisia*, *Centaurea cyanus*, and *Ephedra* in Late Glacial deposits; of *Artemisia*, Chenopodiaceae and Cruciferae side by side with *Hippophaë* in Öland, Sweden, and in the interior of southern Lapland just at or after the disappearance of the last remnants of dead ice). Compare also the finding in the New Siberian Islands of pollen grains of *Artemisia* and chenopodiaceous plants in layers which, it seems, were laid down during a particularly apocratic régime. In our days they no longer live in these places (cf. Gorodkov, 1954).

What is needed are more detailed investigations carried out with refined techniques and sound judgement, without exaggeration of the duration and importance of open ground conditions and so forth.

Pollen morphology, cytotaxonomy, and advanced microscopical techniques. In Scandinavia the number of tree species is quite suitable with regard to pollen statistics. In the U.S.A. the situation is often more complicated owing to the great number of tree species. In Iceland conditions are not ideal either because of the low number of species. Yet it is possible (cf., for example, Praglowski, 1962) to distinguish pollen grains of *Betula nana* from those of the tree birches (*B. pubescens* and *B. tortuosa*), and—if the grains are typical and well preserved—often also between the grains of the two latter species. Hybridism—hitherto not adequately studied from a palynological point of view—will no doubt make the matter more complicated. Attention should be drawn to the importance of suitable embedding media, adequate optical facilities, etc. (Berglund, Erdtman and Praglowski, 1959). Electron micrographs exhibiting the fine relief of the exine surface (Pl. V, 1) are often very instructive and helpful also to those working with an ordinary light microscope. They demonstrate sharply and precisely some of the features which can be seen only dimly by means of the latter. Thus, the white dots and streaks, e.g. in Pl. I, 1, 2, 5, 7 and in Pl. II, 1, 2, 4, 9 and 10, represent small spinules and ridges of more or less the same shape as those shown in Pl. V, 1 and in some places in the UV micrograph Pl. V, 2.

Plates I–IV have no direct bearing on Icelandic Pleistocene problems. They have been inserted, however, as examples of what might be done in the way of making better and safer specific determinations based on pollen grains. Thus, tetraploid pollen grains of *Alnus glutinosa* (Pl. I) are considerably larger than those of diploid specimens and usually also slightly different morphologically (cf. the ringlike "arcus" the center of 9). "Tetraploid" grains have, so far, only been noticed once in Swedish Post-glacial deposits (unpubl.). They are of much the same shape as fossil grains described from the Early Tertiary volcanic districts in Scotland (Simpson, 1961). Detached "arcus" are also found in *Alnus sieboldiana* (Simpson, *loc. cit.*). The apertures in *A. glutinosa* are, as a rule, more narrow than those in *A. incana* (Pl. II). In Sweden the *Quercus robur–Q. petraea* problem (cf. Pls. III and IV) has not yet been tackled with pollen statistics. Investigations are, however, being carried out in order to determine whether some of the features shown in the

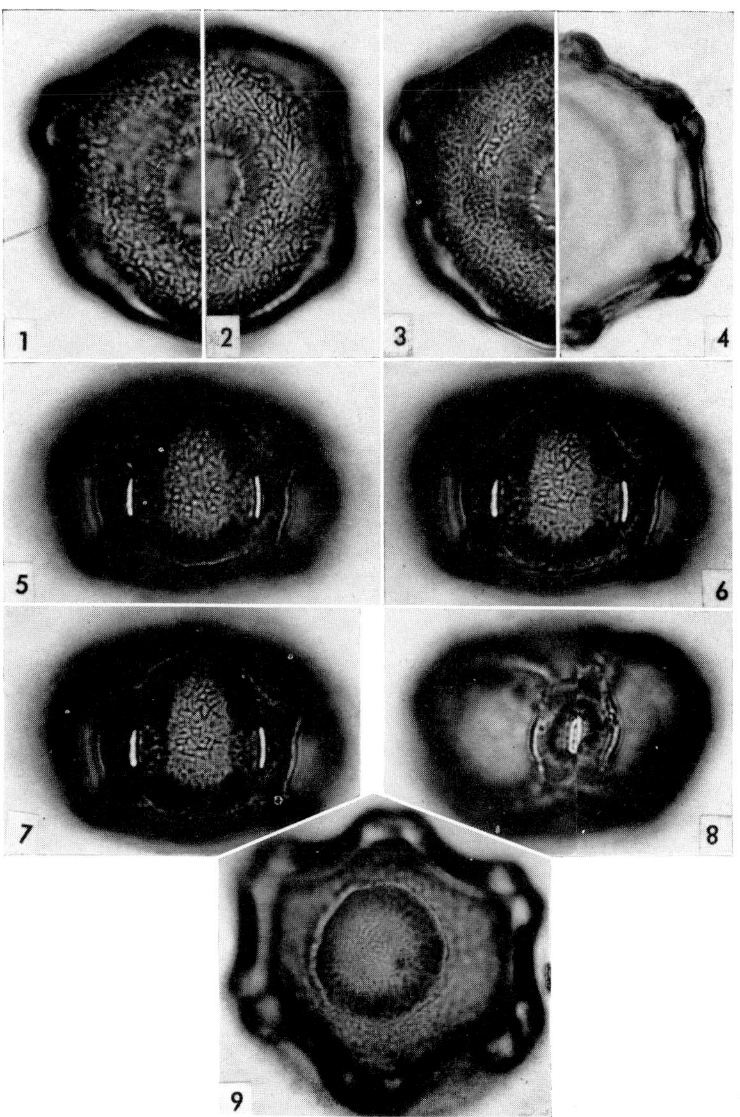

Pl. I. Pollen grains of tetraploid *Alnus glutinosa* from Ekebo, Sweden. ×1300.

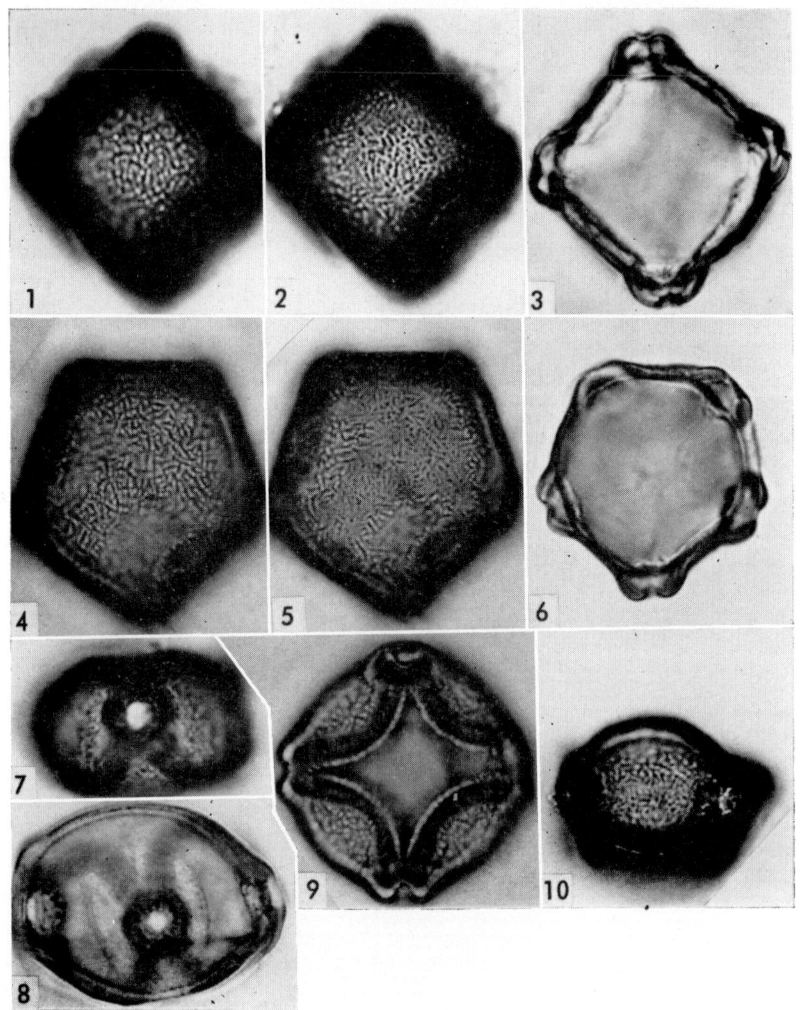

Pl. II. Pollen grains of *Alnus incana* $\times 1300$.

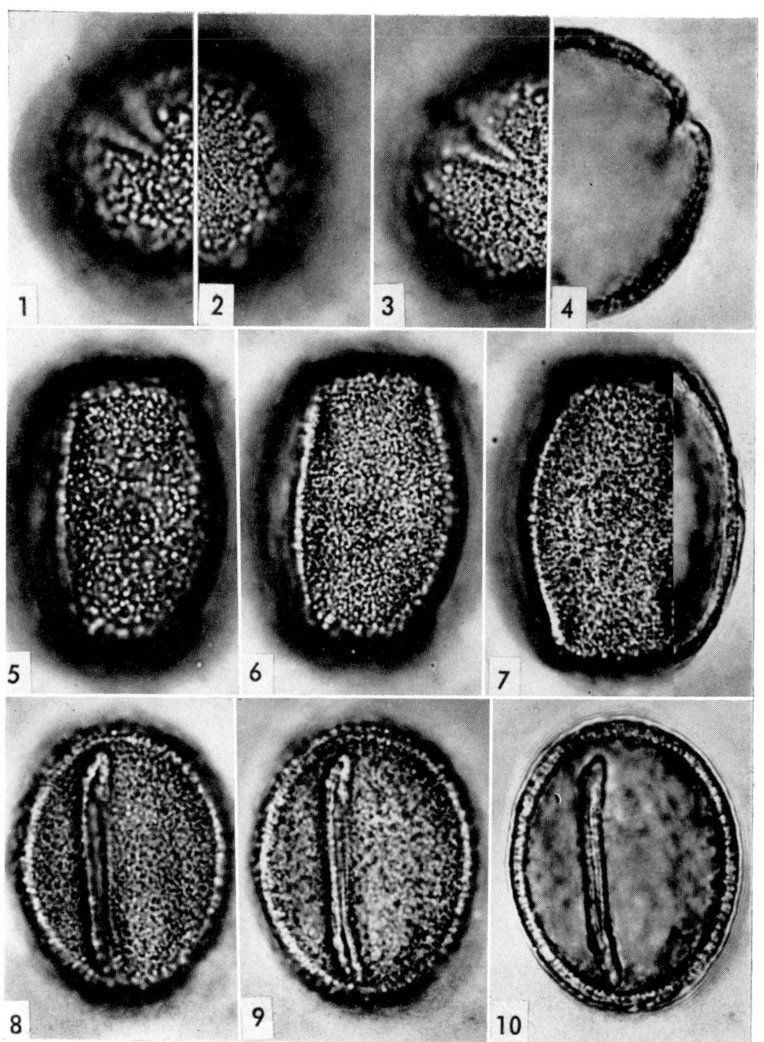

Pl. III. Pollen grains of *Quercus petraea*. ×1300.

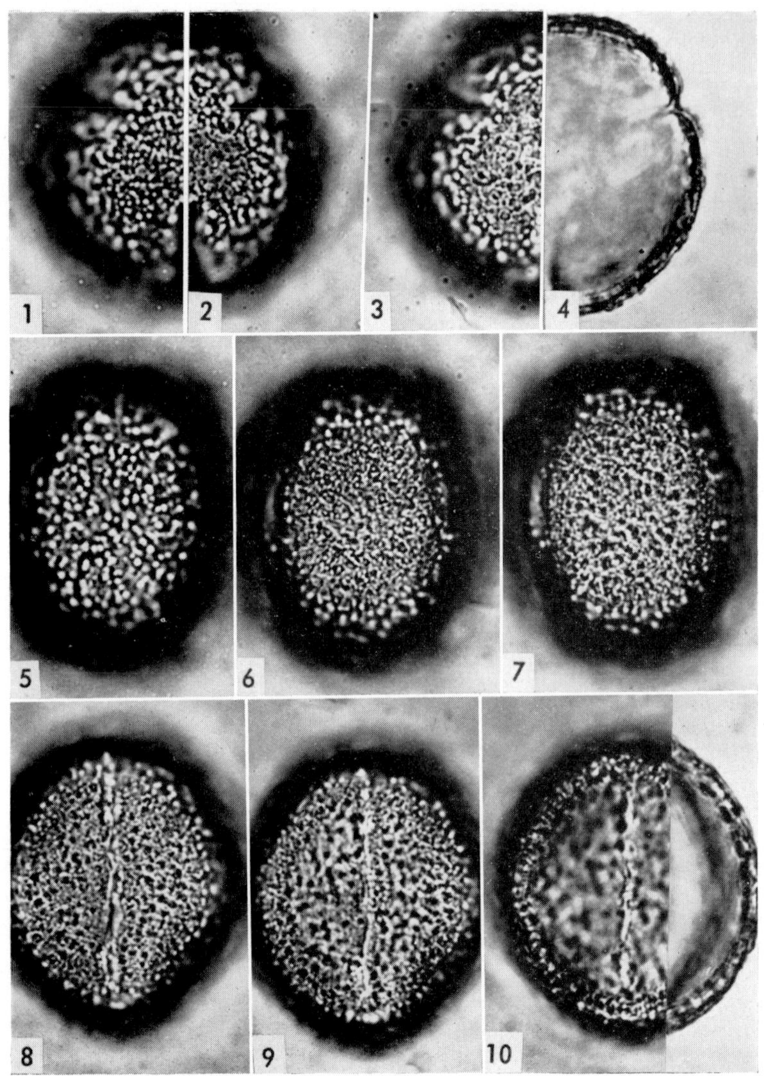

Pl. IV. Pollen grains of *Quercus robur*. ×1300.

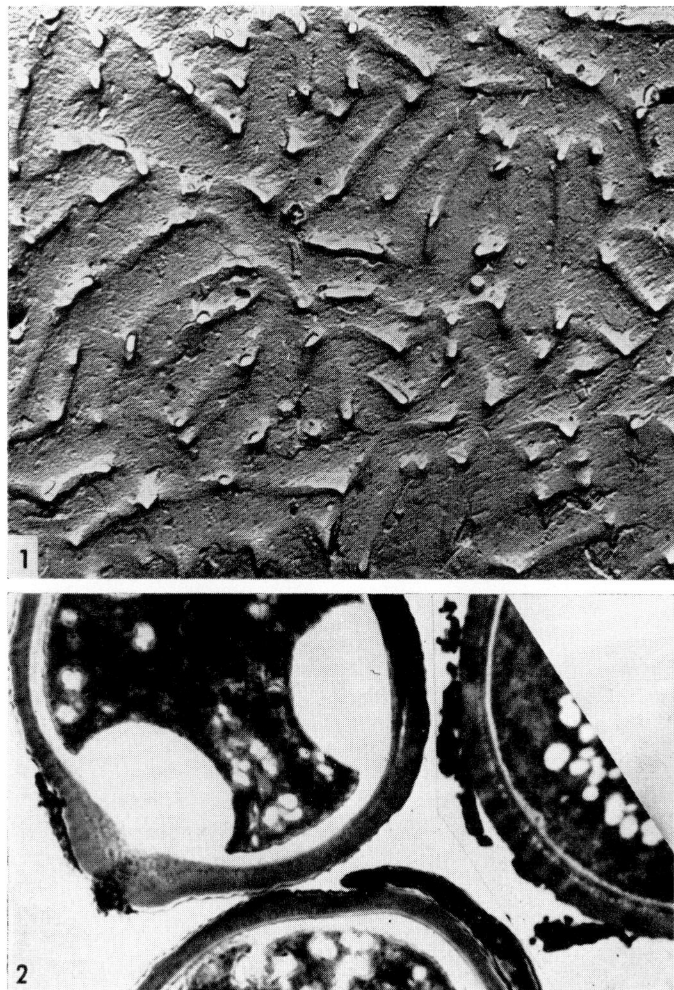

Pl. V. 1, Replica of pollen wall with spinules and ridges of *Betula verrucosa*. Electron micrograph $\times$ 8,000. 2, UV-micrograph of *Corylus avellana* pollen. $\times$ 2000.

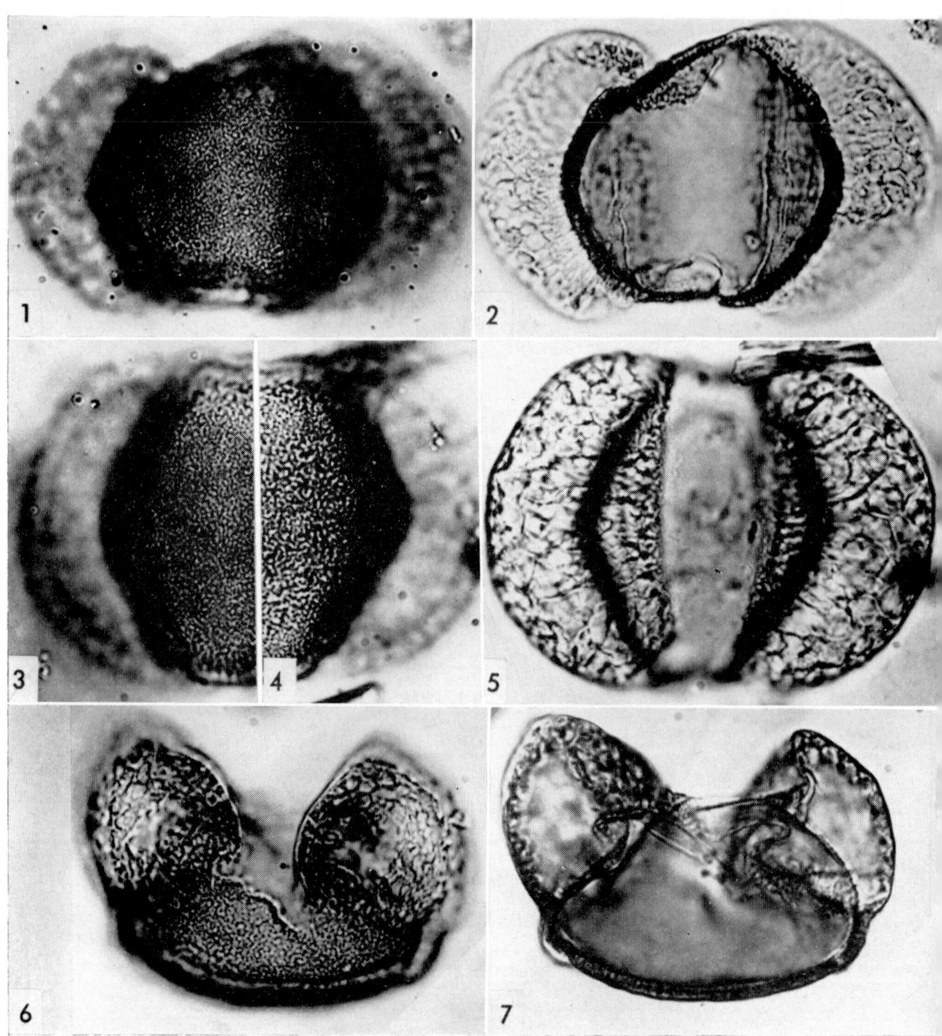

Pl. VI. Pollen grains of the Chinese conifer *Cathaya argyrophylla.* ×950. Pollen grains—as those in Pl. I. 9—embedded in glycerine jelly; the pollen grains in Pl. I: 1–8, II–IV are in distilled water.

plates—small, densely spaced processes in *Q. petraea*, larger, less densely spaced processes in *Q. robur*—are constant or not. Pollen grains of *Tilia cordata* can be easily distinguished from those of *T. platyphylla*.

Furthermore: what is the cytotaxonomic status of *Geranium silvaticum* with comparatively small flowers and pollen grains (Erdtman, unpubl., specimens from Järvsö, Sweden, 1961); and what is that of the large luxuriant specimens of *Sedum acre*, Hammerfest, Norway, etc.?

If someone asks: "Have these things anything to do with the theme 'Palynology and Pleistocene ecology' (with special reference to Iceland)"? the reply is: "Yes and no". My intention has been to stress the importance of basic pollen morphological research, preferably in connection with cytological and cytotaxonomic studies; also to stress the desirability of investigations into the pollen grains and spores of statocrats as well as of apocrats, in surface samples of various kinds; finally, the importance of pollen statistical studies not only of large polliniferous deposits (as in bogs), where pollen grains of statocrats necessarily dominate, but also of podzolized soils and of any small, local, in one respect or another "queer" deposits of peats and sediments. Here interesting, unexpected finds may be made. The palynologist in charge must act as a pathfinder. He will perhaps go astray if he pays too much attention to the routine palynological approach: new problems demand new methods. This may be illustrated by a few words on the début of palynology in Swedish criminology. Four experts, among them a pollen analyst, working independently of one another, arrived at the same conclusion: some dirt adhering to the clothes of a murdered person could not have come from the place where the corpse was found. This statement was of importance to the court. Later another palynologist was asked to undertake a control investigation. As a result he was able to testify to the great care and skill with which his colleague had accomplished his analyses. His conclusion, however, was contrary to that arrived at by the four experts: The dirt, or part of it, must have come from near the very place where the corpse was found. This conclusion was based on the fact that pollen grains of *Trifolium pratense* as well as zygospores of a subterranean phycomycete (*Endogone* sp.; det. by Professor J. A. Nannfeldt, Uppsala) were found in the dirt on the clothes as well as in one or two soil samples from near the place where the corpse was lying. They were not found in any other samples. Compared to these findings, the relative frequencies of tree pollen grains and the locally highly varied non-tree pollen grains must, in my opinion, be considered of minor significance. (cf. Fries in *Nordisk Kriminalteknisk Tidskrift* **31**, 1961; Erdtman, ibid. **32**, 1962).

Does *Endogone* occur in Iceland? What information can be derived from tracing the history of Icelandic apocrats? What is the importance of "apocracy" in the development of biota? Did early Angiosperms live as apocrats, leaving practically no fossil record? Did some apocrats suddenly succeed, appearing in enormous quantities after having been more or less hidden for ages? Did they invade new territories, suppressing the old vegetation? Did they leave the soil, establishing themselves as "preloranthaceous" parasites, eventually killing the Gymnosperms or other plants upon which they lived? What is "*Micropinus*" of which small pinoid pollen grains are encountered in old Icelandic strata? Have they any connection with the small pollen grains in the recently described coniferous genus *Cathaya* from China (cf. Pl. VI)? What about the possibility of picking out fossil birch pollen grains, etc., from Icelandic Interglacial and Post-glacial deposits, and having them subjected to study under the electron microscope? Replicas showing the fine details of the exine relief can, with some training, be made without too great difficulty, as shown by M. Takeoka (unpubl.). Replicas of a number of pre-Quaternary pollen grains and spores have been made at the Palynological Laboratory, Solna. This would mean another approach to the study of stability and instability, in the course of the ages, of certain characteristics in special plants. Which species are static, or which are in statu nascendi? What is, in evolution, the real importance of apocracy versus statocracy?

REFERENCES

ANDERSSON, G. (1909). The climate of Sweden in the Late-Quarternary period. Facts and theories. *Iv. Geol. Unders.* C. 218.

BERGLUND, B., ERDTMAN, G., and PRAGLOWSKI, J. (1959). Några ord om betydelsen av inbäddningsmediets brytningsindex vid palynologiska undersökningar. *Svensk Bot. Tidskr.* **53**, 462–468.

ERDTMAN, G. (1921). Pollenanalytische Untersuchungen von Torfmooren und marinen Sedimenten in Südwest-Schweden. *Ark. f. Bot.* **17** (10), 1–173.

ERDTMAN, G. (1943). Pollen spectra from Swedish plant communities. Addendum: Pollen analytical soil studies in southern Lapland. *Geol. Fören. Stockh. Förhandl.* **65**, 37–66.

ERDTMAN, G. (1949). Palynological aspects of the pioneer phase in the immigration of the Swedish flora II. Identification of the pollen grains in Late Glacial samples from Mt. Omberg, Ostrogothia. *Svensk Bot. Tidskr.* **43**, 46–55.

ERDTMAN, G. (1958). Über die Pollenmorphologie von *Rorippa silvestris. Flora* **146**, 408–411.

ERDTMAN, G., and NORDBORG, G. (1961). Über Möglichkeiten die Geschichte verschiedener Chromosomenzahlenrassen von *Sanguisorba officinalis* und *S. minor* pollenanalytisch zu beleuchten. *Bot. Notiser* **114** 19–21.

FIRBAS, F. (1949, 1952). *Spät- und nacheiszeitliche Waldgeschichte Mitteleuropas nördlich der Alpen.* I, II. Jena.

GODWIN, H. (1960). The history of weeds in Britain. In Harper, J. (ed.): *The Biology of weeds.* Oxford, 1–10.

GORODKOV, B. N. (1954). La palynologie en Russie 1. Paysages pléistocènes peri-glacières en Asie du Nord. *Bot. Notiser* 1954, 90–94.

HALDEN, B. (1917). Om torvmossar och marina sediment inom norra Hälsinglands litorina-område. *Sv. Geol. Unders.* C. 280, 1–227.

HEDBERG, O. (1949). Vegetation och flora inom Ombergs skyddsområde. *Svenska Vetensk. Akad. Avh. Naturskyddsärt.* **5**, 1–64.

HESSELMAN, H. (1919). Iakttagelser över skogsträdspollens spridnings-förmåga. *Medd. Stat. Skogsförsöksanst.* **16**.

IVERSEN, J. (1941). Landnam i Danmarks stenalder. *Danm. Geol. Unders.* II (66), 1–68.

IVERSEN, J. (1958). The bearing of Glacial and Interglacial epochs on the formation and extinction of plant taxa. *Uppsala Univ. Årsskr.* **1958** (6), 210–215.

POST, L. VON (1918). Skogsträdspollen i sydsvenska torfmosselagerföljder. *Forh.* **16.** *Skand. naturforskerm. i Kristiania* 1916.

PRAGLOWSKI, J. (1962). Notes on the pollen morphology of Swedish trees and shrubs. *Grana Palynologia* **3,** 45–65

SIMPSON, H. (1961). The Tertiary pollen-flora of Mull and Ardnamurchan. *Trans. R. Soc. Edinb.* **64** (16).

STEBBINS, G. (1959). Genes, chromosomes and evolution. In Turrill, W. B. (ed.), *Vistas in Botany*, 258–290.

THÓRARINSSON, S. (1944). Tefrokronologiska studier på Island. *Geogr. Ann.* 1944, 1–217.

THE SVÍNAFELL LAYERS
PLANT-BEARING INTERGLACIAL SEDIMENTS IN ÖRÆFI, SOUTHEAST ICELAND

SIGURDUR THORARINSSON
Museum of Natural History, Reykjavík, Iceland

IN early June 1957 a young farmer, Helgi Björnsson, found a small fragment of petrified wood in the scree of Snidagil, a ravine on the western side of Svínafellsfjall in the Öræfi district, southeast Iceland (see Fig. 1 and Pl. I). H. Björnsson is the youngest of the "Kvısker brothers" who live at the farm Kvísker and are renowned as keen observers of nature and very interested in various branches of natural science. One of these brothers, Sigurdur Björnsson, visited Snidagil shortly after his brother had found the petrified wood and discovered at the same place some fragmental leaf impressions. These he sent to the present writer, who went to Öræfi a little later, studied for some days the geology and stratigraphy of the plant-bearing deposits and organized more thoroughly the collecting of leaf impressions; this was carried out mainly by Sigurdur Björnsson who has found all the most important species hitherto collected there. In July 1958 the author continued his stratigraphical studies of Svínafellsfjall with special regard to the remanent magnetism of the rocks. He was accompanied by a young Icelandic geologist, Thorleifur Einarsson, who collected samples from the plant-bearing layers mainly for pollen-analytical and other microscopical studies which he, however, has not yet found time to finish.

The paper here submitted is a short presentation of what is currently known about the Svínafell layers. The author expresses his sincere thanks to his collaborators, S. Björnsson and Th. Einarsson, for their valuable help. He is also indebted to Dr. Svend Th. Andersen (Geological Survey of Denmark) who has determined many of the leaf impressions collected, and to Mr. Tryggvi Samúelsson, Reykjavík, who has photographed them.

THE GEOGRAPHICAL SITUATION

The plant-bearing layers here given the name "Svínafell layers" form a part of the mountain Svínafellsfjall (older name Svínafell) in the district Öraefi, southeast Iceland. Svínafellsfjall (Fig. 2) is a mountain bordering on the Öraefajökull massif and forms the forward section of the ridge that juts

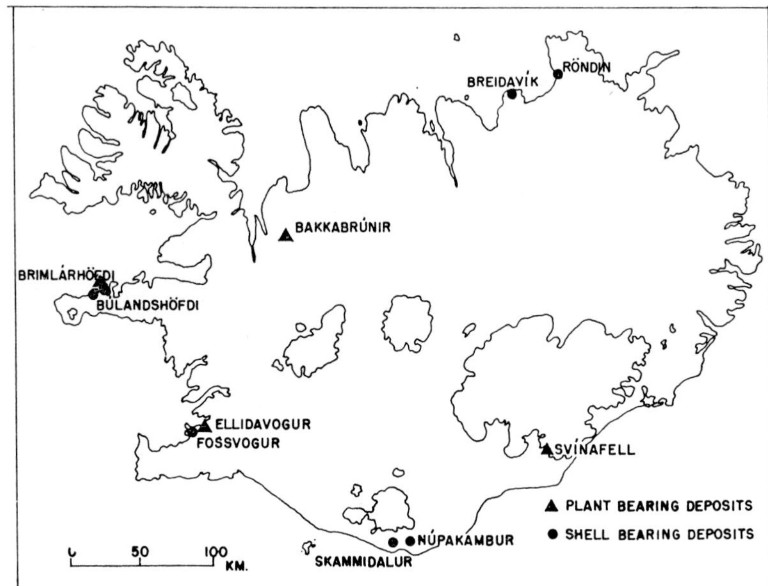

FIG. 1. Location of Pleistocene fossil-bearing deposits in Iceland.

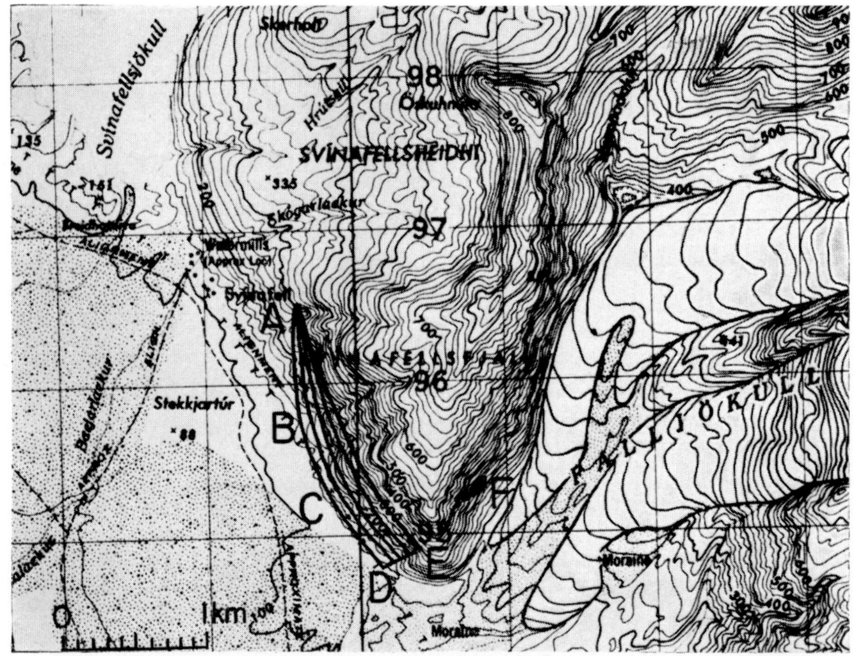

FIG. 2. Svínafellsfjall and its surroundings. Base map: U.S. Army Map Service, Sheet 6018 IV, scale 1:50,000, striated: the Svínafell layers. A, Skjólgil; B, Godagil; C, Breidagil; D, Snidagil; E, Snidabrekka; F, Gapar.

forward between Svínafellsjökull and Falljökull (Pl. II, 1). The gravel plain west of Svínafellsfjall is about 120 m above sea level and from this plain the steep west face of the mountain rises about 450 m. On this west face the Svínafell layers are exposed for a distance of 1.7 km, between the ravine Snidagil in the south and the north edge of Skjólgil in the north. For a distance of 1.2 km between the Godagil and Snidagil ravines, the layers form the base of the mountain and can be clearly seen from the highway to the west where their light yellow–brown color contrasts strongly with the darker surroundings (cf. Pls. II and III). It is really curious that they have not previously attracted the attention of geologists. It should be noted, though, that Henson (1955, p. 45) mentions "a sandstone formation in the succession of Svínafell" without further description. The layers are also exposed in a small spot, named Gapar, on the eastern face of Svínafellsfjall.

S. Björnsson has informed the author that on Skeidarársandur, in the area between the Skeidará river and the tourist hut, are boulders and blocks of material very similar to the Svínafell layers, and in the spring of 1959 he found distinct plant remnants, bits of grass and unclassified foliage, in one such block. These blocks must once have been *in situ* either beneath Skeidarárjökull or in the mountains along the eastern margin of that glacier and thus at least 20 km distant from Svínafell. Whether these sediments are of the same age as the Svínafell layers is an open question. Furthermore it should be mentioned that both Björnsson and the author have observed a layer of bedded sediments, about 30 m in thickness, in Breidamerkurfjall on the eastern side of Öræfajökull. On closer examination Björnsson has not succeeded in finding any plant remnants in these layers, and in the author's opinion they are probably older than the Svínafell layers, although most likely of Pleistocene age. Their bedding is graded and they are probably glaciolacustrine. Petrified boulders of varied glacial sediments from this area have been described by Tryggvason (1952, pp. 96–98).

THE STRATIGRAPHY OF SVÍNAFELLSFJALL AND THE SVÍNAFELL LAYER

As mentioned above, the Svínafell layers form the base of Svínafellsfjall south of Godagil. North of that ravine the base of the layers rises gradually towards the north, but the contact is visible in only a few places because of scree and soil cover. Just north of Skjólgil the base of the layers is about 160 m above the plain and their thickness is about 15 m. The underlying basalt layers there are normally magnetized down to a layer about 100 m below the sediments, but farther down all layers are reversed. In the reverse layers some of the amygdoils are partly filled with crypto-crystalline quartz, and these layers are on the whole more old-looking than the normally magnetized overlaying layers. There may be a hiatus between the two groups, although a clear erosion contact is not exposed (cf. Fig. 3).

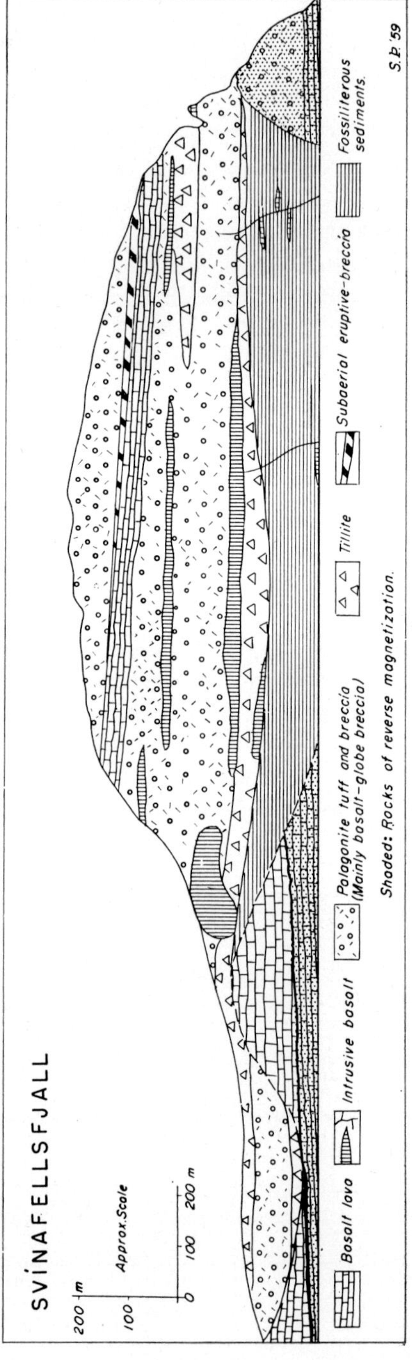

FIG. 3. The west face of Svínafellsfjall (cf. also Pl. I).

Pl. I. Svínafellsfjall viewed from the west. A, Skjólgil; B, Godagil; C, Breidagil; D, Snidagil; E, Snidabrekka. (*Photo S. Thorarinsson.*)

Pl. II. 1, Svínafellsfjall and the glacier Falljökull. The Svínafell layers reach upwards to the line indicated by the arrow. The peak in the background is Hvannadalshnúkur, Iceland's highest peak. (*Photo S. Thorarinsson.*)

2, Snidagil and Snidabrekka (cf. Fig. 4). (*Photo S. Thorarinsson.*)

Pl. III. 1, The Svínafell layers at Breidagil. E, Upper grey layer; B, Lower grey layer. (*Photo S. Thorarinsson.*)

2, Detail of the Svínafell layers near Breidagil. The arrow points to a basalt sill. (*Photo S. Thorarinsson.*)

Pl. IV. 1, The contact between the Svínafell layers and the tillite just north of Breidagil. (*Photo S. Thorarinsson.*)

2, The contact between the Svínafell layers and the tillite just north of Skjólgil. (*Photo S. Thorarinsson.*)

How deep below the plain the Svínafell layers reach between Godagil and Snidagil cannot be said with certainty; in the author's opinion it is hardly more than ten meters or so. A normally magnetized basalt layer at their base at Breidagil is doubtless a sill. Two normally magnetized dykes cut through the layers and sills emerging from these dykes are intercalated between the sedimentary beds. One intrusive sheet connected with the northernmost dyke is only 5 cm thick and thoroughly conformable with the beds (Pl. III, 2). The maximum visible thickness of the sedimentary layers at Snidagil is about 140 m and, as their base a little farther north is at least 10 m lower and the layers are practically horizontal, the total thickness there has been at least 150 m. Towards the south the sediments are limited by Snidabrekka, the base of which consists of reversely magnetized basalt-globe breccia with individually scattered lava nodules.

On the west face of Svínafellsfjall as well as at Gapar on its east face, the Svínafell layers are covered by a 200–300 m thick series of tillites, basalt intrusions, and basalt-globe breccias with irregular layers of globular basalt. This series is capped by beds of subaerial lava. For the most part the tillite rests directly and uncomformably on the Svínafell layers. For a short distance, however, a basalt sill is intercalated between the tillite and the layers. The tillites at Svínafell have been described by Noe-Nygaard (1953, pp. 223–227; Nielsen and Noe-Nygaard, 1936, Figs. 2 and 3). Of their true morainic nature there is no doubt; they certainly contain beautifully striated boulders. In the author's opinion the two tillite beds as well as all tuff breccias between the Svínafell layers and the subaerial basalts 200–300 m higher up belong to the same Glacial, whereas a lower tillite bed in the ravines above the Svínafell farms may well belong—though this is not certain— to an older Glacial (cf. Noe-Nygaard, 1953, p. 224).

The subaerial lava beds capping the subglacially formed rock series could possibly be interpreted as the top layers of a table mountain and in that case could belong to the same Glacial as the underlying tuff breccias. More likely, however, these layers belong to the following Interglacial. These basalts are partly covered by a bed of grayish tuff breccia containing angular boulders. The author, who has had only a hasty glance at this breccia, is inclined to interpret it as subaerial eruptive breccia of the kind found around some Post-glacial explosion craters such as Hverfjall.

Over the subaerial layers is deposited a basalt-globe breccia forming the uppermost part of Svínafellsfjall.

DESCRIPTION OF THE SVÍNAFELL LAYERS

The Svínafell layers are for a great part lacustrine. The lower part of the formation shows a distinct macroscopic and partly graded bedding (rhytmites) which is horizontal except for the upper part of the contact zone towards

Snidabrekka where the layers bend upwards. On the contact with Snidabrekka is found rounded gravel, which in all probability is shore gravel.

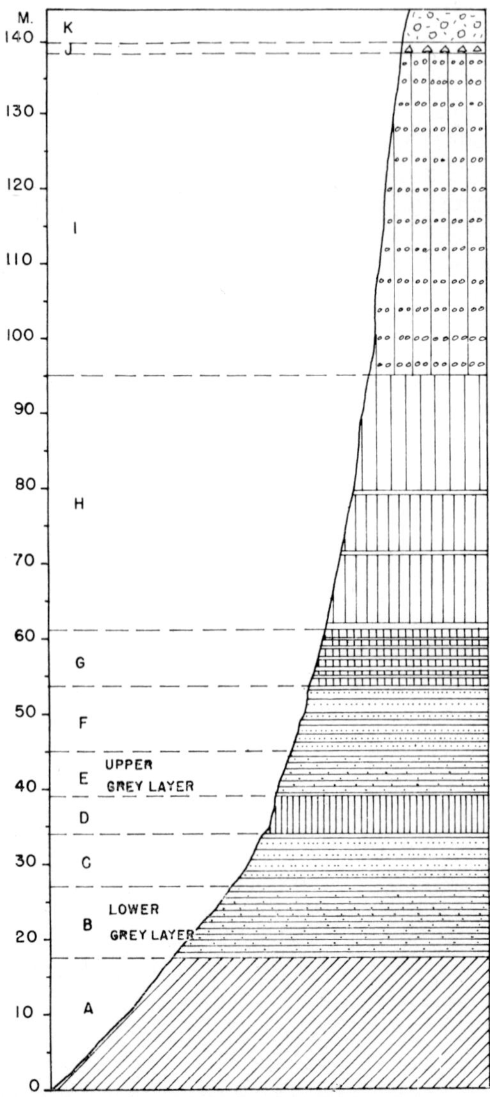

FIG. 4. Section through the Svinafell layers in Snidagil (cf. also Pl. II, 2).

Figure 4 shows a section through the layers in the Snidagil ravine, where the base of the layers is about 130 m above sea level. For the height measurements the author used a Locke level and an aeroplane altimeter (Kollsman Sensitive

Altimeter), but the figures for the altitudes should not be regarded as exact. In the section we find the following layers:

A. Sediment mostly covered by scree. Where visible it is like layer B, although more yellowish-brown in color.
B. "Lower gray layer". Mainly consisting of thin (2–3 mm) silty-clayish strata; here and there fine-sandy strata, about 1 mm thick, are intercalated. The color of this layer and layer E is more grayish than that of the rest of the sediments, which are more or less yellow–brownish.
C. Layers, 10–50 cm thick, of fine-banded silt alternating with unbanded fine-sandy layers.
D. Unbanded, fine-sandy layer.
E. "Upper gray layer". As to color and banding very similar to layer B.
F. Like layer C.
G. Alternating fine-banded and unbanded layers. Average thickness of the unbanded ones about 0.5 m.
H. Unbanded except for three fine-banded layers about 0.5 m thick. Grain size of unbanded sediments gradually increasing upwards from fine to about medium sandy.
I. Unbanded sediment, medium to coarse sandy, with embedded layers of gravel, 5–15 cm thick, and scattered rounded stones the size of a clenched fist.
J. Tillite.
K. Basalt-globe breccia.

In Breidagil and adjacent ravines the layers are fine-banded from the lowest visible base to the tillite-covered erosion surface. Here the rhytmites are more regular than in Snidagii, yet hardly regular enough to be described as varves. The gray layers are discernible here also and at practically the same height as at Snidagil. In the steep-sided Godagil ravine the layers from the base upwards are considerably coarser, mainly sandy, yet here and there one finds thin lenses and even angular fragments of finely banded and silty material of the same type as farther south. There are also thin layers of gravel and scattered rounded stones up to 15 cm in diameter.

Just north of Skjólgil the base of the strata is about 260 m above sea level and the layers about 15 m thick, the contact with the overlying tillite being just about 5 m higher than in Snidagil (Pl. IV). Here the layers consist mainly of sand and rounded gravel with distinct current bedding. On the whole we thus find an increasing coarseness of sediment both upwards and towards the north and it seems to have been transported from the north to a lake that was gradually filling up.

According to the preliminary microscopic studies carried out by Th. Einarsson, the fine grained facies of the Svínafell layers show a microscopic banding. The felspar crystals (labradorite-bytownite), on the whole, lie horizontally. The sediment contains some olivine and occasional grains of augite, but most of the grains are basalt glass. The coating of these glass grains consists of a diffusely double-refracting palagonite which gives the sediments their characteristic yellowish-brown color. The cementing matrix is basalt glass without palagonitization.

The more coarse-grained sediment is more palagonitized. It contains the same minerals: felspar, olivin and augite, as well as magnetite. Even here basalt glass is dominant and the cementing matrix is glass.

The great thickness of the Svínafell layers is rather striking considering that to a large extent they are lacustrine. The thickness of the lacustrine facies probably exceeds 120 m. The deepest lakes now existing in Iceland are found either in tectonic depressions (Öskjuvatn, Thingvallavatn), in valleys over-deepened by glacier erosion (Lögurinn), or in glacier-eroded valleys dammed up by constructive volcanic activity (Hvalvatn). As to the genesis of the basin in which the Svínafell layers were deposited, the diastrophism seems not to have taken any important part in it, whereas glacier erosion and damming up by volcanic activity may have been the main factors. The later exposing of the layers indicates both a great vertical erosion by ice and water and a lateral erosion extending the strandflat area during the latter part of the Pleistocene.

THE PLANT REMNANTS

Macrofossils. As mentioned above, the interest in the Svínafell layers was aroused when plant remnants were found there.

A closer examination revealed that leaf impressions were rather abundant, although far from evenly distributed in the sediments. They are plentiful in Snidagil, fairly close to the old shore of the lake, and are especially frequent in the gray layers B and E (cf. Fig. 4), but they are found in all layers of this section that are accessible for closer study, i.e. all those beneath layer H. At Breidagil they have been found in the entire pack of sediments, and the sandy sediments of Godagil are rather rich in leaf impressions, especially of *Alnus*. Farther north, in Hálsatorfugil, one leaf of a *Salix* sp. was found near the tillite contact.

The following plants have been found:

Alnus. Leaf impressions of alder are by far the most abundant of all found in the Svínafell layers. They are especially frequent in the gray layers B and in E in Snidagil, probably because of proximity to the old lake shore. The species has been determined by Svend Th. Andersen as *Alnus viridis* (cf. Pl. V).

Betula. Only a few impressions of birch leaves have been found and only in fragments. The species has not been determined.

Salix. Leaf impressions of different species of willows have been found. One leaf, found by Helgi Björnsson in a scree in Snidagil, has been determined by Svend Th. Andersen as *Salix reticulata* (Pl. VII): one leaf, found by Th. Einarsson, in layer F in Snidagil, is almost certainly *Salix lanata* (Pl. VII).

Furthermore, there are a lot of willow leaves not yet determined. One type of leaf, probably a willow (Pl. VII, 3, found in two specimens by S. Björnsson in layer C. Snidagil), does not belong to any plant now growing in Iceland.

Sorbus. An impression of one leaf fragment (Pl. VI) was found by S. Björnsson in the uppermost part of layer B in Snidagil. It is not determined with certainty, but looks more like the species now growing in Greenland (*Sorbus decora* (Sarg.) Schneid. var. *groenlandica*) than the recent Icelandic species (*S. aucuparia L.*)

Prunus padus? The impression of one whole leaf (Pl. VI) was found by S. Björnsson in the uppermost part of layer B in Snidagil.

Vaccinium, Empetrum. S. Björnsson has told the author that he has seen impressions of leaves which he thinks are *Vaccinium* sp. Among samples from the Svínafell layers, collected by a young boy from Reykjavík, Sigurdur Sigurjónsson, was one with impressions which in all probability are of *Empetrum*.

TABLE 1

POLLEN COUNTED IN SAMPLES FROM LAYER B IN SNIDAGIL

	I	II	III	Total	%
Alnus	10	24	60	94	72
Betula	1	1	2	4	3
Salix		3		3	2
Gramineae	1	3	3	7	5
Cyperaceae	4	7	5	16	12
Ericaceae			2	2	2
Umbelliferae		1	1	2	2
Rosaceae	1		2	3	2
Total	17	39	75	131	100
Filicinae	7	2	10	19	

Gramineae. Some impressions of straw stalks have been found; the longest one, found in Snidagil, was 17 cm in length.

Polypodiaceae. In three samples are impressions of leaves of some *Dryopteris* sp.

As mentioned above, the first plant remnant found in the Svínafell layers was a petrified twig. Subsequently many twigs have been found, but none has been determined so far.

Pollen and spores. Pollen-analytical study of the Svínafell layers is still at a preliminary stage. In the autumn of 1958, Th. Einarsson counted pollen in some samples from the lower grey layer at Snidagil. This was done in Reykjavík under very poor technical conditions, and the samples were not treated with HF. The sediments seem on the whole to be poor in pollen and some, especially those of *Betula*, were much corroded. The count of pollen in three samples is shown in Table 1. It may be added that one grass pollen is probably *Elymus arenarius* and the Filicinae spores are mainly those of *Dryopteris Linneana*.

On the whole the pollen spectrum gives the same picture as the macroscopic plant remnants. The most characteristic feature is the dominance of *Alnus*. Possibly the *Betula* pollen is somewhat underrepresented, compared with *Alnus*, as it seems to be more sensitive to corrosion.

Further palynological studies of the sediments are highly desirable, both in order to identify more species and to find out possible changes in the flora during the period represented by the Svínafell layers.

THE AGE OF THE SVÍNAFELL LAYERS

Paleomagnetic dating, based on the repeated reversals of the remanent magnetism of the basaltic rocks, was introduced in Iceland by Hospers (1953) and has since been applied in this country mainly by Einarsson (1957 a, b) and Sigurgeirsson (1957). It has proved very useful for the establishment of a chronology for the Tertiary and Pleistocene rocks in Iceland. This method has also been of much help in the determination of the age of the Svínafell layers. The author measured the magnetization of the rock of Svínafellsfjall at many places in the field, and for further checking, a lot of rock samples were measured in the laboratory by Professor Th. Sigurgeirsson.

That the Svínafell layers are interglacial is, in the author's opinion, already evident from the fact that they are definitely younger than the basalt-globe breccia of Snidabrekka, which is a very typical subglacial breccia. The question is then, to which Interglacial do the layers belong? Hospers (1953, pp. 472–473) and Einarsson (1957b, pp. 223–224) agree with Pjeturss (1903), Bárdarsson (1929) and Áskelsson (1938, 1960) in regarding the Búlandshöfdi–Brimlárhöfdi (Stödin) fossiliferous sediments (cf. Fig. 1) as interglacial, and state that they are covered by series of basalt layers of reverse polarity. According to Einarsson, moraine-like sediments are found between some of these basalt beds. The Svínafell layers, on the other hand, rest on normally magnetized basalts that have been greatly eroded, presumably mainly by ice, before the deposition of the plant-bearing sediments. Thus, they cannot belong to the same Interglacial as the Búlandshöfdi–Brimlárhöfdi layers, which in all probability belong to the Günz-Mindel Interglacial (cf. also Áskelsson, 1938, 1960). The Svínafell layers therfore cannot be placed lower than the Mindel-Riss Interglacial. As stated above, the rocks of Svínafellsfjall resting on the Svínafell layers represent two thick series of subglacially formed rocks, separated by subaerial lavas. All these rocks are normally magnetized. In the author's opinion there is hardly any doubt that these rocks represent two Glacials, and the Svínafell layers therefore cannot be placed as high as the Riss-Würm Interglacial. *Consequently they must be placed in the Mindel-Riss*

Pl. V. 1, *Alnus viridis*. $\frac{2}{3}$ nat. size. Snidagil, layer B.

2, *Alnus viridis*. $\frac{2}{3}$ nat. size. Breidagil, layer B.

Pl. VI. 1, *Sorbus* sp. $\frac{2}{3}$ nat. size. Snidagil, layer B.

2, *Prunus padus*? $\frac{2}{3}$ nat. size. Snidagil, uppermost part of layer B.

Pl. VII. 1, *Salix reticulata.* $\frac{2}{3}$ nat. size. Snidagil, scree.

2, *Salix lanata*? $\frac{2}{3}$ nat. size. Snidagil, layer F.

3, *Salix* sp.? $\frac{2}{3}$ nat. size. Snidagil, layer C.

4, *Salix* sp. $\frac{2}{3}$ nat. size. Snidagil, layer B.

5, *Salix* sp. nat. size. $\frac{2}{3}$ Near Breidagil, Layer B.

6, Fragment of leaf with palmate venation. $\frac{2}{3}$ nat. Snidagil, layer E.

Interglacial. As to the intricate question, where to place the first reversal of magnetism in relation to the Pleistocene climatic chronology, we have on one hand Hosper's and Einarsson's observations on Snæfellsnes, which indicate that this reversal did not occur earlier than the end of the Günz-Mindel Interglacial. On the other hand, the reversal took place long before the deposition of the Svínafell layers, as the basalts of normal polarity underlying them are greatly eroded and that erosion is probably by glaciers. From a study of all the evidence it seems most reasonable to conclude that the first magnetic reversal occurred towards the beginning of the Mindel Glacial.

TABLE 2

POLLEN COUNTED IN INTERGLACIAL SEDIMENTS IN ICELAND

	Brimlárhöfdi* (layer H)		Brimlárhöfdi* (layer K)		Bakkabrúnir†		Svínafell	
	n	%	*n*	%	*n*	%	*n*	%
Pinus	2.5	4						
Picea	1	1						
Alnus	1	3	51	44	26	24	94	72
Betula	2	1			21	19	4	3
Salix	7	10	4	3	13	12	3	2
Gramineae	22	32	53	46	40	36	7	5
Cyperaceae	10	15	6	5			16	12
Ericaceae	13	18		2	5	4	2	2
Other herbs	12	16	2	2	6	5	5	4
Total	70.5	100	116	100	111	100	131	100

* According to Áskelsson, 1938, p. 312.
† According to Líndal, 1939, p. 269.

COMPARISON BETWEEN THE FLORA OF THE SVÍNAFELL LAYERS AND OTHER INTERGLACIAL DEPOSITS IN ICELAND

Plant-bearing deposits regarded as interglacial have been described from the above-mentioned Brimlárhöfdi (Stödin) on Snæfellsnes (Áskelsson, 1938, 1960), from Bakkabrúnir in Vídidalur, north Iceland (Líndal, 1935, 1939), and from Ellidavogur near Reykjavík (Thorkelsson, 1935; Löve and Löve, 1956). Common to the sediments in Brimlárhöfdi, Bakkabrúnir, and Svínafellsfjall is the dominance of *Alnus viridis* as shown in Table 2. The occurrence of conifer pollen in layer H in Brimlárhöfdi is somewhat suspect. Áskelsson seems to be doubtful whether to interpret it as secondary or not; the present writer is inclined to regard it as secondary. As to the age of the Bakkabrúnir formation, opinions differ. Líndal and Áskelsson regard it as interglacial, whereas Einarsson (1958) regards it as Pliocene. The present author is inclined to place it in the Günz-Mindel Interglacial. According to Líndal, leaf impressions of *Dryas octopetala* and *Betula nana* are common in these sediments and on the whole they must indicate a somewhat colder climate than does the Svínafell flora. But here one must take into account the difference in climate between the Svínafell and the Bakkabrúnir areas as well.

In the plant-bearing sediments at Ellidavogur no remnants of *Alnus* have been found. If we regard these sediments as most likely belonging to the Riss-Würm Intergalcial, a reasonable although not the only possible conclusion will be that *Pinus* possibly, but not likely, survived the Günz Glacial, that *Alnus* survived both Günz and Mindel, but became thoroughly extinct during the Riss Glacial, and that *Betula* survived all four main Pleistocene Glacials.

The investigation of the Svínafell layers is still in its early stages, and what has been stated about them here is primarily intended to draw attention to the fact that these are layers which require systematic and detailed research, both macroscopic and microscopic, and both of the organic remains and of the sediments as such. Morphometric measurements are particularly desirable. The extent of the layers and their stratigraphy must also be more closely investigated.

What has been stated here about the need for closer investigation of the Svínafell layers also applies to all other fossil-bearing interglacial sediments in Iceland. There is probably no other place where so much of such sediments has been preserved in a country that has been for the most part covered by ice during the Pleistocene Glacials, the conditions for their preservation being rather unique, as volcanoes were very active during both the Glacials and Interglacials and sediments could therefore easily be covered either by lava or tephra and thus be protected against glacial or fluvial erosion. Thorough and systematic study of the fossil-bearing interglacial sediments in Iceland is one of the most urgent tasks in the Quaternary geology of Iceland.

ABSTRACT

The "Svínafell layers" are plant-bearing sedimentary deposits which form the base of the mountain Svínafellsfjall in southeast Iceland. These deposits were discovered in 1955 and have hitherto been only provisionally studied. The minimum thickness of these sediments is 150 metres. Impressions of leaves are abundant. Characteristic for the flora is the dominance of Alnus. *The species has been determined as* A. viridis. *Other trees that have grown in the area are* Betula *sp.*, Sorbus *sp. and probably* Prunus padus, *besides many species of* Salix. *The flora indicates a climate as warm as now or somewhat warmer. Stratigraphical and magneto-geological studies place the Svínafell layers in the*

Mindel–Riss (Yarmouth) Interglacial and indicate that the youngest reversal of the Earth's magnetic field occurred near the beginning of the Mindel (Kansan) Glacial. Other plant-bearing interglacial formations in Iceland are discussed briefly.

REFERENCES

ÁSKELSSON, J. (1938). Quartärgeologische Studien auf Island II. Inter-glaziale Pflanzenablagerungen. *Medd. Dansk Geol. Foren.* **9**, 300–319.

ÁSKELSSON, J. (1960). Pliocene and Pleistocene fossiliferous deposits. *On the geology and geophysics of Iceland. Guide to excursion No. A2, Int. Geol. Congr. 1960*, 28–32.

BÁRDARSSON, G. G. (1929). Nogle geologiske profiler fra Snaefellsnes. *Rep. of the 18th Scandinavian Naturalist Congress, Copenhagen.*

EINARSSON, TR-. (1957a) Der Paläomagnetismus der isländischen Basalte und seine stratigraphische Bedeutung. *Neues Jahrb. Geol. Paläont.* Mh. **4**, 159–176.

EINARSSON, TR-. (1957b). Magneto-geological mapping in Iceland with the use of a compass. *Phil. Mag. Suppl.* 6 (22), 232–239.

EINARSSON, TR-. (1958). Landslag á Skagafjallgardi. *Náttúrufr.* **28**, 1–25.

HENSON, F. H. (1955). The geology of Iceland. *University of Nottingham, Survey* **5**, 34–46.

HOSPERS, J. (1953). Reversals of the main geomagnetic field. I. *Koninkl. Nederl. Akad. van Wetensch. Proc.* Ser. B, 56 (5), 467–476.

LÍNDAL, J. H. (1935). Móbergsmyndanir i Bakkakotsbrúnum og steingervingar theirra. *Náttúrufr.* **5**, 97–114.

LÍNDAL, J. H. (1939). The interglacial formation in Vídidal, Northern Iceland. *Quart. Journ. Geol. Soc. London* **95**, 261–273.

LÖVE, Á and LÖVE D. (1956). Cytotaxonomical conspectus of the Icelandic Flora. *Acta Horti Gotoburg.* **20**, 65–291.

NIELSEN, N. and NOE-NYGAARD, A. (1936). Om den islandske "Palagonitformations" Oprindelse. *Geogr. Tidskr.* **39**, 3–36.

NOE-NYGAARD, A. (1940). Subglacial volcanic activity in ancient and recent times. *Geogr. Dan.* **1** (2), 1–67.

NOE-NYGAARD, A. (1953). Notes on the nature of some indurated moraines in South Iceland. *Geogr. Tidsskr.* **52**, 222–231.

PJETURSS. H. (1903). Shelly boulder-clay in the Palagonite-formation of Iceland. *Quart. Journ. Geol. Soc. London* **59**, 356–361.

SCHWARZBACH, M. (1955). Allgemeiner Überblick der Klimageschichte Islands. *Neues Jahrb. Geol. Paläont.* Mh. 3, 97–130.

SIGURGEIRSSON, TH. (1957). Direction of magnetization in Icelandic basalt. *Phil. Mag. Suppl.* 6 (2), 240–246.

THORARINSSON, S. (1958). The Öræfajökull eruption of 1362. *Acta Nat. Isl.* **2** (2), 1–99.

TRYGGVASON T. (1952). Steinrunninn hvarfleir. *Náttúrufr.* **22**, 96–98.

CONCLUSION

ÁSKELL LÖVE
Institut Botanique de l'Université de Montréal, Montréal, Canada

THE science of biogeography, in the true and wide meaning of the term, may be defined as the exploration of the universe of living beings and the application of the laws of nature to the interpretation of the history of the distribution and dispersal of biota. In this application the laws themselves are put to a test and important explanations are constructed. Such was the case with the theory of evolution which arose from the study of distribution, in time and space, of plants and animals.

It has been said that the most important step in getting a work started is the recognition of a problem. Regarding the North Atlantic biota, this was achieved already by Hooker (1862), or perhaps even by Humboldt (1817) who recognized the close relationships between the biota in the far north of Scandinavia and America. The second important step in the development of this case was the collection of evidence for and against several working hypotheses coined to explain the relationship. Out of this emerged the theory of survival of plants within the glaciated areas of Scandinavia (Blytt, 1876, 1882; Fries, 1913) replacing the now merely historical *tabula rasa* idea.

The theory of glacial survival has been found to be one of the most fertile ideas of biogeography, and much evidence has been sought in support of it for almost a century. Naturally, most of this evidence has come from Scandinavia, but some also from North America, Greenland, Iceland, Svalbard, and the British Isles. Many Scandinavian biogeographers have agreed that this theory is the only available explanation for the distribution patterns of certain biota in Scandinavia (cf. Dahl, 1961; Gjærevoll, 1959; Lindroth, 1958; Nannfeldt, 1958; Nordhagen, 1936; and in this symposium).

Some of the reasoning regarding the North Atlantic biota and their history may seem to have been somewhat circular in that biologists proposed geological possibilites and geologists tended to accept such conclusions as final. Recently, this has changed in such a way that most biogeographers base their conclusions on biological evidence only, at the same time as the conclusions of most geologists rest on geological observations alone. Lately, the latter have tended to doubt the possibility of recognizing ice-free refugia even from the last glaciation (Holtedahl and Rosenquist, 1958; Hoppe, 1959; and in this symposium), though they have not regarded it wise to deny completely this possibility because of the strong biological evidence.

It is extremely difficult to reconstruct biological history when there are no fossils and if all conclusions must be based on the distribution patterns of the surviving populations. This has been the main problem in the investigations of glacial survival in Scandinavia and North America. Although palynologica, studies have added much information on the occurrence, recolonization and extinction of some plants and on certain variations in distribution patterns, such studies usually cover only the Late and Post-glacial periods in areas south of the ice-border or made available by the retreating ice (cf. Deevey, 1949; Godwin, 1956; Iversen, 1958).

One of the most important contributions from this symposium is the furnishing of definite paleobotanical evidence in support of the glacial survival theory. This evidence comes from Iceland, where volcanic activity throughout the Pleistocene has secured the conservation of extensive fossiliferous deposits from the Interglacials (Thorarinsson, Th. Einarsson, in this symposium). In fact, the Icelandic layers show not only that plants, including trees, survived the glaciations within the country, but also that the flora of this island has diminished gradually during the Pleistocene and that some species which were dominant in the first Interglacials have become extinct in the latter. Logically, this must be regarded as a fully satisfactory proof that plants and animals have been able to survive the Pleistocene glaciations also in other countries where no paleological remains have been found and where the only indications left are met with in form of peculiar distribution patterns.

This carries us back to Scandinavia. As mentioned by Fægri (this symposium), it is possible that the bicentric distribution of certain plants in the Norwegian mountains may be explained as a consequence of climatical variations after the glaciations. This argument is, however, considerably weakened by the occurrence of multicentric areas in Iceland for several plants whose present distribution within the country must have been affected by the glaciation, as shown by Steindórsson (this symposium). There are, however, several species in Scandinavia which cannot have invaded their areas from southern or eastern localities in Europe following the retreat of the ice for the simple reason that they have never grown there. These are the species belonging to the element termed "West Arctic" by Blytt (*loc. cit.*), i.e. the American–Arctic element in the European flora. It is apparent from the statements by D. Löve and Dahl (this symposium) that long-distance dispersal over oceans or ice is in this case hardly even a remote possibility, because the radius of dispersability of these plants is much smaller than the present distance to their nearest populations. The hypothesis is also supported by the fact that these plants in Scandinavia are very rare and local though apparently appropriate habitats are available in many localities close by their present areas there. Hence, the "West Arctic" species must have arrived to Scandinavia over some kind of a land-connection and hardly only over the present lands, as partly suggested by Hultén (this symposium). The same sort of dispersal over land may apply also for at least the great majority of the species in the Icelandic flora (E. Einarsson, this symposium). It goes almost without saying that some of the truly Amphi-Atlantic biota in eastern North America must have dispersed westwards in a similar manner. In addition, glacial survival in Arctic America seems even more likely than in Scandinavia for the simple reason that there a much larger land area may have been free from ice north of the glaciation limits (cf. Ewing and Donn, 1956; Ives, this symposium; Terasmae, 1961).

Land-connections have been discussed by several contributors to this symposium. Some biogeographers seem to hold the opinion, based on climatic requirements of the biota, that a land-bridge must have connected at least Iceland and Europe as recently as in late Pliocene (Dahl, this symposium). Others have used paleobotanical data to indicate such a hypothetical connection as late as in the latter part of the Pleistocene (Sörensen, 1953) or during the penultimate glaciation itself (Löve and Löve, 1956). However, the possibility of such relatively recent connections over the Atlantic or parts of it remains a matter of dispute and has so far received only limited support from geologists (Heezen and Tharp, this symposium), but not from paleoclimatologists (Schwarzbach, this symposium). On the contrary, geological (Tr. Einarsson, Schwarzbach, this symposium) and certain botanical (Hultén, this symposium; Steere, 1937; Löve and Löve, 1953) as well as zoological (Waldén, Omodeo, this symposium) evidence seem strongly to uphold the opinion that Iceland (or at least "Great Iceland", cf. Barth, 1941; Tr. Einarsson, this symposium) has been an isolated island ever since the Middle Tertiary, and that its present indigenous biota must be regarded as only remnants of the flora and fauna which became isolated at that time. It follows, if this reasoning is correct, that at least the "West Arctic" plants in Scandinavia are survivors not only of the Pleistocene but relics from a still more distant past when there was some kind of land-connection at least between Greenland and Scandinavia. This is in conformity with the views previously expressed by Nordhagen (*loc. cit.*) and Nannfeldt (*loc. cit.*).

The question arises what kind of connection over the North Atlantic made possible at least a limited exchange of biota until the Middle Tertiary, but because of the limited geological knowledge of the sea bottom in these regions, the answer remains controversial. Though Tr. Einarsson (this symposium) seems to favor the idea of a large Atlantic island (cf. Barth, 1941) somewhat like the Scandic proposed by De Geer (1912), other possibilities remain open and those who prefer, for example, one land-bridge over Iceland and another over Svalbard (Černohorský, Hadač, Rönning, this symposium), or simply some kind of continental displacement (cf. Heezen and Tharp, this symposium) can still find support for these ideas with equally strong evidence. However, the data presented by Lindroth and Waldén and even Dahl (this symposium) seem to back the opinion by Tr. Einarsson (this symposium) that this North Atlantic land-mass had connections northwards and eastwards but hardly all the way to the present American continent. Davis Strait may thus be older than other parts of the North Atlantic Ocean and have acted as an effective barrier to dispersal for a long period of time (cf. Lindroth, 1960). It is, however, also evident that the early Tertiary flora of Iceland was largely American, or, perhaps more correctly, belonged to the so-called "Arcto-Tertiary" or rather "Tertiary-mesophytic" flora that was—and still in part is—common to eastern North America and eastern Asia (cf. Li, 1952). That Denmark Strait—between Iceland and Greenland—apparently has also acted as a strong barrier when this flora was replaced by a more boreal one, seems to be indicated by the fact that the Icelandic flora at present is as typically European as the Greenland flora is typically American, a puzzle not explained at this Symposium.

Although it is possible to draw conclusions like these based on our present knowledge of the history of the North Atlantic and its biota, one ought not to forget that this knowledge still is so limited as to make many of these conclusions very preliminary, and thus, controversial.

Even if we feel that the general picture of the history of the North Atlantic and its biota is emerging into greater clarity, this symposium also has shown that we are in the happy situation of still being confronted by unsolved problems of considerable importance for the problem of the geological and biological history of this region. The answers to even some of the apparently minor questions might affect the major picture considerably. These may be geological as well as biological, and it seems futile to try to mention more than a few problems in need of consideration. Important geological problems are connected with the identification of refugia and unglaciated forelands after the ice has left; these questions need to be investigated in the North Atlantic region where glaciers are still active, although research in the Antarctic may give us some answers. Another geological problem concerns the bottom of the North Atlantic and, then, especially the transatlantic submarine ridges; bottom cores from carefully selected localities might tell us if these ridges ever have been raised above the sea, and if so, when and for how long a time. Such cores taken close to the existing basaltous islands may perhaps reveal in what way the hypothetical land connection has been formed in the Cretaceous. According to a common hypothesis, it should have been formed by eustatic changes in the crust or by some kind of continental drift, whereas another hypothesis assumes that it has been formed by volcanic eruptions only, without drastic changes in sea level (cf. Tr. Einarsson, 1961). If the latter hypothesis is correct, the more than 5000 m thick basalt plateau ought to stand firmly on palagonite formed during suboceanic volcanic eruptions, whereas the lack of such a palagonite formation would at least indicate that the other explanations were more likely. Cores from the deeper parts of the ocean might solve the mystery of the "Scandic", or perhaps of the continental drift, or of the possibility of an expanding earth crust as mentioned by Heezen and Tharp (this symposium; cf. also Dicke, 1962).

A geological question of utmost importance for the ultimate solutions of many problems here discussed concerns detailed examination of the lignites of the North Atlantic basalt formation, which reaches from Scotland and Northern Ireland to the Faeroes, Iceland, and Greenland (cf. Tr. Einarsson, Rasmussen, this symposium). Only such a study can clarify the particulars of the geological and climatological history of life in this part of the world during the Tertiary. Still, these lignites are very sporadically known. As a direct continuation of such studies of the lignites ought to follow detailed investigations of the Icelandic Pleistocene deposits and of Late Glacial and Post-Glacial palynological phenomena in all the countries concerned.

Turning to the biological field, palynological identifications of all the species of the North Atlantic flora is both desirable and essential for the interpretation of past dispersal and distribution areas. Such a background may help in understanding the formation of the limits between the Arctic and Subarctic discussed by Böcher (this symposium). It could probably also find explanation of the peculiar disappearance and reappearance of the vegetation zonation discussed by Sjörs (this symposium), and support or contradict the hypothesis of dispersal of plant communities rather than of individual diaspores as suggested by Hadač (this symposium). Palynology can also be expected to increase our understanding of the importance of the conservative statocrats and the aggressive apocrats (cf. Erdtman, this symposium) in the history of the floras concerned. A combined palynological and cytotaxonomical study based on this concept is also likely to provide new ideas for an explanation of the fact that the frequency of polyploids increases with an increased latitude and is highest in the areas where we expect the highest frequency of glacial survivors (Löve, 1953, 1959; Löve and Löve, 1949, 1957; Reese, 1958, 1961a, b; Favarger, 1961).

Though the general knowledge of the botanical and zoological conditions in the North Atlantic countries is better than almost anywhere else, studies on distribution and sociological behavior still remain insufficient in parts of the area, and the taxonomy of many species is often incomplete and inexact. Detailed studies on minor races need to be intensified, as demonstrated by the excellent results achieved by Nordhagen (1931, 1935) and Nannfeldt (1935, 1940). In addition, the problem of endemism needs special attention by cytogeneticists (cf. Löve and Löve, 1956, 1961). The universally accepted idea that the frequency of endemics should reflect the age of a flora or fauna is still not completely confirmed, at least not in northern lands where populations are medium-sized and competition is limited. Some of the more widely distributed North Atlantic endemics, e.g. *Armeria maritima* ssp. *planifolia*, *Geum rivale* ssp. *islandicum*, and *Papaver Nordhagenianum* ssp. *faeroeënse*, may be old and indicate some late land-connection between Shetland, the Faeroes, and Iceland, but several other local endemics, such as *Sesleria albicans* ssp. *islandica*, *Glyceria fluitans* var. *islandica*, *Roegneria borealis* ssp. *islandica*, *Roegneria Doniana* ssp. *Stefanssonii*, *Dactylorchis maculata* ssp. *islandica*, some species of *Euphrasia*, and the varieties of *Papaver Nordhagenianum* and *P. radicatum* (cf. Löve, 1962a, b) are possibly neoendemics formed in Post-glacial times by strong natural selection in small populations, or simply by genetic drift.

Venturing to summarize the total outcome of this symposium, it seems safe to conclude that although our views on the history of the North Atlantic and its biota have become greatly elucidated by the papers presented, we have also become well aware of the many geological and biological problems which remain unsettled in this part of the world. Many of these problems require thoroughly organized investigations and combined geological and biological efforts on basis of refined chemical, physical, geological, oceanographical, cytogenetical, taxonomical, palynological, biogeographical, and other methods of approach. Most desirable of all, however, are greatly increased facilities for such cooperative studies which could lead to a solution of the complicated but important problems of the history of biota in the North Atlantic area. It seems to us that Iceland, both because of its position and its unique geology, holds the key to many of these problems.

REFERENCES

BARTH, T. F. W. (1941). *Island*. Oslo.

BLYTT, A. (1876). *Essay on the immigration of the Norwegian flora during alternating dry and rainy periods*. Christiania.

BLYTT, A. (1882). Die Theorie der wechselnden kontinentalen und insularen Klimate. *Englers Bot. Jahrb.* **2**, 1–50.

DAHL, E. (1961). Refugieproblemet og de kvartærgeologiske metodene. *Svensk Naturvetenskap* **14**, 81–96.

DEEVEY, E. S. (1949). Biogeography of the Pleistocene. Part I. Europe and North America. *Bull. Geol. Soc. Amer.* **60**, 1315–1416.

DE GEER, G. (1912). Kontinentale Niveauveränderungen im Norden Europas. *Compt. Rend. XIme Congr. Géol. Intern. Stockholm* (1910), 848–860.

DICKE, R. H. (1962). The earth and cosmology. *Science* **138**, 653–664.

EINARSSON, TR. (1961). Upphaf Íslands og blágrýtismyndunin. *Náttúra Íslands*, 11–29.

EWING, M. and DONN, W. L. (1956). A theory of Ice Ages. *Science* **123**, 1061–1066.

FAVARGER, C. (1961). Sur l'emploi des nombres de chromosomes en géographie botanique historique. *Ber. Geobot. Inst. Rübel* **32**, 119–146.

FRIES, T. C. E. (1913). *Botanische Untersuchungen im nördlichsten Schweden*. Uppsala.

GJÆREVOLL, O. (1959). Overvintringsteoriens stilling i dag. *Kgl. Norske Vidensk. Selsk. Forh.* **32**, 1–36.

GODWIN, H. (1956). *The History of the British flora*. Cambridge.

HOLTEDAHL, O. and ROSENQUIST, I. T. (1958). "Refugie-problemet" på den skandinaviske halvöy fra geologisk synspunkt. *Svensk Naturvetenskap* **11**, 108–118.

HOOKER, J. D. (1862). Outline of the distribution of Arctic plants. *Trans. Linn. Soc. London* **23**, 251–348.

HOPPE, G. (1959). Några kritiska kommentarer till diskussionen om isfria refugier. *Svensk Naturvetenskap* **12**, 123–134.

HUMBOLDT, F. A. VON (1817). *De distributione geographica plantarum secundum coeli temperiem et altitudinem montium, prolegomena.* Lutetia Parisiorum.

IVERSEN, J. (1958). The bearing of glacial and interglacial epochs on the formation and extinction of plant taxa. *Uppsala Univ. Årsskr.* 1958, (6), 210–215.

LI, H. L. (1952). Floristic relationships between eastern Asia and eastern North America. *Trans. Amer. Philos. Soc. N.S.* **42**, 371–429.

LINDROTH, C. H. (1958). Istidsövervintrare bland djuren. *Svensk Naturvetenskap* **11**, 134–151.

LINDROTH, C. H. (1960). Is Davis Strait—between Greenland and Baffin Island—a floristic barrier? *Bot. Notiser* **113**, 130–140.

LÖVE, Á. (1953). Subarctic polyploidy. *Hereditas.* **39**, 113–124.

LÖVE, Á. (1959). Origin of the Arctic flora. *Publ. McGill Univ. Museum* **1**, 92–95.

LÖVE, Á. (1962a). Typification of *Papaver radicatum*—a nomenclatural detective story. *Bot. Notiser* **115**, 61–84.

LÖVE, Á. (1962b). Nomenclature of North Atlantic *Papaver*. *Taxon* **11**, 132–138.

LÖVE, Á. and LÖVE, D. (1949). The geobotanical significance of polyploidy. I. Polyploidy and latitude. *Portug. Acta Biol.* (A) R. B. Goldschmidt Vol., 273–352.

LÖVE, Á. and LÖVE, D. (1953). Studies on *Bryoxiphium*. *Bryologist* **56**, 73–94, 183–203.

LÖVE, Á. and LÖVE, D. (1956). Cytotaxonomical conspectus of the Icelandic flora. *Acta Horti Gotob.* **20**, 1–291.

LÖVE, Á. and LÖVE, D. (1957). Arctic polyploidy. *Proc. Genet. Soc. Canada* **2**, 23–27.

LÖVE, Á. and LÖVE, D. (1961). Chromosome numbers of Central and Northwest European plant species. *Opera Botanica* **5**, I–VIII, 1–581.

NANNFELDT, J. A. (1935). Taxonomical and plant-geographical studies in the *Poa laxa* group. A contribution to the history of the North European mountain floras. *Symb. Bot. Upsal.* I (5), 1–113.

NANNFELDT, J. A. (1940). On the polymorphy of *Poa arctica* R. Br. with special reference to its Scandinavian forms. *Symb. Bot. Upsal.* IV (4), 1–86.

NANNFELDT, J. A. (1958). Den skandinaviska fjällfloran och nedisningarna. *Svensk Naturvetenskap* **11**, 119–133.

NORDHAGEN, R. (1931). Studen über die skandinavischen Rassen des *Papaver radicatum* Rottb. sowie einige mit denselben verwechselte neue Arten. *Bergens Mus. Arbok* 1931. *Naturv. rekke* **2**, 1–50.

NORDHAGEN, R. (1935). Om *Arenaria humifusa* Wg. og dens betydning for utforskningen av Skandinavias eldste floraelement. *Bergens Mus. Arbok* 1935. *Naturv. rekke* **1**, 1–183

NORDHAGEN, R. (1936). Skandinavias fjellflora og dens relasjoner til siste istid. *Nord.* (**19**. *skand.) naturforskarmötet i Helsingfors* 1936, 93–124.

REESE, G. (1958). Polyploidie und Verbreitung. *Zeitschr. Bot.* **46**, 339–354.

REESE, G. (1961a) Geobotanische Bedeutung der Chromosomenzahl und Chromosomenstruktur. *Naturw. Rundschau* **14**, 140–145.

REESE, G. (1961b). Karyotype and plant geography. *Recent Advances in Botany*, 895–900.

SÖRENSEN, T. (1953). A revision of the Greenland species of *Puccinellia* Parl. *Medd. om Grönl.* **136** (3), 1–179.

STEERE, W. C. (1937). *Bryoxiphium norvegicum*, the sword moss, as a preglacial and interglacial relic. *Ecology* **18**, 346–359.

TERASMAE, J. (1961). Notes on Late-Quaternary climatic changes in Canada. *Ann. N.Y. Acad. Sci.* **95**, 658–675.

APPENDIX

List of those participating or attending the Symposium.

HUGO ANDERSSON, Lund, Sweden
PÁLL BERGTHÓRSSON, Reykjavík, Iceland
TYGE W. BÖCHER, Copenhagen, Denmark
HÖGNI BÖDVARSSON, Lund, Sweden
EGGERT V. BRIEM, Pennsylvania, U.S.A.
SIGURDUR J. BRÍEM, Reykjavík, Iceland
MAX E. BRITTON, Washington, D.C., U.S.A.
ZD. ČERNOHORSKÝ, Praha, Czechoslovakia
R. CHARPENTIER, Lund, Sweden
EILIF DAHL, Vollebekk, Norway
JEAN DAHL, Vollebekk, Norway
TRULS DAHL, Vollebekk, Norway
INGÓLFUR DAVÍDSSON, Reykjavík, Iceland
MARGARET DAVIS, Ann Arbor, Mich., U.S.A.
PER DOUWES, Lund, Sweden
HEATHER DRUMMOND, Sydney, Australia
KRISTBJÖRG DUADÓTTIR, Akureyri, Iceland
EYTHÓR EINARSSON, Reykjavík, Iceland
THORLEIFUR EINARSSON, Reykjavík, Iceland
TRAUSTI EINARSSON, Reykjavík, Iceland
GUNNAR ERDTMAN, Stockholm, Sweden
GUNNI ERDTMAN, Stockholm, Sweden
JÓN EYTHÓRSSON, Reykjavìk, Iceland
KNUT FÆGRI, Bergen, Norway
STURLA FRIDRIKSSON, Reykjavík, Iceland
WALTER FRIEDRICH, Cologne, Germany
ARNTHÓR GARDARSSON, Reykjavík, Iceland
CAMILLE GERVAIS, Montreal, Canada
GEIR GÍGJA, Reykjavìk, Iceland
OLAV GJÆREVOLL, Trondheim, Norway
FINNUR GUDMUNDSSON, Reykjavík, Iceland
TERESIA GUDMUNDSSON, Reykjavík, Iceland
PÉTUR GUNNARSSON, Reykjavík, Iceland
EMIL HADAČ, Plzeň, Czechoslovakia
HELGI HALLGRÍMSSON, Reykjavík, Iceland
HAYE WALTER HANSEN, Hamburg, Germany

A. M. Harvill, Jr., Murray, Kentucky, U.S.A.
Bruce C. Heezen, Palisades, N.Y., U.S.A.
H. J. Helms, NATO, Paris, France
Steingrímur Hermannsson, Reykjavík, Iceland
Gunnar Hoppe, Stockholm, Sweden
Eric Hultén, Stockholm, Sweden
J. D. Ives, Ottawa, Canada
Sveinn Jakobsson, Reykjavík, Iceland
Bergthór Jóhannsson, Reykjavík, Iceland
Baldur Johnsen, Reykjavík, Iceland
Bengt Jonsell, Uppsala, Sweden
Margareta Jonsell, Uppsala, Sweden
Jón Jónsson, Hafnarfjördur, Iceland
Gudmundur Kjartansson, Hafnarfjördur, Iceland
Britt Kjellqvist, Lund, Sweden
Ebbe Kjellqvist, Lund, Sweden
Carl H. Lindroth, Lund, Sweden
Gun Lindroth, Lund, Sweden
Àskell Löve, Montreal, Canada
Doris Löve, Montreal, Canada
Gunnlaug Löve, Montreal, Canada
Lóa Löve, Montreal, Canada
Thráinn Löve, Reykjavík, Iceland
J. R. Mackay, Vancouver, B.C., Canada
Pierre Morisset, Montreal, Canada
J. A. Nannfeldt, Uppsala, Sweden
Rolf Nordhagen, Oslo, Norway *
Knut Norstog, Springfield, Ohio, U.S.A.
Steinunn Òlafsdóttir, Reykjavík, Iceland
Svandís Òlafsdóttir, Reykjavík, Iceland
P. Omodeo, Sienna, Italy,
U. Omodeo, Siena, Italy
Åke Persson, Lund, Sweden
Sigurdur Pétursson, Reykjavík, Iceland
Frank A. Pitelka, Berkeley, California, U.S.A.
Jóannes Rasmussen, Tórshavn, The Faeroes
Olof I. Rönning, Trondheim, Norway
Martin Schwarzbach, Cologne, Germany
Björn Sigurbjörnsson, Reykjavík, Iceland
Flosi Hrafn Sigurdsson, Reykjavík, Iceland
Sven Th. Sigurdsson, Reykjavík, Iceland

* Did not attend in person, but gave a lecture from a tape.

Thorbjörn Sigurgeirsson, Reykjavík, Iceland
Gudmundur E. Sigvaldason, Reykjavík, Iceland
Hugo Sjörs, Uppsala, Sweden
Ármann Snævarr, Reykjavík, Iceland
Steindór Steindórsson, Akureyri, Iceland
Brita Stenar-Nilsson, Uppsala, Sweden
Marie Tharp, Palisades, N.Y., U.S.A.
Sigurdur Thórarinsson, Reykjavík, Iceland
Günter Timmermann, Hamburg, Germany
Haukur Tómasson, Reykjavík, Iceland
Eysteinn Tryggvason, Reykjavík, Iceland
Tómas Tryggvason, Reykjavík, Iceland
Kári Valsson, Strönd, Iceland
Henrik W. Waldén, Gothenburg, Sweden
Virginia Weadock, New York, N.Y., U.S.A.

AUTHOR INDEX

SUBJECT INDEX